X-RAY MICROSCOPY AND X-RAY MICROANALYSIS

SOLE DISTRIBUTORS FOR THE UNITED STATES OF NORTH AMERICA:

D. VAN NOSTRAND COMPANY, INC.

120 Alexander Street, Princeton, N. J. (Principal office)

24 West 40th Street New York 18, N.Y.

SOLE DISTRIBUTORS FOR CANADA:

D. VAN NOSTRAND COMPANY (CANADA), LTD.

25 Hollinger Road, Toronto 16

SOLE DISTRIBUTORS FOR THE BRITISH COMMONWEALTH EXCLUDING CANADA:

D. VAN NOSTRAND COMPANY, LTD.

358 Kensington High Street, London, W. 14

X-RAY MICROSCOPY

and

X-RAY MICROANALYSIS

PROCEEDINGS OF
THE SECOND INTERNATIONAL SYMPOSIUM
(Stockholm, 1960)

Edited by

A. ENGSTRÖM
Professor of Medical Physics
Karolinska Institute, Stockholm (Sweden)

V. COSSLETT
Lecturer in Physics, Cavendish Laboratory
Cambridge (England)

H. PATTEE
Department of Physics and Biophysics
Laboratory Stanford University
Stanford, California (U.S.A.)

ELSEVIER PUBLISHING COMPANY
AMSTERDAM/LONDON/NEW YORK/PRINCETON
1960

Library of Congress Catalog Card Number 60-12354

With 436 illustrations and 27 tables

PRINTED IN THE NETHERLANDS BY

DIJKSTRA'S DRUKKERIJ V.H. BOEKDRUKKERIJ GEBR. HOITSEMA N.V., GRONINGEN

PREFACE

At the first international symposium on *X-ray Microscopy and Microradiography* which was held in Cambridge, England, 1956, it was decided to hold a second symposium in Stockholm, in 1959. The period between the two conferences saw a further development in the general field of X-ray micromethods, but the main emphasis was shifted somewhat. At the 1956 meeting the major interest was focused on X-ray microscopic procedures *per se*, that is on the methods of obtaining enlarged X-ray images as well as procedures to obtain chemical information from these absorption images. To-day more interest is directed towards X-ray microprobe techniques or scanning methods, such as emission and diffraction analysis. Therefore the title of the symposium was chosen as *X-ray Microscopy and X-ray Microanalysis.*

The development of the microprobe methods has been rapid and as the proceedings of this symposium indicate, instruments are now commercially available which permit the recording of X-ray emission spectra from areas as small as one micron in diameter.

The lectures at this second symposium were divided into three main groups, namely X-ray microanalytic procedures based on absorption, emission and diffraction of X-rays respectively. Accordingly, the papers in this volume are classified in the corresponding categories. A panel discussion treating the merits and results of the various methods was held after each main group of papers. Some of the results of these panel discussions are outlined in the three introductions to the three main sections of this book.

The third symposium in this series is planned for the summer of 1962 at Stanford University, Stanford, California.

Stockholm and Cambridge, February, 1960.

A. ENGSTRÖM

H. H. PATTEE

V. E. COSSLETT

CONTENTS

II. X-Ray Microemission

A. INTRODUCTION

B. APPARATUS AND TECHNIQUES

C. APPLICATIONS

III. X-Ray Microdiffraction

A. INTRODUCTION

B. APPARATUS AND TECHNIQUE

C. METALLURGICAL APPLICATIONS

D. BIOLOGICAL APPLICATIONS

SECTION ONE

X-RAY MICROABSORPTION

A. INTRODUCTION

HOWARD H. PATTEE

Biophysics Laboratory, Stanford University, Stanford, Calif. (U.S.A.)

The first section of these proceedings contains papers on improvements and refinements of the existing methods of producing and interpreting X-ray images. Theoretical data have been added on ultrasoft X-ray absorption and reflection, on microphotometry, and on reflection optical systems. Instrumental improvements include new recording materials for both light- and electron optical enlargement, as well as special screens for direct viewing, and high intensity sources of small dimensions. New methods of operation of X-ray instruments and of collecting data are also included. In the last half of this section are papers on the application of X-ray imaging methods to diverse fields of biology, medicine, mineralogy, and metallurgy.

Unfortunately, none of the papers produced in the three years since the first X-ray symposium have reported striking advances in spatial resolution. At the time of this conference none of the X-ray imaging methods in actual use could claim resolution significantly different from that of the ordinary light microscope. On the other hand, new evidence is presented that significant improvement in spatial resolution is practicable, using electron optical enlargement of contact X-ray images, and we may expect such results in the near future.

X-ray imaging and recording materials have been produced which extend the useful range of both the contact and projection methods. These include a radiation-sensitive dye which can record an X-ray image, which appears grainless under light microscopic enlargement; a Xerographic process for high-speed X-ray recording; and a fine-grained fluorescent screen which allows direct viewing of a soft X-ray image at high optical magnification.

The interpretation of absorption data from soft X-ray images now rests on firmer ground, since an extensive amount of new data is presented on absorption coefficients, as well as on the possible sources of error resulting from reradiation and photometric measurement of the image.

Improvements reported in the projection method of imaging are largely concerned with refinement of the design and operation of existing microfocus X-ray sources. These include a discussion of electron diffusion in the target, a calculation of the maximum intensities available from microfocus targets of various materials, observations on the fine structure of the X-ray absorption edges, and new techniques of focusing by the use of electrons scattered from the target.

Reflection methods of imaging are represented by only one paper on optical theory and one paper on the construction of a reflection system.

The last half of this section is devoted to applications of these absorption X-ray microscopic image techniques. By far the greatest number of applications are biological, including studies of mineralized tissue, vascular structures, animal and plant tissues. Two papers on mineralogical and one on metallurgical applications were also presented. As indicated in the following sections, the methods of emission and micro-diffraction analysis appear more suitable for the problems of mineralogy and metallurgy.

The future value of absorption images will depend largely on the spatial resolution which can be achieved. As long as the spatial resolution of X-ray imaging methods does not significantly exceed the resolution available with standard light microscopes, it will remain more advantageous in most cases to use light optical methods for localizing the specimen areas to be analyzed by X-ray microprobe techniques. However, if an X-ray resolution of several hundred angströms can be reached, a new region of structural detail will be opened for study in both physical and biological problems. X-ray microscopy, as such, would then have a unique function in studying structures beyond the resolution of the best light optics but without many of the specimen preparation and interpretation problems of electron microscopy in this range of sizes. It is to be expected that such significant improvements in spatial resolution will be reported at the next conference planned for 1962.

B.   GENERAL PRINCIPLES

XEROGRAPHY AS A RECORDING MEDIUM FOR X-RAY MICROSCOPY

J. H. AULD

Australian Defence Scientific Service, Aeronautical Research Laboratories, Melbourne

and

J. F. McNEIL

A.D.S.S., Defence Standards Laboratories, S.A. Branch, Adelaide (Australia)

ABSTRACT

In methods for X-ray microscopy utilising diffracted beams for image formation, the resolution is often limited by the grain size of the film required for recording the low intensity beams in a reasonable time. Xerography using liquid developers, however, offers hope for substantial improvements in this direction. In preliminary experiments, resolutions comparable with those given by ultra-fine grained X-ray films have been obtained with exposure times similar to those for the fastest X-ray films.

Improvements in technique should also make the method advantageous for applications to microradiography.

In recording X-ray images, the sensitivity of silver halide emulsions is approximately proportional to the inverse square of the resolving power so that increased resolving power is only possible at the expense of a considerable reduction in radiographic speed. In methods of X-ray microscopy which utilize diffracted beams for image formation, particularly those using polychromatic rather than characteristic wavelengths, the resolution obtainable can therefore be limited by the grain size of the silver halide-coated film necessary to give acceptable exposure times.

Xerography (or electro-photography) which utilizes entirely different principles of image formation appears to offer advantages which make it worth investigating as an image-recording system for X-ray microscopy. In this technique a photoconductive coating on a backing material is uniformly charged in the dark and on exposure to light or X-rays the charge is conducted away, in proportion to the quantity of radiation incident at any point thus leaving an electrostatic latent image on the coating surface. Either amorphous photoconductive coatings such as vacuum-evaporated selenium or particulate coatings such as zinc oxide powder dispersed in a resin matrix may be used. In the latter case, however, the resolving power is limited by the particle size of the photoconductor so that where highest resolving power is required amorphous coatings, normally of vitreous selenium, must be used. As such coatings are grainless and since no evidence of sideways spreading of the charge has yet been obtained, it is clear that the latent electrostatic image on vitreous selenium is one of high resolution.

METHOD

In the conventional xerographic process the image is rendered visible by development with charged dry powder particles which adhere to the selenium in proportion to the charge remaining on the plate. Due to the relative coarseness of the powders which must be employed and to aggregation effects, no dry development technique has been able to take the advantage of the inherent resolving power of the selenium plate.

The liquid development process which was originated by METCALFE and WRIGHT[1,2] enables much finer particles to be employed and therefore gives much better resolution than dry development techniques. Using liquid development and high quality selenium coatings McNEIL and JOLLY[3] have produced line images by optical means which show resolutions in excess of 600 lines/mm. This work also suggests that, at least up to resolutions of the order of 1000 lines/mm, it is the development stage which controls the resolving power of the selenium-plate – liquid-developer combination.

Where maximum resolving power is required, the selenium coating however must be free from defects such as scratches and discrete particles thrown up during evaporation; it must also be uniformly vitreous and free from even microscopic crystallites. Such coatings must therefore be deposited either on highly polished metal substrates or on good quality glass plates upon which an electrically conducting layer of cadmium oxide has been deposited by vacuum sputtering prior to deposition of the selenium. McNEIL and JOLLY have shown that image defects and artefacts become less numerous the thinner the selenium coating is made and for high resolution applications involving optical images they recommend the use of selenium coatings only 0.2 to 2.5μ in thickness. Such thin coatings however have relatively low sensitivity to X-rays and for the following experimental work a coating thickness of 10μ was selected as offering a reasonable compromise between radiographic sensitivity and freedom from artefacts and other image defects.

The plates were produced on 7.5 cm × 5 cm glass substrates which were first coated with a sputtered layer of cadmium oxide 0.05μ in thickness. The selenium (99.998 grade) was then evaporated from a molybdenum boat *in vacuo* and in the dark, the plate temperature being controlled so as not to exceed 20° C during evaporation.

APPLICATION

To investigate the applicability of xerography to this type of work it was decided to apply it to the SCHULZ technique[4] which we have been using to study deformation in aluminium single crystals[5]. SCHULZ photographs are essentially high resolution Laue diffraction images obtained by using a microfocus X-ray source; detail produced in the images is a result of disturbances to the perfection of the lattice planes. The experimental arrangement is shown in Fig. 1.

The microfocus X-ray unit had a focal spot size of 50μ dia. and was operated at 40 kV with a current of 250 μA. The selenium plates were charged negatively by means of a 10 kV corona discharge which produced a saturation charge on the plates in 30 sec. The plates were developed by means of positively charged pigment particles suspended in a volatile petroleum fraction. Used under these conditions the speed of the selenium plates is only about half that available with positive charging, however difficulty has been experienced in obtaining reproducible plate behaviour when positive charging is used.

Electron micrographs showed the developer particles to be acicular in shape with an average length of approximately $1\,\mu$. The plates were developed for 30 sec after which they were dried in a current of warm air. Developed images could be removed by gently brushing the plate in water containing a detergent; by this method the plates could be used many times but scratches due to brushing gradually accumulated. For permanent records the images were photographed either with glancing or normal illumination.

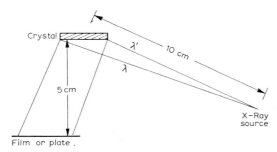

Fig. 1. Experimental arrangement of SCHULZ technique.

A series of tests showed that satisfactory xerographs of SCHULZ images could be obtained with exposure times of $1\frac{1}{2}$ h whereas a coarse grained industrial X-ray film (with one emulsion of the double-sided film removed) required $\frac{1}{2}$ h. There was less evidence of grain in the xerographs and the detail appeared sharper but from the lack of finer detail it was clear that we were limited by the resolution of the X-ray technique. It had not been possible to check this previously by the use of ultra-fine grained X-ray films as the movement of the focal spot during the long

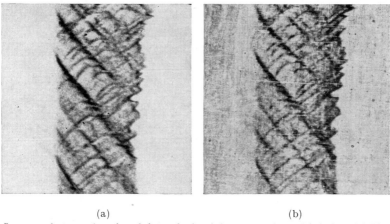

(a)   (b)

Fig. 2. SCHULZ photographs of a deformed aluminium crystal on (a) industrial X-ray film, (b) xerographic plate. Magnification 10×.

exposures involved (up to 6 h) has sometimes resulted in even less sharp photographs than those on coarse grained film. The most likely factor limiting the resolution is the focal spot size although the appreciable depth of material which contributes to the diffraction may be a factor in the case of aluminium specimens. Fig. 2 shows comparative SCHULZ photographs taken on industrial X-ray film and on a xero-

References p. 9

graphic plate. The black lines correspond to deformation bands in the aluminium single crystal which has been strained 1 % at −196° C.

RESULTS

To obtain some measure of the radiographic resolving power of the plates, a corner of a 500 mesh/in. copper grid was folded and contact microradiographs were made of it at a distance of 45 cm from the microfocus source using 40 kV and 250 μA. The grid was actually located 1 mm in front of the selenium plate. Similar exposures were also made on industrial and ultra-fine grained X-ray films. The results are

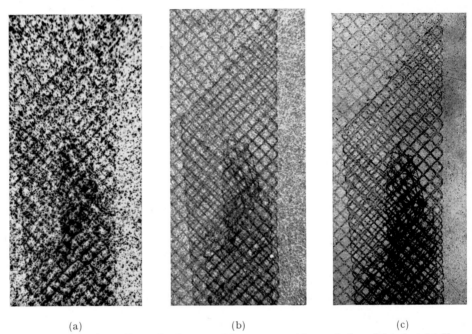

(a)   (b)   (c)

Fig. 3. Contact microradiograph of 500 mesh/in. copper grid recorded on (a) industrial X-ray film, (b) ultra-fine grained X-ray film, (c) xerographic plate. Magnification 50×.

shown in Fig. 3 at 50 × magnification. The estimated resolving powers together with the required exposure times are given in Table I.

TABLE I

	Resolving power	Exposure time
	lines/mm	sec
Industrial X-ray film	20	1
Ultra-fine grained X-ray film	100	25
Xerograph	120	15

The exposure time of the xerograph relative to that of the industrial film was longer in this case than for the SCHULZ photographs. However, in spite of this there is still a considerable gain in speed over that of a silver halide emulsion for the resolution obtained.

References p. 9

These preliminary results thus indicate that xerography can be used with advantage in X-ray diffraction methods of microscopy and should permit improvements to be made in the resolution of these techniques by modifications which involve some loss of X-ray intensity. It could also have application to low magnification contact microradiography especially where short exposures are required such as for living tissues. Further work is being undertaken to investigate the possibilities of taking advantage of the two fold increase in speed which results from positive charging of the selenium plates and of further improving the resolving power of the plate – developer combination.

ACKNOWLEDGEMENTS

The authors wish to thank Dr. R. I. GARROD for advice and encouragement, Mr. B. E. WILLIAMS for assistance in the work, and Messrs. K. A. METCALFE, R. J. WRIGHT and A. S. CLEMENTS for xerographic materials. This paper is published by permission of the Chief Scientist, Australian Defence Scientific Service, Department of Supply.

REFERENCES

[1] K. A. METCALFE, *J. Sci. Instr.*, 32 (1955) 74.
[2] K. A. METCALFE and R. J. WRIGHT, *J. Sci. Instr.*, 33 (1956) 149.
[3] J. F. McNEIL and D. JOLLY, *J. Phot. Sci.*, in the press.
[4] L. G. SCHULZ, *Trans. Am. Inst. Mining. Met. Eng.*, 200 (1954) 1082.
[5] R. A. COYLE, A. M. MARSHALL, J. H. AULD and N. A. McKINNON, *Brit. J. Appl. Phys.*, 8 (1957) 79.

ULTRASOFT X-RAY INTERACTION COEFFICIENTS

BURTON L. HENKE

Millikan Laboratory of Physics, Pomona College
Claremont, Calif. (U.S.A.)

ABSTRACT

Ultrasoft X-ray interactions as absorption, diffraction, grazing incidence reflection and transmission are being investigated as bases for the analysis of microscopic systems for structure, mass and chemical information. The complex atomic scattering factors for the light elements C_6 to Ge_{32} and for the long wavelength X-ray region have been calculated from mass photoelectric absorption coefficients[1] using an integral relationship given by the quantum mechanical theory of dispersion[2]. The anomalous scattering due to electron "resonances" at the K and the L critical absorption edge wavelengths has been found to be more extensive than that predicted by the older dispersion theories. The reflection efficiency as a function of both angle of reflection and of wavelength has been calculated for a quartz and an aluminum mirror from the atomic scattering coefficients. The predicted reflection curves are found to be in good agreement with those obtained experimentally.

I. INTRODUCTION

For two important reasons ultrasoft X-radiations are appropriate for the micro-analysis of systems in the micron size range, and particularly for the light element

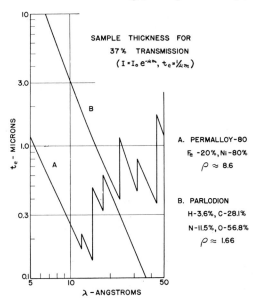

SAMPLE THICKNESS FOR
37% TRANSMISSION
$(I = I_0 e^{-\mu m}, t_e = 1/\mu m)$

A. PERMALLOY-80
F_e -20%, Ni -80%
$\rho \approx 8.6$

B. PARLODION
H-3.6%, C-28.1%
N-11.5%, O-56.8%
$\rho \approx 1.66$

Fig. 1. The thickness which is required for approximately 60 % absorption as a function of X-ray wavelength for an organic sample, Parlodion, and for Permalloy-80.

References p. 29

materials: (1) these yield the required absorption signal for precise analysis, and (2) such wavelengths include the critical absorption-edge wavelengths, either K or L, which often can form the bases for analysis of maximum sensitivity and uniqueness. In Fig. 1, the thickness which will yield 60 % absorption signal (as approximately required for optimum absorption or diffraction analysis, for example) is shown to be of the order of 1 μ for the low atomic number materials, (A) Permalloy and (B) Parlodion and for the ultrasoft wavelength region. The presence of the critical absorption edges is also illustrated here. In Table I, the K and L emission and critical absorption wavelengths for the light elements are given.

TABLE I

Z	Element	$K_{\alpha12}$	K_{ab}		Z	Element	$L_{\alpha12}$	L_{Iab}	L_{IIab}	L_{IIIab}
1	H		911		13	Al		142	170	172
2	He		504		14	Si		105	125	126
3	Li	238	225		15	P		81.0	96.1	96.8
4	Be	112	107		16	S		64.2	75.6	76.0
5	B	67.0	64.6		17	Cl		52.1	61.1	61.4
6	C	44.0	43.8		18	A		43.2	50.2	50.6
7	N	31.6	31.1		19	K		36.3	41.7	42.2
8	O	23.7	23.3		20	Ca	38.0	31.1	35.2	35.5
9	F	18.3	18.0		21	Sc	31.4	26.8	30.2	30.5
10	Ne	14.6	14.2		22	Ti	27.4	23.4	26.9	27.3
11	Na	11.6	11.5		23	Va	24.3	20.5	23.9	24.2
12	Mg	9.88	9.51		24	Cr	21.7	18.3	21.3	21.6
13	Al	8.34(α1)	7.95		25	Mn	19.5	16.3	19.1	19.4
					26	Fe	17.6	14.6	17.2	17.5
					27	Co	16.0	13.3	15.6	15.9
					28	Ni	14.6	12.2	14.2	14.5
					29	Cu	13.4	11.3	13.0	13.3
					30	Zn	12.3	10.3	11.9	12.1
					31	Ga	11.3	9.54	10.9	11.1
					32	Ge	10.4	8.73	9.93	10.2

The $K_{\alpha12}$ and $L_{\alpha12}$ emission lines and the K and L absorption edges in the ultrasoft region as derived from the compilation of emission and absorption edge energies given by S. FINE and C. F. HENDEE, *Nucleonics*, 13, 3 (1955) 36.

Ultrasoft X-ray interactions are, in general, much simpler than those for light and for conventional X-radiation. (See Fig. 2.) In transmission through uniform, isotropic samples, nearly all of the absorption is photoelectric. The energy is re-emitted essentially as photo- and Auger electron emission, and for C, N and O, for example, the fluorescent yields are less than 1 %; there is negligible incoherent scattering. The coherently scattered energy is often measurable in low-angle diffraction or, in grazing incidence, "total reflection" from surfaces.

In order to design optimum microanalysis methods based upon these effects, it is usually necessary to have detailed quantitative information on the interaction coefficients. Below, the work accomplished in this laboratory on the semi-empirical determination of such coefficients which have been found to be useful for absorption, diffraction, and reflection microanalysis is summarized.

References p. 29

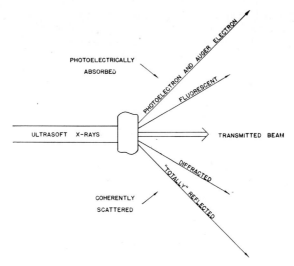

Fig. 2. Ultrasoft X-ray interactions.

II. PHOTOELECTRIC ABSORPTION COEFFICIENTS

A fundamental interaction coefficient, most directly measurable, is the mass absorption coefficient, μ, defined by the usual law

(1) $$I = I_0 \exp(-\mu m)$$

in which I and I_0 are the transmitted and incident intensities respectively and m is the mass per unit area of the sample; m is equal to the sample mass density multiplied by the sample thickness. The photoelectric absorption coefficient, μ, *unlike* the linear absorption coefficient, should depend only upon the elementary chemistry of the sample. In microanalysis, the thickness of the sample is usually best determined as the directly measured mass-per-unit area "thickness", m. The density and the linear thickness values are secondary variables, much less amenable to direct measurement and are therefore much less useful parameters. We have found that the mass photoelectric absorption coefficient can only very approximately be described by simple power law expressions as, for example,

(2) $$\mu = \text{Const.} \times Z^p \lambda^q$$

in which Z is the atomic number and λ is the wavelength. Nevertheless, because the absorption coefficients for many materials are extremely difficult to measure precisely in the ultrasoft X-ray region, it was felt very important to find some kind of "universal" absorption curves which could permit precise interpolation of a complete set of coefficients based upon those which can be measured accurately. Such functions have been found[1], as suggested by quantum mechanical theory of photoelectric absorption, and are of the form

(3) $$(\mu_K A / \lambda) = F_1(\lambda/\lambda_1)$$

in which μ_K is the mass absorption coefficient associated with the removal of K electrons from the atom, A is the atomic weight, λ is the incident wavelength and

λ_1 is a wavelength number characteristic of the K shell of the particular atom which is only approximately equal to the corresponding critical absorption edge wavelength. The characteristic wavelengths, λ_1, and the universal function $F_1(\lambda/\lambda_1)$, have been determined empirically from available ultrasoft X-ray absorption coefficients and in a similar manner a universal function $F_2(\lambda/\lambda_2)$ and associated characteristic wavelengths for the photoelectric absorption due to mainly the L shell electrons have also been derived. The absorption functions are shown in Fig. 3 along with the cor-

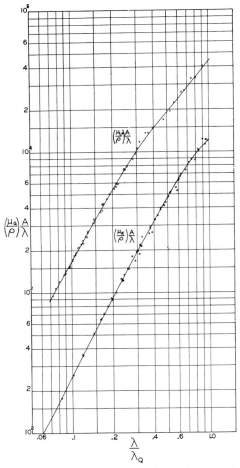

Fig. 3. Plots of the empirically derived "universal" absorption function $F_1\ (\lambda/\lambda_1)$ and $F_2\ (\lambda/\lambda_2)$ along with the experimental points obtained from all of ALLEN's non-interpolated photoelectric absorption coefficients which have been reported for the ultrasoft X-ray region.

responding points obtained from all of the non-interpolated experimental data given by ALLEN[3]. In Fig. 4 is shown the empirically derived characteristic wavelengths, λ_1 and λ_2, plotted against the atomic number, Z, as a Moseley plot. It is seen here that the variable $1/\sqrt{\lambda_q}$ for these empirical wavelength numbers follow nearly linearly with Z as it does for the critical absorption edge and characteristic emission wavelengths. This linear relation provides a good interpolational basis

References p. 29

for the derivation of a complete set of characteristic numbers, λ_1 and λ_2, for the light elements. With these, and using the universal functions, a table of ultrasoft X-ray photoelectric absorption coefficients has been calculated. (See Table II).

TABLE II

MASS ABSORPTION COEFFICIENTS FOR SOME USEFUL ULTRASOFT WAVELENGTHS DERIVED SEMIEMPIRICALLY[1] WITH A PROBABLE ERROR OF ABOUT ± 2 %

Absorber	Atomic Number	Al Kα12 8.34 Å	Cu Lα12 13.3 Å	Fe Lα12 17.6 Å	Cr Lα12 21.7 Å	O Kα12 23.7 Å	Ti Lα12 27.4 Å	C Kα12 44.0 Å
H	1	7.5	30	70	130	170	260	1100
He	2	30	120	275	500	660	1000	4300
Li	3	78	280	640	1200	1450	2300	9400
Be	4	151.7	581	1288	2292	2965	4532	17430
B	5	323.7	1233	2711	4784	6130	9200	32540
C	6	605	2290	4912	8440	10730	15760	
N	7	1047	3795	7910	13120	16270	22590	3647
O	8	1560	5430	10740	16610	983	1473	5470
F	9	1913	6340	11600	1015	1301	1949	7280
Ne	10	2763	8240	1079	1863	2379	3575	13180
Na	11	3129	661	1402	2429	3100	4651	16650
Mg	12	3797	981	2085	3601	4592	6830	22850
Al	13	322.6	1146	2441	4189	5310	7840	24910
Si	14	510	1813	3812	6420	8040	11510	33840
P	15	640	2259	4661	7670	9470	13280	38610
S	16	814	2839	5710	9160	11190	15520	45230
Cl	17	990	3364	6530	10210	12450	17330	50100
A	18	1163	3795	7110	11070	13540	18820	
K	19	1429	4504	8310	12960	15820	22030	
Ca	20	1706	5150	9450	14800	18030	24910	
Zapon		998	3571	7270	11690	6500	9470	
Parlodion		1177	4167	8390	13320	5450	7870	
Animal proteins		854	3095	6391	10480	8719	12584	
H_2O		1388	4830	9554	14779	893	1338	4984

Zapon (H 5.3 %, C 46.7 %, N 6.6 %, O 41.4 %), Parlodion (H 3.6 %, C 28.1 %, N 11.5 %, O 56.8 %), Animal proteins (H 7 %, C 52.5 %, N 16.5 %, O 22.5 %, S 1.5 %)

These coefficients have an average deviation of ± 2.4 % from the weighted and averaged experimental data of ALLEN. This method for computing absorption coefficients has been found to be very valuable in the development of microanalysis methods. It is evident, however, that more directly measured absorption data is needed for the ultrasoft X-ray region in order that the indeterminacy of the absorption coefficients be not the limiting effect on accuracy of measurement.

III. ATOMIC SCATTERING FACTORS

Directly measured effects, as absorption, diffraction, etc., are necessarily the result of many atomic interactions within the finite sample thickness traversed by the

X-ray beam. In order to correctly interpret the total integrated effects and/or to be able to deduce microscopic information from such, a knowledge of the atomic interaction coefficients is required.

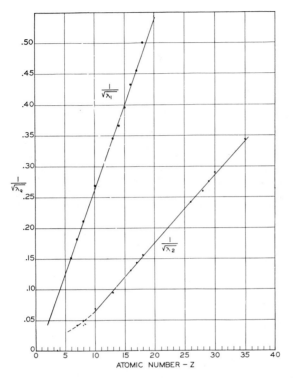

Fig. 4. Moseley plots of the empirically determined values for λ_1 and λ_2 as derived from available photoelectric absorption data. These nearly linear curves permit the interpolation of a complete set of the characteristic numbers, λ_1 and λ_2, for the lighter elements.

The interaction of X-radiation with a single many-electron atom is, in general, a complex process described by the quantum theory[4] only in varying degrees of approximation. Fortunately, a relatively simple and precise quantum mechanical expression for the atomic interaction coefficient obtains for the ultrasoft X-ray wavelengths which are of interest here. The great simplification in the theory results for several reasons: first of all, as already mentioned, since the low energies associated with ultrasoft X-ray quanta are of the same order of magnitude as the binding energies of the effective interacting atomic electrons, incoherent scattering as Raman or Compton scattering is negligible. Also, due to the relatively low energy of these radiations, the atomic electrons respond as bound oscillators, resulting in the anomalous dispersion of the radiation, and the contribution due to terms usually associated with free electron scattering may also be neglected.

For the ultrasoft region, therefore, the quantum mechanical expression for the atomic scattering factor (total amplitude scattered by the atom relative to that which would be scattered by a free classical electron for the same polarization of the primary wave) becomes:

(4)
$$f = \Sigma_q' \int_{\omega_q}^{\infty} \frac{\omega_i^2 (dg/d\omega)_q \, d\omega}{(\omega_i^2 - \omega^2) - i\gamma\omega_i}$$

Here, ω_i is the incident X-ray frequency and ω_q is the critical absorption frequency characteristic of the q-type electrons as K, L, M etc. Now recalling the expression for the dispersion of X-radiation by a single, bound electronic oscillator on the basis of classical theory, viz.

(5)
$$f = \Sigma_q \frac{\omega_i^2 g_q}{(\omega_i^2 - \omega_q^2) - i\gamma_q\omega_i}$$

we note a correspondence between this and the quantum mechanical result in (4). In (5) g_q represents the number of q-type oscillators within the atom and the total amplitude scattered by the atom is given as a summation of the amplitudes scattered by each type. Here, γ_q is a radiative damping factor for the q-type electrons.

We may now give the quantum mechanical result (4) the following convenient, classical interpretation: The atom "scatters" as an assemblage of virtual oscillators, each of resonance frequency within a continuous band from ω_q to infinitely large values. $(dg/d\omega)d\omega$, then, represents the number of oscillators having a resonance frequency in the ω to $\omega + d\omega$ interval, and $(dg/d\omega)$ is thus an oscillator density function. Quantum mechanically, this function is proportional to the transitional probability associated with the photo ejection of a q-type electron from the ground state to a state in the positive energy continuum of energy $h\omega/2\pi$.

By invoking the sum rule (setting $\Sigma_q \int_{\omega_q}^{\infty}(dg/d\omega)d\omega = Z$) and restricting ω_i to values outside the region very close to a critical absorption frequency, $\omega_q \pm \Delta\omega_q$, where $\Delta\omega_q$ is of the order of magnitude of the natural line breadth of the associated characteristic radiation (and thus not accessible to experimental measurement) (4) reduces to

(6)
$$f = f_1 + if_2 = Z + \Sigma_q \int_{\omega_q}^{\infty} \frac{\omega^2 (dg/d\omega)_q \, d\omega}{\omega_i^2 - \omega^2} + i\Sigma_q \frac{\pi\omega_i}{2} \left(\frac{dg}{d\omega_i}\right)_q$$

From (6) it is evident that both the real and the imaginary components of the atomic scattering factor can be completely determined if the oscillator density function is known, since the damping factor does not appear in the final result. Although the function $(dg/d\omega)$ can be calculated theoretically in terms of transition probabilities, it may also be determined directly from the atomic photoelectric absorption cross sections. As would be expected, the number of virtual oscillators per unit frequency interval of a certain resonant frequency, ω, is proportional to the atomic absorption coefficient for the same type of electrons and at the same frequency, and is given by the relation

(7)
$$(dg/d\omega)_q = (mc/2\pi^2 e^2)\mu_a(\omega)_q$$

We have used our universal absorption functions, F_1 and F_2, described in section II, in order to obtain semi-empirical functions for the atomic interaction coefficients[5]. We write for the oscillator density functions for the K and for the L type electrons respectively:

(8)
$$\left(\frac{dg}{d\omega}\right)_K = K \frac{F_1\left(\frac{\omega_1}{\omega}\right)}{\omega} \quad \text{and} \quad \left(\frac{dg}{d\omega}\right)_L = K \frac{F_2\left(\frac{\omega_2}{\omega}\right)}{\omega}$$

For the corresponding oscillator strengths:

$$(9) \qquad g_K = K \int_{\omega_K}^{\infty} \frac{F_1\left(\frac{\omega_1}{\omega}\right) d\omega}{\omega} \quad \text{and} \quad g_L = K \int_{\omega_L}^{\infty} \frac{F_2\left(\frac{\omega_2}{\omega}\right)}{\omega} d\omega$$

For the real part of the atomic scattering factor:

$$(10) \qquad f_1 = Z + \Delta f_1 = Z + K \int_{\omega_K}^{\infty} \frac{\omega F_1\left(\frac{\omega_1}{\omega}\right) d\omega}{\omega_1^2 - \omega^2} + K \int_{\omega_L}^{\infty} \frac{\omega F_2\left(\frac{\omega_2}{\omega}\right) d\omega}{\omega_i^2 - \omega^2}$$

And finally, for the imaginary part of the atomic scattering factor:

$$(11) \qquad f_2 = \tfrac{1}{2}K\left[F_1\left(\frac{\omega_1}{\omega}\right) + F_2\left(\frac{\omega_2}{\omega}\right) \right]$$

In the above expressions, the constant K is given by the relation

$$K = 10^8 \, (mc^2/\pi N e^2) = 5.890 \times 10^{-4}$$

in which e and m are the charge and mass of the electron, N is Avagadro's number, and c is the velocity of light.

The relations (10) and (11) obtain for the light elements and for the ultrasoft X-ray region — that is, for interactions involving the dispersion of X-radiation in which the K electrons play the dominant role. It has been assumed that the incident wavelength is large compared with the diameter of the K electron orbit. The Thomas-Fermi diameter of the first orbit is given as

$$(12) \qquad d = 2a_0/Z^{1/3} \sim 1/Z^{1/3} \text{ angstroms}$$

where a_0 is the first Bohr radius of the hydrogen atom. Often in microanalysis it is desirable to use wavelengths near a critical absorption discontinuity. We shall note the ratio of the K-orbital diameter to wavelength for two cases, copper K radiation (1.54 Å) scattered by the copper atom and oxygen K radiation (23.7 Å) scattered by the oxygen atom. For the former case, with a conventional X-ray wavelength, this ratio is $(1/29^{1/3})/1.5 = 1/4.5$ and for the latter, with the ultrasoft wavelength, the ratio is $(1/8^{1/3})/23.7 = 1/48$. For wavelengths near the K absorption discontinuity, the atomic diameter to wavelength ratio is proportional to $Z^{5/3}$ since, by Moseley's law, the critical absorption wavelengths are proportional to $1/Z^2$.

Generally, the atomic scattering factor decreases with the angle of scattering. This is observed for conventional X-rays and is due to the fact that the amplitudes scattered from different parts of the atom will be at different phases. When, however, the atomic dimensions are very small compared with wavelength, as for wavelengths of interest here, all parts of the atoms scatter nearly in the same phase except, perhaps, for angles of scattering in the region of 90°. For this reason the expression above for the atomic scattering factors for the ultrasoft X-ray region may be applied for most angles of interest in microanalysis applications.

It is thus evident that for atomic interactions involving long wavelengths and light elements, the total scattering can be predicted in terms of the complex atomic scattering factor. By definition, the scattered amplitude from the atom is given by multiplying the scattering factor by the amplitude scattered from a free, classical electron, $viz.$

$$(13) \qquad E_e = -E_0\left(\frac{e^2}{mc^2}\right) \frac{\sin \phi}{|R|} e^{i\omega\left(t - \frac{|R|}{c}\right)}$$

The quantity (e^2/mc^2) is the classical radius of the electron, r_0, and is equal to 2.818×10^{-13} cm. E_0 is the electric field intensity and ω the frequency of the incident wave; e and m have their usual meanings; R is the distance in cm to the point of observation of the scattered amplitude, E; and c is the velocity of the

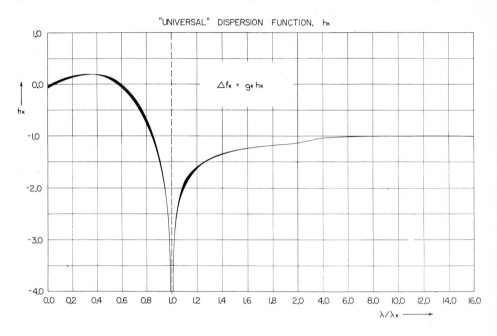

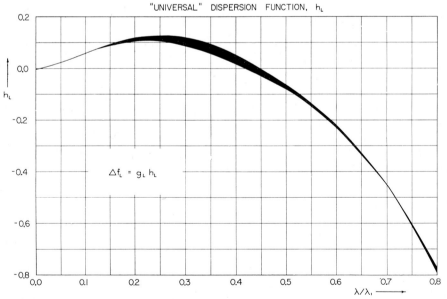

Fig. 5. Plots of h_K and h_L for the light elements demonstrating the degree of universality for these functions. The real part of the atomic scattering factor is given by the relation
$$f_1 = Z + \Delta f_K + \Delta f_L.$$

References p. 29

wave. The angle, ϕ, is that between the direction of observation and the direction of polarization (hence of E_0) of the incident wave. The intensity that is scattered by the atom is proportional to the square of this factor and hence to $\sin^2 \phi$. If the incident radiation is unpolarized, the intensity must then be proportional to the

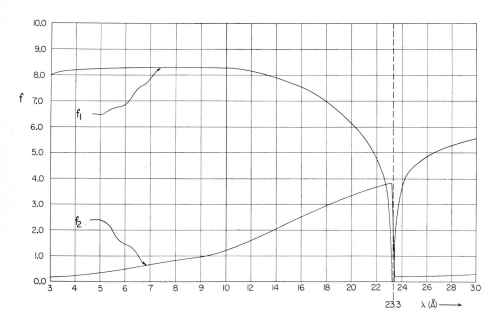

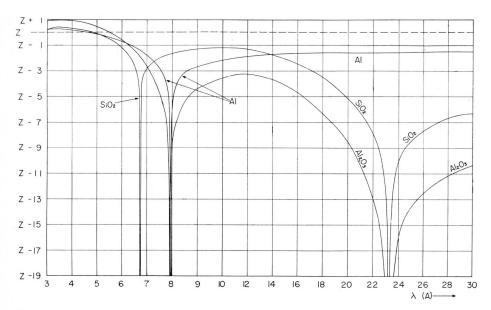

Fig. 6. (a) Atomic scattering factor for oxygen, $f = f_1 + if_2$. (b) The real part of the atomic structure factors for small angle of scattering for Al, Al_2O_3 and SiO_2. The imaginary part of the atomic structure factors are calculated directly from the photoelectric absorption coefficients.

References p. 29

average value of $\sin^2 \phi$ and thus to $\frac{1}{2}(1 + \cos^2 \theta)$ where θ is the angle of scattering.

For the purposes of numerical integration it is convenient to rewrite the first integral in (10) as

$$(14) \qquad f_{1K} = Km^2 h^2 \int_0^N \frac{F_1(x)\,dx}{x(x^2 - m^2 h^2)}$$

Here, x is the variable λ/λ_1 of the tabulated F_1 and h is the interval of the table. The incident wavelength ratio λ_i/λ_1 is set equal to mh, where m is an integer (1 to 100). N_K is the ratio of the characteristic wavelengths, λ_K/λ_1. It is evident that Δf_{1K} is a function of not only the incident wavelength ratio λ/λ_1, but also of N_K. In order to express the results of the integration in terms of a function which varies relatively slowly with N_K (a "nearly universal" function), Δf_{1K} is normalized by dividing it by its value for $mh \gg 1$, which is equal to the negative of the oscillator strength g_K. This normalized function is defined as h_K, which has been tabulated for values of λ_i/λ_1 from 0.10 to 16.0 and for values of N_K from 0.90 to 1.10. In order to indicate its departure from universality, h_K is plotted in Fig. 5 (a) for the light elements up through Z equal to 20.

An analogous expression for the contribution of the L type electrons to the anomalous dispersion, h_L, has been tabulated and is given in Fig. 5 (b), similarly plotted for the light elements.

With the tabulated g_K, g_L, h_K and h_L functions, it becomes relatively easy to calculate the atomic scattering factors for the light elements and for the ultrasoft wavelengths, and to combine these to form the structure factors for molecular groups. It must be remembered that unlike the atomic diameters, the molecular diameters may not be very small compared to the incident wavelengths so that if the atomic scattering factors are simply added, assuming no phase differences between their scattered amplitudes, the resulting structure factors are valid only for the small angles of scattering. Since most applications of the ultrasoft X-rays to microanalysis involve only small-angle effects (as refraction, low-angle diffraction and total reflection) this is not usually a serious limitation.

In Fig. 6 (a) is shown a plot of the calculated components of the atomic scattering factor for oxygen. In Fig. 6 (b), the calculated values of f_1 are plotted for Al, Al_2O_3 and for SiO_2. It should be noted that the anomalous contribution to the scattering of X-rays cannot be neglected in any part of the wavelength region of interest here.

Often in the calculation of reflection or diffraction intensities for conventional X-rays, damping effects are neglected. For the ultrasoft region, this is usually not possible, and it is necessary to replace the f^2 factor in the conventional analysis for intensities by the modulus squared of the atomic scattering factor (or structure factor), viz. $(f_1^2 + f_2^2)$. In order to illustrate the magnitude of the effect of f_2 upon intensity, the factor $(1 + f_2^2/f_1^2)$ is plotted as a function of wavelengths for SiO_2 in Fig. 7 (a).

The phase of the scattered wave from a molecule will not only depend upon its position relative to the point of observation, but also, because of the term f_2, it will depend upon the wavelength. This contribution to the phase shift is given by the relation

$$(15) \qquad \Delta \psi = \tan^{-1} (f_2/f_1)$$

The magnitude of $\Delta\psi$ for the SiO_2 molecule (and for the smaller angles of scattering) is shown in Fig. 7b.

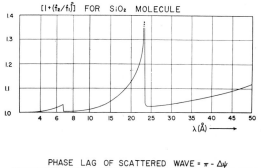

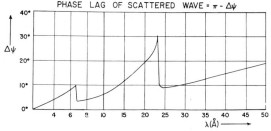

Fig. 7. The effect of the term f_2 due to damping upon (a) the modulus of the scattering factor (or structure factor for small angles of scattering) equal to $f_1(1 + (f_2/f_1)^2)$ and (b) the phase of the scattered wave.

IV. ULTRASOFT X-RAY SCATTERING

Often a microscopic sample may be considered as a more or less packed collection of particles, each particle unit containing a large number of atoms. For such, the next step in the analysis for the effect of the total sample on an X-ray beam is to determine the interaction with the single particle unit of the matter. This would depend not only upon the type of atoms involved, but also upon the size and the shape of the particle.

It should be mentioned here that sometimes a more precise model for the real sample is obtained by defining a continuous density distribution through the sample space which fluctuates according to the irregularities of the sample. A vast amount of work[6] has been carried out on X-ray scattering from both points of view. It is desired here to give one simple example, the prediction of the total amplitude scattered by a uniform sphere which is of dimensions that are large compared with the X-ray wavelength — in order to indicate the method and the assumptions involved, to introduce the "unconventional" effects associated with ultrasoft X-ray scattering, and finally to present a result which is useful for predicting "order of magnitude" effects, in connection with the design of microanalysis methods.

It is desired to obtain the total amplitude scattered at any angle, θ, out of a collimated beam of ultrasoft X-rays, summing over the molecular scattered amplitudes from all parts of the sphere. We make the following assumptions: (1) The sphere radius is sufficiently large compared with the wavelength $(a/\lambda > 10)$ so that only small-angle scattering will be appreciable and therefore the angular dependence of the molecular scattering factor (the structure factor) may be neglected. This is not a serious limitation in as much as only the small-angle scattering is sufficiently concentrated for most ultrasoft X-ray scattering measurements. (2) The ratio a/λ is sufficiently small ($a/\lambda < 100$ for ultrasoft radiations) so that only single non-refractive scattering occurs. (3) The density of molecules is considered as uniform and isotropic throughout the sphere and equal to that which obtains for differential volume elements which are small compared with the total volume.

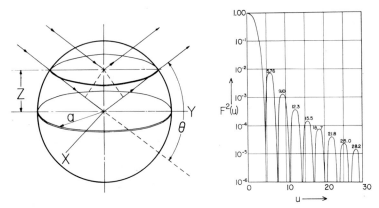

Fig. 8. Scattering by a spherical particle. (a) The constant-phase geometry for the scattering of a plane wave at an angle θ by a non-absorbing and non-refractive sphere of radius equal to a, and (b) the integrated intensity distribution function, $F^2(u)$, versus the parameter u which is equal to $(4\pi a/\lambda) \sin \theta/2$.

The total scattered amplitude, then, may be obtained by integrating over the limits of the sphere the differential amplitudes scattered by circular sections which contribute scattered amplitudes of constant phase throughout the section. See Fig. 8 (a). Using (13) and (15), this differential amplitude measured R cm from the center of the sphere, may be written as

$$(16) \qquad dE = -E_0 \left(\frac{r_0 \sin \phi}{R}\right) |f| \, n\pi(a^2 - z^2) \, dz \exp\{i\,[\omega(t - R/C) - Kz - \Delta\psi]\}$$

in which $k = \dfrac{4\pi \sin \theta/2}{\lambda}$ and where $\pi(a^2 - z^2)dz$ is the differential volume of the constant phase section and n is the number of molecules per unit volume, each of structure factor modulus $|f| = (f_1^2 + f_2^2)^{\frac{1}{2}}$. The integral over the spherical volume becomes (setting $e^{ikz} = \cos kz + i \sin kz$)

$$(17) \qquad E = -E_e |f| e^{i\Delta\psi} (n\pi) \left\{ \int_{-a}^{a} dz(a^2 - z^2) \cos kz + i \int_{-a}^{a} dz(a^2 - z^2) \sin kz \right\}$$

The second integral is equal to zero (odd integrand and symmetric limits). The first is easily integrated to give

$$(18) \qquad E = -E_e |f| e^{i\Delta\psi} (4/3) \pi a^3 \, n \, \frac{3 \, (\sin ka - ka \cos ka)}{(ka)^3}$$

The flow of energy per unit area at the position R from the sphere, i.e. the intensity, is given by multiplying the square of the modulus of the electric field intensity by the factor $c/4\pi$. By denoting the incident intensity as $(c/4\pi)E_0^2$, we obtain

$$(19) \qquad I = I_0\,(f_1^2 + f_2^2)\,[(4/3)\pi a^3 n]^2\,(r_0/R)^2\,[F(u)]^2$$

$F(u)$ is equal to $3(\sin u - u \cos u)/u^3$, $(u = ka)$, and is plotted in Fig. 8 (b). It may be noted that a strong central scattering occurs, nearly Gaussian in form, and of inflection-point half-width at a scattering angle given by

$$(20) \qquad 2 \sin (\theta/2) \approx \lambda/4a \approx \theta \text{ for small angles}$$

By integrating (19) for the total energy scattered over a spherical area of $4\pi R^2$, and dividing by the incident intensity, I_0, the cross section for small angle scattering by a sphere is readily obtained as

$$(21) \qquad S = 2\pi\, n^2\, r_0^2 (f_1^2 + f_2^2)\, R^4 \lambda^2$$

In the above expressions the only modification to the conventional theory for the scattering of X-rays by a sphere has been the introduction of the f_2 term which cannot be neglected, compared to f_1, in the ultrasoft X-ray wavelength region. The application of these results is limited mainly by the assumption that the wavelet scattered by a particular atom within the sphere proceeds radially to the point of measurement without any further interactions and without interfering with the direct X-ray beam — hence without any refraction effects.

In order to determine the degree to which these results are an approximation for the long wavelengths, different and more exact derivations of the scattering equations have been studied[7]. MIE obtained the complete solution, in series form, using Maxwell's equations and introducing the material properties through the dielectric constant, or, equivalently, through the refractive index. By examining the work of VAN DE HULST, HART and MONTROLL reduced the MIE solution finally to closed form for the case of relatively "soft" spheres, i.e. for the refractive index approaching unity. We have introduced a complex refractive index, $m = 1 - \delta - i\beta$, into their expressions and have retained only the terms which are significant for the region in which the quantity $(\delta^2 + \beta^2)$ is very small compared with unity. We obtain a very similar expression to that of (19), viz.

$$(22) \qquad I = I_0(\delta^2 + \beta^2)\,(\tfrac{4}{3}\pi a^3)^2\,\frac{4\pi^2}{\lambda^4 R^2}\,[F(w)]^2 \text{ where } w = u\left\{1 + \frac{\delta^2\left[1 + \left(\frac{\beta}{\delta}\right)^2\right]}{2\,(\delta/2 \sin \theta/2)^2}\right\}$$

from which we may deduce the relations between the increments of the refractive index and the components of the atomic scattering factors, viz.

$$(23) \qquad \delta = (nr_0/2\pi)f_1$$

$$(24) \qquad \beta = (nr_0/2\pi)f_2$$

We note, finally, that the reduction of the exact theory for the scattering of radiation from a uniform, homogeneous sphere reduces to that obtained for the single-scattering non-refractive case in (19) when the variable w becomes equal to u, hence when the quantity $(\delta/2 \sin (\theta/2))^2$ is small compared with unity. And, if one is interested in the scattering in the central maximum region, this restriction requires, using (20), that the quantity $(a\delta)$ be very small compared with the wavelength. Since for the ultrasoft region, $\delta \approx 10^{-3}$, effects of refraction, etc., are not appreciable for (a/λ) less than about 100.

References p. 29

V. ULTRASOFT X-RAY REFLECTION

WOLTER[8] has given the general solution of Maxwell's equations applied to the reflection of electromagnetic waves from an n-layered surface. We have assumed

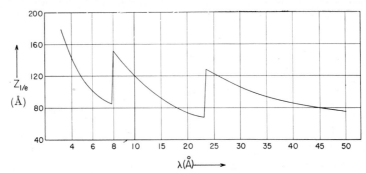

Fig. 9. Depth of penetration reflection at θ_c off Al_2O_3. The penetration depth for an angle of reflection equal to θ_c and off an aluminum oxide surface at which the intensity has dropped to $(1/e)$th value. The reflected intensity is mainly determined by the material within this layer.

that these may be applied to the X-ray region, setting permeability equal to unity, and replacing the dielectric constant by its equivalent, $m^2 - 1$, in which the refractive index, m, is set equal to $1 - \delta - i\beta$ as in the preceding section. By calculating tables for the refractive index increments, δ and β, using the relations (23) and (24) we have completed detailed tabulations[5], using a digital computer, for the following examples of predicted ultrasoft X-ray reflections: (1) intensity of reflection as a

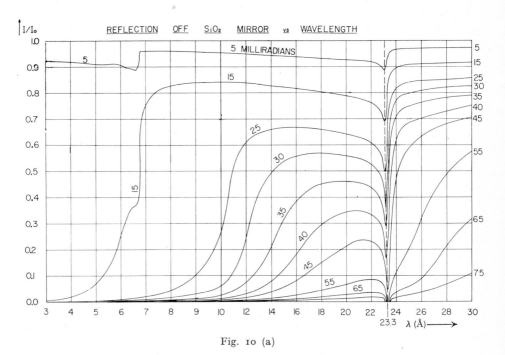

Fig. 10 (a)

References p. 29

function of both the angle of reflection and of wavelength for mirror surfaces of
aluminum, aluminum oxide, and quartz (see Fig. 10), (2) intensity of reflection

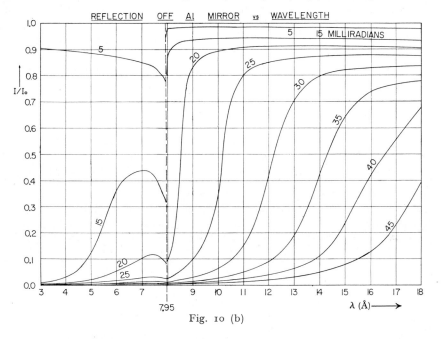

Fig. 10 (b)

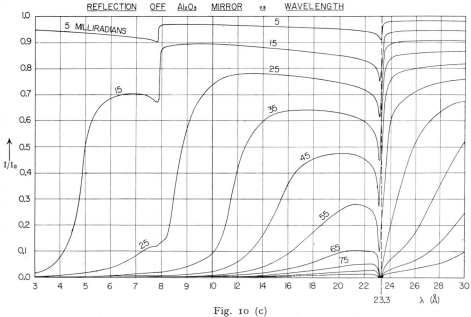

Fig. 10 (c)

Fig. 10. The predicted intensity of reflection relative to incident intensity, I/I_0, for angles near
the critical values for total reflection, and wavelengths near the critical absorption edge wavelengths. The shape of these curves are very sensitive to both the real and to the imaginary parts
of the refractive index decrements, δ and β, which characterize the mirror surfaces.

References p. 29

from a thin film of quartz evaporated upon an aluminum substrate (see Fig. 11), and (3) intensity of reflection from an oxidized layer on aluminum for various oxide thicknesses (see Fig. 12).

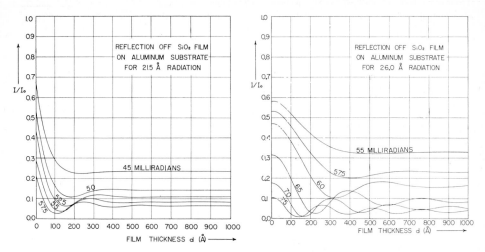

Fig. 11. The extent of the thin film interference predicted for wavelengths on each side of the critical absorption edge of oxygen (23.3 Å) off a SiO$_2$ film evaporated upon an aluminum substrate and at several film thicknesses.

It may be readily derived from theory[8] that the layer thickness which effectively determines the resultant reflected intensity is given by the penetration depth at which the X-ray beam has been reduced to $1/e$ (37 %) of its initial value

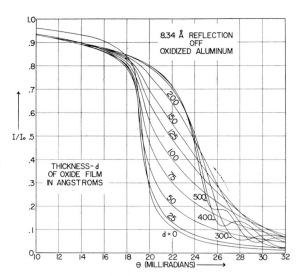

Fig. 12. Illustrating the effect of oxide film thickness upon the reflection intensity of 8.34 Å radiation from an aluminum mirror. A pure, uniform density Al$_2$O$_3$ film is assumed for these calculated curves.

which is given by

$$(25) \qquad z_{1/e} = \lambda/4 \, \pi \beta^{\frac{1}{2}}$$

for angles of reflection near the critical angle for total reflection, θ_c. (θ_c is the largest angle for which there is total reflection for the ideal non-absorptive mirror and is given by the relation, $\theta_c = (2\delta)^{\frac{1}{2}}$). The effective penetration depth, $z_{1/e}$, is plotted in Fig. 9 as a function of wavelength for an Al_2O_3 surface, showing the penetration to be of the order of 100 Å and changing appreciably only at the absorption edges. It should be noted that the effective layer thickness for reflection is relatively insensitive to wavelength — unlike the penetration for normal incidence. This is due to the fact that β varies approximately as λ^2.

For the homogeneous surface (two media case) the reflected intensity may be written as

$$I = I_0 \frac{(1 - A)^2 + B^2}{(1 + A)^2 + B^2}$$

where

$$(26) \qquad \begin{aligned} A &= x\{[(x^2 - 1)^2 + y^2]^{\frac{1}{2}} + (x^2 - 1)\}^{\frac{1}{2}} \\ B &= x\{[(x^2 - 1)^2 + y^2]^{\frac{1}{2}} - (x^2 - 1)\}^{\frac{1}{2}} \end{aligned}$$

and

$$x = \sin \theta / (2\delta)^{\frac{1}{2}} \approx \theta/\theta_c$$
$$y = \beta/\delta = f_2/f_1$$

We note from the above equations that the intensity ratio may thus be written as

$$I/I_0 = f[\theta^2/(n r_0 f_1/\pi), \; f_2^2/f_1^2]$$

using (23) and (24) for δ and β. The variable, f_2^2/f_1^2, depends only upon the elementary chemistry and wavelength. It is critically sensitive to the chemical nature of the surface at certain wavelengths as illustrated in Fig. 7a and 10.

The effect of the density of the surface material is to translate the characteristic curve of I versus θ in amount proportional to the value $n^{\frac{1}{2}}$. ($n =$ the number of molecules per cm³ $= \rho N/M$ where ρ is the mass density, N is Avogadro's number and M is the molecular weight.) The position of the curve for I versus θ where a sharp change in intensity occurs may thus be used for the determination of surface film densities. Such a sharp variation in this curve can often be achieved for the ultrasoft wavelengths by choosing an angle of reflection and a wavelength so as to combine the effects of the total reflection cut-off and the "break" at the absorption discontinuities.

Figs. 11 and 12 are intended to illustrate how the intensity of reflection may change markedly due to the effect of a very thin layer of material on a substrate of a different density and/or chemistry. The position of the interference peaks as shown in Fig. 12, shifts along the θ axis according to the film thickness. Also, it is seen here that, for a 22-milliradian reflection, the intensity of reflection increases uniformly from 10 to 65 % for oxide film thicknesses from about 20 to 200 Å. Such curves would also be sensitive to the nature of the change in density of the material between the oxide and the pure aluminum if it is not an abrupt change as assumed here[9].

References p. 29

VI. COMPARISON TO EXPERIMENTAL RESULTS

In the preceding sections we have outlined methods for predicting photoelectric absorption, scattering and reflection of ultrasoft X-rays that might be useful in the design of microanalysis measurements. For the prediction of X-ray reflection intensities, for example, the steps involved were as follows: (1) The atomic absorption cross-sections were obtained for the lighter elements from universal absorption functions based upon the best available mass absorption coefficient data for the ultrasoft wavelengths. (2) The atomic photoelectric cross-sections were then used to deduce the density of the quantum mechanical oscillators which account for atomic scattering as well as emission and absorption processes. (3) With the oscillator density functions established universally for the lighter elements, the quantum dispersion formulae which are valid for the ultrasoft X-ray region were then numerically integrated to yield universal functions for the atomic scattering factors. And, (4) the averaged effects of atomic scattering within a uniform distribution of atoms were obtained to deduce the refractive index for a given density of matter, which material property finally permitted the application of Maxwell's equations to predict the total effect of X-ray reflection.

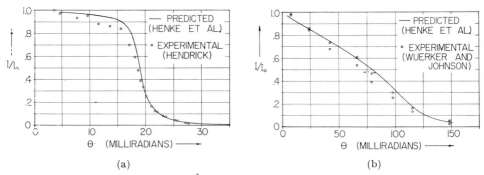

(a)   (b)

Fig. 13. (a) Reflection of Al K (8.34 Å) radiation off aluminized mirror. (b) Reflection of CK (44 Å) radiation off quartz mirror. Predicted reflection curves calculated for (a) 8.34 Å radiation off an aluminized surface of assumed density equal to 2.702 g/cm³ and for (b) 44 Å radiation off a quartz surface of assumed density equal to 2.657 g/cm³ compared to experimental data of HENDRICK and of WUERKER and JOHNSON.

The comparison of the predicted reflection intensities to that obtained experimentally is a good test of the quantum theory of ultrasoft X-ray interactions and of the procedures used here because it is very sensitive not only to photoelectric absorption directly, but also, in prediction, to the assumed resonance and damping characteristics of the quantum mechanical virtual oscillators. We have chosen two experimental measurements for comparison. In Fig. 13 (a) is shown the reflection of radiation of wavelength very near an absorption discontinuity, Al K (8.34 Å) off an aluminum surface. In this reflection the cut-off is appreciably sharpened by the effect of the absorption edge at 7.95 Å [see also Fig. 10 (b)]. The fact that the measured reflected intensity falls somewhat lower than that predicted for the ideally smooth aluminum surface might be explained by the effect of low-angle scattering due to microscopic irregularities in the aluminized surface and also to the effect of a thin oxide film as illustrated in Fig. 12. In Fig. 13 (b) is shown a reflection from a quartz surface which could be highly polished and free of surface films. CK (44 Å) radiation was used, illustrating the strong effect of absorption characteristic of the longer wavelength (and not due to proximity to an absorption edge) on the shape of the critical cut-off.

It is believed that the approach used here for the prediction of ultrasoft X-ray interactions, based upon introducing measured mass absorption coefficient data in order to evaluate quantum mechanical expressions, can be quite successful. Its reliability may be improved in several ways. First of all, more mass photoelectric absorption measurements should be obtained for the long wavelength region. Secondly, the theoretical framework for the calculation of the interaction coefficients should be clearly defined for the ultrasoft region with the underlying assumptions critically established[5]. And finally, averaging techniques employed in the integration of atomic interactions into total effects should be extended in order to more accurately describe the real sample.

ACKNOWLEDGEMENTS

This work was supported by the Office of Scientific Research, Air Research and Development Command, U.S. Air Force.

The experimental points shown in Fig. 13 were weighted and averaged values compiled for us by Mr. GEORGE JOHNSON, Physics Dept., Stanford University, Stanford, California.

REFERENCES

1 B. L. HENKE, R. WHITE and B. LUNDBERG, *J. Appl. Phys.*, 28 (1957) 98.
2 R. W. JAMES, *Optical Principles of the Diffraction of X-rays*, G. Bell and Sons, Ltd., London, 1954.
3 ALLEN, in A. H. COMPTON and S. K. ALLISON, *X-rays in Theory and Experiment*, Van Nostrand, New York, 1946, p. 799.
4 L. G. PARRATT and C. F. HEMPSTEAD, *Phys. Rev.*, 94 (1954) 1593 and their ref. 1.
5 B. L. HENKE and J. C. MILLER, in preparation.
6 A. GUINIER and G. FOURNET, *Small Angle Scattering of X-rays*, (with bibliography by K. L. YUDOWITCH), John Wiley and Sons, New York, 1955.
7 B. L. HENKE and JESSE W. M. DuMOND, *J. Appl. Phys.*, 26 (1955) 903.
8 H. WOLTER, in S. FLUGGE, *Handbuch der Physik*, Vol. 24, Springer-Verlag Berlin, 1956, p. 461.
9 L. G. PARRATT, *Phys. Rev.*, 95 (1954) 359.

THE SCHWARZSCHILD-VILLIGER EFFECT IN THE PHOTOMETRY OF X-RAY MICRORADIOGRAMS.

D. H. HOWLING AND P. J. FITZGERALD

Department of Pathology, State University of New York, Brooklyn, N.Y. (U.S.A.)

ABSTRACT

The Schwarzschild-Villiger effect has been experimentally demonstrated with the optical system used in this laboratory. Using a photographic mosaic specimen as a model, it has been shown that the conclusions of NAORA are substantiated and that the SV effect, in large or small magnitude, is always present in optical systems. The theoretical transmission error arising from the presence of the SV effect has been derived for various optical conditions of measurement. The results have been experimentally confirmed. The SV contribution of the substage optics of microspectrophotometers has also been considered. A simple method of evaluating a flare function $f(A)$ is advanced which provides a measure of the SV error present in a system. It is demonstrated that measurements of specimens of optical density less than unity can be made with less than 1 per cent error, when using illuminating beam diameter/specimen diameter ratios of unity and uncoated optical surfaces.

REFERENCE

D. H. HOWLING and P. J. FITZGERALD, *J. Biophys. Biochem. Cytol.*, 6 (1959) 313.

DIE INFORMATIONSÜBERTRAGUNGSKAPAZITÄT VON RÖNTGENSTRAHLMIKROSKOPEN

GÜNTHER LANGNER

*Institut für Elektronenmikroskopie an der Medizinischen Akademie,
Düsseldorf (Deutschland)*

ABSTRACT

TRANSMISSION CAPACITY OF X-RAY MICROSCOPES

The notion of transmission capacity (TC) deriving from the theory of communication is known to be an objective measure of the imaging quality in optical instruments, specifically in microscopy. The TC yields more information than the resolution defined variously according to the measuring technique applied. At given mean-square deviation of the object contrast, the TC is determined by the contrast transmission function (CT) and the statistics of the background noise (quanta noise, photo-granularity). CT is a function of spatial frequency (*e.g.* lines/mm). The various components involved in image formation are characterized by their share in the CT. Assuming contrasts to be small and transmission to be linear, the CT of the microscope can be derived as the product of the components. This assumption holds good for microradiography, point-projection microscopy and the flying-spot microscope. With the methods currently employed with these three types of microscopes, the theoretical limit of the TC (in bits per unit surface of the object) is plotted against the acceleration voltage and the thickness of the target for gold as target material. By these criteria, the method best suited for a given research target can be decided on.

EINFÜHRUNG

Üblicherweise kennzeichnet man die Leistungsfähigkeit von optischen Geräten, insbesondere Mikroskopen durch das „Auflösungsvermögen''. Es sind verschiedene Messmethoden bekannt, die voneinander abweichende Ergebnisse liefern können und an bestimmte Testobjekte gebunden sind. Bei der Berechnung des Auflösungsvermögens muss man von bestimmten Objektstrukturen ausgehen und willkürliche Annahmen darüber machen, was man als „noch trennbar'' bezeichnen will. Die angeführten Mängel haben eine Kritik am Begriff des Auflösungsvermögens wach gerufen. Es wurde daher versucht, einen physikalisch logischeren Begriff zur Kennzeichnung der Leistungsfähigkeit optischer Abbildungsgeräte zu finden. Man hat eine Anleihe bei der Nachrichtentheorie gemacht und die Begriffsbildung und Theoreme der Informationstheorie (I. Th.) übernommen, die vornehmlich von SHANNON[1, 2] begründet worden ist. In der I. Th. definiert man die mit einer Nachricht übertragene Information $\Im$ über ein Ereignis folgendermassen:

(1) $\quad \Im = \mathrm{ld} \, \dfrac{\text{Wahrscheinlichkeit für das Eintreffen eines Ereignisses}}{\text{Wahrscheinlichkeit für das Eintreffen des Ereignisses}}$

Wahrscheinlichkeit für das Eintreffen eines Ereignisses nachdem die Nachricht darüber empfangen worden ist

Wahrscheinlichkeit für das Eintreffen des Ereignisses bevor eine Nachricht darüber empfangen worden ist ($\mathrm{ld} = \log_2$)

Eine Nachricht über das Ergebnis eines Wurfes einer Münze (Beispiel für eine ja-nein-Entscheidung) kann demnach höchstens die Information $1 = \mathrm{ld}\ 1/0{,}5$ enthalten, eine Nachricht über das Ergebnis eines Wurfes eines Würfels kann entsprechend höchstens eine Information $\mathrm{ld}\ 1/\frac{1}{6} \approx 2{,}6$ enthalten. In einen Mikroskop und anderen optischen Apparaten wird Information vom Objekt zum Bild übertragen. Die I.Th. wird daher in zunehmenden Masse zur quantitativen Kennzeichnung der Übertragungseigenschaften optischer Geräte angewendet. Hier soll speziell der Versuch gemacht werden, sie auf die Röntgenstrahlmikroskope anzuwenden.

DIE INFORMATIONS-ÜBERTRAGUNGS-KAPAZITÄT

Als Kennzeichen der Leistungsfähigkeit von Mikroskopen wollen wir die sogen. Informations-Übertragungskapazität (IÜK) verwenden. Sie gibt die maximale Information an, die ein Übertragungssystem übertragen kann, in unserem Falle die maximale Information, die in einem Mikrogramm vorhanden sein kann, das mit dem fraglichen Mikroskop gewonnen wurde. Es wird sich ausserdem erweisen, dass eine der üblichen Methoden zur Messung des Auflösungsvermögens die IÜK näherungsweise zu bestimmen gestattet. Ein Bild ist durch seine (z.B. Schwärzungs-) Werte an endlich vielen Stellen, den n Bildpunkten, vollständig bestimmt. Dabei ist pro Bildpunkt nur eine endliche Zahl L von Schwärzungs- oder Kontraststufen von einander sicher unterscheidbar. Das Mikroskop kann dann nicht mehr als L^n voneinander sicher unterscheidbare Bilder aus einer unendlichen Menge von Objekten liefern. Die IÜK des Mikroskopes beträgt dann günstigstenfalls $\mathfrak{J} = \mathrm{ld}\ L^n = n \cdot \mathrm{ld}\ L$. Die Aufgabe der Berechnung der IÜK ist also gelöst, wenn es gelingt, n und $\mathrm{ld}\ L$ zu berechnen. Um den Gang der Rechnung anzudeuten, wenden wir uns nun der formalen Behandlung einer Nachrichtenübertragung zu.

DIE INFORMATIONSGEWINNUNG IM MIKROSKOP

Die eigentliche Nachricht besteht beim Röntgenstrahlmikroskop in der Verteilung der Massendicke eines bestimmten chemischen Elements oder der morphologischen Struktur des Objekts. Vermöge der Eigenschaften der Objekte gegenüber Röntgenstrahlung, wie ihre u.a. von der Wellenlänge abhängigen Durchlässigkeit τ, wird diese Nachricht in Form der Durchlässigkeit verschlüsselt (codiert). Die Durchlässigkeit ist dann die „gesendete'' Signalfunktion. In Abb. 1 ist der Vorgang der Übertragung von Signalfunktionen schematisch dargestellt. Am Ausgang des Übertragungssystems erscheint die „empfangene'' Signalfunktion als Bild-Leuchtdichte B, die mittels des Code gedeutet werden muss. Zur Vereinheitlichung führen wir die Kontraste ein, und zwar den Objektkontrast

$$(2) \qquad\qquad k_0 = \frac{\tau(x) - \overline{\tau}}{\overline{\tau}}$$

und den Bildkontrast

$$(3) \qquad\qquad k_b = \frac{B(x) - \bar{B}}{\bar{B}}$$

Der Einfachheit halber beschränken wir uns auf Funktionen einer Veränderlichen. Überstreichung bedeutet Bildung des arithmetischen Mittelwertes. Der Objektkontrast sollte im Idealfall dem Bildkontrast gleich sein. In jedem Mikroskop wird aber der Objektkontrast bei der Übertragung Veränderungen unterworfen.

Ausserdem überlagern sich ihm unvermeidlich im Einzelnen nicht vorhersehbare Störsignale, die man unter dem Begriff Rauschen (noise) zusammenfasst.

Die formale Behandlung der Übertragung macht, wie in Abb. 1 angedeutet, Gebrauch von der Zerlegung der gesendeten Signale in Sinus- und Kosinuskomponenten nach FOURIER. Wir greifen nun eine einzelne Sinuskomponente der Frequenz N heraus und verfolgen ihren Weg durch das Übertragungssystem. Unter der notwendigen und hinreichenden Voraussetzung der Linearität der Übertragung verändert das Übertragungssystem nur die Amplitude und gegebenenfalls die Phasenlage jeder Komponente unabhänging davon, was mit den zu anderen Frequenzen N gehörenden Komponenten geschieht. Den frequenzabhängigen Faktor $Y(N)$, mit dem die Amplitude multipliziert wird, nennen wir im optischen Fall die Kontrastübertragungsfunktion (KÜF). Sie ist von der Objektstruktur völlig unabhängig und eine Eigenschaft des Übertragungssystems allein.

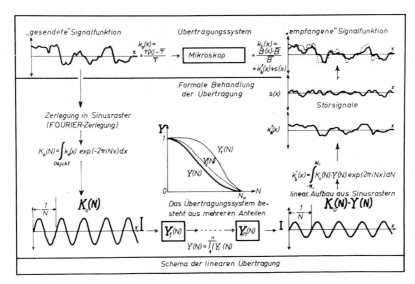

Abb. 1. Schematische Darstellung der Übertragung einer Signalfunktion einer Variablen durch ein lineares Übertragungssystem und ihre formale Behandlung.

Man strebt bei Übertragungssystemen Linearität an. Wo diese nicht erreichbar ist, wie z.B. bei der Belichtung photographischer Schichten mit sichtbarem Licht, gelten die Gesetze der linearen Übertragung nur näherungsweise für kleine Kontraste. Ein Übertragungssystem kann aus einzelnen Gliedern bestehen, die hintereinander auf das gesendete Signal wirkend gedacht werden können. Sind alle diese Glieder linear, so setzt sich die KÜF des gesamten Systems multiplikativ aus den Anteilen der einzelnen Glieder zusammen, wie in Abb. 1 angedeutet. So ist die als Beispiel eingezeichnete KÜF $Y(N)$ durch Multiplikation der Anteile $Y_1(N)$ und $Y_2(N)$ entstanden.

Bei linearer Übertragung erhalten wir das Bild als empfangene Signalfunktion, indem wir die einzelnen in ihrer Amplitude und Phase veränderten Sinus- u. Kosinuskomponenten wieder linear zusammensetzen. Dies wird wieder durch eine Fourier-Transformation beschrieben, die in Abb. 1 angegeben ist. Die wirklich empfangene

Signalfunktion $k_b(x)$ unterscheidet sich von der auf die beschriebene Weise gewonnenen Signalfunktion $k_b'(x)$ dadurch, dass sich letzterer statistisch im Einzelnen
nicht vorhersehbare Störsignale überlagern, z.B. der Quantenschrot und die Körnigkeit der photographischen Emulsion. Wenn die KÜF und die statistischen Eigenschaften der Störsignale bekannt sind, so kann man prinzipiell die IÜK berechnen.
Falls die nun eine flächenhafte Übertragung beschreibende KÜF $Y(N_x, N_y)$ nur
von $N = \sqrt{N_x{}^2 + N_y{}^2}$ abhängt und die Störsignale einer Normalverteilung mit dem
ebenfalls nur von $N = \sqrt{N_x{}^2 + N_y{}^2}$ abhängigen Schwankungsquadrat $\sigma_s{}^2(N)$ unter-
liegen, so erhält man für die KÜF pro Bildpunkt

$$(4) \qquad \Im n = \frac{1.44}{N_0{}^2} \int_0^{N_0} \ln\left[1 + \frac{\sigma_0{}^2\, Y^2(N)}{\sigma_s{}^2(N)} \right] N dN$$

$\sigma_0{}^2$ ist das Schwankungsquadrat des Kontrastes aller zu erwartenden Objekte. Jedes
Übertragungssystem hat einen endlichen Frequenz-Durchlassbereich. N_0 in Abb. 1
und in Gl. (4) ist die endliche Grenzfrequenz des Übertragungssystemes. Nach dem
sogen. Sampling-Theorem der I.Th. ist der endliche Frequenz-Durchlassbereich
eines Übertragungssystems der Grund dafür, dass (im Falle optischer Übertragung)
das Bild durch die Kontrastwerte an endlich vielen Bildpunkten hinreichend
bestimmt ist.

ANWENDUNG DER BEGRIFFSBILDUNG AUF DIE RÖNTGENSTRAHLMIKROSKOPIE

Wir wenden uns nun den Röntgenstrahlmikroskopen zu, beschränken uns aber auf
die Röntgenstrahlmikroskope, bei denen sich zwischen Objekt und Bild keine
abbildenden Elemente befinden. Wir fassen diese Mikroskope unter dem Begriff
Röntgenstrahl-Projektionsmikroskope zusammen und verstehen darunter

a. die Kontaktmikroradiographie (KMR),
b. die Punkt-Projektionsmikroskope (PPM) und
c. die Raster- oder Flying-spot-Mikroskope (RM).

Für diese Mikroskope treffen die Voraussetzungen der Gl. (4) weitestgehend zu.

　　Abb. 2 stellt das allgemeine Schema eines Röntgenstrahlprojektionsmikroskopes dar. Die KÜF setzt sich aus einzelnen Anteilen multiplikativ zusammen.
Jeder dieser Anteile beschreibt ein an der Abbildung mitwirkendes Element, das
vermöge seines Zerstreuungs- oder Fehlerscheibchens mit einer charakteristischen
Gewichtsfunktion eine Verunschärfung des Bildes bewirkt. Die Fourier-Trans-
formierte dieser Gewichtsfunktion liefert bei linearer Übertragung den jeweiligen
Anteil $Y_i(N)$ an der KÜF. Durch die multiplikative Zusammensetzung dieser Anteile
ist auch das Problem der richtigen Superposition der Fehlerscheibchen automatisch
gelöst. Im Einzelnen müssen wir folgende Elemente der Röntgenstrahlprojektionsmikroskope berücksichtigen, die je einen Anteil $Y_i(N)$ an der KÜF liefern:

1. die Röntgenstrahlquelle, gekennzeichnet durch den Anteil $Q(N)$, der wiederum
   aufgebaut wird aus dem Anteil $Q_B(N)$ des Elektronenbrennflecks und dem
   Anteil $Q_D(N)$ der Elektronendiffusion im Target. Der Brennfleckanteil $Q_B(N)$ selbst
   setzt sich wieder zusammen aus dem Anteil $Q_s(N)$ des (verkleinerten) Bildes des
   Crossovers im Elektronenstrahler bzw. der Kathode bei Feldemissionskathoden,
   und dem Anteil $Q_A(N)$ der Abbildungsfehler der Elektronenoptik. Der Anteil
   $Q_D(N)$ der Elektronendiffusion im Target ist am schwierigsten zu ermitteln.

Deshalb wollen wir uns mit ihm in einem gesonderten Beitrag (s.S. 90 dieses Bandes) befassen.

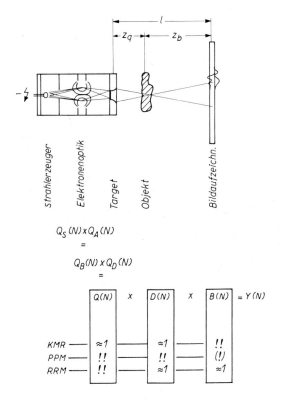

Abb. 2.   Schematische Darstellung des Röntgenstrahlprojektionsmikroskopes und der verschiedenen Anteile seiner Kontrastübertragungsfunktion.

2. die Fresnel'sche Beugung, im Falle kleiner Kontraste durch den Anteil $D(N)$ an der KÜF gekennzeichnet. Im Prinzip vermindert die Fresnel'sche Beugung die Information nicht. Vielmehr kann man mit Hilfe der Beugungsmikroskopie oder der ,,Mikroskopie mit rekonstruierten Wellenfronten'' nach GABOR[3], die für Röntgenstrahlen von BAEZ[4] diskutiert worden ist, die im Fresnel'schen Beugungsbild enthaltene Information nutzbar machen. Wo das nicht geschieht, muss man die Beugung wie Abbildungsfehler behandeln. Man kann übrigens aus der Erkennbarkeit der Beugungssäume auf die Ausdehnung der Röntgenstrahlquelle beim PPM schliessen, worauf schon NIXON[5] hingewiesen hat;

3. die Bildaufzeichnung, gekennzeichnet durch den Anteil $B(N)$ an der KÜF. Sie enthält beim RM auch den Frequenzgang des Videoverstärkers und die endliche Ausdehnung des Schreibflecks der Bildröhre.

Die Abb. 3 und 4 zeigen Beispiele für berechnete KÜF von Röntgenstrahl-Projektionsmikroskopen. Die zu Grunde gelegten Apparateparameter und Betriebswerte gehen aus den Bildunterschriften hervor. Man erkannt deutlich die Rolle der einzelnen Anteile an der KÜF. Der Unterschied zwischen dem Brennfleckanteil

$Q_B(N)$ und dem gesamten Quellenanteil $Q(N)$ wird von der Diffusion der Elektronen im Target verursacht. Man erkennt ferner, dass die Fresnel'sche Beugung bei höheren räumlichen Frequenzen N eine Kontrastumkehr erzeugt (negative Werte von $Y(N)$,

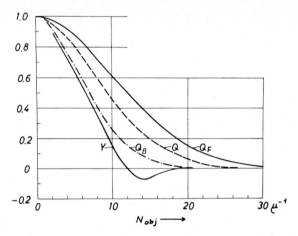

Abb. 3. Beispiel einer Kontrastübertragungsfunktion eines Punkt-Projektionsmikroskopes. Es sind folgende Parameterwerte zugrunde gelegt: Strahlspannung $U_0 = 10$ kV; Expositionsdauer $t = 300$ sec; Kameralänge $1 = 5$ mm; $z_q = a = 20\mu$; Au-Target, Dicke $d \approx 0{,}15$ μ; maximaler Richtstrahlwert $j_0 = 4 \cdot 10^4$ A $\cdot$ cm^{-2} sterad^{-1}; Linse 1,5 mm Brennweite mit Stigmator; Diapositivfilm.

ähnlich wie dies von einer Defokussierung bei optischer Abbildung durch Linsen bekannt ist). Macht man unter sonst gleichen Bedingungen, u.a. auch gleicher Expositionszeit t, das Target dünner, so wird zwar der Anteil $Q_D(N)$ günstiger, aber der

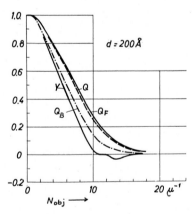

Abb. 4. Weiteres Beispiel einer Kontrastübertragungsfunktion eines Punktprojektionsmikroskopes. Die Parameterwerte sind die gleichen wie bei Abb. 3, nur ist die Targetdicke $d \approx 200$ Å.

Anteil $Q_B(N)$ wird ungünstiger, weil nun der Verlust an im Target nicht zur Wirkung kommenden Elektronen durch eine grössere Apertur oder geringere Verkleinerung des Crossover wieder ausgeglichen werden muss. Ausserdem hat man im Falle dünner Targets mit einer Kontamination des Objektes durch die Elektronen zu rechnen.

Literatur S. 40

BEISPIELE VON KONTRAST-ÜBERTRAGUNGS-FUNKTIONEN

Die Zahl der Bildpunkte beträgt theoretisch für das Objektfeld F unter den Voraussetzungen, dass zur Berechnung der IÜK Gl. (4) gilt, $n = \pi N_0^2 F$. Es erweist sich nun, dass die Form der KÜF bei den Röntgenstrahlprojektionsmikroskopen ziemlich ähnlich ist und dass sich die KÜF in erster Näherung nur duch ihre Grenzfrequenz N_0 unterscheiden, so dass die Grenzfrequenz N_0 zur Kennzeichnung einer KÜF oft genügt. Als ein Beispiel zur Lösung eines speziellen Problems mit Hilfe der informationstheoretischen Betrachtungsweise haben wir daher die Abhängigkeit der Grenzfrequenz N_0 der KÜF für ein RM und PPM ohne Berücksichtigung der Fresnel'schen Beugung als Funktion der Strahlspannung U_0 und der Targetdicke d berechnet. In Abb. 5 ist für Gold-Targets und Bremsstrahlung das Ergebnis der

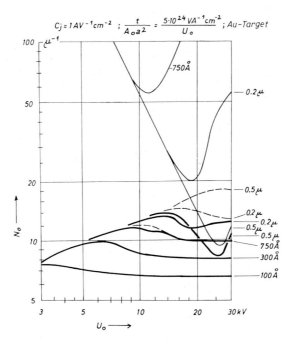

Abb. 5. Grenzfrequenz N_0 der KÜF eines Röntgenstrahl-Rastermikroskopes bzw. eines Röntgenstrahl-Punktprojektionsmikroskopes ohne Berücksichtigung der FRESNEL'schen Beugung in Abhängigkeit von der Strahlspannung U_0 und der Dicke d des Gold-Targets zur Erzeugung von Bremsstrahlung.

Rechnung aufgetragen. Der Parameterwert C_j charakterisiert den maximalen Richtstrahlwert j_0 des Elektronenstrahlers, wobei angenommen wurde, dass die Beziehung

(5) $$j_0 = C_j \cdot U_0$$

Gültigkeit hat. t bezeichnet die Expositionszeit, a hier den Abstand Objekt-Quelle (in Abb. 2 mit z_q bezeichnet) und A_0 die Bildpunktarbeit der Bildaufzeichnung zur Erreichung der Schwärzung 0,5. In Abb. 5 sind die Grenzfrequenzen des Diffusionsanteils $Q_D(N)$ (dünner Strich) und der übrigen Anteile zusammen (gebrochen gezeichnet) getrennt herausgezeichnet. Das Ergebnis der Superposition beider Anteile, also die Grenzfrequenz N_0 der KÜF ist stark ausgezogen. Man erkennt deutlich eine Einsattelung als Folge der Elektronendiffusion im Target. Es ist wegen der zu erwartenden Kontamination des Objektes durch die Elektronenstrahlen und dem Ansteigen des Störpegels nicht empfehlenswert, rechts von der Einsattelung, also bei höheren Strahlspannungen zu arbeiten. Die von den Experimentatoren bei den besten bisher bekannt gewordenen PPM (Nixon[5]) als günstig herausgefundenen Werte der Strahlspannung liegen etwa im theoretisch optimalen Bereich, was man als eine gewisse Bestätigung der Theorie werten kann.

ALLGEMEINE ERGEBNISSE

Die Anwendung der informationstheoretischen Überlegungen auf die Röntgenstrahlprojektionsmikroskope hat in grossen Zügen folgende Ergebnisse gezeigt:

Für eine vorgegebene Massendicke und eine vorgegebene elementare Zusammensetzung des Objektes gibt es stets eine oder einige Wellenlängen, bei denen der Kontrast und damit die Zahl der pro Bildpunkt sicher unterscheidbaren Kontraststufen optimal ist. Wenn diese optimalen Wellenlängen nicht im Vorhinein bekannt sind, empfiehlt es sich stets, die Untersuchung mit Bremsstrahlung durchzuführen und dabei die Strahlspannung zu variieren, um so eine optimale Wellenlänge zu ermitteln.

Der Störpegel hängt in erster Linie von der Wellenlänge der verwendeten Röntgenstrahlung ab. Er nimmt mit zunehmender Wellenlänge ab. Die Zahl der Bildpunkte ist beim PPM und RM eine ziemlich komplizierte Funktion der Strahlspannung, was den Quellen-Anteil $Q(N)$ betrifft, und eine Funktion der Wellenlänge, was den Beugungsanteil $D(N)$ und den Bildaufzeichnungsanteil $B(N)$ betrifft. Bei Verwendung von Bremsstrahlung ist die Wellenlänge eine Funktion der Strahlspannung, so dass dann die Strahlspannung U die entscheidende Variable für die Zahl der Bildpunkte pro Flächeneinheit Objektfläche ist. Beim KMR ist in erster Linie, wie schon weiter oben gesagt, der Anteil $B(N)$ der Bildaufzeichnung entscheidend. Daher ist die KMR am besten bei weicher und ultraweicher Röntgenstrahlung geeignet ($\lambda \geqq 5\text{Å}$), ferner bei charakteristischer Strahlung leichter Elemente, wo die Verwendung von Targetmaterialien erforderlich wird, die man technologisch nicht leicht in Form dünner Folien herstellen kann. Die mehrstufigen Verfahren, seien es die Verwendung von Mikro-Bildwandlern mit nachfolgender elektronenoptischer Vergrösserung nach Huang[6] und Möllenstedt[7] oder seien es die chemischen Ätzverfahren mit nachfolgender elektronenmikroskopischer Vergrösserung der Lackabdrucke nach Ladd[8], versprechen für das KMR wesentliche Fortschritte. Bei Verwendung von Bremsstrahlung und charakteristischer Strahlung von Al, Cu usw. werden das PPM und RM überlegen. Ein weiterer Vorteil charakteristischer Strahlung ist, dass man die für optimalen Kontrast geeignete Wellenlänge und beim PPM und RM einigermassen unabhängig davon für maximale Bildpunktzahl die geeignete Strahlspannung wählen kann.

VERGLEICHENDE BETRACHTUNG DER VERSCHIEDENEN RÖNTGENSTRAHLMIKROSKOPE

Normalerweise liefert die Integration der Gl. (4) für die IÜK weniger als Eins pro Bildpunkt, wenn man bis zur wirklichen Grenzfrequenz N_0 der KÜF integriert. Dies ist eine Folge des praktisch nicht unterschreitbaren Störpegels. Es sind dann zwei benachbarte Bildpunkte nicht mehr sicher zu unterscheiden. Dies ist vielmehr erst dann der Fall, wenn man die IÜK von Eins pro Bildpunkt zur Verfügung hat. Es ist dann in Gl. (4) statt N_0 eine neue, praktische Grenzfrequenz N_1 einzusetzen, die sich durch die Forderung ergibt, dass die Integration nach Gl. (4) genau Eins liefern soll. Die Zahl der effektiv vorhandenen Bildpunkte beträgt daher nicht mehr $n = \pi N_0^2 \cdot F$, sondern nur noch $n_{\text{eff}} = \pi N_1^2 \cdot F$ für das Objektfeld F. Es besteht dann ein Zusammenhang zwischen der IÜK pro Bildpunkt und dem Auflösungsvermögen δ, wie es im Beispiel der Elektronenmikroskopie an Aufdampfschichten gemessen wird. Es gilt $\delta \approx 1/\sqrt{\pi} \cdot N_1$. Dieser Tatbestand ermöglicht es, aus bekannten

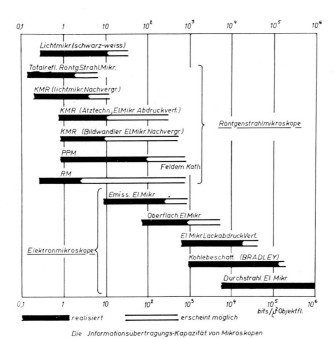

Die Jnformationsübertragungs-Kapazität von Mikroskopen

Abb. 6. Zusammenstellung über die realisierten oder theoretisch möglich erscheinenden Informationsübertragungskapazitäten mikroskopischer Verfahren.

Daten des auf geeignete Weise gemessenen Auflösungsvermögens auf die IÜK zu schliessen. Wir haben in Abb. 6 eine Zusammenstellung gemacht über die bisher mit den verschiedenen Mikroskopen und mikroskopischen Verfahren erreichten und den theoretisch möglich erscheinenden Informationsübertragungskapazitäten. Man erkennt, dass die Röntgenstrahlungs-Mikroskope eine Mittelstellung zwischen den Licht- und den Elektronen-Mikroskopen einnehmen. Dies bedeutet aber kein Werturteil, weil das Röntgenmikroskop die Gewinnung spezifischer Informationen ermöglicht und in dieser Hinsicht unersetzbar ist.

DANK

Herrn Dr. LENZ bin ich für viele klärende Diskussionen, der Landesregierung Nordrhein-Westfalen für finanzielle Förderung der Arbeiten zu Dank verpflichtet.

Literatur S. 40

ZUSAMMENFASSUNG

Der aus der Nachrichtentheorie stammende Begriff der Informationsübertragungs-kapazität (IÜK) kann bekanntlich als objektives Mass für die Informationsübertragung in optischen Geräten, insbesondere Mikroskopen verwendet werden. Die IÜK sagt mehr aus als das je nach Messverfahren verschieden definierte Auflösungsvermögen. Die IÜK wird bei vorgegebener mittlerer quadratischer Abweichung des Objektkontrastes von der Kontrastübertragungsfunktion (KÜF) und der Statistik der Störsignale (Quantenschrot, photogr. Körnigkeit) bestimmt. Die KÜF ist eine Funktion der räumlichen Frequenz (z.B. in Linien/mm). Die einzelnen an der Bildentstehung beteiligten Komponenten werden durch ihre Teil-KÜF beschrieben. Unter den Voraussetzungen kleiner Kontraste und linearer Übertragung gewinnt man die KÜF des Mikroskops als Produkt der Teil-KÜF. Für die Mikroradiographie, das Punktprojektionsmikroskop und das Raster-(Flying spot-)Mikroskop treffen diese Voraussetzungen zu. Für die gängigen Verfahren dieser drei Mikroskoparten wird theoretisch die Grenze der IÜK (in bits pro Flächeneinheit des Objektes) in Abhängigkeit von der Strahlspannung, dem Targetmaterial und der Targetdicke bestimmt. Man ersieht daraus das für ein vorgegebenes Untersuchungsziel am besten geeignete Verfahren.

LITERATUR

[1] C. E. SHANNON, *Bell Syst. Tech. J.*, 27 (1948) 379, 623.
[2] C. E. SHANNON, *Proc. I.R.E.*, 37 (1949) 10.
[3] D. GABOR, *Proc. Roy. Soc. (London)*, A 197 (1949) 454.
[4] A. V. BAEZ, *J. Opt. Soc. Am.*, 42 (1952) 756.
[5] W. C. NIXON, *Proc. Roy. Soc. (London)*, A 232 (1955) 475.
[6] LAN YU HUANG, *Z. Physik.*, 149 (1957) 225.
[7] G. MÖLLENSTEDT und L. Y. HUANG, in *X-ray Microscopy and Microradiography*, Academic Press, Inc., New York, 1957, p. 392.
[8] W. A. LADD und M. W. LADD, in *X-ray Microscopy and Microradiography*, Academic Press, Inc., New York, 1957, p. 323.

THE OBSERVATION OF X-RAY ABSORPTION FINE STRUCTURE IN VERY SMALL SPECIMENS

J. V. P. LONG

Cavendish Laboratory, University of Cambridge
(Great Britain)

ABSTRACT

The fine structure of the X-ray absorption edge of an atom is related to its chemical valency. The observation of this structure in the absorption edges of elements contained within areas of thin sections a few microns in diameter is discussed.

Experimental results obtained with a point-focus X-ray tube and a curved-crystal spectrometer are described.

THE NATURE OF THE FINE STRUCTURE

When the apparently sharp X-ray absorption discontinuities are examined at high resolution, they are found to contain a fine structure extending in some cases to about 300 eV on the short wavelength side of the main edge, although the major features occur within about 70 eV of the edge.

From the point of view of the present discussion, the structure close to the edge is of the greatest interest, since it has been shown to be related to the valency of the absorbing atom. For example, clearly defined similarities in position and magnitude of the absorption maxima and minima occur within groups of ferrous and ferric compounds and cyanide complexes of iron, and marked differences are observed between the different groups[1]. Early work of BERGERGREN[2] and LINDH[3,4] also showed that the position of the absorption edge was dependent on the state of chemical combination of the element; for example, in hexavalent inorganic sulphur compounds, the K edge showed a shift of 10.3 eV compared with the edge in crystalline sulphur.

It does not fall within the scope of the present paper to discuss the theory of the absorption fine structure; it is clear, however, that even a semi-empirical interpretation of the data may give information on the valency state of constituent elements in the absorber. The object of the preliminary experiments described here has been to explore the possibility of making measurements on small selected areas in thin sections, in order that variation in oxidation states of elements may be studied on a microscopic scale, for example, within different parts of small zoned mineral grains.

METHODS OF OBSERVING THE STRUCTURE

The resolution required for the observation of the fine structure is of the order of 0.2—2 eV. This can be attained by the use of spectrometers employing crystals with very narrow natural widths of reflection and three principal experimental arrangements have been described:

1. The flat crystal spectrometer of large dimensions, *e.g.* COSTER and KIESTRA[5].
2. The double crystal spectrometer, in which the first crystal acts as a collimator for the second.
3. Curved crystal spectrometers, which have the advantage of increased aperture and consequently reduced exposure time, *e.g.* YOSHIDA[1].

The use of a point focus X-ray tube with a curved crystal spectrometer

Previous work with curved crystals has been carried out with X-ray tubes having broad foci. With a very intense point source of X-rays it is possible to use the curved crystal in two distinct ways, illustrated in Fig. 1. In the first arrangement the source

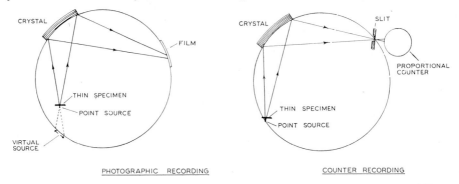

Fig. 1. Alternative arrangements of curved crystal spectrometer with a point source of X-rays.

is displaced from the focussing circle and radiation may be considered to come from points extended along the circle. With the crystal stationary, a range of wavelengths, whose magnitude depends on the displacement of the source from the circle, is brought to a focus as a spectrum on the photographic film. In the second arrangement, the source is located accurately on the focal circle, so that only a very narrow range of wavelengths is reflected, and brought to a sharp focus at the position of the slit. To record other wavelengths the slit and crystal are moved round the focussing circle. This arrangement has the advantage of increased sensitivity over the photographic technique, and also allows the use of a pulse height discriminator in conjunction with the proportional counter for the removal of high order reflections.

In both cases, the transmission of small areas in a thin section placed close to the source may be examined, in exactly the same way as in the elementary analysis procedure already described[6].

In assessing the possibility of using a crystal spectrometer in this way it is necessary first to estimate the available intensity and also the precision required in the construction of the spectrometer.

Intensity

The quantum intensity in narrow energy bands of the continuous spectrum has already been calculated[7] and for a semi-angular aperture of $1°$ should be of the order of 50—500 quanta/sec/eV interval in the range 4—17 keV. For a specimen with

30 % transmission, the time required for a measurement accuracy of 1 % at one wavelength will thus be in the range 300—3000 sec for an energy resolution of 0.2 eV.

Geometrical factors and the necessary mechanical precision

In considering the precision necessary in the construction of the spectrometer an effective aperture of semi-angle 1° will be assumed. In practice this will involve a beam divergence of ~ 4° in the plane of the focussing circle in order that the divergence perpendicular to this plane may be kept small. For a nearly monochromatic reflected beam, all rays must be incident on the crystal planes within a certain range of Bragg angle given by equation (1),

$$\Delta E = E \cdot \cot \theta \cdot \Delta \theta. \tag{1}$$

where ΔE is the energy interval, and θ is the Bragg angle. For $E \sim 10$ keV, $\Delta E / E$ may be set at $2 \cdot 10^{-5}$ and $\cot \theta = 1$ giving $\Delta \theta = 2 \cdot 10^{-5}$.

The angle subtended by a $1\ \mu$ source at any point on a crystal placed d cm from it is $10^{-4}/d$ radians so that for a focussing circle of 25 cm radius, the contribution of the source to $\Delta \theta$ is small and may be neglected.

In order to fulfill the focussing conditions over an angular aperture of 4° it is necessary to use a curved and ground crystal in which the crystal planes are bent to a radius twice that of the focussing circle, whilst the surface is ground so that it lies on the circle. The radius to which the surface of a parallel sided flat crystal must be ground before bending is thus $2r = R$ where r is the radius of the focussing circle. The improvement in focussing resulting from grinding over that obtainable in a simple curved crystal is given in terms of the parameter $V = \Delta R/R$ (JOHANSSON[8]) where ΔR is the amount by which the grinding radius differs from the optimum value of $2R$. (For an unground crystal $V = 1$). Since the variation in angle of incidence in the case of an unground crystal of aperture 4° and radius of curvature 50 cm is of the order of 10^{-3} radians, an improvement of about 50 is required for $\Delta \theta = 2 \cdot 10^{-5}$. Thus to a first approximation $V = 0.02$, or for $r = 25$ cm ΔR must not exceed 1 cm. This should be fairly easily achieved in practice.

It is now necessary to know with what accuracy the source and crystal must be located on the focussing circle, since displacement of the source from the circle results in the reflection of a polychromatic beam. The angular error resulting from such a displacement may be shown by simple geometry to be given for small angles of α (the full angular aperture) by

$$\Delta \theta = \frac{\alpha \cdot \Delta r}{2r \sin^2 \theta} \tag{2}$$

where Δr is the radial displacement of the source. Or substituting in eqn. (1),

$$\Delta r = \frac{\Delta E}{E} \cdot \frac{2r}{\alpha} \cdot \sin^2 \theta \cdot \tan \theta \tag{3}$$

For $\Delta E/E = 2 \cdot 10^{-5}$, $\theta = 45°$, $r = 25$ cm and $\alpha = 4°$ we obtain $r = 75\ \mu$ or $3/1000''$.

A high but not impossible accuracy is thus necessary in placing the source on the circle if a very narrow waveband is to be selected with high efficiency.

The spectrometer

The spectrometer which has been constructed in an attempt to achieve this resolution is shown diagrammatically in Fig. 2. It consists essentially of three arms which form radii of the focussing circle. Micrometers allow the lengths of these arms to be set to an accuracy of $\sim 5\mu$. The angular movement of the arm carrying the proportional

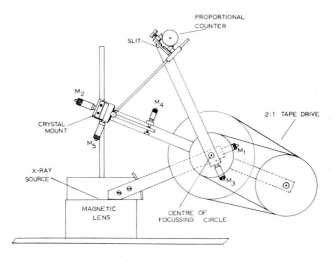

Fig. 2. Diagram showing arrangement of curved crystal spectrometer. The length of the arms determining the distances of the source, crystal and slit from the centre of the circle are adjustable by means of the micrometers M_1 M_2, M_3. Micrometer M_4 allows the tangent to the crystal surface to be set normal to radius of the circle. Micrometer M_5 allows fine adjustment of the Bragg angle.

counter is achieved by a drive using steel tapes and accurately turned drums, which give a ratio of 2 : 1 with respect to the crystal arm.

The mount for the crystal, consisting of two blocks of radii 50 cm and 25 cm respectively, was formed by methods similar to those described by DuMond, Lind and Cohen[9]. The quartz crystal was cut parallel to $\{1011\}$ and was $3 \times 1.5 \times 0.04$ cm before grinding. One surface of the crystal was polished optically flat, while the other, originally parallel to it, was ground to a radius of 50 cm. When placed with the flat surface in contact with a concave metal block of 50 cm radius and compressed by means of a 25 cm convex block, the crystal planes assume a radius of 50 cm, while the radius of curvature of the reflecting surface becomes 25 cm.

RESULTS

The measurements so far made with the instrument have been confined to observations of the resolution and intensity of the $CuK\alpha_1\alpha_2$ doublet. Fig. 3 shows an early result obtained with the full aperture of the crystal and of the counter. The X-ray intensity was plotted with a ratemeter and pen recorder as the crystal was moved slowly and in discrete steps round the focussing circle. The separation of the two peaks is considerably poorer than that obtained from the flat side of the unbent crystal when this was mounted above the X-ray source and the resultant spectrum recorded on a photographic film. The discrepancy indicates either a degree of misalignment of the spectrometer, faulty bending of the crystal, or possibly "block misorientation" in the quartz, similar to that commonly found in lithium fluoride.

References p. 46

A second experiment, again made with the full aperture of the crystal, but with the second order reflection and with a narrow slit in front of the counter, gave a

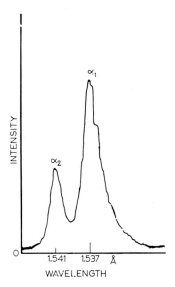

Fig. 3. Pen recorder trace showing 1st order 10Ī1 reflection of $CuK\alpha_1\alpha_2$ from quartz. No apertures used.

considerably improved resolution as shown in Fig. 4. The true separation of the $CuK\alpha_1\alpha_2$ peaks is 21 eV and the natural full widths of the X-ray lines at half peak

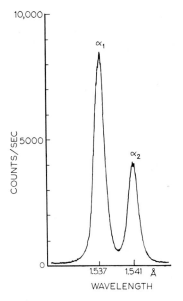

Fig. 4. Pen recorder trace showing 2nd order 10Ī1 reflection of $CuK\alpha_1\alpha_2$ from quartz. Narrow slit used in front of counter.

height are 3.0 and 4.0 eV respectively[10]. The result obtained thus indicates an instrumental broadening of the order of 5 eV.

Whilst this resolution is almost adequate for the observation of the major features of the absorption fine structure, an improvement by a further factor of 10 is desirable. More important is the fact that the resolution here is obtained only by the use of a narrow slit in front of the counter, and the overall efficiency of the spectrometer, as estimated from the known output of the X-ray tube, is only about 10 %. Thus only about 10 % of the crystal surface is being effectively used.

An increased resolution and intensity may be expected to result from repolishing of the crystal mount, further alignment of the instrument, and possibly from the substitution of a different quartz crystal.

REFERENCES

[1] S. YOSHIDA, *Sci. Papers Inst. Phys. Chem. Research Tokyo*, 38 (1941) 272.
[2] J. BERGERGREN, *Compt. rend assoc. franc. avances sci.*, 171 (1920) 624.
[3] A. E. LINDH, *Z. Phys.*, 6 (1921) 303.
[4] A. E. LINDH, *Thesis*, Lund, (1923).
[5] D. COSTER and S. KIESTRA, *Physica*, 14 (1948) 175.
[6] J. V. P. LONG, *J. Sci. Instr.*, 35 (1958) 323.
[7] J. V. P. LONG, this volume, p. 98.
[8] T. JOHANSSON, *Z. Phys.*, 82 (1933) 507.
[9] J. W. M. DuMOND, D. A. LIND and E. R. COHEN, *Rev. Sci. Instr.*, 18 (1947) 617.
[10] S. K. ALLISON, *Phys. Rev.*, 44 (1933) 63.

C. THEORY AND TECHNIQUE OF CONTACT MICRORADIOGRAPHY

A HIGH-OUTPUT ROTATING ANODE SHOCK-PROOF TUBE (DEMOUNTABLE) FOR X-RAY MICROSCOPY

R. V. ELY

Guildford, Surrey (Great Britain)

ABSTRACT

The experimental tube as described at the First Symposium has been further developed. The target is now insulated from the supporting tube passing through the vacuum-sealed bearings and the insulated high tension supply is applied directly to the target.

Any part of the tube can be handled with complete safety during operation so that the target can be rotated manually to permit a substantial increase in loading.

The tube operates satisfactorily in the range 8 to 30 kV.

In order that the substantially grainless, but very slow, emulsions now available for contact X-ray microscopy can be employed more freely it is essential, for most practical purposes, to effect a considerable reduction in the exposure times normally required when using very fine focus tubes.

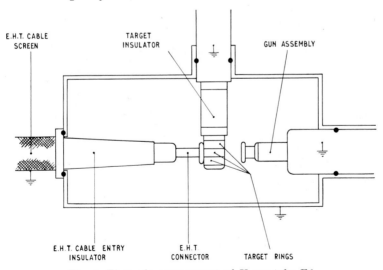

Fig. 1. Electrode arrangement of X-ray tube E6.

Since target pitting and contamination are the factors which normally prevent an increase in tube current when the focal spot size is maintained within specified limits, rotation of the target, either continuously or at short intervals during operation, was the obvious approach to greater outputs.

With a little alteration it was found that the form of vacuum seal between the target and body of the tube, as described at the Cambridge symposium[1], could be made to maintain a satisfactory vacuum when the target was rotated by external manipulation.

Since that target was at high potential, it was decided to redesign the tube so that the external extremity of the target support could be at earth potential.

Fig. 2. Front view of tube E6.

The method adopted is shown diagramatically in Fig. 1 and Figs. 2 and 3 are external views of the completed tube. As at present constructed, the arrangement of the oil cooling supply tubes does not permit of continuous rotation. This may be altered for the future, but, as the target can also be moved laterally, it may prove more convenient to arrange the return traverse in conjunction with a small lateral shift for maximum loading of the target.

Lateral movement may also be used to bring alternative targets into use, as described at Cambridge, but if a single material only is employed, the available lateral traverse may be sufficient to permit an increase in loading above normal, which may be adequate for some purposes.

With focal spot sizes as small as those required, *i.e.* less than 25 μ, any movement of the target is bound to produce some degree of spot enlargement however accurate the mechanical construction may be, and it may prove that lateral movement only is better in that respect.

Fig. 3. Rear view of tube E6.

Nevertheless, it is in the foreshortened plane that variation in target position is likely to be most affected and some movement in that plane can be tolerated more than would be permissible in the other.

The normal maximum current at which the tube can be run for lengthy periods is 250 μA when the target is static, and the focussing test applied makes use of 1500 per inch silver mesh positioned 1″ from the target. The emulsion to target distance is 6″ and at this direct magnification of $\times$ 6 the mesh is clearly resolved.

The tube was completed so recently that it has not been possible to do any serious work with it, but preliminary tests have shown that at four times normal load, *i.e.* at 1,000 μA, no damage occurred to the target after a run of 30 minutes.

Fig. 4 shows a part of the body of a moth taken at 20 kV in contact with a Kodak Maximum Resolution plate at 13 cm from the target. Exposure 90 sec at 1 mA with manual rotation of the target. Subsequent optical magnification to × 250.

Precise comparisons have yet to be made, but results so far confirm that the tube current can be greatly increased by rotation of the target without serious enlargement or displacement of the focal spot. To what extent the current can be further increased is not known at present, but a very recent test at 20 kV and 2 mA for a few minutes was quite satisfactory.

Fig. 4. Part of body of a moth. Magnification 190×.

At very low voltages the focussing is not as good as was expected, judged by results with the previous tube, but characteristic radiation from a manganese target may be adequate for a good deal of work requiring longer wavelengths.

At 30 kV the tube tended to become unstable and in order to test the possibilities of the design at high voltage, a 6″ diameter vacuum camera is now being converted into an experimental tube in which the high-tension insulated cable and the target insulator should both be satisfactory at 70 kV. What characteristics this tube will have remains to be determined, but it appears likely that, if high voltage microfocus tubes are to be available at a moderate cost, they will have to be of the demountable type — and preferably shock-proof.

REFERENCE

[1] R. V. ELY, in V. E. COSSLETT, A. ENGSTRÖM and H. H. PATTEE, *X-ray Microscopy and Microradiography*, Academic Press, Inc., New York, 1957, p. 59.

A NEW SCANNING MICRO-ANALYSER FOR DATA COLLECTION AND EVALUATION FROM X-RAY MICRORADIOGRAMS

HOLGER HYDÉN and SUNE LARSSON

Department of Histology, University of Göteborg (Sweden)

ABSTRACT

A rapid quantitative evaluation of the sample is of great importance for the application of contact X-ray microradiography to biological problems. A scanning cell analyser, previously constructed by the authors, gives information: (*a*) of the distribution of the amount of the X-ray absorbing elements or substances within the sample, and (*b*) of the total amount of X-ray absorbing substances within the sample as one single value, based on up to 12,000 measurements, performed in 4 min by mechanical scanning.

A new construction is presented with which the total amount of X-ray absorbing substances is determined by electronic scanning 1,000 times more rapidly than was possible with the previous cell analyser. The X-ray absorption can be directly evaluated by combining the scanning part with the camera tube.

Using contact X-ray microradiography the best available lateral resolution lies around 0.3 μ according to our experience. Leaving aside this part of the technique, there are still the pertinent problems of the treatment of the biological material and the quantitative evaluation of the X-radiograms.

We have found fresh, untreated cells, directly and rapidly taken out from the fresh tissue to represent the best material now available for such analyses. The cells, in Fig. 1 represented by nerve cells, are rapidly freed from surrounding cells in a drop of isotonic sucrose solution and placed on a 0.2—0.5 μ-thick Al foil. When the sucrose solution is sucked off, they spread out on the metal foil and are allowed to dry, preferably *in vacuo* and at $-20°$ C. Fig. 1 shows such a cell exposed at 8—12 Å for mass determination. There are several advantages to this way of preparing the samples. No material available for 8—12 Å X-ray analysis has disappeared from the cells and the mass of the whole cell will be obtained, including that of the delicate processes. Furthermore, the organic material is mostly evenly distributed within the fresh cells. There are no disturbing gradients, and errors due to *e.g.* the Eberhard effect, so frequently occurring in X-radiograms from sections through fixed tissues, can be avoided.

An example of the latter case is shown in Fig. 2. This shows a 5 μ-thick section through two nerve cells of the same type as that demonstrated in Fig. 1. These are, however, taken from a Carnoy-fixed tissue, embedded in paraffin wax and sectioned. This treatment has caused a loss from the nucleus of around 90 % and from the cytoplasm of around 50 % of the organic mass. Furthermore, the cell material is highly shrunken and false gradients have been produced[1, 2]. Although the resolution

References p. 55

is good in this radiogram, around 0.2 μ, disturbing adjacency effects are present, increasing further the errors due to the Schwarzschild-Villiger effect in the photometric evaluation. We have found that nerve cell material fixed in such a way is useless for quantitative measurements.

The question to be discussed below is the best way to evaluate a suitable radiogram and a new construction for this purpose will be presented.

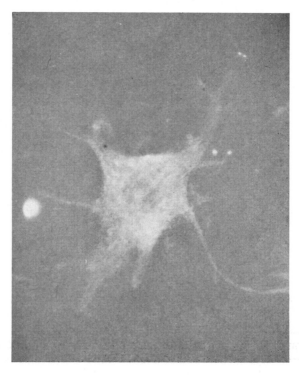

Fig. 1. A fresh, isolated nerve cell, spread out on an Al foil, exposed at 8—12 Å and photographed with a 40× objective, n.a. 0.65, and 5× ocular. Magn. × 300. Kodak emulsion 649—0.

According to our view this is best made by scanning and integrating. By an instrument described some years ago[3] this is done by mechanical scanning. The scanning device is a three-layered table where the three plates are movable against each other in pairs[4]. The velocity of the scanning is adjusted to the measuring frequency of the cell analyser, which is 50 measuring points per second. The sample can be moved 100—300 μ. During this movement 100 small areas are measured, ranging in size from 0.75 to 6 μ^2. The start of the measurement is actuated by a signal from a synchronous motor. Each signal also actuates the movement in the other dimension by 1 to 3 μ. The sample is thus divided into 12,000 small areas. It is, of course, not permissible to add the transmission values from each small area to a sum-up value of the mass. The mass value from each area is obtained by letting the signals pass an electronic function transformer. This function transformer converts the non-linear transmission curve to a linear curve form, where every point is proportional to the mass.

References p. 55

In practice, this is done by calibrating the function transformer against a reference system (where each step has the same wavelength dependence as the sample). At the same time it is corrected for non-linear γ-values in the film.

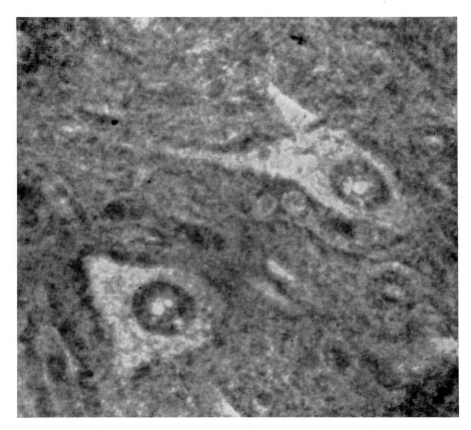

Fig. 2. A 5μ-thick section through two Carnoy-fixed nerve cells of the same type as those demonstrated in Fig. 1. Exposed at 8—12 Å and photographed as in Fig. 1.

The construction of the function transformer is the following.

The radiation intensity of the paraxial rays in the microscope system coming from each measuring area is transformed to amplified and rectified potentials, proportional to the intensity. The potentials are fed into the function transformer which acts as a voltage-dependent resistance. Ten diodes are connected and each diode is provided with a variable resistance. Each unit can be set at a certain voltage. The diodes can successively be made conducting by the incoming voltage. Thus, in this way can the function transformer be calibrated against the reference system of each preparation, usually containing many cells.

The determination of 12,000 values by mechanical scanning takes 4 min. It is hardly possible to increase the speed in such an instrument.

In the instrument to be described, the principle of the functional transformer is kept, but the speed is much increased by electronic scanning.

Some instruments have already been described using a television microscope system to visualize the sample by suitable counting techniques[5-8]. Our purpose, on the other hand, has been to utilize a flying spot tube for scanning in the microscope and to make the analysis quantitative. Fig. 3 gives a diagram of the instrument.

A flying spot tube is used as illuminating source for the two inverted microscopes I and II. The two optical systems are identical and each provided with a photo-multiplier tube. One of the microscope systems is connected with the grid of the flying spot tube *via* a broad-band amplifier II in a feed-back system to keep the light intensity constant. Thus are eliminated the lack of uniformity of the screen and the optical error of the microscope.

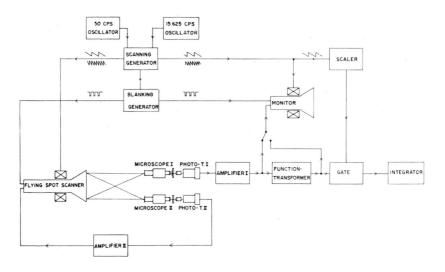

Fig. 3. Diagram of the scanning micro-analyser.

The multiplier I is connected to an integrating unit *via* a video amplifier I and a function transformer. In the integrator (a) the information in one whole frame or in many whole frames is summed up, or (b) the integrator tells by a scaler how many whole frames are needed to give a certain mass value.

The function transformer is also here used to convert the non-linear trans-mission curve to a linear curve which is proportional to the mass value. The in-tegrator is thus calibrated in mass values. The sample, *e.g.* the cell is visualized on a monitor, and the signal is taken out before the function transformer, where it is non-linear and gives better contrast.

The scanning of the flying spot tube and the monitor is done by a single scanning generator. This generator is synchronized with the mains (50 cycles/sec) for the frame sweep and with a standard oscillator (15,625 cycles/sec) for the line sweep. Interlace system is not used. In this way 50 frames per second with 312 lines are obtained and the band width of the video-amplifier can be kept at 3 Mc.

The advantage with this integrating instrument is that a mass value of a cell is directly obtained in a fraction of a second and is based on maximally 120,000 values in each frame.

References p. 55

The use of ultraviolet-producing and sensing components in the instrument would give a direct-measuring and scanning cell-analyser, especially suited for rapid quantitative analysis of living cells.

REFERENCES

1 H. HYDÉN, *J. Embryol, Exptl. Morphol*, 1 (1953) 315.
2 H. HYDÉN and O. HALLÉN, *Exptl. Cell Research, Suppl.* 4 (1957) 197.
3 H. HYDÉN and S. LARSSON, *J. Neurochem.*, 1 (1956) 134.
4 S. LARSSON, *Exptl. Cell Research*, 12 (1957) 666.
5 F. ROBERTS, J. Z. YOUNG and D. CAUSLEY, *Electronics*, 26 (1953) 137.
6 L. E. FLORY, *Cold Spring Harbor Symposia Quant. Biol.*, 16 (1951) 505.
7 V. K. ZWORYKIN, L. E. FLORY and R. E. SCHRADER, *Electronics*, 24 (1952) 150.
8 W. E. TOLLES, *Trans. N. Y. Acad. Sci. Ser. II*, 17 (1955) 250.

CONTRIBUTION TO THE THEORY OF QUANTITATIVE MICRORADIOGRAPHY IN BIOLOGY

B. LINDSTRÖM and F. C. HOH

Department of Medical Physics, Karolinska Institute, Stockholm (Sweden)

ABSTRACT

Using contact microradiography, three different types of quantitative analysis may be performed on a cytochemical scale, *viz.* total dry weight determinations utilizing soft polychromatic X-rays and a reference system, elementary analyses utilizing monochromatic X-rays on each side of the absorption edge of the particular element, and determination of the mineralization in bone and teeth from microradiograms registered by means of filtered K-radiation from copper, chromium, or vanadium. In the wavelength range utilized, only the photoelectric absorption is important, and secondary to this absorption process three different kinds of radiation may be produced, *viz.* direct fluorescence, (characteristic X-rays), photo- and Auger electrons, and indirect fluorescence (polychromatic, low-energy radiation). The influence of these kinds of re-radiation has been evaluated for the three quantitative microradiographic procedures. In mass (total dry weight) determinations re-radiation is completely negligible. In elementary analyses and in determinations of the mineralization, only direct fluorescence influences the results. However, it has been possible to calculate appropriate corrections which are relatively independent of the composition and the thickness of the specimens.

REFERENCE

F. C. HOH and B. LINDSTRÖM, *J. Ultrastruct. Research*, 2 (1959) 512.

ELECTRON OPTICAL ENLARGEMENT OF CONTACT X-RAY IMAGES

H. H. PATTEE

Biophysics Laboratory, W. W. Hansen Laboratories of Physics, Stanford University, Stanford, Calif. (U.S.A)

ABSTRACT

A theoretical comparison is made between reflection, point projection, scanning, and contact methods of X-ray microscopic imaging, with respect to resolution, field, and speed. The contact geometry is shown to have significant theoretical advantages. The use of electron optical enlargement is necessary to realize these advantages, and some of the practical considerations of this technique are mentioned.

It is the purpose of this paper to set forth some of the most general criteria for good microscopic images, and then attempt a comparison of the theoretical possibilities of the known X-ray imaging systems with respect to these criteria. The following paper by ASUNMAA, p. 66, will present some of the practical problems and the preliminary experimental results of the approach to X-ray imaging to which we are led by these theoretical considerations.

We shall take *resolution, width-of-field,* and *speed* as the primary criteria for good X-ray microscopic images. For the purposes of our analysis and comparison we shall differentiate between *geometric resolution* and *diffraction resolution*, although in fact there is no precise separation possible in the physical sense. We shall not discuss the different definitions of resolving distance or width-of-field, but shall use a common definition in our comparisons whenever possible. A discussion of the relative speeds of X-ray image systems has been presented by NIXON and PATTEE[1]. We shall continue to use their assumption that the detector is ideal in each case, that is, limited in speed only by the noise generated by random fluctuations of the X-ray photons passing through the specimen. For detectors of radiation as energetic as X-rays this would appear to be a reasonable assumption, in the sense that single photons of this energy are quite easily detectable, and therefore the detector need not be the slowest link in the imaging process.

As secondary criteria for the quality of an X-ray imaging system we should, of course, include such concepts as simplicity or cost, accuracy of measurement, and ease of operation. However, these are not easy to define for purposes of comparison since they are not independent properties of the instrument itself but depend upon conditions within a laboratory and the skills and preferences of the user. We shall only mention our own views on these points, but shall lay the greatest weight on the more quantitative arguments involving resolution, width-of-field and speed. These three quantities are fundamental in a special way, since if speed is defined in terms of a minimum detectable intensity change, the product of these quantities gives a measure of the information recorded per unit time within the system. This is perhaps the only *single* quantity which, stated by itself, has much value for comparing a group of different data-collecting instruments. On the other hand one should not overemphasize the meaning of comparisons based on such a single "figure of merit" as long as the quantities involved in its derivation have individual significance and can be analyzed separately in more detail.

The resolution and width-of-field of focusing X-ray microscopes is difficult to state for purposes of comparison since the aberration theory of true focusing is developed with entirely different parameters than those used in the shadow methods, and furthermore there is such great variety possible in optical design that few figures for image quality may be stated without reference to particular mirror contours. However, we may base an estimate of resolution on diffraction alone using an aperture of about one-fifth the critical angle which is generous for most of the grazing systems yet designed*. Since the critical angle increases with wave length, this allows us to estimate a diffraction-limited resolving distance of about 500 Å for all wavelengths. It is furthermore unlikely that a field resolving more than 1,000 lines at this resolution can be designed in a practical system involving only a few mirrors. This figure is based on the order of magnitude quality of axial optical systems which are, at worst, much more tractable than grazing incidence systems. It should also be stated that no reflection instrument has yet approached this image quality, and consequently this must be considered as an optimistic estimate even for possible realization in the future.

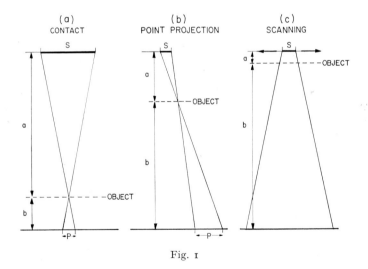

Fig. 1

The behavior of the shadow methods of image formation, which include the contact, point projection and scanning systems, is more easily stated. Fig. 1, a, b, c, illustrates the geometries of these three methods. The parameters used in the comparison are defined below:

---

* It is possible that normal incidence, high aperture X-ray optics may be used at wave lengths greater than 200 Å; however, this region is at present too undeveloped to allow useful predictions.

References p. 60

$s \equiv$ effective X-ray source diameter
$a \equiv$ source-to-object distance
$b \equiv$ object-to-detector distance
$t \equiv$ specimen thickness
$F \equiv$ width-of-field
$\lambda \equiv$ wave length of image-forming radiation

From these quantities we may write expressions for the width of penumbra and image magnification:

$$P = \frac{bs}{a} \equiv \text{width of penumbra of source cast at image plane by opaque screen}$$
$$\text{in object plane,}$$

$$M = \frac{a+b}{a} \equiv \text{image magnification.}$$

We may also write the geometric and diffraction resolving distances in a general form for all three systems:

$$r_g = \frac{P}{M} = \frac{bs}{a+b} \equiv \text{geometric resolving distance,}$$

$$r_d = \left(\frac{ab\lambda}{a+b} \right)^{\frac{1}{2}} \equiv \text{diffraction resolving distance (first Fresnel fringe width).}$$

For the contact and point projection geometries the useful width-of-field, F, can seldom be larger than the source-to-object distance, a. Beyond this the X-ray intensity drops rapidly from target absorption, and the image becomes distorted from the obliquity of rays passing through the specimen. We may also define the number of resolvable lines per field, L, by the expression $L = F/r_m$ where r_m is the optimum resolving distance obtained when the geometric and diffraction resolving distances are made equal. The lines per field is a common measure of picture quality which takes into account the necessity for the observer to orient details, whatever their size, to the specimen as a whole. A picture which resolves only a few lines in its entire width does not convey much meaning unless the surrounding area is already mapped.

TABLE I

Approximations		Contact $M = 1$ $b \leq t \ll a$	Point projection $M > 1$ $a < b$	Scanning $M \gg 1$ $a \leq t \ll b$
	r_g	$\dfrac{b}{a} s$	$\sim s$	s
	r_d	$\leq (t\lambda)^{\frac{1}{2}}$	$(a\lambda)^{\frac{1}{2}}$	$\leq (t\lambda)^{\frac{1}{2}}$
	F	$\sim a$	$\sim a$	—
	L	a/r_m	r_m/λ	—

Table I summarizes the resolution, width-of-field, and lines per field relationships for the shadow methods. The top row indicates the approximations which are applicable for each system. Thus, for the contact method the image magnification is unity and the object-to-detector distance, b, is less than or equal to the specimen thickness, t.

In the second row we see that the geometric resolving distance, r_g, is equal to the equivalent source diameter for the point projection and scanning methods, whereas with the contact geometry the resolving distance may be less than the source diameter by the ratio b/a. We also see that the diffraction resolving distance in both the contact and scanning methods does not involve the effective width-of-field, F. For the point-projection system the dependence of resolving distance on width-of-field is a serious disadvantage, especially at long wave lengths. This is shown in the last row where lines per field is expressed as a ratio involving resolving distance. For the point-projection geometry either a small resolving distance or a long wave length necessarily means a small number of picture elements. Substituting a wave length value of 20 Å and a resolving distance of 500 Å we find that a point-projection picture could not give more than 25 resolvable lines.

The resolving distance and width-of-field in the contact geometry, on the other hand, are not interdependent in a deleterious sense. In general, whenever the source-to-object distance is increased in a contact image system, both the width-of-field and resolution increase, the only disadvantage being a loss of intensity.

The width-of-field in the scanning system depends on the electron optical aberration of the deflected electron beam, which easily allows several hundred resolvable lines in the field. Here as in the contact method, the speed will suffer as the number of picture elements is increased.

Finally we come to comparison of speed. As shown by NIXON and PATTEE[1] it is unlikely that any X-ray imaging system will not suffer from low intensity. Much earlier, ZWORYKIN et al.[2] despaired entirely of point projection solely on the grounds of its slow speed at high resolution. Both point-projection and scanning systems must suffer a direct loss of intensity as the resolution is improved since the source diameter must decrease. The corresponding increase in specific loading means an increase in source brilliance, but the net effect for a given wave length leaves the speed very nearly inversely dependent on resolving distance. As wave length is increased, as it must be for contrast at high resolution, the intensity will suffer a further decrease.

The reflection system must use a source diameter approximately equal to the width-of-field in order to give uniform illumination. This means that the advantage in brilliance of microfocus sources cannot be used. However, the intensity need not change appreciably as resolution is improved, since the source size is not intimately linked to resolving distance, and since the allowable aperture increases with wave length. At the higher resolutions and longer wave lengths, therefore, the reflection system may surpass the point projection and scanning systems. Whether or not reflection optics can achieve good enough imaging properties to make use of this advantage is yet to be determined.

However, it is only the contact geometry which can utilize the great brilliance of microfocus X-ray tubes, and which does not at the same time require a proportional decrease in source diameter as resolution is increased. At the high, light optical resolutions it is possible to build contact systems with at least an order of magnitude greater speed than other systems[3], and this advantage increases significantly at the higher resolutions towards which we are working.

References p. 60

The basic problem in realizing these advantages in contact imaging lies in the development of recording materials which can be enlarged beyond the light optical limit. The most hopeful method of enlargement would utilize the unexcelled resolution of electron optical systems, and it is along these lines which our present work is directed.

Although the criteria so far discussed are of primary importance for microscope design, there are several other considerations which should be mentioned briefly. The cost of any method which requires electron optical enlargement must necessarily be significant. However, in comparison with point projection or scanning systems there seems to be little choice, since the latter must put a greater fraction of effort into the source electron optics instead of the enlarging electron optics. The existence of so many electron microscopes and the availability of low-priced commercial models with more-than-adequate resolution for contact X-ray image enlargement would seem to make such methods economically sound.

The simplicity of specimen preparation and instrument operation are certainly worth mentioning, although it is as yet uncertain exactly what may be involved in future contact techniques. In general, as discussed in the following paper, we have not departed from standard electron microscope techniques any more than necessary. The initial X-ray recording material has been mounted on standard specimen grids; and specimen mounting, X-ray exposure, development, if any, and final electron optical viewing is accomplished without transfer of material. The X-ray exposure is done in air while under direct visual microscopic observation. The total X-ray path length need not be more than 100 microns which means that the X-ray absorption is slight, even at very long wave lengths. Exposure times of over 30 min are considered impractical, and fortunately we find that for most materials the exposure may be held to shorter times.

The operation of the microfocus X-ray source is relatively simple compared to point-projection systems, since the source diameter need not be smaller than a few microns even for resolving distances in the hundreds of angstroms. By using fine-grained evaporated screens[3] it is an easy matter to align and focus the electron system using the same microscope which is used for viewing the mounted specimens.

Although it is too early to guess whether or not a practical contact recording material can be developed, there is now no reason to believe that X-ray resolutions an order of magnitude better than what is possible with the light microscope may be achieved. If we believe the comparisons stated in the earlier paragraphs, it would be most reasonable to work towards such resolutions by employing some form of contact image geometry.

REFERENCES

[1] W. C. NIXON and H. H. PATTEE, in COSSLETT et al., X-ray Microscopy and Microradiography, Academic Press, Inc., New York, 1957, p. 397.
[2] V. K. ZWORYKIN, MORTON, RAMBERG, HILLIER and VANCE, Electron Optics and the Electron Microscope, John Wiley & Sons, Inc., New York, 1945.
[3] H. H. PATTEE, Science, 128 (1958) 977.

HIGH RESOLUTION RADIOSENSITIVE MATERIALS FOR MICRORADIOGRAPHY AT LONG WAVELENGTHS

H. H. PATTEE

Biophysics Laboratory, W. W. Hansen Laboratories of Physics, Stanford University, Stanford, Calif. (U.S.A.)

ABSTRACT

The resolution of contact X-ray images is limited by the quality of the recording material. Silver emulsions continue to suffer from granularity which is visible at high optical magnification. Several new X-ray recording materials with no microscopically visible structure have been investigated. The characteristics and possibilities of these materials are discussed.

The oldest and simplest method of producing X-ray images, which is called *contact microradiography*, continues to be one of the most practical forms of X-ray microscopy for a wide range of biological and metallurgical problems. Some of its advantages are obvious, especially to investigators who are inexperienced in the use of electron optical devices, or who cannot afford to invest large sums of money for special point-projection equipment. Some of the less obvious, but no less important, advantages of the contact image geometry are covered in detail in the following papers. These advantages include the highest possible intensity of any X-ray imaging system, wide field of view, and a resolution limited only by the properties of the recording material, even at very long X-ray wavelengths.

Notwithstanding some improvements in fine-grained silver emulsions, the structure of photographic recording material is still a troublesome element in the interpretation of contact images at high, light-optical resolutions. The extension of the contact method to electron optical enlargement which was begun by LADD[1], RECOURT[2] and MÖLLENSTEDT and HUANG[3] continues to offer promise for high resolution X-ray images, and this aspect of our work will also be covered in the following chapters. This paper will describe radiosensitive materials for light-optical viewing at high magnification.

A visible image may be produced by X-rays in a uniform sheet of material either by a change of optical absorption or by a change of optical path length. These two general types of alteration may be brought about by many processes, both direct and indirect, involving staining or bleaching reactions, dye synthesis, solubility changes, density changes, or mass changes by etching. The detailed chain of reactions which may give rise to the final image is seldom easy to interpret, although the general principles of the process are understood.

It is well known, for example, that many ionic crystals take on a characteristic color as a result of irradiation[4]. This change in optical absorption is ascribed to the trapping of the photoelectrons released by the X-rays at the vacant lattice points of the crystal. It was at one time thought that these *Farbcentren* or *F-centers* could not occur with enough density in normal crystals to produce strong coloration;

but it is now known that the X-ray photons themselves produce lattice defects, and that on prolonged exposure, very deep coloration is possible[5]. Reasonably good images of 1500 bar/in. grids were made by the author in 1953 on the surface of single crystals of rocksalt and cesium bromide after prolonged irradiation with a chromium target tube. There are by now many examples of both crystalline and amorphous materials which undergo a color change upon irradiation without any subsequent chemical or physical processing.

The basic practical difficulty with this type of direct image formation is its lack of efficiency. At the ultrasoft X-ray wavelengths especially, even with the optimum source design and image geometry, there are so few photons available that lack of sensitivity in the recording material presents a serious obstacle, even for the contact method.

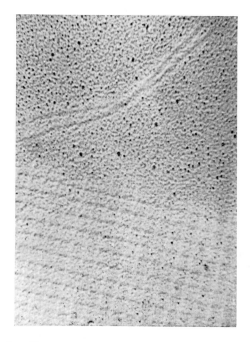

Fig. 1. Light micrograph of X-ray image of 1500 bar/in. mesh produced on vinylidene chloride (Saran). Note bubbles produced by high dose rate. This image appeared after 1.6 h exposure, 10 cm from a vanadium target tube operated at 12.5 kV and 10 mA. No development process was used.

Another well known effect of the absorption of energetic radiation in plastics is a change of solubility produced by cross-linking or alteration of polymer length. This effect was used by the LADDS[1] in their study of microradiographic materials for electron optical enlargement. However, by the use of phase or interference light optics this same effect can be made to produce excellent light images. Some work along these lines was done by WARNES[6] in our laboratory in 1956, using a variety of common plastic materials available in thin sheets. Exposure was made using a vanadium target tube (Machlett AEG-50) operated at 12.5 kV. The target was located 10 cm from the test material. Test objects were 500 bar/in. and 1500 bar/in. grids.

The most responsive of the common plastics was vinylidene chloride (Saran) which gave a visible image of a 1500 bar/in. mesh after 1.6 h exposure at 10 mA target current, and with no subsequent treatment (Fig. 1). This image suffers from gas bubbles which are the result of too high a dose rate. A much improved image is obtained by exposing longer at a lower target current. The image contrast in either case is greatly enhanced by washing for several hours in a 20 % solution of NH₄OH. Fig. 2a shows such an image microphotographed with transmitted light. The topographic nature of the image is seen more easily in Fig. 2b which is made with oblique illumination. This method was not pursued further because again the exposure times, even for the relatively hard radiation used, was too long to be practical.

A third type of material remained to be examined, namely photoreactive dye derivatives which become dyes on exposure to sufficiently energetic radiation.

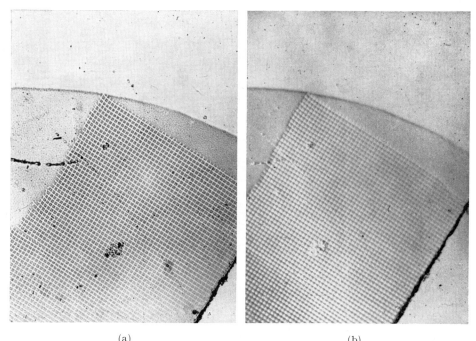

(a)   (b)

Fig. 2a. Micrograph by transmitted light of X-ray image of 1500 bar/in. mesh produced on Saran. Dose rate was much less than that used in Fig. 1 and image is enhanced by washing in 20 % NH₄OH for several hours.

Fig. 2b. Light micrograph by oblique illumination of identical image as shown in (a).

Ordinary photographic dyes used to extend the spectral range of emulsions have the function of absorbing the low energy incident photons and efficiently transferring the absorbed energy to a silver grain so that it can undergo a permanent chemical change. The function of a dye derivative material for microradiographic recording is to utilize the high energy photon to initiate a chemical change which results in an efficient *in situ* dye synthesis. One material of this type has been described by CHALKLEY[7] for recording the ultraviolet spectrum at wavelengths shorter than 3200 Å. Through the courtesy of Dr. E. RYSKIEWICZ of the International Business Machines Corporation Research Laboratory, San Jose, California, samples of a similar material, pararosanaline leuconitrile, were obtained for our use for contact X-ray imaging. Samples of the dyestuff were dissolved either in gelatin or Nylon. The thickness of the sensitive layer was about 15 μ. Exposure was made using a micro-focus X-ray source with a 10-μ diameter. The target was a 6-μ aluminum foil, and the excitation voltage was 15 kV. Target to specimen distance was 0.1 to 0.2 mm.

Since the dyestuff is insensitive to visible light, and since the image appears immediately upon exposure without additional treatment, it is possible to view the specimen and the image during the X-ray exposure, provided that a suitable optical illumination system is available. The equipment used in this investigation was the same as that comprising the microfluoroscope which is fully illustrated in a subsequent chapter, page 79. This arrangement allowed simultaneous high intensity X-ray exposure and high-magnification optical viewing of the film and specimen. Exposure times for this arrangement were from 5 to 20 min depending on the target

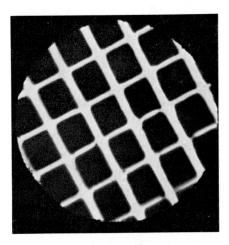

Fig. 3. Micrograph by transmitted light of X-ray image of 1500 bar/in. mesh produced on para-rosanaline leuconitrile film. Exposure was made with aluminum target tube with 10-μ source diameter. Resolution is limited by thickness of image which greatly exceeds depth of focus of microscope objective.

to specimen spacing. This places the X-ray sensitivity of the dyestuff at about one-tenth that of Lippmann-type emulsions.

Except for the inevitable dust and scratches, the gelatin-base dye shows no background structure at the highest possible optical magnification. The present resolution of the material is limited by the thickness of the sensitive layer which greatly exceeds the depth of focus of the microscope objective used for viewing. There is also the possibility that diffusion of the dye may occur over distances comparable to the optical resolution, but there is no clear experimental evidence of this occurring. The high optical absorption which can be achieved with the 15 μ thickness indicates that a reduction in thickness by a factor of three or four should be possible. This would improve the resolution as well as provide a better filtering effect so as to record only the ultrasoft X-rays. Fig. 3 shows a 1500 bar/in. test grid image enlarged with a Leitz 90 $\times$, N.A. 1.32 objective. A green filter was used to utilize the maximum absorption band of the dye, but there is no photographic enhancement of the contrast. Fig. 4 shows a light and an X-ray image of a mica flake to indicate the gray scale of the dye.

The slow speed of the material compared with silver halide emulsions is a disadvantage unless a semi-microfocus source of 10 or 20-μ diameter is available.

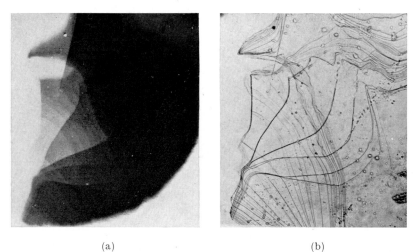

(a)   (b)

Fig. 4a. Micrograph by transmitted light of X-ray image of mica flake produced on pararosanaline leuconitrile film illustrating the contrast range of this recording material.
Fig. 4b. Light micrograph of identical mica flake as shown in (a).

With such a tube, using an aluminum target within a fraction of a millimeter of the specimen, it is possible to keep the exposure time within 10 or 15 min. Since the image appears directly, and can be viewed safely in visible light during exposure, this material is ideal for preliminary surveys of specimens as well as for quantitative absorption measurements. In the latter case the image may be photometrically monitored during exposure so that any given density may be reproduced closely without the possibilities of error which arise from the normal developing process.

REFERENCES

[1] W. A. LADD, W. M. HESS and M. W. LADD, *Science*, 123 (1956) 3192.
[2] A. RECOURT, in V. E. COSSLETT *et al.*, *X-ray Microscopy and Microradiography*, Academic Press, Inc., New York, 1957, p. 234.
[3] G. MÖLLENSTEDT and L. Y. HUANG, *ibid.*, p. 392.
[4] R. W. POHL, *Physik. Z.*, 39 (1938) 36.
[5] F. SEITZ, *Rev. Modern Phys.*, 18 (1946) 384.
[6] R. WARNES, see discussion by PATTEE, in V. E. COSSLETT *et al.*, *X-ray Microscopy and Microradiography*, Academic Press, Inc., New York, 1957, p. 387.
[7] L. CHALKLEY, *J. Opt. Soc. Am.*, 42 (1952) 387.

X-RAY-SENSITIVE RECORDING MATERIALS FOR ELECTRON OPTICAL CONTRAST*

SAARA K. ASUNMAA

*Biophysics Laboratory, W. W. Hansen Laboratories of Physics,
Stanford University, Stanford, Calif. (U.S.A.)*

ABSTRACT

The quantitative properties of an X-ray absorption image can be recorded in electron micrographs if the photographic densities in the EMG's are studied in areas of large dimensions, compared with the resolution attained, and if the recording material has uniform thickness and a homogeneous or amorphous structure. A thickness corresponding to the "reference thickness" or a single electron scattering on the average allows the optimum conditions for quantitative evaluation of the image contrast. Good recording materials must have not only radiosensitivity and minimum structure, but also stability in the electron beam. A chemical reaction of the recording material with an electron stain activated by the irradiation is preferable to dissolution processes, which easily produce swelling, especially in the organic materials (*e.g.*, polymers), and consequently can change the distribution of the structural details.

INTRODUCTION

Electron microscopy has been used to magnify several types of contact X-ray images by LADD and LADD[1], RECOURT[2], and MÖLLENSTEDT and HUANG[3]. The advantages of this general approach have been discussed by PATTEE in a previous paper[4].

The application of electron microscopy to the evaluation of the quantitative properties of an X-ray absorption image prerequires certain conditions. *First,* the proper use of an electron microscope for investigation of mass distribution requires a study of areas and details which are large compared with the resolution attained. *Second,* only in specimens of *reference thickness* (a *characteristic* or *transparency thickness*) or less is the image formation easily interpreted[5, 6]. *Third,* the theory of image formation is developed for amorphous scatterers[7, 8]; and therefore only structureless materials, or at least substrates with a random distribution of the smallest structural components, must be selected as X-ray-sensitive recording materials for subsequent electron optical investigations. *Fourth,* the energy loss of electrons interacting with a solid is characteristic of the material. Therefore, for all kinds of quantitative evaluations of the electron image and its contrasts, the chemical consistency and the distribution of the different chemical components in the X-ray record, must be known.

No simple relationship exists between electron scattering and dry mass. Scattering, absorption and diffraction simultaneously produce the variations of image intensities. Therefore, as a *fifth* prerequisite, the physical properties of the X-ray-sensitive

---

* The research reported here was supported by the U.S. Navy (Office of Naval Research).

recording material, its microcrystallinity and electron diffraction, must be known. The stability of the substrate in the electron beam is a requirement above all the forementioned. Approximate evaluation of relative mass thicknesses can thus be attained only if a calibration system is applied.

Finally, if an electron contrast is introduced by means of irradiation-activated chemical reactions and heavy components incorporated or removed, then the reaction mechanism and kinetics give new problems. The electron contrast should preferably show a simple relationship to the irradiation dose; *i.e.*, the X-ray quantum yield of the contrast-producing reaction should be constant over a wide range of incident intensity.

Development of convenient methods for reproducing the quantitative properties of an X-ray-absorption image in electron micrographs is accordingly subject to evident difficulties. However, the superior resolution available and the speed of X-ray recording under favorable irradiation conditions call for a closer study of possibilities and requirements.

EVALUATION OF POSSIBILITIES

The first requirement (referring to details larger than the resolution) is fortunately fulfilled for electron micrographs of X-ray images taken by means of the present X-ray microscopes. An optimum resolution of about 200—500 Å for the contact X-ray method, as referred to in this paper, shows minimum details of dimensions of one or two orders of magnitude larger than the routine resolving power of the present commercial electron microscopes. The other requirements stated guide the selection of the most convenient recording materials among a number of possibilities.

Structure and absorption

The silver grain of the finest photographic emulsions is about 50 mμ. Nevertheless, the fluctuation of granularity causes an unevenness much larger than the minimum resolvable distance of the X-ray contact method. Many other X-ray-sensitive materials show considerably smaller grain, if any.

Several noncrystalline materials with minimum structure are radiation-sensitive and applicable as recording materials for soft X-rays. The quantum yield for a few polymers, for example, increases up to 10^8-fold in the short wave-length region[9]. Furthermore, a large number of organic degradative dyes and inorganic single crystals, as well as several metals, are high-energy-sensitive.

An initial step of irradiation effect and excitation must involve introduction of energy by means of absorption, directly or indirectly. The X-ray record itself can be used as an electron microscope specimen if it has the appropriate characteristic thickness according to the second prerequisite[5-7]. The characteristic thickness, corresponding to one single elastic scattering on the average per incident electron on its path through the specimen, is about 400 Å for carbon and 1,000 Å for organic materials, but considerably less for compounds of higher density. Thin films with a linear thickness down to 100 Å can be prepared from many synthetic plastics. These films are not only thin enough for electron microscopy; they are almost structureless submicroscopically and can be sufficiently stabilized for the electron beam. The absorption of soft X-rays with a wave length below 10 Å, however, is

References p. 77

very limited in these ultrathin layers of organic compounds, especially if the substrates do not contain any heavy inorganic radicals. (About 1 % of the aluminum radiation of 8.32 Å is absorbed in a foil of nitrocellulose with a thickness of 500 Å, if the chemical composition is 3.6 % H, 28.1 % C, 11.5 % N, and 56.8 % O.) For obtaining optimum absorption for a certain wave length from a certain X-ray source operating in the atmosphere with constant intensity, only the radiation dose, *i.e.*, the exposure time, can be varied. As another alternative the reaction rate can be enhanced by means of activators.

Low concentrations of organic degradative dyes, homogeneously distributed in plastics, can be used for X-ray recording for subsequent electron microscope studies. The characteristic thickness, the microstructure, and the absorption properties are about the same as for pure polymers.

The characteristic thickness in terms of g/cm^2 does not vary essentially as a function of the atomic number. In terms of centimeters it is considerably lower for the common metals than for lighter atoms. However, thin evaporated metal layers supported on carbon or plastic films and with an "optical thickness" of a few hundred Å are transparent also in the 50 kV electron beam, mainly because of the distribution and size of crystallites. The evaporated metal films show an electron diffraction which is characteristic for random distribution of crystallites. According to HAINE and AGAR[10] the single scattering theory can be expanded to lattices of atoms, and according to measurements of LIPPERT[11] the electron optical transparency of carbon, aluminum, palladium, and tungsten films shows a direct exponential relationship to the film thickness. Several metals and metal salts are irradiation-sensitive, especially under atmospheric conditions. Further experiments are needed to investigate the suitability of the applied reactions for electron-optical dosimetry.

Electron contrast

Electron contrast is produced by differences in mass thicknesses in a chemically uniform substrate or by distribution of components with differentiating electron-scattering properties.

An electron staining refers to introduction of heavy atoms, radicals, and components, as well as to removal of these. An irradiation-activated reaction often occurs as oxidation under atmospheric conditions, or other changes in mass thickness can be produced under accurately controllable conditions. Macromolecules are able to retain the incident ionizing radiation energy; most polymers, therefore, are sensitive to high-energy radiation. Fortunately they can be stabilized for subsequent irradiation. Condensation, cross-linking, or degradation characterize the irradiation-initiated reactions. The degree of polymerization (DP) thus is changed and, accordingly, solubility in addition to other physical properties. Fractions of certain DP can be removed and evaluated as a measure for the absorbed quantity of radiation or under optimum conditions for the incident intensity. A transfer of energy occurs along the macromolecular chains to the most sensitive links. Distribution of sensitive regions determines the localization of changes, and it prescribes whether or not a latent image is produced, capable of being developed as an original true image. Further investigations have to decide to what extent the possible multiple ionization allows a dosimetry of incident radiation.

Free radicals of considerable lifetime are radiation intermediates giving opportunity not only for further polymerization and copolymerization, but also for secondary reactions with other reagents, so-called inhibitors present in the solid. Incorporation of known radicals of high electron scattering in the exposed portions of molecules — preferably localized only in the irradiated areas — produces an "electron image." An experimental calibration will show in what manner a certain fraction of collisions and reactions corresponds to the incident energy and can be used to relate the incident radiation and the electron contrast. If the additional reagent can be applied in the gas phase, no further preparation is required, and no preparation artifacts are introduced.

The decomposition products of irradiation-degradative dyes often show differentiating solubilities or vapor pressure, applicable for development of an electron image. Reaction mechanism and preparation technique hence remain the main problems. Metal surfaces are easily oxidized in air if activated by light or high-energy photons. They also react with halogens and oxides or give alloys with adjacent metals if favorably activated. Changes in optical and electrical properties are not always recorded as an electron contrast. Differentiating solubility or chemical reactivity of the reactants and the reaction products on the other hand can fortify an electron contrast more or less quantitatively.

Instead of introduction of a new electron contrast as an irradiation record into the specimen itself, an indirect method is available: replication of relief surfaces onto thin plastic membranes or evaporated films. This successful preparation method for morphological electron microscopy can be used for replication of mass thicknesses for the corresponding investigation of electron-scattering densities under careful modification of conditions and preparation. The uniform chemical consistency of a "quantitative" replica simplifies the evaluation of relationship between dry mass and electron scattering.

PROCEDURES

The X-ray source was a microfocus tube with a 10-μ beam diameter, 8 kV excitation voltage, and 6-μ aluminum target. This source is described in the following chapter of this volume[12].

The irradiation occurred under atmospheric conditions at a distance of about 1 cm down to 0.8 mm from the target. Irradiation times shorter than 30 min were intended. The X-ray beam was carefully focused on a certain labeled area on the specimen holder.

The X-ray-sensitive materials were dried as a thin layer of uniform thickness (about 0.1 μ) on a supporting membrane carried by an electron microscope specimen grid. For specimens with subsequent chemical treatment, only grids of gold or stainless steel were used, with formvar, nitrocellulose, or silicon oxide as supporting films.

Single polymers and mixtures of two different polymers were investigated, as well as mixtures of polymers with an inorganic activator. Metals were correspondingly evaporated as thin films on a supporting membrane and sometimes activated by oxides.

The Hitachi HU-10 electron microscope with double condenser and interchangeable objective aperture (10-, 20-, 50-μ) was used. Electron optical magnifications of 600—5,000 were taken on Kodak lantern slide contrast plates, and photographic enlargements (up to five times) of the electron micrographs were made.

Test specimens of different geometry and chemical constitution were employed, namely: silver grid 1500/inch, copper grid 500/inch, diatoms with openings down to 100 Å diameter, pollen grains (about 7 μ), wood sections with various structural dimensions, polystyrene spheres from 1.8 μ down to 0.2 μ diameter. The specimens were placed directly on the X-ray-sensitive membrane in order to give a perfect contact. Most specimens could be easily removed.

The following synthetic plastics were selected: nylon; carboxymethylcellulose, with and without sodium (CMC); polyvinylpyrrolidone (PVP); methylmethacrylate; polyethylene glycol dimethacrylate; polyvinyl alcohol; and Saran, the copolymer of vinylidene chloride with vinyl chloride. Hemocyanin and serum globulin represented the native macromolecules. The irradiation occurred under atmospheric conditions or under iodine or osmium tetroxide vapor. For removal of degradation products only solvents of moderate efficiency were used in order to avoid unnecessary swelling of the unmodified original material. Changes of the physical properties of nylon were recorded as an increased diffusion rate of osmium tetroxide from water solution into the plastic film. The inorganic activator in a mixture of PVP and CMC was soluble in water and easy to remove from the areas without radiation reaction.

Of the degradative dyes erythrosin and 2,3,5-triphenyl-2H-tetrazolium chloride were most interesting.

EXPERIMENTAL DETAILS AND RESULTS

The preliminary results are described by means of a few examples and prints.

1. The polymers polyvinylpyrrolidone (PVP) and sodium carboxymethylcellulose (CMC) show a pronounced increase in degree of polymerization after a high-energy irradiation. The exact reaction mechanism has not been investigated. However, from observation of similar effects on corresponding polymers, a crosslinking between adjacent molecules is assumed. Both original materials are water soluble and fairly soluble in acetone and ethyl ether. The mixture 1:1 (equal parts of 5 % PVP and 1 % CMC in water) gave satisfactory results, a considerable reaction rate, a convenient strength, and flexibility of the film.

The film (about 1 μ) was cast on a glass surface and dried for 3 days in air. During the irradiation — 20 min at a distance of 1 cm from the target — the film was in direct contact with the glass surface and the specimen (500/inch copper grid) in immediate contact with the film. A subsequent treatment with acetone and ethyl ether for about 5 min developed a relief surface on the irradiated area. The original film thickness remained approximately constant on the areas corresponding to the grid bars and protected by them from the exposure. In the X-ray-irradiated areas a fraction of the polymers was easily soluble in the solvents. Further polymerization occurred in the whole irradiated film. A more pronounced effect was observed on the membrane areas protected from the immediate X-ray radiation by the copper bars.

There is a certain evidence that the X-ray "image" obtained is not only a direct absorption image but an irradiation effect of more complicated character, produced to a certain extent by means of some kind of contact reaction in areas with perfect contact between the substrate and the irradiated metal. The thickness of the metal bars, a few microns, excludes a possible excitation by photoelectrons. An initial overall polymerization is superposed by radiation degradation.

Fig. 1 shows a phase contrast photograph of a relief surface, representing an X-ray-produced image of a 500/inch copper grid. The X-ray penumbral blurring is visible on outer areas of the print. This film and the relief image can be magnified in an electron microscope; the variations in mass thickness give an electron contrast. For a sharp reproduction of the relief bars, this particular membrane was too thick and the background scattering of electrons too pronounced. An original film thickness of about 0.1 μ allows a better electron image, as illustrated in Fig. 2.

Sodium carboxymethylcellulose is more electron-opaque than pure plastic films of the same linear thickness; it acts as an X-ray pigment and allows, therefore, a considerably higher speed of polymerization than that observed by previous investigators.

2. Carboxymethylcellulose and polyvinylpyrrolidone, activated by inorganic oxidants and irradiated at a short distance — 0.8 mm — for 15 to 20 min, gave sharp irradiation images of 1.8 μ polystyrene particles according to Figs. 3 and 4. Some heterogeneity is observed in the distribution of the inorganic component. The granularity, however, is much smaller than the finest photographic grain. The highly electron-opaque areas surrounding the image and visible also inside a group of three or more spherules need further investigation.

3. Erythrosin (tetraiodofluorescein) is a fluorescent dye, which is photo-degradative according to NATASON[13]. The same decomposition probably occurs as in one of the high-energy-initiated reactions, since the dark color of free iodine is observed after a treatment with soft X-rays. Formation of a leuco-color probably intensifies the observed differences in color intensity as an irradiation product. The distribution of color corresponds to an optical image, and an electron contrast is produced if one of the decomposition products is removed.

A thin film was cast from a solution consisting of 1.5 % pyroxylin and 0.4 % erythrosin, dissolved in a mixture of alcohol and ethyl ether. Metal grids were used as control specimens for an irradiation of 10 min at a distance of 1 cm from the target. Fig. 5 shows a light micrograph of the X-ray-produced image of a 500/inch copper grid, and Fig. 6 of a 1500/inch silver grid on a thin film which is supported by an electron microscope 200/inch gold grid. The dark color, and consequently the reaction, is obtained mostly in the X-ray-protected areas under the X-ray-irradiated grid bars. An irradiation excitation owing to photoelectrons, as first suggested, is less probable because of the thickness of the grid bars: about 5 μ. The reaction observed is therefore interpreted at the present time as a kind of contact reaction by the irradiated metal. It requires further study. The equidistant distribution of the very dark spots on the borders of the grid-bar images confirms the importance of an immediate contact. The dark areas with high concentration of free iodine correspond to the unevenness in the surface of the electrolytically prepared copper grids and to the highest points.

4. A commercial nylon film, 25 μ thick, was irradiated for 20 min at a distance of 1 cm from the target, using a 500/inch copper grid as protecting specimen. Fig. 7 shows an optical micrograph of the film after treatment with 1% water solution of osmium tetroxide for 1 h. The X-ray-irradiated areas corresponding to the openings of the metal grid show a dark color of metallic osmium.

References p. 77

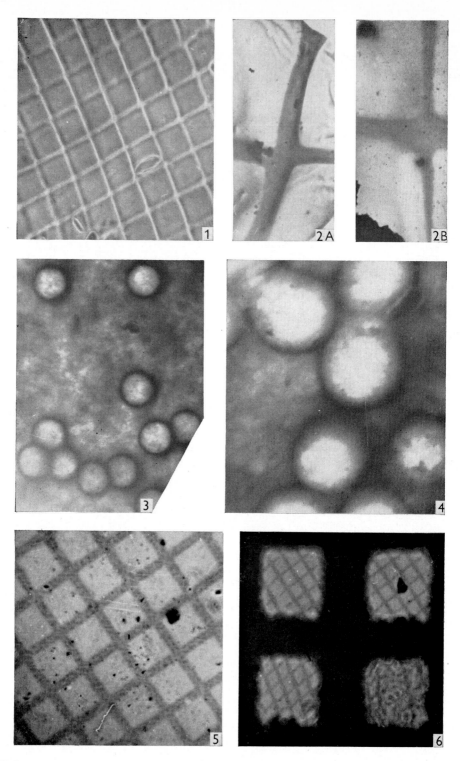

The physical properties of the film are changed in the X-ray-exposed areas; the diffusion rate of water solutions into the solid increases and allows a faster penetration of osmium tetroxide into the irradiated film than into the metal-protected areas and the original foil. The oxide then is easily reduced to metallic osmium, giving a dark color. Osmium metal, free or in compounds, is a well-known electron scatterer. The fine striation on the film surface in Fig. 5 corresponds to the calendering of the commercial film. No granularity is visible. Fig. 8 confirms the results and illustrates a nylon film irradiated as in Fig. 7 after a treatment with sulfuric acid instead of osmium. The fraction of low DP as a degradation product is dissolved, and a relief image produced. A good optical resolution illustrates a sharp localization of the irradiation effect. The radiation-initiated reaction occurred in the X-ray-exposed areas, producing an absorption image.

Exactly the same method was applied to several degradative polymers: methacrylates, polyethylene compounds such as polyethylene glycol methacrylate, vinyl polymers and their copolymers such as vinylidene chloride copolymer with vinyl chloride. The electron staining, applying differences in diffusion rate, allows a considerably easier preparation than removal of degradation products by means of solution. See Fig. 15.

5. Evaporated metal films of silver, copper, tin, and aluminum were irradiated for 15 to 20 min at a short distance from the target: about 0.8 mm or less. Diatoms, silver grid, and polystyrene particles with diameters of 1.8 to 0.2 μ were applied as irradiation-protecting specimens.

Surface oxidation and the accessibility of nonreacted surfaces to oxygen determine the general kinetic scheme of reaction with a true activating radiation effect.

Figs. 9, 10, and 11 illustrate irradiation images on silver films. They give an impression of true absorption-shadow images, probably owing to the more pronounced oxidation and increase of mass thickness on the X-ray-exposed areas. However, a change of crystallite size in the electron beam in the areas protected by the specimen increases the electron transparency and the electron contrast of the image. A quantitative interpretation, therefore, is complicated by the superposition of the two different effects.

In Fig. 12 a shadow-absorption image of a round diatom on aluminum foil

---

Fig. 1. Phase contrast micrograph of an X-ray image of 500/inch copper grid, irradiation for 20 min at a distance of 1 cm from the target. Substrate PVP plus CMC. Details in text.

Fig. 2. Electron micrographs A and B of a corresponding X-ray image as in Fig. 1 of 1500/inch silver grid, irradiation 1 h at a distance of 0.4 mm from the target. Imaging defects due to X-ray penumbra illustrated in Fig. 2B.

Fig. 3. Electron micrograph of an X-ray-produced image of 1.8 μ polystyrene particles, irradiation 15 min at a distance of 0.8 mm from the target. Substrate PVP plus CMC plus an inorganic activator. The dark areas around images need further studies.

Fig. 4. Electron micrograph of an X-ray-produced image of 1.8 μ polystyrene particles with the same method as in Fig. 3. The fluctuation of mass thickness in the substrate less than 0.1 μ.

Fig. 5. Light micrograph of an X-ray-produced image of 500/inch copper grid, 10 min, 1 cm from the target on erythrosin in nitrocellulose. The black spots are dust particles on the film. Note the regular distribution of dark points on the grid borders corresponding to closest contact between the substrate and the grid.

Fig. 6. Light micrograph of a corresponding X-ray image as in Fig. 5, 1500/inch silver grid, recorded on an ultrathin film, supported by an electron microscope specimen grid. The membrane in the right lower corner shows a preparation artifact.

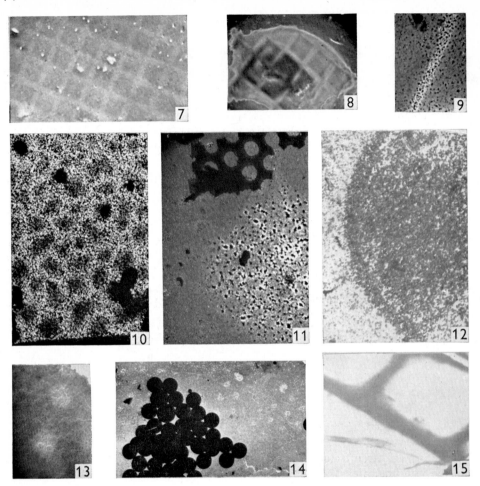

Fig. 7. An X-ray absorption image of 500/inch copper grid recorded on a commercial nylon film. The image is developed by treatment with a solution of osmium tetroxide. Details in text.

Fig. 8. A corresponding X-ray absorption image as in Fig. 7. Development with sulfuric acid. The relief surface is photographed under a drop of sulfuric acid in phase contrast.

Fig. 9. Electron micrograph of an X-ray irradiation image of a diatom fiber (silica) on evaporated silver. Irradiation for 20 min at 0.8 mm from the target. Oxidation in addition to changes in crystallinity produces the electron contrast.

Fig. 10. Electron micrograph of an X-ray irradiation image of a diatom recorded on a film of evaporated silver. The crystallinity is more pronounced after the irradiation. The dark areas correspond to openings in the diatom shell. The five black areas are remnants of inorganic material remaining on the silver film after removal of the specimen.

Fig. 11. Electron micrograph of a silver film. The crystallites in the irradiated area at the upper right corner are different from the crystallites in the original silver film. Diatom at the left.

Fig. 12. Electron micrograph of an X-ray irradiation image of a diatom shell at low magnification, recorded on an evaporated aluminum film, 20 min, 0.8 mm from the target. The irradiation effect produces a high electron contrast after treatment with a dilute solution of ammonium carbonate.

Fig. 13. Electron micrograph of an X-ray irradiation image of 1.8 μ polystyrene particles recorded on an evaporated film of copper.

Fig. 14. Effect of overexposure of polystyrene particles irradiated by soft X-rays. The image is recorded on an aluminum film.

Fig. 15. Electron micrograph of an X-ray absorption image of 1500/inch silver grid on polyethylene glycol methacrylate after development in organic solvents. Irradiation 1 h at a distance of 0.4 mm from the target.

References p. 77

Fig. 16 and 17. Light micrographs of X-ray irradiation images of a 1500/inch silver grid recorded on a substrate of triphenyltetrazolium chloride and fructose suspended in gelatin and irradiated for 1 h at a distance of 0.5 mm in nitrogen atmosphere. The dark vertical lines correspond to a replication effect.

is fortified by treatment with a dilute solution of ammonium carbonate.

In Fig. 13 and 14 the dimensions of the absorption images of polystyrene particles on copper (Fig. 13) and on aluminum (Fig. 14) are compared with the original size of the specimen. An accurate selection of conditions enables us to avoid an "over-exposure" of this kind.

6. Irradiation reactions are guided by the environmental conditions such as pH value, temperature, partial pressure of oxygen and irradiation rate. In Figs. 16—20, 2,3,5-triphenyl-2H-tetrazoliumchloride (TTCl) as a degradative dye was selected to illustrate the importance of the supporting polymer and its reactivity for the electron contrast obtained. The TTCl is decomposed into 2,3-diphenylen-5-phenyltetrazoliumchloride (DPTCl) and 2,3,5-triphenylformazan (TPF) according to WEYGAND and FRANK[14] as a photochemical reaction. The red color of DPTCl gives an optical contrast, and the removal of TPF and TTCl in water produces an excellent electron contrast. Figs. 16 and 17 are light micrographs of an X-ray irradiation image of 1500/inch silver grid and show the distribution of DPTCl in gelatin after an irradiation for 1 h in nitrogen atmosphere at a distance of 0.5 mm from the target. Fructose was used as activator. The image is an absorption image and shows a good resolution in the central area of the field. The swelling of gelatin, however, easily produces a preparation artifact in the submicroscopic dimensions.

When nitrocellulose (11 % nitrogen) was used as a supporting polymer and the irradiation occurred in a mixture of air and ammonium vapor, the nitrocellulose was degraded and became soluble in water. Fig. 18 (light micrograph) shows that

Fig. 18. Light micrograph of an X-ray irradiation image of a 1500/inch silver grid recorded on a substrate of triphenyltetrazolium chloride and fructose in nitrocellulose (11 % nitrogen) and irradiated for 1 h at a distance of 0.5 mm from the target in a mixture of air and ammonium vapor. Degradation of the polymer gives a true absorption image.

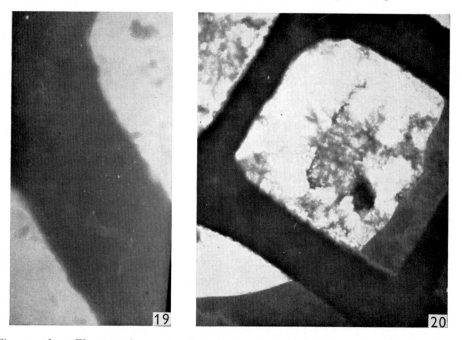

Fig. 19 and 20. Electron micrographs of the image of a few grid bars and one single grid bar from Fig. 18. They show a good resolution at the transit areas between the irradiated and the protected areas, but they show also a preparation artifact particularly produced during the drying of the specimen. Magnification in Fig. 19 is 6,500 times; in Fig. 20 the magnification is only 300 times.

References p. 77

the image of a 1500/inch silver grid is a proper X-ray irradiation image and an absorption image. The X-ray penumbral effect is visible on the outside areas, and the upper left corner shows a low incident intensity.

Electron micrographs (Figs. 19 and 20) show selected areas of the X-ray image in Fig. 18. They illustrate a good resolution owing to the thinness of the recording film and the X-ray imaging geometry in the central field, as well as to a sufficient exposure time and X-ray effect, which allow a good preparation with distinct transit between the irradiated and protected areas. The electron microscope aperture of about 20 μ allows a high contrast in the electron micrograph. The granularity of the X-ray recording membrane is visible in Fig. 20 on the grid-bar images; this granularity can, however, be eliminated or made less pronounced by a proper choice of preparation conditions. The material in the grid-bar openings consists of remnants of the decomposed recording substrate. It may be a preparation artifact, or it may represent a lower incident intensity in that particular area. The critical point method for drying of the specimen will be taken up in our next experiment.

CONCLUSIONS

A number of X-ray-sensitive materials show a localized irradiation effect. The X-ray irradiation image is an absorption image, provided that a sufficient dose of radiation is absorbed in the recording substrate and the radiation-activated reaction shows a higher speed than do the secondary reactions (see Figs. 2, 7, 8, and 15).

Plastics without additional dyes or inorganic activators supply structureless recording materials (Figs. 2 and 15). By sufficient absorption of energy, the irradiation effect is stabilized, and an image without artifacts can be developed.

A degradation mechanism provides a dosimetry needed for absorption records; a polymerization, on the other hand, is initiated and allows a study of reaction kinetics only under accurately controlled conditions. The degradation of radiosensitive dyes often is monomolecular in solution and easily calibrated also in solids, giving a great advantage over the surface reactions of metal foils.

Simplicity of energy record hence requires a submicroscopic structure in the recording substrate, a structure essentially below the resolving power of a light microscope.

ACKNOWLEDGEMENT

The author wishes to express her thanks to Dr. H. H. Pattee and Professor Paul Kirkpatrick for criticism of the manuscript.

REFERENCES

[1] W. A. Ladd and M. W. Ladd, in V. E. Cosslett et al., X-ray Microscopy and Microradiography, Academic Press, Inc., New York, 1957, pp. 383—389.
[2] A. Recourt, ibid., pp. 234—239.
[3] G. Möllenstedt and L. Y. Huang, ibid., pp. 392—396.
[4] H. H. Pattee, Symposium on X-ray Microscopy, Stockholm, 1959, this volume, p. 56.
[5] B. von Borries, Z. Naturforsch., 4a (1949) 51.
[6] F. Lenz, Z. Naturforsch., 9a (1954) 185; Bildentstehung und Bildkontrast, Vierter Internationaler Kongress für Elektronenmikroskopie, Berlin, 1958, Lecture No. 1.07, Springer Verlag, Berlin, in the press.

[7] R. UYEDA, *Proceedings of the Third International Conference on Electron Microscopy, London,* 1954, Royal Microscopical Society, London, 1957, p. 61.

[8] H. NIEHRS, Kritisches zu gewohnten Auffassungen über Kontrastentstehung, *Vierter Internationaler Kongress für Elektronenmikroskopie, Berlin,* 1958, Lecture No. 26.11, Springer Verlag, Berlin, in the press.

[9] A. SIPPEL, *Textil-Praxis,* 11 (1955) 1131, as quoted in E. TREIBER, *Die Chemie der Pflanzenzellwand,* Springer-Verlag, Berlin, 1957, p. 343.

[10] M. E. HAINE and A. W. AGAR, in F. S. SJÖSTRAND and J. RHODIN, *Electron Microscopy, Proceedings of the Stockholm Conference,* Sept., 1956, Academic Press, Inc., New York, 1957, p. 64.

[11] W. LIPPERT, *ibid.,* p. 74.

[12] H. H. PATTEE, *Conference on X-ray Microscopy, Stockholm,* 1959, this volume, p. 79.

[13] G. L. NATASON, *J. Phys. Chem. (U.S.S.R.),* 14 (1940) 16.

[14] F. WEYGAND and I. FRANK, *Z. Naturforsch.,* 3b (1948) 377, as quoted in A. SCHÖNBERG, *Präparative organische Photochemie,* Springer-Verlag, Berlin, 1958, p. 166.

QUANTITATIVE MEASUREMENTS WITH THE MICROFLUOROSCOPE

H. H. PATTEE

*Biophysics Laboratory, W. W. Hansen Laboratories of Physics,
Stanford University, Stanford, Calif. (U.S.A.)*

ABSTRACT

The microfluoroscope is an instrument which allows direct visual observation of a soft X-ray contact image at high optical magnification. This
is accomplished by means of a microfocus X-ray source, a very fine-grain
evaporated fluorescent screen, and a special viewing microscope. The
screen is thick enough to stop the Al K radiation from the microfocus
target, but allows most of the harder components to pass through. Knowing
the effective spectrum producing the fluorescence, one can make direct
photometric intensity measurements in order to determine the mass of
specimen structures. By using standard stage and eyepiece micrometers,
a simple stereoscopic method of measuring thickness dimensions is possible.
Other parameters, such as X-ray source diameter and source-to-specimen
spacing, may be adjusted and measured with the viewing optical microscope.

The microfluoroscope is a contact X-ray system producing a fluorescent X-ray
image which may be viewed directly with a high-power light microscope, or photometrically monitored to measure X-ray absorption. The two essential requirements

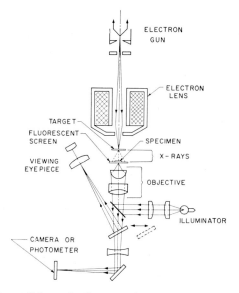

Fig. 1. Schematic diagram of the microfluoroscope.

for such an instrument are a microfocus X-ray source and an ultrafine-grained
fluorescent screen to record the image details with the maximum resolution possible
with the light microscope. The advantages of the contact image geometry are

discussed on pp. 56—60 in this volume, and more details of construction are given by the author in *Science*, 128 (1958) 977.

The design of the present microfluoroscope is shown schematically in Fig. 1. The microfocus X-ray tube at the top consists of a standard electron gun followed by a single magnetic lens which provides the demagnification of the source. The target is located at the outer surface of the lens polepiece so that the specimen and

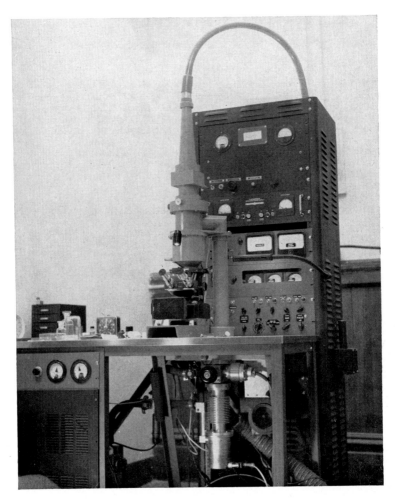

Fig. 2. The microfluoroscope.

fluorescent screen, mounted on the light microscope stage, can be brought into contact with the outer surface of the target. It is important that the source-to-screen distance be adjustable, and preferably calibrated so that both specimen thickness and source-to-screen distances can be measured directly to within a few microns.

The image which appears on the fluorescent screen is viewed with the inverted light microscope which has provision for a plate camera or the photomultiplier head of a photometer. A source of light and optics for incident light illumination is also useful, since the X-ray source completely obscures the upper side of the specimen.

The actual instrument is shown in Fig. 2. The viewing microscope may be displaced from the X-ray axis on a short optical bench to permit changing targets or specimens. A micrometer stop assures exact repositioning under the X-ray source.

Two basic types of direct measurements may be made with this instrument without handling the specimen or employing photographic processes. First, the relative X-ray intensity of any part of the image may be measured photometrically, and second, the distance from any point in the specimen to the fluorescent screen may be measured stereoscopically. These are the essential data which allow calculation. of mass in the specimen.

The X-ray absorption may be measured by employing the following procedure. The specimen is mounted on the fluorescent screen which rests on the movable stage of the inverted microscope. The photometer head is placed at the back focal plane of the microscope objective, which is then masked off to expose only the selected region of the specimen image. A better way of isolating the region of measurement is to place an X-ray mask with appropriate aperture directly on the specimen. This reduces the errors resulting from scattered light, but is technically more difficult. The reference intensity of the direct X-ray beam is measured by displacing the specimen stage until the fluorescent screen alone is in the beam. The specimen is then shifted into the beam and a second intensity measurement made. To make sure that any intensity change is solely the result of X-ray absorption it is necessary to check the surface of the fluorescent material to make certain it has uniform response, and to check the stability of the X-ray source by remeasuring the reference intensity from the direct beam. Intensity measurements should always be made at the lowest value of objective aperture consistent with the resolution requirements. If the highest resolution is desired, a correction for stray light must be made by subtracting the background intensity from an opaque test spot on the screen. Stray light may be reduced considerably by evaporating a thin coat of aluminum on the fluorescent screen and by using oil immersion objectives. An adjustable metallurgical-type objective iris is also useful for controlling the stray light.

The use of the stereoscopic principle to measure thickness is illustrated in Fig. 3. The distance, a, from the source to fluorescent screen is measured with the calibrated fine-focus adjustment of the microscope. The microscope is then shifted forward the same distance on its optical bench by a micrometer. The position of the reference point in the specimen whose distance to the screen, b, is to be determined is matched with the cross hair in the eyepiece micrometer. The microscope is then shifted backward on the optical bench by a distance 2a, and the displacement of the reference point is measured with the micrometer eyepiece. This displacement is 2b. Using this method we may obtain a vertical distance measurement with an accuracy of one-half the minimum resolving distance of the light microscope with no mechanical measurements more accurate than $\pm$ 0.001 cm. By taking into account the shape of an inclusion in the specimen, its thickness may be determined by measuring its projections on the screen when the source is shifted a known distance.

Contact microradiography using photographic recording can, of course, provide this same type of information. However, the microfluoroscope has several advantages. In some instances the specimen may undergo changes which are sufficiently rapid to make long exposure times impossible. These changes could be viewed directly with the microfluoroscope. Also densitometric and photodevelopment errors are absent. In the case of thickness measurements the stereoscopic image may be obtained without remounting the specimen on a new area of the recording emulsion.

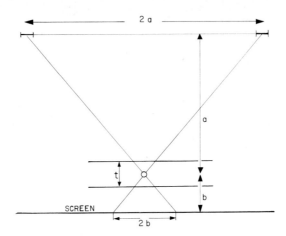

Fig. 3. Diagram of thickness measurement.

Finally, the problem of specimen mounting is greatly simplified since it may be done under normal illumination and the specimen need not be placed in a vacuum during exposure.

D. THEORY AND TECHNIQUE OF PROJECTION MICRORADIOGRAPHY

AUFBAU EINER MIKROFOKUS-RÖNTGENRÖHRE UND VERWENDUNG VON CHARAKTERISTISCHER K-STRAHLUNG IN DER PROJEKTIONSMIKRORADIOGRAPHIE

WOLFGANG HINK

I. Physikalisches Institut, Freie Universität Berlin, Berlin-Dahlem (Deutschland)

ABSTRACT

CONSTRUCTION OF A MICROFOCUS X-RAY TUBE AND THE USE OF CHARACTERISTIC K-RADIATION IN PROJECTION-MICRORADIOGRAPHY

A microfocus X-ray tube with Ti-membrane anticathode is described giving at single-stage reduction a focal spot diameter of about 0,4 μ. The conditions for an optimal run of the electron gun are discussed using an example. Resolution and contrast are demonstrated with test microradiographs. Using a Ti-membrane anticathode of 9,5 μ thickness in place of a W-membrane the gain in intensity under increase of contrast allows purely visual focussing and considerably shorter exposure times.

EINLEITUNG

Die in der Projektionsmikroradiographie[1a] als Röntgenlichtquelle verwendeten Mikrofokus-Röntgenröhren sind fast ausschliesslich mit dünnen Antikathodenfolien (0,1—1 μ) aus Elementen mit hoher Ordnungszahl und grosser Dichte wie Gold und Wolfram ausgerüstet. Die beiden folgenden Gesetzmässigkeiten sprechen insbesondere für die Wahl derartiger Elemente. Der Wirkungsgrad für die Erzeugung von Röntgen-Bremsstrahlung wächst mit der Ordnungszahl, und die Reichweite der in die Antikathode eindringenden Elektronen ist umgekehrt proportional der Dichte. Die Reichweite bestimmt bei gegebener Antikathodenfolie die untere Grenze des Brennfleckdurchmessers und damit die erzielbare Auflösungsgrenze für die Projektionsaufnahmen. Die geringe Dichte der Elemente mit niedriger Ordnungszahl, die allein für die Erzeugung langwelliger charakteristischer K-Strahlung interessieren, bedingt somit eine grosse Reichweite der Elektronen und lässt daher nur vergleichsweise grosse Brennfleckdurchmesser (0,5 μ und grösser bei Anodenspannungen von 10—15 kV) erwarten. Für eine intensive Anregung der K-Strahlung ist aber ein Vielfaches der Anregungsspannung als Anodenspannung wünschenswert[1b].

Bei Untersuchungen zur Erzielung einer hohen Strahlungsdichte in einem Mikro-Brennfleck mit möglichst hohem langwelligem Strahlungsanteil wurden dicke Folien aus Kupfer und Titan (etwa 10 μ dick) als Antikathode verwendet. Es zeigte sich hierbei, dass die die Folie in Elektronenstrahlrichtung verlassende Röntgenstrahlung (Durchsichtbeobachtung) einen hohen Anteil an charakteristischer K-Strahlung besitzt[2,3]. Über die spektrale Zusammensetzung der aus Folien tretenden Röntgenstrahlung, deren Dicke etwa der Reichweite der auffallenden Elektronen

entspricht, liegen wenig Angaben vor. Nur von BESSEN[4] sind spektrale Verteilungs-
kurven für die massive Antikathode (Aufsichtbeobachtung) und die Membran-
Antikathode (Durchsichtbeobachtung) einiger Materialien bei gleichen Anodenspannungen aufgenommen worden. Nach diesen Kurven hebt sich beispielsweise
bei einer massiven Antikathode und der Anodenspannung 15 kV die CuK-Strahlung
kaum vom Kontinuum ab, während bei einer 12μ dicken Cu-Folie und der gleichen
Anodenspannung in Durchsicht das Kontinuum neben der intensiven CuK-Strahlung
kaum auszumachen ist. BESSEN schliesst aus seinen Messungen, dass unter Ein-
haltung von bestimmten Bedingungen für die Foliendicke und das Verhältnis von
Anoden- zu Anregungsspannung im wesentlichen K-Strahlung die Folie verlässt.
Die unten mitgeteilten Ergebnisse zeigen nun ferner, dass trotz der grossen Reichweite
in Elementen niedriger Ordnungszahl Brennfleckdurchmesser von weniger als 1 μ,
also einem Bruchteil der praktischen Reichweite[5], erzielt werden kann.

Im folgenden wird eine Mikrofokus-Röntgenröhre beschrieben, die für Untersuchungen zur Erzielung einer hohen Strahlungsdichte mit grossem langwelligem
Strahlungsanteil entwickelt wurde.

APPARATUR

Die zerlegbare Röntgenröhre wird durch eine Hg-Dampfstrahlpumpe Typ Hg 12
bis zu einem Enddruck von $1 \cdot 10^{-5}$ Torr oder besser evakuiert. Die Verkleinerung
des engsten Strahlquerschnitts wird durch eine magnetische Polschuhlinse kurzer
Brennweite erzielt. Diese nur einstufige Verkleinerung bedingt einen grossen Abstand
zwischen Kathode und Antikathode, der wahlweise durch verschiedene Zwischen-
rohre mit Leybold-Kleinflanschen NW 10 eingestellt werden kann. Abb. 1 zeigt
die für die Strahlausbildung und die Strahljustierung wesentlichen Bauelemente der

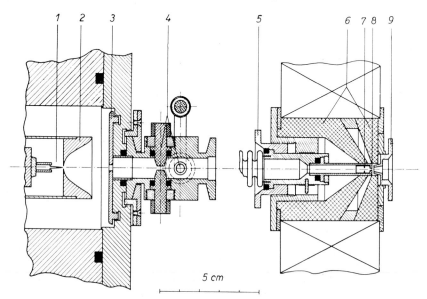

Abb. 1. Masstabgerechte Teil-Schnittzeichnung der für die Strahlausbildung und Strahljustierung
wesentlichen Bauelemente der Röntgenröhre. Haarnadelkathode (1), Steuerelektrode (2), Anode
(3), Magnetablenkung (4), axiale Verschiebung (5) der Antikathode (8), Polschuhe der Magnetlinse (6), Aperturblende (7) und Objektträger (9).

Literatur S. 89

Röntgenröhre in einer masstabgerechten Teil-Schnittzeichnung. Die Haarnadel-
kathode (1) (Wolframdraht von 125 μ Durchmesser) ist während des Betriebes
(also unter Vakuum bei angelegter Hochspannung) axial und lateral verschiebbar.
Sie taucht in die Bohrung (0,9 mm Durchmesser) der Steuerelektrode (2), die die
Form einer tiefen Schale hat. Die Anode (3) ist eine flache Scheibe mit einer zentralen
Bohrung von 3 mm Durchmesser. Sie ist während des Betriebes axial verschiebbar.
Die stufenlos regelbare Steuerspannung von maximal $\pm$ 1 kV gegen Kathode
liefert ein Batterieaggregat. Die Heizung der Kathode geschieht durch Wechselstrom
von Netzfrequenz. Der durch das Triodensystem gebündelte Elektronenstrahl durch-
läuft die Zwei-Koordinaten-Magnetablenkung (4), die eine mechanische Strahljustierung ersetzt. Die Magnetablenkung, zwei gekreuzte Elektromagnete, kann
wahlweise mit Gleich- oder Wechselspannung gespeist werden. Die statische Ablenkung dient zum normalen Betrieb. Die dynamische Ablenkung ist für das Auf-
suchen der optimalen Betriebsbedingungen des Strahlerzeugungssystems* vor-
gesehen (an die Stelle der Magnetlinse tritt hierbei ein Faradaybecher; der Auffängerstrom steuert einen Oszillographen, dessen Zeitablenkung synchron zur
Strahlablenkung läuft). Nach Durchlaufen einer Aperturblende (7) wird der Elektronenstrahl durch die Magnetlinse mit den Polschuhen (6) auf die Antikathode (8)
fokussiert. Die Antikathodenfolie ist mit Gummilösung auf eine auswechselbare
Patrone vakuumdicht geklebt. Die Verstellung (5) gestattet eine axiale Verschiebung
der Antikathode, wodurch das Arbeiten bei verschiedenen Brennweiten ermöglicht
wird. Das Objekt wird mit dem Objektträger (9) in das Innere des vorderen Pol-
schuhs dicht an die Antikathode gebracht.

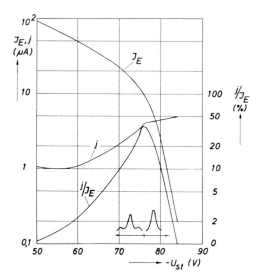

Abb. 2. Abhängigkeit von der Steuerspannung U_{St} der Grössen Emissionsstrom I_E, Auffängerstrom
j und Verhältnis j/I_E. Anodenspannung 38 kV. Im Maximum von j liegt optimaler Betrieb vor.

* Der optimale Betrieb des Strahlerzeugungssystems wird hier wie folgt definiert: Die
Kathode arbeitet in Sättigung, also mit dem grösstmöglichen Richtstrahlwert bei vorgegebener
Kathodentemperatur. Der Elektronenstrahl ist ein reiner Kernstrahl ohne Nebenmaxima mit
einer Strahlapertur von etwa $1 \cdot 10^{-3}$ rad.

Literatur S. 89

Strahlerzeugungssystem

Der optimale Betrieb des Strahlerzeugungssystems wurde in Voruntersuchungen unter Änderung der geometrischen und elektrischen Grössen des Elektrodensystems festgelegt. An einem Beispiel (Abb. 2) sei für feste geometrische Daten und Anodenspannung 38 kV die Abhängigkeit der Grössen Emissionsstrom I_E, Auffängerstrom j in Strahlmitte im Abstand 28 cm von der Kathode mit einer Blende von 0,5 mm Durchmesser und Verhältnis j/I_E von der Steuerspannung U_{St} der Steuerelektrode angegeben. Es tritt bei einer optimal genannten Steuerspannung ein Maximum der Stromdichte auf. Lassen die geometrischen Daten des Elektrodensystems die Ausbildung eines derartigen Maximums zu, so ist bei der optimalen Steuerspannung in dem untersuchten Anodenspannungsbereich von 10—40 kV stets der optimale Betrieb gewährleistet. Vergrösserung der negativen Steuerspannung führt zum Raumladungsbetrieb mit stark abfallenden Strahlströmen, Verkleinerung zur Ausbildung von Nebenmaxima der Stromdichteverteilung über den Öffnungswinkel des Strahles (angedeutet in Abb. 2) wie auch über den engsten Strahlquerschnitt. Bei optimaler Steuerspannung sind diese Stromdichteverteilungen durch Gauss-Kurven gegeben. Die exponentielle Abhängigkeit des Emissionsstroms I_E von der Heizung der Kathode deutet auf den Sättigungszustand der Kathode.

Magnetlinse

Die Polschuhe der Magnetlinse[6] haben eine Bohrung von 5,95 mm Durchmesser, ihr Abstand beträgt 2,2 mm. Bei der maximalen Erregung von 2365 AW wird für eine Anodenspannung von 16 kV eine Brennweite von 2 mm erreicht. Nach den Daten von LIEBMANN-GRAD[7] ist hierbei eine Öffnungsfehlerkonstante C_δ von 1 mm zu erwarten. Bei einem Durchmesser der Aperturblende von 0,35 mm berechnet sich damit der Radius des Öffnungsfehlerscheibchens δ_δ zu 0,7 μ, woraus ein möglicher Brennfleckdurchmesser von 0,35 μ folgen würde. Bei höheren Anodenspannungen wächst wegen der begrenzten Erregung die Brennweite an.

Brennfleckgrösse

Von den mit der beschriebenen Röntgenröhre erhaltenen Projektionsmikroaufnahmen seien zwei Beispiele herausgegriffen, um die Auflösung und den Kontrast der Aufnahmen zu demonstrieren. Abb. 3 zeigt ein Testobjekt (Ag-Gitter mit 1500 Maschen/inch, Dicke etwa 2 μ). Die praktische Reichweite berechnet sich bei den vorliegenden Aufnahmebedingungen — Anodenspannung: 16 kV, Antikathodenfolie: 9,5 μ Titan — zu 1,2 μ, während der Brennfleckdurchmesser aus der an den Kanten des Objekts auftretenden geometrischen Unschärfe zu 0,5 μ oder kleiner geschätzt wird. Das Auftreten eines schwachen Fresnelschen Beugungssaums an den Kanten des Objekts, der unter bestimmten geometrischen Aufnahmebedingungen zu beobachten ist[8], lässt auf einen Brennfleckdurchmesser von 0,4 μ schliessen. Bei einer Erhöhung der Anodenspannung auf 21 kV (praktische Reichweite 2 μ) wächst der Brennfleckdurchmesser nicht merklich, wie die Abb. 4 zeigt. Diese Projektionsaufnahme einer in Luft getrockneten *Drosophila melanogaster* (vgl. hierzu die Aufnahmen von COSSLETT und NIXON[9]) lässt Objektdetails von weniger als 1 μ Durchmesser erkennen. Das Testobjekt der Abb. 3 ist zur Kontrolle der Schärfe mitprojiziert. Schärfe und Kontrast des Gitters sind im Vergleich zu Abb. 3 unverändert.

Die Aufnahmen mit Titanstrahlung können bei einer erheblich geringeren

Literatur S. 89

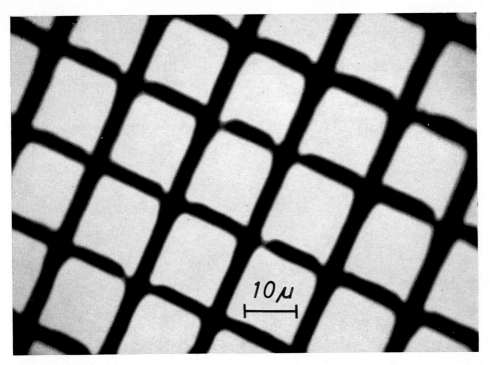

Abb. 3. Projektionsmikroaufnahme eines Testobjektes (Ag-Maschengitter 1500 Maschen/inch, 3 μ Stegbreite) mit der Strahlung einer Titan-Antikathodenfolie von 9,5 μ Dicke. Die Aufnahme dient zur Abschätzung des Brennfleckdurchmessers, welcher etwa 0,4 μ beträgt. Anodenspannung: 16 kV; Elektronenstrom an der Antikathode: 1,5 μA; Aufnahmeabstand: 2,3 cm; Vergrösserung mit Röntgenstrahlen: 170 $\times$; Photoplatte: Perutz Diapositiv hart; Belichtungszeit: 45 sec.

Belichtungszeit als Aufnahmen mit Wolfram-Bremsstrahlung gewonnen werden, wie die Verwendung einer 1 μ dicken Wolfram-Antikathode zeigte. So ist bei einer 1 μ Wolfram-Antikathode und der Anodenspannung 10 kV die erforderliche Belichtungszeit 10- bis 15mal grösser als bei einer 9,5 μ Titan-Antikathode und der Anodenspannung 16 kV. Der Kontrast ist mit Titanstrahlung trotz der höheren Anodenspannung grösser, was auf eine grössere effektive Wellenlänge schliessen läßt.

Aus der Grösse des mit einer Titanfolie erzielten Brennfleckdurchmessers kann man folgern, dass bei Durchsichtbeobachtung die effektive Strahlung in einer Halbkugel von maximal 1/3 bis 1/4 der praktischen Reichweite erzeugt wird. Genauere Aussagen können bei der Brennfleckgrösse von 0,4 μ nicht gemacht werden, da der Durchmesser des kleinsten Zerstreuungskreises (vgl. Abschnitt Magnetlinse) von gleicher Grösse ist. Messungen an Kupferfolien (14 μ dick), die bei Anodenspannungen bis zu 38 kV durchgeführt wurden, liefern das gleiche Ergebnis.

Bis auf die von COSSLETT[10] angegebene Abschätzung, die allerdings zu ungünstig ist, liegen keine Aussagen über den Einfluss der Elektronenstreuung auf die effektive Grösse des Brennflecks vor. Lediglich aus den Messungen von CASTAING[10b], der die Emission eines Schichtelements einer Antikathode als Funktion der Tiefe des Schichtelements in der Antikathode bei der Anodenspannung 29 kV gemessen hat, kann man schliessen, dass bis zu einer Tiefe von 1/3 der praktischen Reichweite

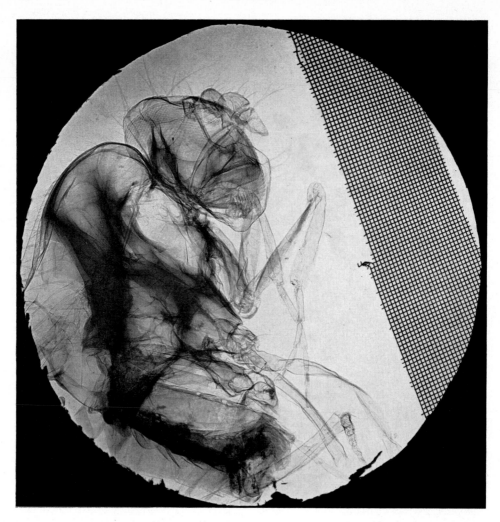

Abb. 4. Projektionsmikroaufnahme einer in Luft getrockneten *Drosophila melanogaster* mit Testobjekt von Abb. 3. Die Aufnahme zeigt den Kontrast, der bei einem biologischen Objekt trotz der hohen Anodenspannung (21 kV) mit einer Titan-Antikathodenfolie von 9,5 μ Dicke erzielt werden kann. Aufnahmeabstand: 3,6 cm; Vergrösserung mit Röntgenstrahlen: je nach Objektdetail 8 bis 14 $\times$, Testobjekt 9 $\times$; Photoplatte: Perutz Diapositiv hart; Belichtungszeit: 75 sec. Elektronenstrom an der Antikathode: 3 μA.

etwa 70 % der gesamten K-Strahlung emittiert wird. Hierbei ist der Anteil an Fluoreszenzstrahlung, der auf dem Umweg über die Bremsstrahlung bis zu dieser Tiefe erzeugt wird, nicht erfasst.

Für die Praxis der Projektionsmikroradiographie bringt die Verwendung von charakteristischer K-Strahlung, die in dicken Folien erzeugt wird, wesentliche Vorteile. Einmal erlaubt der Gewinn an Intensität unter Steigerung des Kontrastes die rein visuelle Scharfstellung bei wenig adaptiertem Auge und eine erhebliche Verkürzung der Belichtungszeiten. Zum andern lassen sich die dicken Folien ohne jegliche Vakuumschwierigkeiten bequem handhaben.

Literatur S. 89

ZUSAMMENFASSUNG

Es wird eine Mikrofokus-Röntgenröhre mit Ti-Membranantikathode beschrieben, deren Brennfleckdurchmesser bei einstufiger Verkleinerung etwa 0,4 μ beträgt. Die Bedingungen für den optimalen Betrieb des Elektronenstrahl-Erzeugungssystems werden an einem Beispiel diskutiert. An Testaufnahmen werden Auflösung und Kontrast demonstriert. Der Gewinn an Intensität unter Steigerung des Kontrastes bei Verwendung einer 9,5 μ dicken Ti-Membranantikathode an Stelle einer W-Membran erlaubt die rein visuelle Scharfstellung und eine erhebliche Verkürzung der Belichtungszeiten.

LITERATUR

[1] *Handbuch der Physik*, Bd. XXX, Springer, Berlin-Göttingen-Heidelberg, 1957, a) S. 315 ff; b) S. 6 ff.
[2] W. HINK, *Dissertation*, Berlin, 1956.
[3] W. HINK und W. PETZOLD, *Z. angew. Phys.*, 10 (1958) 135.
[4] J. J. BESSEN, *Norelco Reptr.*, 4, Heft 6 (1957).
[5] *Handbuch der Physik*, Bd. XXII, 2, Springer, Berlin, 1933, S. 35ff.
[6] H. WEBER, *Diplomarbeit*, Berlin, 1954.
[7] M. v. ARDENNE, *Tabellen der Elektronenphysik, Ionenphysik und Übermikroskopie*, Bd. I, VEB Deutscher Verlag der Wissenschaften, Berlin, 1956, S. 60 ff.
[8] W. C. NIXON, *Proc. Roy. Soc. (London)*, A 232 (1955) 475.
[9] V. E. COSSLETT und W. C. NIXON, *Proc. Roy. Soc. (London)*, B 140 (1952) 422.
[10] V. E. COSSLETT, *Intern. Conf. Electron Microscopy, London*, 1954, Royal Microscopical Society, London, 1956, a) S. 311; b) S. 300.

ÜBER DEN EINFLUSS DER ELEKTRONENDIFFUSION IM TARGET VON FEINSTFOKUS-RÖNTGENRÖHREN

GÜNTHER LANGNER

Institut für Elektronenmikroskopie, Düsseldorf (Deutschland)

ABSTRACT

ON THE INFLUENCE OF ELECTRON DIFFUSION IN THE TARGET OF MICROFOCUS X-RAY TUBES

Microfocus X-ray tubes are known to be employed in X-ray point-projection and flying-spot microscopes. The actual diameter of the X-ray source is larger than that of the focus, due to electron diffusion. According to the theory of paraxial diffusion of LENZ, it is comparatively simple to calculate the diffusion. By taking photographs of X-rays produced in atmospheric air with a pinhole camera and a slot camera, the range and the appropriate constants of the theory were experimentally determined. Using these constants and LENZ's theory, the broadening of the X-ray source as a result of diffusion was calculated for some elements as a function of the acceleration voltage and the target thickness.

Die effektive Linearausdehnung der Röntgenstrahlquelle (Target einer Röntgenröhre) ist als Folge der Elektronendiffusion grösser als der Elektronenbrennfleck (Fokus). Dieser Umstand fällt bei den Feinstfokus-Röntgenröhren ins Gewicht, wie sie bei Hochleistungs- Punktprojektions-Mikroskopen und Raster- (Flying spot-) Mikroskopen verwendet werden müssen. Wir wollen daher den Anteil $Q_D(N)$ der Kontrastübertragungsfunktion im Sinne des Beitrags "Die Informationsübertragungskapazität von Röntgenstrahlmikroskopen" (S. 31 ds. Bds.) zu ermitteln versuchen.

PROBLEMSTELLUNG

Mit W bezeichnen wir die Röntgenstrahlenenergie, mit $\dot{W}$ die Röntgenstrahlleistung. Der Winkel zwischen der Elektroneneinschussrichtung (z_t-Richtung im Target) und der Emissionsrichtung der Röntgenstrahlen sei Θ. x, y, z_t sind die Koordinaten im Target.

$\frac{\partial^3}{\partial x \partial y \partial z_t}\left(\frac{\partial \dot{W}}{\partial \Omega}\right)\,\mathrm{d}x\,\mathrm{d}y\,\mathrm{d}z_t\,\mathrm{d}\Omega$ ist dann die von einem Volumenelement $\mathrm{d}x\,\mathrm{d}y\,\mathrm{d}z_t$ des Targets in das Raumwinkelelement $\mathrm{d}\Omega$ emittierte Röntgenstrahlleistung. Die Dicke des Targets sei D. Zur Bestimmung des Diffusionsanteils $Q_D(N)$ müssen wir die Fouriertransformierte von $\int_0^D \frac{\partial^3}{\partial x \partial y \partial z_t}\left(\frac{\partial \dot{W}}{\partial \Omega}\right)^{\Theta=0^0}\mathrm{d}z_t$,

also

$$(\mathrm{1}) \qquad Q_D(N_x N_y) = \text{const.} \iint_{-\infty}^{+\infty} \exp\left[-2\pi i(N_x x + N_y y)\right]\int_0^D \frac{\partial^3}{\partial x \partial y \partial z_t}\left(\frac{\partial \dot{W}}{\partial \Omega}\right)^{\Theta=0^0}\mathrm{d}z_t \mathrm{d}x \mathrm{d}y$$

bilden. Eine Berechnung der Verteilungsfunktion $\frac{\partial^3}{\mathrm{d}x \mathrm{d}y \mathrm{d}z_t}\left(\frac{\partial \dot{W}}{\partial \Omega}\right)$ kann aus zwei Schnitten bestehen. Der erste Schnitt ist die Lösung des Problems der Vielfachstreuung der Elektronen im Target, als dessen Ergebnis man eine Verteilungs-

Literatur S. 97

funktion für die Orts-, Richtungs- und Energieverteilung der Elektronen im Target erhält. Der zweite Schnitt besteht darin, dass man die Richtungs- und Frequenzverteilung der von dieser Elektronenströmung emittierten Röntgenstrahlung berechnet, indem man die Richtungs- und Frequenzverteilungen der von jedem Elektron emittierten Röntgenstrahlung über die Verteilungsfunktion der Elektronen integriert.

Der erste Schnitt besteht in der Lösung der Transportgleichung von Boltzmann unter den entsprechenden Randbedingungen. Eine gute Übersicht über das Problem gibt eine Arbeit von WANG und GUTH[1]. Die Kenntnis der für den zweiten Schnitt benötigten Richtungs- und Frequenzverteilung der von einem Elektron emittierten Röntgenstrahlung liefert im Fall der *Bremsstrahlung* die Sommerfeld'sche Theorie, die experimentell gut bestätigt ist. Wir haben deren numerische Auswertung von KIRKPATRICK und WIEDMANN[2] sowie eine Arbeit von SCHEER und ZEITLER[3] über eine einfache Formel für die Richtungsabhängigkeit der Bremsstrahlungsemission verwendet, die streng aus der Sommerfeld'schen Theorie folgt. Für die *charakteristische* Röntgenstrahlung bestehen noch keine befriedigend mit den Experimenten übereinstimmende Theorien, es gibt aber brauchbare empirische und halbempirische Näherungsformeln, auf die wir hier nicht näher eingehen wollen. Die strenge Ausrechnung der Gl. (1) scheiterte bisher an rechnerischen Schwierigkeiten. Es ist daher verschiedentlich versucht worden, insbesondere für die Lösung der Transportgleichung einfache Näherungen zu finden. Im Folgenden werden wir eine solche Näherung verwenden und ihren Gültigkeitsbereich durch Anpassung der vorkommenden Konstanten an experimentelle Werte zu erweitern suchen.

NÄHERUNGSWEISE LÖSUNGSMETHODE

Wir führen folgende Vereinfachungen zur Lösung des Problems ein:

1. Die Elektronenenergie εU sei eine Funktion von z_t allein;

2. Wir setzen näherungsweise an, dass die Verteilungsfunktion $\dfrac{\partial^3}{\partial x \partial y \partial z_t}\left(\dfrac{\partial W}{\partial \Omega}\right)$ für die Orts- und Winkelverteilung der emittierten Röntgenstrahlung als Produkt aus der am Emissionsort herrschenden Elektronenstromdichte $i(x, y, z_t)$ und einer nur von der Elektronenenergie $\varepsilon U(z_t)$ und der Emissionsrichtung abhängigen Funktion geschrieben werden kann:

$$(2) \qquad \frac{\partial^3}{\partial x \partial y \partial z_t}\left(\frac{\partial W}{\partial \Omega}\right) = i(x, y, z_t) \cdot \Phi\Big(\Theta,\ U(z_t)\Big)$$

Gl. (2) ist streng gültig für charakteristische Strahlung. Bei Bremsstrahlung gilt sie nur näherungsweise. Wenn R die Elektronenreichweite in Einschussrichtung ist, so haben für $z_t/R \ll 1$ fast alle Elektronen noch praktisch die Einfallsrichtung, und $\Phi(\Theta, z_t)$ ist nichts anderes als die Winkelverteilung der Bremsstrahlung nach der Sommerfeld'schen Theorie bei parallel einfallenden Elektronen. Für Werte von z_t, die sich der Elektronenreichweite R nähern, entnimmt man $\Phi(\Theta, z_t)$ besser aus Messungen der Winkelabhängigkeit der Bremsstrahlemission von massiven Targets, die sich in der Literatur finden. Im Zwischengebiet kann man eine Interpolation verwenden. Die Ungenauigkeit ist dabei nicht so erheblich, dass die Zuverlässigkeit von $Q_D(N)$ darunter allzu stark litte, zumal die noch erfolgende Integration glättende Eigenschaften hat.

Als Beziehung zwischen der Elektronenenergie εU und z_t haben wir das Thomson-Whiddington'sche Gesetz

$$(3) \qquad \frac{\mathrm{d}U}{\mathrm{d}z_t} = -\frac{\kappa \cdot \rho}{-U}$$

mit $\varkappa = 2 \cdot 10^{11}$ V²cm²g⁻¹ (1923) nach TERRILL[4] verwendet (ρ = Dichte des Targetmaterials). Für die Elektronenvielfachstreuung benutzen wir die paraxiale Theorie von LENZ[5, 6]. Aus dieser Theorie ergibt sich die Elektronenstromdichte zu

$$(4) \qquad i(x, y, z_t) = \frac{I(z_t)}{\pi}\, \Psi(z_t) \cdot \exp\left[-\Psi(z_t) \cdot (x^2 + y^2)\right]$$

Die Funktion $\Psi(z_t)$ gewinnt man dabei mit einem bekannten Zusammenhang zwischen U and z_t als Lösung eines Systems gewöhnlicher Differentialgleichungen. Wählt man für den gen. Zusammenhang Gl. (3), so lautet $\Psi(z_t)$ für die Koordinate $\zeta = z_t/R$ geschrieben nach LENZ

$$(5) \qquad \Psi(\zeta R) = \frac{L}{R^3} \cdot \left[-(1-\zeta)^2 \cdot \ln(1-\zeta) + \tfrac{3}{2}\zeta^2 - \zeta\right]^{-1}$$

(L ist dabei, wie R, eine materialabhängige Funktion von U). Für kleine ζ gilt also

$$(6) \qquad [\Psi(\zeta)]^{-1} = \frac{L}{R^3}\left(\frac{\zeta^3}{3} + \mathrm{o}(\zeta^4) \cdot \cdot\right)$$

Wir haben den Gültigkeitsbereich der paraxialen Theorie für in atmosphärischer Luft gestreute 60 kV-Elektronen experimentell untersucht.

EXPERIMENTELLER TEIL

Abb. 1 zeigt die Versuchsanordnung. Sie besteht aus:

1. einer Elektronenstrahlquelle, die einen dünnen in atmosphärischer Luft austretenden monochromatischen Elektronenstrahl kleiner Apertur liefert, dessen Anfangsenergie von 20—70 kV geregelt werden kann. Diese Elektronenstrahlquelle

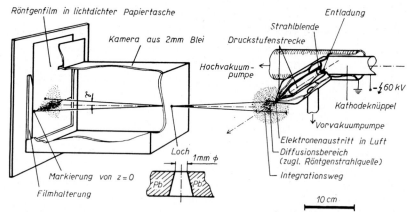

Abb. 1. Versuchsanordnung zur Aufnahme der Diffusion eines in Luft austretenden Elektronenstrahles in der eigenen Röntgenstrahlung (Röntgenstrahl-Lochkamera und Elektronenstrahler).

wurde von HAHN[7] für andere Zwecke gebaut und arbeitet nach dem Prinzip der „behinderten Gasentladung" nach INDUNI[8]. Sie ermöglichte störungsfrei Dauerbelichtungen bis zu 100 Stunden und mehr.

2. einer Röntgenstrahl - „Lochkamera" aus dickem Bleiblech, die es gestattet,

auf einem Röntgenfilm eine Röntgenstrahlquelle genügend grosser räumlicher Ausdehnung in ihrer eignen Röntgenstrahlung aufzunehmen.

Die Aufnahmen der Quelle wurden photometrisch ausgewertet. Verwendet man als „Objekt" ein Loch, so registriert die Kamera eine Grösse, die nach Einführen einiger geometrisch bedingter Korrekturen proportional ist zu

(7)
$$\int_{-\infty}^{+\infty} \frac{\partial^3}{\partial x \partial y \partial z_t} \left(\frac{\partial \dot{W}}{\partial \Omega}\right)_{90^0} dy = \frac{\partial^2}{\partial x \partial z_t} \left(\frac{\partial \dot{W}}{\partial \Omega}\right)_{90^0}$$

Verwendet man dagegen einen schmalen Spalt (siehe Abb. 2), so registriert die

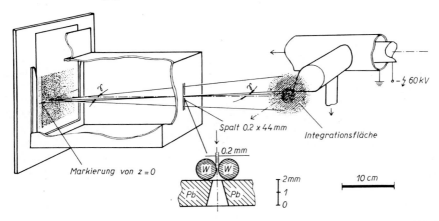

Abb. 2. Versuchsanordnung wie bei Abb. 1, nur Röntgenstrahl-Schlitzkamera statt Röntgenstrahl-Lochkamera. Diese Anordnung misst das Integral über x dessen, was auf der Lochkamera gemessen wird.

Kamera eine Grösse, die proportional ist zu

(8)
$$\iint_{-\infty}^{+\infty} \frac{\partial^3}{\partial x \partial y \partial z_t} \left(\frac{\partial \dot{W}}{\partial \Omega}\right) dx dy = \frac{\partial}{\partial z_t} \left(\frac{\partial \dot{W}}{\partial \Omega}\right)_{90^0}$$

Da es auf gleichmässige Schlitzbreite sehr ankommt, haben wir die Backen aus gezogenen und geschliffenen Wolfram-Rundstäben hergestellt, bei denen ausserdem die Korrektur auf Vignettierung besonders einfach durchzuführen war.

Zum Vergleich haben wir die Grössen (7) und (8) nach Gl. (2) berechnet und für $i(x, y, z_t)$ die Lenz'sche Näherung (4) mit Gl. (5) und (3) eingesetzt. Für $I(z_t)$ haben wir einmal einfach $I(z_t) = I_0$ $(I_0 = I(0))$ und dann nach einem Vorschlag von LENZ[5, 6]: $I(z_t) = (1 - z_t/R)^{7,5}$ mit zwei verschiedenen Werten für die Reichweite R nach TERRILL[4] und nach SCHONLAND[9] gewählt. Die gemessenen und berechneten Werte für die Symmetrielinie $(x = 0)$ zeigt Abb. 3. Die Übereinstimmung der mit $I(z_t) = I_0$ berechneten Werte mit den gemessenen Werten ist bis etwa $z_t/R = 0,15$ gut. Auch für die Halbwertsbreiten der längs der x-Koordinaten gemessenen Röntgenstrahlintensität zeigte bis etwa $z_t/R = 0,15$ eine gute Übereinstimmung mit der paraxialen Theorie. Für Schichtdicken, die mit der Elektronenreichweite vergleichbar sind, darf man die Gültigkeit der paraxialen Theorie natürlich nicht mehr erwarten. Die Darstellung der Elektronenstromdichte $i(x, y, z_t)$ in Form einer Gauss'schen Fehlerfunktion ist aber insbesondere für die Fourier-Transformation (1) so bequem, dass wir versucht haben, eine auch für grössere Werte von z_t/R noch hinreichend gültige Näherung dadurch zu gewinnen, dass wir den Ansatz

(9)
$$i(x, y, z_t) = A(z_t) \cdot \exp\left[-B(z_t) \cdot (x^2 + y^2)\right]$$

gemacht und die Funktionen $A(z_t)$ und $B(z_t)$ experimentell bestimmt haben. Zu

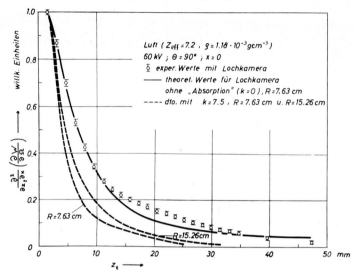

Abb. 3. Vergleich der mit der Lochkamera erhaltenen Messergebnisse mit den aus der paraxialen Theorie der Elektronenvielfachstreuung berechneten Werten.

diesem Zweck haben wir aus der gemessenen Grösse (7) nach Gl. (2) und unserem oben erwähnten Ansatz für $\Phi(\Theta, z_t)$ die Funktion

$$(10) \qquad \int_{-\infty}^{+\infty} i(x, y, z_t)\mathrm{d}y = \frac{\frac{\partial^2}{\partial x \partial z_t}\left(\frac{\partial W}{\partial \Omega}\right)_{90^0}}{\Phi(90^0, z_t)} = \frac{\sqrt{\pi}\cdot A(z_t)}{\sqrt{B(z_t)}}\exp\left[-B(z_t)\cdot x^2\right]$$

und aus den gemessenen Grössen (8) entsprechend die Funktion

$$(11) \qquad \iint_{-\infty}^{+\infty} i(x, y, z_t)\mathrm{d}x\mathrm{d}y = I(z_t) = \frac{\frac{\partial}{\partial z_t}\left(\frac{\partial W}{\partial \Omega}\right)_{90^0}}{\Phi(90^0, z_t)} = \frac{\pi A(z_t)}{B(z_t)}$$

ausgerechnet. Dass die Messungen keine absoluten, sondern nur relative Werte ergaben, stört bei der Berechnung der normierten Fourier-Transformierten nicht. Abb. 4

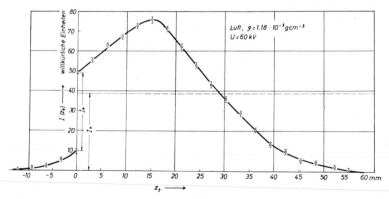

Abb. 4. Gesamtelektronenstrom $I(z_t)$ durch die Ebene z_t, ermittelt aufgrund der mit der Schlitzkamera erhaltenen Messergebnisse.

Literatur S. 97

zeigt die so gewonnenen Ergebnisse für den Strom $I(z_t)$. Man erkennt deutlich die Wirkung der Rückdiffusion an dem Buckel etwa bei $z_t = 15$ mm und den Werten für negative z_t.

ERGEBNISSE

Setzt man (9) in (2) und (2) in (1) ein, so erhält man für $\Theta = 0$ nach Durchführung der Integration über x und y

$$(12) \qquad Q_D(N) = \text{const} \int_0^D \frac{\pi A(z_t) \cdot \phi(0^0, z_t)}{B(z_t)} \exp\left[-\frac{\pi^2 N^2}{B(z_t)}\right] dz_t$$

Die Konstante wird so gewählt, dass für $N = 0$ $Q_D(N) = 1$ wird. Den uns allein interessierenden Absolutbetrag des so normierten Diffusionsanteils $Q_D(N)$ zeigt Abb. 5 über einer reduzierten Raumfrequenz πN_q^* aufgetragen, damit die Kurven

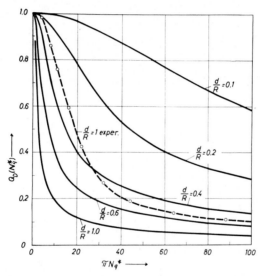

Abb. 5. Anteil $Q_D(N)$ der Elektronendiffusion im Target an der Kontrastübertragungsfunktion von Röntgenstrahlmikroskopen. Berechnet unter Zugrundelegung der paraxialen Theorie der Elektronenvielfachstreuung nach LENZ [5,6] (ausgezogene Kurven) und nach der an die gemessenen Werte angeglichene Näherung für die Vielfachstreuung (gebrochen gezeichnete Kurve).

unabhängig von der Strahlspannung und der Ordnungszahl des Targetmaterials gelten. Um die wahre Raumfrequenz N zu erhalten, ist πN_q^* mit einem Faktor zu multiplizieren, der von der Strahlspannung und dem Targetmaterial abhängt. In Abb. 6 ist dieser Faktor für Gold und Aluminium aufgetragen. Für Gold bewirkt die Elektronendiffusion beispielsweise bei 10 kV Strahlspannung eine Vergrösserung des Quellendurchmessers von etwa 0,08 μ wenn die Dicke des Targets etwa 0,1 μ beträgt. Bei Aluminium und 20 kV sind es bei 2 μ Targetdicke 0,8 μ. In Abb. 5 liegt den ausgezogenen Kurven die paraxiale Theorie der Elektronenvielfachstreuung von LENZ und die Elektronenreichweite nach der Formel von TERRILL zu Grunde. Bei der gestrichelt gezeichneten Kurve sind die experimentell angepassten Werte für die Stromdichte nach Gl. (9) verwendet worden. Für kleine Werte von z_t/R kann man die ersteren Kurven verwenden, für Werte von z_t/R in der Nähe von Eins die letztere Kurve. Dazwischen müsste man interpolieren.

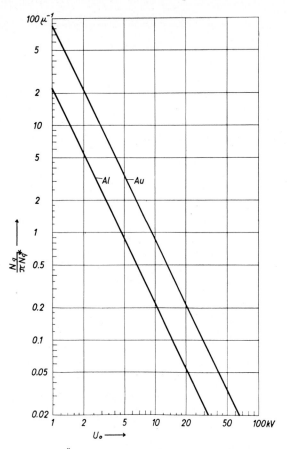

Abb. 6. Umrechnungsfaktor $\dfrac{N_q^*}{\pi N_q^*}$ zur Ermittelung der wahren Raumfrequenz $N_q = N$ der Funktion $Q_D\,(N)$ nach Abb. 5, für Gold und Aluminium in Abhängigkeit von der Strahlspannung U_0.

Zum Gültigkeitsbereich der experimentellen Ergebnisse ist noch folgendes zu sagen: Bei unseren Experimenten (Luft, $U_0 = 60$ kV) ist der Wert von U/Z^2 (Z-Ordnungszahl) viel höher als bei den in der Röntgenmikroskopie üblichen Verhältnissen. Es wäre daher empfehlenswert, die Experimente etwa an Hg-Dampf mit 10 kV-Elektronen zu wiederholen und dann mit Hilfe der charakteristischen Strahlung zu messen, für die Gl. (2) streng gilt. Trotzdem glauben wir, einen gangbaren Weg beschritten zu haben, um über die Verhältnisse der Elektronenvielfachstreuung in Materie quantitative Aussagen machen zu können und sie in Form handlicher Näherungen darzustellen.

DANK

Herrn Dr. LENZ danke ich für viele klärende Diskussionen und der Landesregierung Nordrhein-Westfalen für finanzielle Förderung der Arbeiten.

Literatur S. 97

ZUSAMMENFASSUNG

Feinstfokus-Röntgenröhren werden bekanntlich in den Röntgenstrahl-Punkt-projektionsmikroskopen und -Raster-(Flying spot-) Mikroskopen verwendet. Der effektive Durchmesser der Röntgenstrahlquelle ist infolge der Elektronendiffusion grösser als der effektive Durchmesser des Fokus. Die paraxiale Diffusionstheorie von LENZ gestattet, die Diffusion verhältnismässig einfach zu berechnen. Auf dem Wege von Lochkamera- und Schlitzkamera-Aufnahmen der in atmosph. Luft erzeugten Röntgenstrahlen wurden Gültigkeitsbereich und geeignete Konstante der Theorie experimentell ermittelt. Die Verbreiterung der Röntgenstrahlquelle durch die Diffusion wurde für einige Elemente in Abhängigkeit von Strahlspannung und Dicke des Targets nach der Lenzschen Theorie berechnet.

LITERATUR

[1] M. CH. WANG und E. GUTH, *Natl. Bur. Standards (U.S.), Circ.* 527 (1954) 39.
[2] P. KIRKPATRICK und L. WIEDMANN, *Phys. Rev.,* 67 (1945) 321.
[3] M. SCHEER und E. ZEITLER, *Z. Phys.,* 140 (1955) 642.
[4] H. M. TERRILL, *Phys. Rev.* 22 (1923) 101.
[5] F. LENZ, *Z. angew. Phys.,* 10 (1958) 31.
[6] F. LENZ, *Habilitationsschrift,* T. H. Aachen, (1958).
[7] M. HAHN, *Vortrag auf dem 4. Intern. Kongr. f. Elektronenmikroskopie, Berlin,* Sept. 1958.
[8] G. INDUNI, *Helv. Phys. Acta,* 20 (1957) 463.
[9] B. F. J. SCHONLAND, *Proc. Roy. Soc. (London),* A 104 (1923) 235.

SOME FACTORS AFFECTING THE RANGE AND ACCURACY OF THE POINT-PROJECTION METHOD OF X-RAY ABSORPTION MICROANALYSIS

J. V. P. LONG

Cavendish Laboratory, University of Cambridge, Cambridge
(Great Britain)

ABSTRACT

The useful quantum intensity obtainable from a point-focus X-ray tube with given combinations of target material and monochromator crystal has been calculated and the results compared with experimental measurements. The computed values are presented in a form which allows estimation of the statistical error of absorption measurements in the wavelength range 0.6—7 Å. The magnitude of systematic errors of the method is also discussed.

INTRODUCTION

Elementary absorption microanalysis of thin sections by measurement of transmission at two wavelengths near an absorption edge may be carried out either by contact or projection techniques. In the former case the experimental error, due

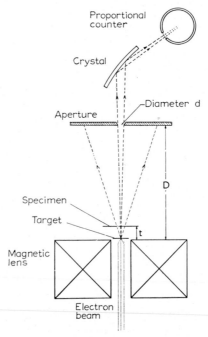

Fig. 1. Arrangement of point-projection tube for absorption microanalysis.

largely to the reference system and the photographic-photometric procedure, has been evaluated[1,2]. In this paper the experimental or random error of the projection method is discussed, and the sources of systematic error are briefly considered.

The experimental arrangement employed for the point-projection method[3] is shown in Fig. 1. The distance D may be of the order of 10 cm, $d \sim$ 1 mm and $t \sim$ 0.2 mm, so that the area examined is $\sim 2\mu$ diameter, the limit to the resolution being set by the X-ray source size.

The experimental error, corresponding to the photographic-photometric error of the contact method is fixed by X-ray intensity available at the wavelengths to be used. Since the target of the point focus tube must be in the form of a stable thin foil, the choice of target materials is restricted, and only in special cases can characteristic radiation be employed. It is therefore assumed that a monochromator crystal will be used to select narrow wavebands from the continuous spectrum generated by the target. The counting rate at the detector then depends principally on two factors: the output of the target, and the properties of the monochromator, the efficiency of the detector being assumed to approach unity.

INTENSITY OF CONTINUOUS RADIATION

The intensity in the continuous spectrum may be calculated from the following relationship, originally due to KUHLENKAMPFF[4]

(1) $$I_E \cdot dE = aZ (E_0 - E) dE$$

where a is a constant, E is the quantum energy and E_0 the limiting energy, equal

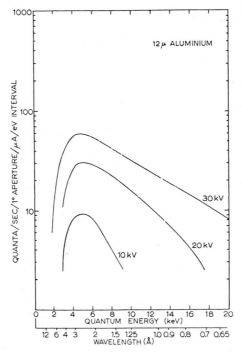

Fig. 2. Quantum intensity of continuous radiation from aluminium (calculated).

References p. 104

to that of the incident electrons. Setting $a = 2.2 \times 10^{-3}$ (COSSLETT and DYSON[5]) and writing the intensity as N_E, the number of quanta of energy $E/\text{sec}/\mu A/$ unit

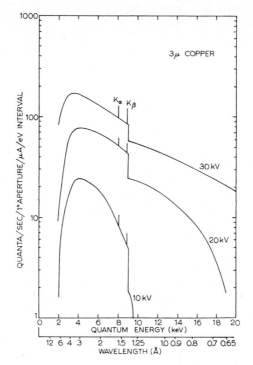

Fig. 3. Quantum intensity of continuous radiation from copper (calculated).

solid angle/eV interval, with the unit solid angle chosen to be a cone of semi-angle $1°$, we obtain

$$(2) \qquad N_E = 1.32 \cdot \frac{Z}{E} (E_0 - E) \cdot e^{-\mu(T-t)}$$

where $e^{-\mu(T-t)}$ is a correction term for absorption by the target of thickness T, when the effective depth of electron penetration is t.

The results obtained from this equation in the case of $12\,\mu$ aluminium are shown in Fig. 2, and for 3μ copper in Fig. 3, for accelerating voltages of 10, 20 and 30 kV in each case.

The maximum output obtainable from a given target depends on its thermal properties. On the assumption that at the point of impact the maximum temperature shall not exceed half the melting point of the target material, and that the electron spot is 2μ in diameter, then for the two targets considered the maximum currents at 20 kV are 9.3 μA and 10.9 μA respectively. Under these conditions the X-ray outputs are as shown in Fig. 4, this diagram showing in addition the output from a gold target 2μ thick.

EFFICIENCY OF MONOCHROMATOR

In order to estimate the quantum intensity at the detector it is necessary to know what proportion of the incident beam is reflected by the monochromator. The

reflecting power of a given set of lattice planes in a crystal is expressed in terms
of an interval of Bragg angle, over which total reflection of a monochromatic radiation

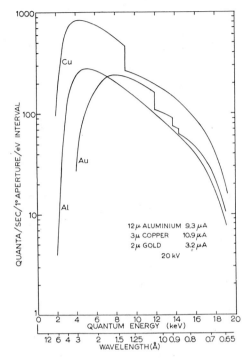

Fig. 4. Quantum intensity of continuous radiation from Al, Cu, Au, at maximum permissible
beam current for target temperatures equal to half the melting point. (X-ray source size $= 2\mu$).

is considered to occur. This angle, usually denoted by ρ and measured in micro-
radians, is known as the integrated reflection.

   If a crystal is maintained at a fixed angle and illuminated by a parallel beam
of continuous radiation, the intensity of the reflected beam but not necessarily its
wavelength range, can be stated in terms of ρ. If the Bragg relationship is written as

$$nkE^{-1} = 2d \cdot \sin\theta$$

then by differentiation and substitution we may obtain

$$-\mathrm{d}E = E \cot\theta \cdot \mathrm{d}\theta.$$

Thus the energy range over which 100 % reflection can be considered to occur is
given by

(3) $$\Delta E = E \cot\theta \cdot \rho.$$

The number of quanta/second obtained with a given combination of crystal and
target is then obtained from

(4) $$\Delta N_E = E \cot\theta \cdot \rho \cdot N_E$$

where N_E is given by eqn. (2).

   The calculated values of ρ for the 200 reflection in perfect and ideally imperfect
crystals of lithium fluoride are given in Fig. 5 for the energy range considered above.
The same diagram also shows the calculated intensity obtained with a copper target
operated at 20 kV and 1 μA with the two extreme types of crystal.

References p. 104

The experimental values, obtained with the same combination of target and crystal confirm the general predictions of the calculations since the crystal used, which

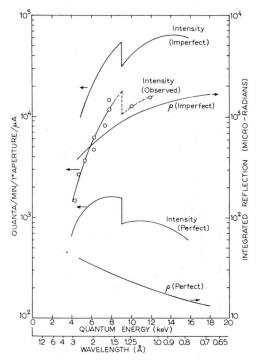

Fig. 5. Calculated and observed quantum intensities of continuous radiation from 3μ copper target at 20 kV and lithium fluoride monochromator.

had been slightly deformed after cleaving from a larger block, would not be expected to conform exactly to either the perfect or ideally imperfect states.

MEASUREMENT TIME

The calculations may be summarized in terms of the measurement period t required for a given proportional error $\sigma N/N$ in the total number of quanta recorded. The error is given by

(5) $$(\sigma N/N)_E = (\triangle N_E \cdot \varepsilon \cdot t)^{-\frac{1}{2}}$$

where ε is the efficiency of the detector for quanta of energy E. Setting $\sigma N/N = 0.01$ or 1%, and assuming that an argon-filled proportional counter with an absorption path of 5 cm is used as detector, the values of t for the energy range considered will be as in Fig. 6. In computing these curves, it has been assumed that a pulse height analyser is used to eliminate high order reflections, and that the channel width is set so that a constant fraction, (0.68), of the total number of quanta is recorded at each energy.

The curves show that in the region of 4—17 keV (corresponding to K edges from ^{20}Ca to ^{42}Mo, and L edges from ^{48}Cd to ^{83}Bi), the measurement times for 1% accuracy range from ~ 0.1 min for an ideally imperfect crystal to ~ 5 min with a perfect crystal.

References p. 104

A further experimental confirmation of the validity of this conclusion is provided by results obtained in the micro-estimation of calcium[3,6], when the combination

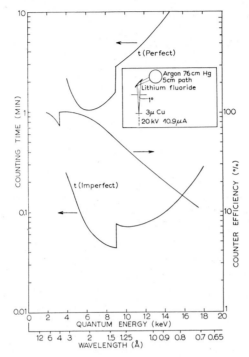

Fig. 6. Measurement periods giving 1 % standard deviation, for copper target and argon counter with perfect and ideally imperfect lithium fluoride monochromators.

of a 12 μ aluminium target and a pentaerythritol crystal was found to give a counting rate of 2000/min at 3.0 Å, with a beam semi-angle of 0.5°, corresponding to a standard deviation of 1 % in 2.5 min for a semi-angle of 1°.

SYSTEMATIC ERRORS

The principal sources of systematic error which could occur in the determination of elementary composition by a two-wavelength projection method are listed below:
1. Diffraction in the specimen, producing an increase or decrease in the intensity of the transmitted beam.
2. Fluorescence of the specimen, not only in the area analysed, but also in the whole area irradiated by the X-ray beam.
3. Incomplete elimination by the pulse height analyser of pulses produced by radiation scattered from the crystal monochromator, and by high order reflections.

An examination of these possible effects has shown that the last is the most important in an experimental arrangement of the type shown in Fig. 1. It has been found[3], however, that provided the effective wavelength and intensity of the radiation are known, corrections may be applied so that the residual error does not exceed 1 %.

Detailed geometrical considerations of the various possibilities of error due to diffraction, (*i.e.* increase or reduction of intensity in both monocrystalline and polycrystalline specimens) are somewhat lengthy, but lead to the conclusion[7] that errors greater than 1 % will not occur provided that beam semi-angles greater than 0.5° are used. Moreover, it may be shown that the probability of an error of this magnitude is very small.

Similar arguments may be used to show that, provided the illuminated area of the specimen is restricted by an aperture above the target, fluorescence radiation produced in the specimen is not recorded by the spectrometer.

CONCLUSIONS

The theoretical calculations, which are supperted by experimental measurements, thus indicate that a standard deviation of less than 1 % may be achieved in transmission measurements on 1—2 μ diameter areas of thin specimens in the energy range 4—17 keV. Extension beyond this range is clearly possible; for example, the continuous output of a silver target in the 5—6 Å region may be shown to be high, making it a very suitable target for the determination of ^{15}P and ^{16}S.

The experimental error thus compares favourably with that of the contact technique, in which the standard deviation of a single photometric determination is of the order of ± 1.5 % (ref. [1]).

No quantitative estimates of the systematic errors due to diffraction and fluorescence appear to have been made in the case of the contact method. The large solid angle subtended by the recording medium at the specimen would suggest that such errors could be appreciable, and almost certainly greater than those encountered in the projection technique.

REFERENCES

[1] S. O. BRATTGÅRD, O. HALLÉN and H. HYDÉN, Biochim. Biophys. Acta, 10 (1953) 486.
[2] B. LINDSTRÖM, Acta Radiol., Suppl. 125 (1955).
[3] J. V. P. LONG, J. Sci. Instr., 35 (1958) 323.
[4] H. KUHLENKAMPFF, Ann. Physik, 69 (1922) 548.
[5] V. E. COSSLETT and N. A. DYSON, X-ray Microscopy and Microradiography, Academic Press, Inc., New York, 1957, p. 405.
[6] H. RÖCKERT, Acta Odont. Scand., 16, Suppl. 25 (1958).
[7] J. V. P. LONG, Thesis, Cambridge University, 1958.

PROJECTION X-RAY MICROSCOPY WITH FORWARD SCATTERED ELECTRON FOCUSING

W. C. NIXON

Cavendish Laboratory, Cambridge University, Cambridge
(Great Britain)

ABSTRACT

The X-ray projection image finally becomes too faint to use for focusing when the X-ray source is about 0.2μ in diameter using existing electron guns and lenses. Eventually improvements in the electron optics and the use of soft X-ray image intensifiers should overcome the present limitations. As a temporary expedient it is still possible to focus the electron beam without seeing the X-ray image. One such method is to use the multiply scattered electrons that have passed through a thin metal foil target and emerge as a cone of approximately 60° along the axis of the initial electron beam. The sharpness of the projection image of a fine mesh grid placed close to the point of scatter may be used as a focusing guide. The X-ray specimen and film are placed to one side of the transmitted electron beam. The exposure time has not been reduced by this indirect method and electrical and mechanical instability over many minutes still limits the resolution.

Projection X-ray microscopy resolution is limited by the enlargement of the X-ray source size due to electron diffusion in a thick target. The electron penetration may be reduced by lowering the kilovoltage to a few kV but this leads to a severe loss of intensity. Alternatively, a thin target may be used at 7 to 10 kV and a resolution

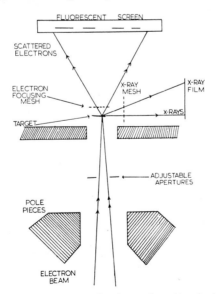

Fig. 1. Experimental arrangement for forward scattered electron focusing.

of 0.1 to 0.2 μ has been demonstrated[1]. The intensity is also very low with a thin target and it is difficult to focus the electron beam while observing the X-ray image under these conditions. An indirect method of focusing has been developed by using the transmitted electrons that have passed through such a thin target after multiple scattering.

Soft X-rays and a vacuum camera are necessary for high resolution X-ray microscopy by any method in order to provide sufficient contrast in the image. With the projection system this means vacuum on both sides of a thin target, leading to the use of the transmitted electrons as shown in Fig. 1. The pole pieces of the

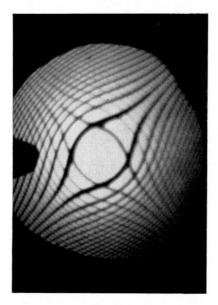
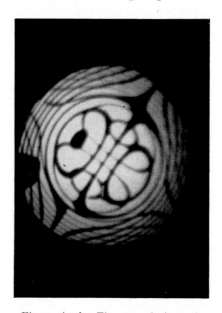

Fig. 2. Direct electron image of 1500 mesh/inch grid, no target or aperture present, overfocused.

Fig. 3. As for Fig. 2, underfocused.

final magnetic reducing lens are shown together with the apertures, target and meshes. With no aperture in position and no target, a direct electron projection image is formed of the electron focusing mesh that is at right angles to the electron beam. The fluorescent screen image is as shown in Fig. 2 when the axial electron beam is focused in the plane of the grid. The barrel distortion is due to the spherical aberration of the electron lens and this constant may be measured from such a picture knowing the geometry of the system. If the lens current is slightly changed under similar conditions the grid image alters to that shown in Fig. 3. In this case the pin-cushion distortion is also due to spherical aberration and now a ring around the axis is in focus in the plane of the grid.

An aperture of 100 μ is placed in the beam and the target (thin aluminium or carbon) is moved in just below the grid. The thickness of the target is chosen so that some 50 % of the electrons are transmitted and these will have been multiply scattered at the voltages used. As a result the electrons are spread over a cone of about 60° and pass through the spaces of the focusing mesh giving rise to the

References p. 109

image as seen in Fig. 4. There is no distortion due to aberration in this picture as all of the electrons come from the same small volume in the target as if that point were

Fig. 4. Scattered electron image of the same grid as in Fig. 2, both target and aperture present. Magnification about 750 times.

self-luminous. There is some geometrical distortion at the edge of the field of view since the projection angle is large. This fluorescent screen image is observed while focusing the final lens and the minimum beam cross-section at the target corresponds with the sharpest grid image. The magnification is given by the ratio of distances in the usual way, *i.e.*, with the grid 40 μ and the screen 40 mm from the target foil the magnification is 750 $\times$ as seen in Fig. 4. This image is viewed with a 10 $\times$ lens.

The X-ray specimen is placed to one side of the main electron beam as shown in Fig. 1 with the X-ray film 4 mm from the X-ray source. The emulsion used is 16 mm, cut to take 9 exposures by rotating a small drum. If the horizontal focusing grid is large enough the edge will be imaged by the X-rays as shown in Fig. 5 with severe foreshortening. When the grid is in the proper place parallel to the electron beam the X-ray image recorded on the 16 mm film is as shown in Fig. 6. In this case the field of view at the specimen is about 100 μ across without the distortion seen at the top of this figure. A faint white Fresnel fringe is seen along the grid bars indicating a resolution of about 0.2 μ, as expected from the target thickness and overall electron beam reduction. This X-ray image is too faint to be seen on a fluorescent screen and yet it has been recorded in focus by using an indirect method based on the transmitted electron image.

It is possible to give an estimate of the ratio of the fluorescent screen brightness for direct X-ray focusing and indirect electron focusing. For the former we assume a conversion efficiency of 10^{-4} from electrons to X-rays and that these X-rays are

spread uniformly over a sphere of 1 cm radius or 4π cm² in order to compare the
energy density at the fluorescent screen. The transmitted electrons in the second

Fig. 5. X-ray image of electron focusing grid perpendicular to electron beam and almost parallel
to X-ray beam.

Fig. 6. X-ray image of the same grid now placed parallel to the electron beam and perpendicular
to the X-ray beam. A faint white Fresnel fringe may be seen along the edge of the grid bars
indicating a resolution of about 0.2 μ, roughly equal to the thickness of the target.

References p. 109

case are taken to be half of the total beam current. These are scattered through approximately one radian or fall on an area of 1 cm^2 of a fluorescent screen placed 1 cm away as in the X-ray case, for the same test grid enlargement. If we also assume that the X-rays and electrons are equally efficient in causing the screen to fluoresce, the ratio of quantum densities will give a comparison of the brightness of the fluorescent screen under the two conditions. For X-ray focusing we have $10^{-4}/4\pi$ cm^2 quanta/cm^2/incident electron and for electron focusing $\frac{1}{2}/1$ cm^2 quanta/cm^2/incident electron. The ratio of these two, $(\frac{1}{2} \times 4\pi)/(1 \times 10^{-4})$ or 6.3×10^4, gives the increase in brightness for focusing when using an electron image. A similar calculation may be made for the back-scattering electron focusing method[2] where a gain of up to 10^4 is found over direct X-ray focusing.

However, neither of these methods reduces the exposure time necessary to record the focused X-ray image. In principle, either method could be used to focus an X-ray image with 100 Å resolution since direct focusing fails at about 2000 Å and the X-ray intensity falls with the cube of the electron spot size. The electron image at 100 Å would then be just as dim as the present direct X-ray image. In practice, the resultant exposure time would be up to $10^4 \times$ the 5 to 10 minutes at present (or 70 days) with impossible demands on electrical and mechanical stability, filament life and operators patience! In conclusion, although it is possible to avoid the consequence of low X-ray intensity at high resolution as far as focusing is concerned, it is impossible at present to record such an X-ray image. Further improvements in resolution will have to wait for brighter electron sources, improved electron lenses or soft X-ray image intensifiers.

REFERENCES

[1] W. C. NIXON, *Proc. Roy. Soc. (London), A* 232 (1955) 475.
[2] S. P. ONG and J. B. LE POOLE, *Appl. Sci. Research, B* 7 (1958) 233.

MINIATURE POINT X-RAY SOURCES FOR POINT-PROJECTION MICROSCOPY AND DIFFRACTION STUDIES

B. M. ROVINSKY, V. G. LUTSAU and A. I. AVDEYENKO

Institute of Machine Sciences of the U.S.S.R., Academy of Sciences, Moscow (U.S.S.R.)

ABSTRACT

The source of X-rays with a "point" focus for point-projection microscopy is built in the form of a needle anode, with electrostatic focusing of the electron beam. The source has an effective focus about 0.2 μ in diameter and works at voltages of 1 to 12 kV. It is very small and is placed in a chamber connected to a vacuum system with a window for letting X-rays into the air. In this form it is used for obtaining X-ray point projection with direct X-ray magnification up to $\times$ 600. In order to obtain point X-ray projection in vacuum, the specimen, film and radiation source are placed in a vacuum chamber. In this form pictures can be taken with magnification up to $\times$ 800.

The source of X-rays for diffraction studies is built according to the same principle. The diameter of its operating part is 15 mm and its construction allows diffraction patterns to be taken at short distances. Effective diameter of the point source is 1 or 2 μ and the total power of the source is increased correspondingly. Operating voltage is also increased to 18 kV. The source of X-rays is placed in a chamber connected to a vacuum system with a window through which the X-rays emerge into the air.

Due to their small size the sources of X-rays can also be placed in sealed chambers.

INTRODUCTION

The paper describes the design and some data on the experimental application of point X-ray sources to point-projection microscopy and diffraction studies. The point sources described are experimental laboratory models used in our research work. The small size and simplicity of the device allows point sources of sealed-off type to be designed.

X-RAY SOURCE FOR POINT-PROJECTION MICROSCOPY

The improved point X-ray source for projection microscopy has been designed on the principle of the needle microprojector proposed by us some time ago[1]. That first model had many O-ring seals, which exerted a negative influence on the life of the cathode loop and needle-anode because of oxidation and atomization. Moreover, the adjustment of the main elements of the projector, which determines the size of the radiation source and consequently its resolution, was carried out in the assembled device in vacuum. The inaccuracy of adjustment considerably reduced the quality of the projector. The horizontal position of the projector axis had also a bad influence on the image sharpness because of the vibration of the apparatus. Some of these drawbacks have been eliminated in the new model described in this paper. The X-ray path in the new model is vertical and it has only one rubber O-ring seal.

References p. 117

The projection device itself is a separate miniature unit containing all the main elements of a point source of X-radiation. It is shown in vertical section in Fig. 1.

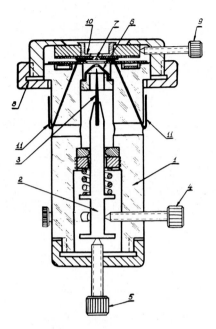

Fig. 1. Vertical section of the X-ray point-source projector.

In the casing 1, made of teflon, there is an anode holder 2 with a needle-anode 3. Three side screws 4 and an advancing screw 5 accurately center the anode and bring it to the necessary height. The needle-anode, focusing diaphragm 6 and cathode-heating filament in the form of a ringshaped loop 7 are mounted and centered under an optical microscope. For this purpose the casing 1 with mounted parts, *i.e.* the whole unit shown in Fig. 1, is fixed by a special holder on the microscope table. With the aid of a coupling nut 8 and three screws 9 the cathode is centered and fixed at the required distance from the focusing diaphragm. The specimen is placed in a holder 10. The high voltage is applied to the anode, and cathode heating current is supplied to the terminals 11, one of which is earthed.

After adjustment, the assembled projection device, shown in Fig. 2, is placed in the vacuum chamber of the projector. We have made two variants of the projector vacuum chamber: metallic and glass. The metallic vacuum chamber, shown in Fig. 3 and Fig. 4, consists of a base plate *a* soldered to the sleeve of a vacuum system *b*, and a covering tube. Through the bottom of the base plate pass vacuum contacts for heating the cathode *c* and delivering high voltage *d*. On the upper side of the plate there is a holder *e*, in which the projection device *f* is placed. The cover is a metal tube, sealed at one end, which is placed on the rubber O-ring seal of the foundation (Fig. 4). When pictures are taken in vacuum, the film is placed in a special adapter, which is fixed in the tube at the required distance from the object. In this case, under optimal conditions, the direct magnification is up to × 800. For taking pictures in air there is a shorter covering tube, on the upper side of which is a cellophane window for letting the radiation out into the atmosphere. In this case both the specimen and film can be placed outside the vacuum.

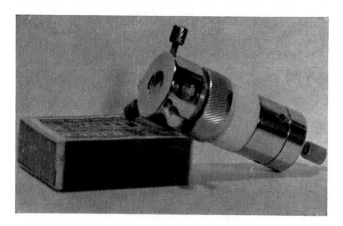

Fig. 2. Assembled projection device.

The glass vacuum chamber consists of a glass funnel, the lower part of which is connected to a vacuum system through a conical glass joint; the upper part is connected to the camera tube. Soldered-in metallic terminals allow delivery of cathode heating current and high voltage from a generator. At the same time the terminals for cathode heating are used to fasten the projector casing in the chamber.

Fig. 3. Vacuum chamber of the point-source projector with projection device *f* in position, but with cover removed.

Fig. 4. Vacuum chamber of the point-source projector with metal cover in place for taking pictures in vacuum.

References p. 117

For taking pictures in the air the upper chamber is replaced by a rubber O-ring seal with a cellophane window.

The specimen can be placed not nearer than 0.6 mm from the needle-anode. Pictures can be taken at voltages of 1 to 12 kV and a current of 1 to 5 μA. The needle-anodes are best made of tungsten or molybdenum, but for obtaining monochromatic radiation nickel, cobalt, iron and chromium needle-anodes have also been used.

The resolution of the X-ray point-source projector was determined by taking photographs of a grid and by the detectability of details in microphotographs of various objects. However, X-ray point-projection photographs of a copper grid with a bar width of 5 μ and at a total magnification of $\times$ 2000 do not provide a reliable evaluation of the resolution, if it is less than 0.5 μ. We therefore determined the resolution from objects photographed both by a point-source microprojector and by an electron microscope; for instance, the hairs on the leg of a gnat (*Anopheles*), could be clearly seen in the X-ray image. Electron microscope pictures of the hair showed that the hair tips are less than 0.1 μ in diameter. We therefore suppose that the resolution of the X-ray point source projector is about 0.2 μ.

In order to evaluate the qualities of this new X-ray point projector, we have investigated the structure of alloys subjected to different kinds of heat treatment and mechanical tests[2]. Some results of the analysis of minerals and of medical investigations are described elsewhere[3,4].

Figs. 5, 6 and 7 show microstructures in an alloy of aluminium with copper

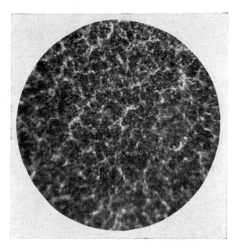

Fig. 5. Aluminium alloy (4.7 % of Cu, 0.8 % of Mn, 0.2 % of Ti) in the cast state. Radiographic magnification $\times$ 360; tungsten L-radiation.

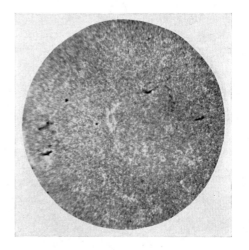

Fig. 6. Structure of the alloy after quenching. (Conditions as in Fig. 5.)

(4.7 %), manganese (0.8 %), and titanium (0.2 %), examined in different states. Fig. 5 shows the structure of the alloy in the cast state. The picture was taken in tungsten L-radiation, at a magnification of $\times$ 360. The large white areas are the $CuAl_2$ phase, and the finely dispersed inclusions are the T phase ($Al_{12}Mn_2Cu$). Fig. 6 shows the structure of the alloy after quenching, taken again in tungsten L-radiation at a magnification of × 360. The general background is lighter due to the matrix being enriched with copper from the CuAl₂, the T phase remaining in the form of a finely dispersed inclusion with a size of about 1 μ. As a result of ageing and testing

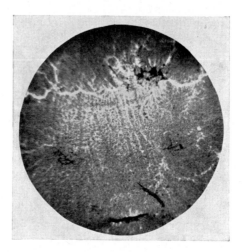

Fig. 7. The same alloy after ageing and testing at 300° C, under a load of 6.5 kg/mm², during 100 hours; × 360.

the alloy at a temperature of 300° C and under a load of 6.5 kg/mm² during 100 hours, the CuAl₂ phase is again segregated from the solution. In Fig. 7 (× 360) one can clearly see the isolation of the CuAl₂ phase mainly on the grain boundaries (the white zigzag line) and in the grains themselves on the subgrain boundaries, with a certain

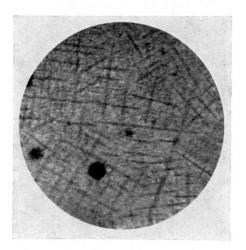

Fig. 8. Microstructure of tin bronze after deformation and long homogenizing annealing at 450° C, showing microdendrites in the grains. Nickel radiation; × 520.

direction with respect to the applied force. As a result of the simultaneous action of the stress and the temperature, the segregating particles of the brittle CuAl₂ phase form continuous chains in which starting points of failure are formed as microscopic cracks, which were detected in later microradiographs. Fig. 8 shows a radiograph of tin bronze in the cast state, taken in nickel radiation at a magnification of × 520, after being deformed and subjected to long homogenizing annealing. The alloy contains microdendrites with a thickness of 1 to 2 μ and pores about 10 μ in size.

X-RAY SOURCES WITH A FOCAL SPOT OF 1 TO 2 μ FOR DIFFRACTION STUDIES

The point X-ray source for diffraction is designed according to the same principle as the microprojector. However, the special features of diffraction methods necessitated some structural changes in the device. First of all it was necessary to reduce the diameter of the working part of the source, in order to have the possibility of bringing the object and film as near to the focus as possible. The effective diameter of the focus was increased to 1 or 2 μ, which made it possible to increase the total power of the source somewhat. The operating voltage was increased to 18 kV.

Constructionally two variants of the point source for diffraction have been made: one with horizontal and the other with vertical exit of the X-rays. Fig. 9

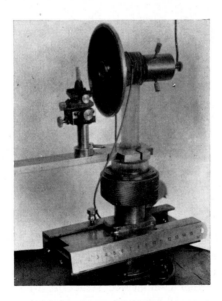

Fig. 9. Point X-ray source for diffraction work with horizontal path of X-rays, arranged for taking epigrams.

shows the source in the horizontal arrangement and with a device for obtaining epigrams. On the source casing an exit window of cellophane is situated at a distance of 0.6 mm from the focus, and either a miniature powder camera or a flat adapter is used. The source of X-radiation is connected to the vacuum system through a valve. The source with vertical exit of X-rays consists of a glass flask connected to a vacuum system through a conical glass joint. Inside the flask on metallic supports,

References p. 117

soldered to it, there is an X-ray source made as a separate unit, similar to that shown in Fig. 2. On the upper part of the source either a miniature powder camera or a flat adapter with a film can be mounted. For taking epigrams and back reflection patterns the specimen is placed in a holder mounted on a separate support. The radiation source is connected to a high voltage generator and the cathode filament is heated by a battery of accumulators. A powder pattern obtained in a miniature camera of 14 mm in diameter, the specimen being an 0.1 mm tungsten wire, required an exposure of only 10 min. The voltage was 15 kV, the current 4 μA, and the needle anode was of iron.

To obtain an epigram, the distance between the source focus and the specimen is 6 mm, the distance between the specimen and the film is 10 mm. At a voltage of 18 kV, current of 4 μA and with a tungsten needle-anode the exposure is 15 min. Fig. 10 shows a radiograph of a thin specimen made of aluminium alloy, obtained

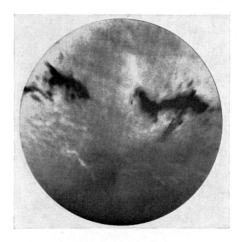

Fig. 10. Radioscopic picture of a thin specimen of aluminium alloy. Voltage 18 kV, 3 μA, tungsten anode and radioscopic magnification; × 280.

by the transmission method at a magnification of × 280. In the general background one can see the boundary of two grains (a light zigzag line), *i.e.* this is a usual X-ray projection picture. In addition to the projection picture, one can clearly see two Laue spots (black) of rather complicated structure, which are evidence that the irradiated grains are structurally complicated. The picture was taken at a voltage of 18 kV, current intensity of 3 μA, exposure time 15 min, with tungsten anode.

In the literature there is very little information on the application of X-ray point sources to microdiffraction techniques[5]. Our experience suggests that in some cases it is advantageous to use a point focus in the study of the substructure of metals and alloys. In order to obtain high resolution in diffraction methods when the usual "macroscopic" radiation sources are used, it is necessary to use very thin slits, which involves considerable increase in exposure time and difficulties in making the experiment.

References p. 117

REFERENCES

1 B. M. ROVINSKY, V. G. LUTSAU and A. I. AVDEYENKO, in V. E. COSSLETT et al., X-ray Microscopy and Microradiography, Academic Press, Inc., New York, 1957, pp. 269–277.
2 I. F. KOLOBNEV, V. G. LUTSAU and N. A. ARISTOVA, Metallovedenie i Obrabotka Metallov, in the press, 1960.
3 B. M. ROVINSKY, V. G. LUTSAU and A. I. AVDEYENKO, Izvest. Akad. Nauk S.S.S.R., Ser. Fiz., 23 (1959) 545.
4 V. A. POLIAKOV and V. G. LUTSAU, Experimentalniai Hirurgia, in the press, 1960.
5 W. C. NIXON, in V. E. COSSLETT et al., X-ray Microscopy and Microradiography, Academic Press, Inc., New York, 1957, pp. 326–344.

E. THEORY AND TECHNIQUE OF REFLECTION X-RAY MICROSCOPY

THE OBLIQUITY ABERRATION OF REFLECTION X-RAY MICROSCOPY*

JAMES F. McGEE and JOHN W. MILTON

Saint Louis University, Saint Louis, Mo. (U.S.A.)

ABSTRACT

The obliquity aberration causes the image plane to recline with respect to the principal ray. The insertion of a stop of vanishing aperture at the proposed distance $D_0 = R \sin i/3$ in image space is shown to result in the erection of one image point into the Gaussian plane. For systems of finite magnification M and mirrors of finite length s the position of the stop is shown to be $D = D (M, f, s)$ where f is the focal length. The latter function reduces to D_0 when M is infinite and s is zero. The analysis is further extended to include the positioning of a *finite* aperture stop. Extensive ray tracing with the aid of an IBM-610 computer has resulted in a more complete understanding of the role of aperture stops and the prediction of the performance of a complete reflection X-ray microscope.

INTRODUCTION

The focusing X-ray microscope described by KIRKPATRICK and BAEZ[1] consists of two concave X-ray reflectors mounted one behind the other. The reflectors which may be sections of much larger polished glass mirrors are oriented so that the tangent planes at the center of each mirror are mutually perpendicular. This disposition succeeds in removing the extreme astigmatism which is characteristic of a single reflecting mirror. Because of the extreme astigmatic nature of a single reflector the optical analysis may be confined to two dimensions in the meridian plane, where the image and object positions are related for a mirror of small length by

$$(1) \qquad \frac{1}{p} + \frac{1}{q} = \frac{2}{R \sin i} = \frac{1}{f_m}$$

with R, the radius of the mirror segment, f_m, the focal length in the meridian plane and i, the angle of grazing incidence (complement of the ordinary angle of incidence). For total reflection of X-rays to take place, the angle of grazing incidence i has to be less than the critical angle i_c which is at most a few degrees. The latter is a function of the wavelength and the electron density of the reflecting surface. For glass and radiation of wavelength 1.54 Å, the critical angle is about 4.5 milliradians. With radiation of 8.34 Å incident on gold, the critical angle increases to approximately 35 milliradians.

Beside the meridional focal length f_m there exists a sagittal focal length f_s which is many thousands of times the meridian focal length for a typical X-ray microscope system. The sagittal focal length is given by

$$f_s = \frac{R}{2 \sin i}.$$

---

* This research was supported by a grant from the Research Corporation.

References p. 128

GEOMETRICAL ABERRATIONS

In common with other optical devices, the X-ray microscope does not produce images which are exact reproductions of the object. It further differs from most other optical systems by not possessing a symmetry axis. Accordingly it is to be expected that the reflection X-ray microscope will produce the common geometrical aberrations, such as spherical, comal, etc., together with some aberrations not possible in symmetrical systems.

The formation of spherical aberration by a concave spherical reflector is illustrated in Fig. 1. A narrow pencil of rays from the point object O, incident on a small section of mirror at C is imaged perfectly at I according to Gaussian optics.

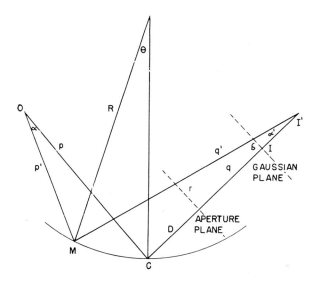

Fig. 1. Spherical aberration formed by a concave spherical reflector.

However, it is seen that another narrow pencil from O, incident on the reflector at M, will be focused at I'. A photographic plate placed in coincidence with the Gaussian plane would thus record an image of width δ. The length δ is a measure of the transverse spherical aberration. The defect could also be specified by $\varDelta = \overline{II}'$, the *longitudinal* spherical aberration. The transverse and longitudinal spherical aberrations are related by the aperture angle α',

(2)
$$\delta = \alpha'\varDelta.$$

KIRKPATRICK and BAEZ show that, for large magnification ($M \equiv q/p$) and a *small* mirror segment $\overline{CM} = s$, the transverse spherical aberration is

(3)
$$\delta_{02} = \frac{3}{2} \cdot \frac{Ms^2}{R}.$$

The projection of the mirror length s into the aperture plane of Fig. 1, located adjacent to the mirror, shows that for large magnification M the separation of the pencils in the aperture plane is given approximately by $r = si$ where i is the angle of incidence of the principal reference ray $\overline{OCI}$. The transverse spherical aberration

References p. 128

may then be written as

(4)
$$\delta_{02} = \frac{3}{2} \cdot \frac{Mr^2}{i^2R} = a_{02}\, r^2 .$$

which indicates that the spherical aberration is a function of the square of the aperture opening r. It is readily seen that mirrors of large radii of curvature are desirable if the spherical aberration coefficient a_{02} is to be held to a minimum.

Spherical aberration is but one of the many geometrical aberrations which comprise the total transverse aberration δ_t. KIRKPATRICK and BAEZ found that an extended object perpendicular to the principal reference ray $\overline{OCI}$ has an image plane which makes a small angle γ with the principal reference ray. The seriousness of the situation is evidenced by the fact that $\gamma \simeq i/M$ for large magnifications. This defect is called the obliquity aberration.

Since it is convenient to treat each aberration type as if the others did not exist, it will be assumed in Fig. 2 that a bundle of rays of angular aperture α' originating at the extreme end of a line object h, not shown, is focused free of spherical

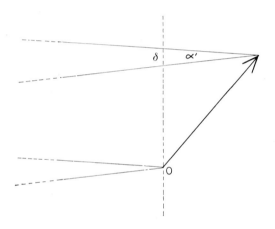

Fig. 2. Obliquity aberration.

aberrations in the origin of the Gaussian (dotted) plane. Because of the obliquity aberration, the bundle of rays from the other end of the object is focused behind the Gaussian image plane. It is clear from Fig. 2 that one bundle of rays will intersect the Gaussian plane over a distance δ while the other will have an interception of zero extent. Ray bundles from intermediate field points will correspondingly intercept the Gaussian plane with overlapping intercepts varying in extent from zero to δ. Because of obliquity, the transverse aberration δ associated with any one field point is a function of its perpendicular distance h measured from the principle reference ray in object space and the aperture r of the system.

In Fig. 2 the longitudinal aberration due to obliquity alone is approximately given by $\varDelta \simeq Mh/\gamma$. As stated above $\gamma \simeq i/M$ so that $\varDelta \simeq M^2h/i$. The aperture angle $\alpha' \simeq r/q$ and $q \simeq iRM/2$ so that $\alpha' \simeq 2r/iRM$. The transverse aberration due to obliquity alone is approximately

(5)
$$\delta_{11} = \varDelta \cdot \alpha' = (M^2h/i)(2r/iRM) = (2M/i^2R)hr = a_{11}\, hr.$$

References p. 128

The transverse aberrations δ_{02} and δ_{11} may be considered as terms in a power series expansion of the total transverse aberration δ_t which is expressed as

(6)
$$\begin{aligned}
\delta_t = \; & a_{00} + a_{01}r + a_{02}r^2 + a_{03}r^3 + \cdots \\
& \cdots + a_{10}\,h + a_{11}hr + a_{12}hr^2 + \cdots \\
& \cdots + a_{20}\,h^2 + a_{21}h^2r + \cdots \\
& \cdots + a_{30}\,h^3 + \cdots .
\end{aligned}$$

Since the optical system is unsymmetrical, the power series may contain even as well as odd powers.

The definition of the Gaussian plane requires that δ be zero when h and r are respectively zero. Thus the coefficient a_{00} should be zero. It is possible to interpret other terms of the power series as due to a particular type of geometrical aberration. When δ depends only on r^2, the coefficient a_{02} would be called the primary spherical aberration coefficient. The coefficient a_{11} is associated with the obliquity defect while the coefficient a_{12} is associated with coma and a_{21} with curvature of field.

Correction of obliquity

The usual approach to correcting alterations in an optical system is either an alteration of the optical surfaces, the insertion of apertures, or both. DYSON[2] considered the insertion of an aperture of *vanishing width* at a distance $D = Ri/3$ from the mirror in image space. It will be shown that a narrow aperture at this position will erect but one conjugate field point and then only for a mirror of vanishing length, adjusted for infinite magnification.

To determine the position D of a narrow aperture which will correct the obliquity defect, consider the object $\overline{OA}$ and the erect image $\overline{IB}$ which are located at distances p_c and q_c respectively from the mirror center C of Fig. 3. The object $\overline{OA}$ has been erected perpendicular to the principal reference ray. It is desired to find the condition

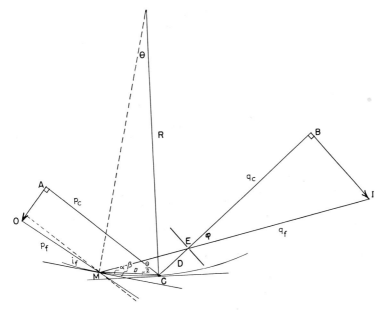

Fig. 3. Correction of obliquity defect.

or position D of the aperture which will result in the image being perpendicular to the principal reference ray in image space. The extreme rays drawn from the line object of Fig. 3 are considered to be narrow bundles of rays which after reflection at C and M respectively are brought to a focus in the extreme points of the image $\overline{BI}$ after being forced to cross over at the narrow aperture opening E. If the ray p_c is incident at an angle i_c on the concave reflector of radius R while the ray p_f is incident at an angle i_f at point M it follows from the geometry of Fig. 3 that for small angles $i_f = \beta + \alpha$ with $\alpha \cong \theta/2$ and

$$\theta \cong s/R$$

or

(7) $$i_f = \beta + s/2R \cdot$$

In triangle MCE the following relationship holds

(8) $$\beta + \varphi - \frac{\theta}{2} - i_c = 0 \cdot$$

The application of the law of sines to triangles MCE yields

(9) $$\frac{s}{\varphi} = \frac{D}{\beta} \cdot$$

In order that the object point O be imaged in the Gaussian plane through BI the following conditions must hold at small angles.

(10) $$p_c \cong p_f + s$$

(11) $$q_c \cong q_f - s$$

(12) $$1/p_c + 1/q_c = 1/f_c$$

(13) $$1/p_f + 1/q_f = 1/f_f$$

where $f_f = Ri_f/2$ and $f_c = Ri_c/2$. In the subsequent analysis it will be convenient to have equation (12) in the two forms

(14) $$p_c = \frac{1 + M}{M} \cdot f_c$$

(15) $$q_c = (1 + M) \cdot f_c$$

where

$$M = q_c/p_c \cdot$$

Also equation (13) is better expressed as

(16) $$p_f = \frac{q_f f_f}{q_f - f_f} \cong \frac{(q_c + s)f_f}{q_c + s - f_f} \cdot$$

Successive substitutions in eqn. (10) of p_c, p_f, and q_c, f_f and i_f from equations (14), (16), (15), (13) and (7) respectively and of f_f and f_i results in the following expression for the angle β

(17) $$\beta = \frac{4(1 + M)^2 f_c^2 + (3 - 5M)(1 + M)sf_c - 4Ms^2}{2f_cR(1 + M)^2} \cdot$$

Another expression for β can be developed from eqn. (8) by first eliminating φ with eqn. (9) and subsequently using $\theta \cong s/R$ and $f_c = Ri_c/2$ as substitutes for θ and i_c with the result that

(18) $$\beta = \frac{D(s + 4f_c)}{2R(s + D)} \cdot$$

References p. 128

The final step is the equating of eqns. (17) and (18) and solving for D to give

(19)
$$D = \frac{4(1+M)^2 f_c{}^2 + (3-5M)(1+M)f_c s - 4Ms^2}{2(1+M)(3M-1)f_c + 4Ms}.$$

For *infinite magnification* eqn. (19) reduces to

(20)
$$D = \frac{Ri_c}{3} - \frac{5}{6}s.$$

If s approaches zero, then $D = Ri_c/3$, which is just DYSON's result for a *narrow* aperture. For unity magnification and zero length of mirror

(21)
$$D = 2f_c = Ri_c$$

and the aperture would coincide with the image position.

With due consideration of Fig. 3 and eqn. (19) it becomes evident that the infinitesimal ray bundles originating at intermediate object points must intersect the mirror at different values of s and cross the principle reference ray at different points if they are to focus in the Gaussian plane $\overline{\text{IB}}$. Thus a single narrow aperture will cause but one field point to be focused in the Gaussian plane. It would seem that an infinite number of narrow apertures would be required if each and every point of the field is to be focused into the Gaussian plane and a completely erect image obtained. The prospect of accomplishing this looks discouraging until a few key rays are drawn as shown in Fig. 4. The intersections a and b are readily determined for each extreme ray through an application of eqn. (19).

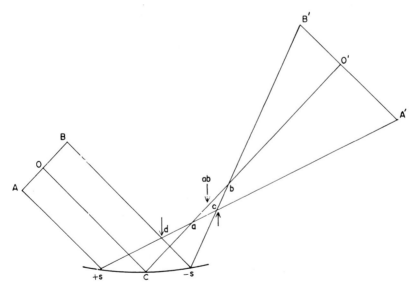

Fig. 4. Effect of several apertures on focusing.

In Fig. 5, D is plotted *versus* s for various magnifications M with $f_c = Ri_c/2$ constant $= 17.875$ which corresponds to $R = 325$ cm and $i_c = 0.55$ radians.

The distance D for the intersections a and b can conveniently be read from Fig. 5 for a reflector of maximum length $2s$. It is obvious in Fig. 4 that the placing of *narrow* apertures at the intersections a and b will not be satisfactory because of the blockage of rays. Perhaps half-apertures (single knife-edges) at the three intersections a, b, and c would still insure that the rays cross at the proper distance *D*? The latter solution is tenable until one plots the paths of ray from intermediate field points. It is found that they will intersect the principal reference ray at points *between* a and b with the end result that the knife edges previously placed at a

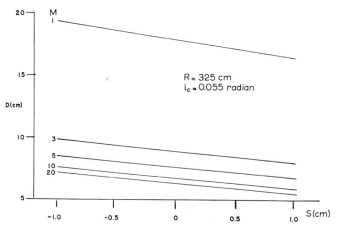

Fig. 5. *D* plotted *vs.* *s* for different values of *M*.

and b would cut off rays from intermediate points of the field! Thus if one wishes to image intermediate field points, the half-apertures originally placed at a and b of Fig. 4 have to be moved toward one another until they finally coalesce into one at some intermediate point *almost* directly above point c. It now becomes clear that the half aperture between a and b together with the half aperture at c constitute but one *finite* aperture as distinguished from the narrow (infinitesimal) apertures previously considered but tacitly assumed to be finite in practice! However, this *finite* aperture is not of itself capable of directing the limiting rays of Fig. 4 to cross the principal reference ray at the correct point as given by eqn. (19). To by-pass some of the original logic, let it be assumed that a half-aperture is placed at point d. The edges of the half-apertures c and d determine a straight line which coincides with the desired direction of the extreme ray AA'. Likewise the single edge at c and the edge d determine the direction of the remaining extreme ray BB' after an intermediate reflection. Thus a finite aperture (ab), c and a half-aperture d serve the function of the infinite number of narrow apertures placed along the principal reference ray as required by eqn. (19). It appears that the lower edge c of the finite aperture and the edge d of the half-aperture define the correct direction for the extreme rays; in one case, after one intermediate reflection.

   If each image point is considered the source of a bundle of rays of angular width α' which are traced backward through the system, it is evident that one end of the image will be "vignetted" by the combination of the finite aperture and the half-aperture. Before becoming alarmed at this and other possible ill effects it would be wise to determine more completely by ray tracing exactly what happens in detail.

References p. 128

RAY TRACING ANALYSIS

(a) Image contours

A preliminary step is the determination of how well the expression $D = D(M, s, f_c)$ removes obliquity. Again the reverse approach is helpful. If obliquity is to be totally absent, then the infinitesimal *bundle* of rays from any image point in the Gaussian plane which strikes the reflector at a point s should cross the principle reference ray at a point D cm from C as given by eqn. (19). The computation starts with a directed ray passing *through* the desired Gaussian image point and striking the reflector at s and crossing at D as computed from eqn. (19). This is sufficient to fix the reverse reflected ray direction so that its intersection with the Gaussian plane in object space can be computed. From the latter intersection point and the reflector intersection point at s the object distance p_i can readily be computed. An application of the focusing condition expressed by eqn. (1) allows the determination of q_i which should fall in the Gaussian image plane. The above calculation is repeated for values of s between -0.8 cm to $+0.8$ cm. It is an easy matter to compute the coordinates of each image and object point in a ξ, η co-ordinate system whose origin is at C, the ξ axis tangent to the reflector at C and the η axis along the radius R. The image contours of Fig. 6 were computed for three different cases. Case I was for $R = 850$ cm and $i_c = 0.015$ radians; Case II for $R = 325$ cm and $i_c = 0.015$ radians; Case III for $R = 325$ cm and $i_c = 0.055$ radians. A Gaussian image plane if drawn in Fig. 6

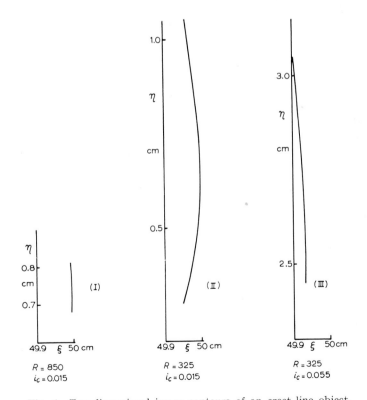

Fig. 6. Two-dimensional image contours of an erect line object.

would be almost perpendicular to the ξ-axis and touch each image contour at its approximate center.

The width of field corresponding to the image contour of Case I is 192 μ. It should be noted that the width of mirror ($2s$) used for this case was only 1.0 cm. The width of field corresponding to the image contour of Case III is 1288 μ. It is now evident that an image relatively free of obliquity may be produced by causing the rays from a given field-point to cross the principal reference ray of Fig. 4 at the point determined by eqn. (19). The resulting image planes do not depart significantly from their Gaussian planes. It is seen that some deviations are less than the thickness of the photographic emulsion which would ordinarily be positioned in or close to the Gaussian plane to record the image. It should be remembered that each image point has been computed with zero spherical aberration because an infinitely narrow beam or ray was used in the calculation.

(b) Total geometrical aberration

A separate ray-tracing study using the IBM 610 computer was next undertaken to determine the total geometrical aberration produced by the system. Each object point was considered the source of a divergent bundle of rays with uniform density and of sufficient divergence to fill the aperture. In the actual machine calculation the program was arranged so that a larger than necessary bundle of equally spaced rays could be sent through the computer. Mathematical limits representing the edges of the full and half apertures would automatically reject those rays which should hit the sides of the physical apertures. The computer would then start over with the next adjacent ray.

Assuming object and image planes have been erected, then the path of any ray through the optical system is completely determined if h the distance of the object point from the principal reference ray and r the coordinate of the rays' intersection with an aperture plane are specified. In Gaussian optics, a field-point at h would intersect the Gaussian image plane at a distance Mh units from the principal reference ray. An aberrant ray intersects the Gaussian plane with an error δ_t which may be expressed as a function of h and r by the power series of eqn. (6). Its coefficients are of course functions of various system parameters such as object distance, magnification, angle of incidence i_c, radius R of the reflector, etc. Provided the foregoing analysis of obliquity is correct, the coefficient a_{11} should be extremely small.

An attempt to determine the coefficients of eqn. (6) was made assuming that terms beyond the third order could be neglected. The computation was carried out for a mirror of radius $R = 325$ cm and $i_c = 0.055$ radians. Sufficient input information covering a large range of field h and aperture r was available from the previous ray tracing study. A standard method was used for triangulation of the matrix in (h, r) and the coefficients were improved in accuracy by a technique due to CROUT[3]. A considerable loss in precision may result through cumulative round-off errors and failure to evaluate the coefficients in the proper order. The resulting coefficients are tabulated in Table I. They should be divided by the magnification.

(c) Intensity distributions

The final study is concerned with the distribution in the image contour of a uniform angular distribution of rays emanating from one field-point. Once tha

TABLE I

$a_{01} = -\ 0.0086267$	$a_{10} =\ \ \ 0.0010645$	$a_{20} =\ \ 3.9670$
$a_{02} = -\ \ 1.8874$	$a_{11} = -0.53659$	$a_{21} = 22.387$
$a_{03} = -680.60$	$a_{12} =\ \ 56.179$	$a_{30} =\ \ 4.4605$

coefficients of eqn. (6) have been determined, it is an easy step to program the computer for calculating a large number of intersections for a particular case. The linear density of the intersections was converted to an arbitrary intensity scale and plotted as a function of distance from the intersection of the chief ray (zero aperture) as shown in Figs. 7 and 8. In the case of Fig. 7 the above process was repeated for another field-point displaced 0.1 μ from the original point at $h = 400\ \mu$. While time did not permit making computations for two points closer than 0.1 μ, it is clear that

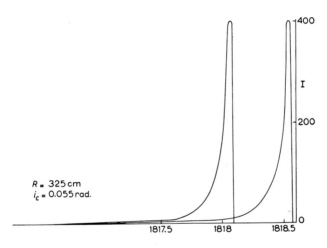

Fig. 7. Intensity *vs.* image field in microns. Object points 0.1 μ apart.

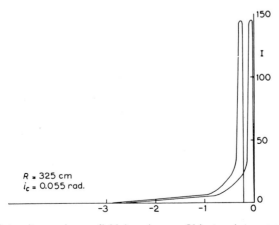

Fig. 8. Intensity *vs.* image field in microns. Object points 0.05 μ apart.

References p. 128

adopting almost any reasonable resolution criterion, the geometrical resolution for this case is much less than 0.1 μ. In the computations leading to Fig. 7 the original point was taken at the center of field $h = 0$ and the displaced point at a distance of 0.05 μ from the center of field.

REFERENCES

[1] P. KIRKPATRICK and A. V. BAEZ, *J. Opt. Soc. Am.*, 38 (1948) 766.
[2] J. DYSON, *Proc. Phys. Soc. (London)*, 65 (1952) 580.
[3] PRESCOTT D. CROUT, *Trans. AIEE*, 60 (1941) 1235, 1240.
[4] J. F. McGEE, in V. E. COSSLETT, A. ENGSTRÖM and H. H. PATTEE, JR., *X-ray Microscopy and Microradiography*, Academic Press, Inc., New York, 1957, p. 164.

NOUVELLES RÉALISATIONS DE MICROSCOPIE X À RÉFLEXION TOTALE

MARC MONTEL

Laboratoire de Chimie Physique de la Faculté des Sciences, Paris (France)

ABSTRACT

NEW X-RAY MICROSCOPIC TECHNIQUES USING TOTAL REFLECTION

A new apparatus and its proposed applications are described. A new method is given for a more accurate calculation of the influence of diffraction on resolving power. The author reports briefly on a study in progress concerning surface defect.

Depuis le Symposium de Cambridge, les recherches sur la déviation des faisceaux par réflexion totale, au Laboratoire de Chimie Physique de la Faculté des Sciences de Paris, ont porté essentiellement dans trois directions:

(1) Réalisation d'un nouveau microscope, basé sur le même principe optique que le précédent, mais mieux adapté à nos recherches.

(2) Étude théorique de l'influence des aberrations — et en particulier de la coma — en présence de diffraction, sur la limite de résolution.

(3) Étude théorique de l'influence des défauts de surface sur la structure de l'image, à partir d'un calcul simple dû à EHRENBERG[1]. Nous allons détailler successivement ces trois points.

L'APPAREIL

Nous ne nous étendrons pas sur la description du nouvel appareil. Il ne comporte, en effet, que des améliorations de détail, telles que, par exemple, le remplacement des commandes manuelles par des micromoteurs qui permettent la télécommande des déplacements et des réglages. La démultiplication des mouvements a été choisie de manière à assurer, avec une meilleure précision que dans le modèle initial, des déplacements linéaires de 20 μ par seconde, qui facilitent les réglages fins. Une partie de ce microscope, englobée dans une maquette de démonstration, a d'ailleurs été présentée à l'Exposition Universelle de Bruxelles en 1958. Ce microscope, mis au point en 1957, n'est revenu du Palais International de la Science que depuis peu, et nous n'avons, par suite, pu en étudier toutes les caractéristiques. Je rappellerai seulement, pour mémoire, que la partie optique se compose d'un prisme en toit à faces latérales sphériques. Le professeur COSSLETT avait eu l'amabilité de nous donner une grille d'argent de 1500 mesh. Cette grille nous a servi à déterminer à nouveau la limite de résolution de notre microscope (Fig. 1); on peut estimer cette limite à 1 μ, comme une méthode plus complexe que nous avions exposée précédemment nous l'avait déjà suggéré[2]. Une autre étude est en cours avec un fil Wollaston. On sait qu'un tel fil est constitué par un fil de platine enrobé d'une gaine d'argent. Le tout est ensuite étiré de manière à obtenir un fil très fin de platine, de quelques μ de diamètre. Malheureusement, les résistances à la traction des deux métaux étant très différentes, il se produit de fréquentes ruptures du fil de platine dans sa gaine, rupture qui, vu le diamètre du fil, est difficilement décelable par radiographie ordinaire. Nous étudions actuellement la possibilité d'un déplacement continu du fil, joint à un enregistrement continu de l'image, mais nous heurtons à de grosses difficultés d'asservissement au grandissement 100 ×.

Un autre problème à l'étude est celui de l'utilisation de l'objectif pour irradiations localisées. Ce problème nous a été posé en particulier, dans le cas de petites tumeurs peu profondes, mais non superficielles, telles que celles de l'œil ou de l'oreille. Il se rencontre d'ailleurs, une difficulté: celle de pouvoir réfléchir un rayonnement assez pénétrant pour franchir les parties surperficielles des organes, sans leur faire subir une dose d'irradiation trop élevée.

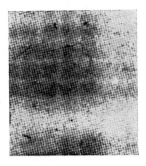

Fig. 1. Photographie d'une grille de 1500 mesh.

ÉTUDE THÉORIQUE DE L'INFLUENCE DES ABERRATIONS

PRINCE[3] avait proposé de prendre pour ouverture optimale du microscope à réflexion totale, celle qui donne des élargissements égaux pour la diffraction et les aberrations, considérées comme indépendantes. Un calcul un peu plus poussé que le sien conduit à une limite de résolution de l'ordre de 3.200 Å avec les valeurs numériques qu'il utilise, pour G = 100 ×. Il semble qu'une telle manière d'opérer conduise à un résultat trop pessimiste (en se plaçant d'un point de vue purement théorique, car d'autres causes viennent modifier la valeur calculée). En effet, qui ne connait certains vieux objectifs photographiques qui, examinés du point de vue des aberrations, ne devraient rien donner de correct, et qui donnent, cependant, des résultats meilleurs que certains objectifs mieux corrigés. Nous pensons que le raisonnement de PRINCE est inexact, car il place sur le même plan, la diffraction et les aberrations. Ces deux quantités sont de nature différente, et ne peuvent, par conséquent, être valablement comparées. Pour faire une étude correcte, il faut utiliser les courbes de répartition de l'énergie dans les images optiques en présence de l'aberration considérée — ici la coma. Nous donnons, sur la Fig. 2, les courbes de MARECHAL[4], qui donne la répartition lumineuse en fonction de la déformation maximale de la surface d'onde, pour divers défauts de mise au point. Dans les courbes reproduites, nous avons supposé ce défaut nul: en effet, vu le champ, l'aberration „courbure" est généralement négligeable. Le calcul montre que la déformation comatique $\triangle$ est de l'ordre de 1 à 2 λ. Cette valeur peut sembler faible, mais il ne faut pas oublier que $\triangle$ varie comme le cube de l'ouverture-image. Les courbes sont tracées en prenant pour

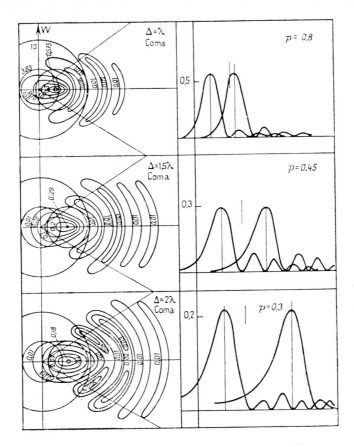

Fig. 2. Courbes de MARECHAL.

échelle, la distance $w = \frac{2\pi}{\lambda} y\alpha$, le premier anneau de la tache d'Airy correspondant à $w = 3{,}83$. Pour utiliser ces courbes, nous allons considérer deux couples, chacun relatif à un point, faire la somme des intensités correspondantes, et prendre comme critère la distance des points qui correspond à une baisse relative d'intensité égale à 0,8 (c'est le critère habituel en diffraction). Quand on compare les résultats, donnés par des points pris dans divers azimuts, on voit que la limite maximale correspond à deux points situés sur l'axe horizontal de la figure. On en a déduit, dans les trois cas, les performances de l'instrument, c'est-à-dire le rapport entre la limite de résolution réelle et la limite donnée par la diffraction. Il reste maintenant à faire une correction sur cette valeur. En effet, les courbes utilisées sont celles de la coma du troisième ordre et nous avons affaire à une coma du second ordre. Une évaluation numérique sur l'exemple 1,5 λ nous a montré qu'il fallait multiplier la valeur trouvée par un facteur sensiblement égal à $\sqrt{G}$, soit, dans notre cas, 10. On trouve donc, pour limite de résolution, 763 Å pour $\triangle = \lambda$, 1.355 Å pour $\triangle = 1{,}5\,\lambda$ et 2.034 Å pour $\triangle = 2\,\lambda$. La valeur de PRINCE correspond sensiblement à un $\triangle$ de 3λ et on voit, sur les courbes, que dans ce cas, on peut en effet négliger les pieds des courbes et considérer les phénomènes comme additifs.

Bibliographie p. 132

Dans le cas d'objets non totalement absorbants, — et c'est généralement le cas pour les fins détails — la méthode ci-dessus n'est plus applicable. Nous avons utilisé la méthode de STEEL[5] qui évalue la perte de contraste de l'image due à l'instrument en fonction des coefficients d'aberration exprimés en longueur d'onde pour une pupille de rayon unité, et de la fréquence spatiale de l'objet — rapport entre sa périodicité et la limite de diffraction pure pour l'ouverture considérée. On trouve, dans ce cas, des valeurs qui peuvent atteindre le micron et même parfois, le dépasser, selon le récepteur utilisé.

ÉTUDE THÉORIQUE DES INFLUENCES DES DÉFAUTS DE SURFACE

Pour terminer, nous signalerons les points suivants à l'étude:

(1) À partir de l'idée d'EHRENBERG[1], nous essayons un calcul plus complet qui permette de connaître la forme de la surface à partir des striations de l'image d'une fente fine. Nous avons en particulier, cherché les conditions de cohérence d'éclairage de la fente. La méthode habituelle, utilisant le tube placé juste derrière la fente ne peut convenir, car l'ouverture du faisceau avant la fente est nettement supérieure à celle utilisée effectivement. On peut y remédier en faisant une première focalisation à l'aide d'un premier miroir, en prenant soin d'étudier l'influence des défauts de ce premier focalisateur et les inégalités de brillance de la tache émettrice de l'anti-cathode. Nous avons calculé également, les largeur et hauteur optimales de la fente pour que la superposition des striations, dues aux différentes tranches de la fente, ne produise pas de recouvrement des stries. On trouve une largeur de $1\,\mu$ et une hauteur angulaire, vue à partir du centre du miroir, de 0,02rd, en assez bon accord avec les valeurs de BUTEUX[6].

(2) Comparaison des résultats obtenus ainsi avec l'expérience, en utilisant l'interférométrie multiple, système TOLANSKY. L'appareil est en cours de montage.

Je rappellerai, enfin, que le Dr. J. DESPUJOLS[7] poursuit ses études sur les cristaux courbes et leurs applications à la focalisation et la monochromatisation des faisceaux X. Ses efforts ont porté principalement sur l'aluminium.

RÉSUMÉ

L'auteur décrit sommairement le nouvel appareil réalisé, ainsi que les applications envisagées. Il décrit une méthode pour calculer avec plus de précision, le rôle de la diffraction sur la limite de résolution. Il mentionne enfin une étude en cours sur les défauts de surface.

BIBLIOGRAPHIE

[1] W. EHRENBERG, *J. Opt. Soc. Am.*, 39 (1949) 741.
[2] M. MONTEL, dans V. E. COSSLETT *et al.*, *X-ray Microscopy and Microradiography*, Academic Press, Inc., New York, 1957. p. 177.
[3] E. PRINCE, *J. Appl. Phys.*, 21 (1950) 698.
[4] A. MARECHAL, *Communs. lab. Inst. Opt.*, 2 (1953) No. 4.
[5] W. H. STEEL, *Thèse*, Paris, 1953.
[6] R. H. BUTEUX, *Thèse* Londres, 1952.
[7] J. DESPUJOLS, *Compt. rend.*, 236 (1953) 282.

F. METALLURGICAL APPLICATIONS

THE APPLICATION OF MICRORADIOGRAPHY IN MINERAL DRESSING

E. COHEN and I. SCHLOEGL

Department of Mineral Dressing, Royal School of Mines, London
(Great Britain)

ABSTRACT

The technique of microradiography developed for the study of thin sections of iron ores and sinters has been further evolved for application to mineral dressing problems. It is used for examination of granular mill products in which assessment of the distribution of values is difficult. Such difficulty may be caused by fine grain size or by lack of visual criteria for distinction between different mineral species. The necessity for recognition and identification of value-bearing constituents generally arises in mineral dressing when difficulties are encountered in maintaining an acceptable grade of concentrate or an economic rate of recovery of values. It is then desirable to assess the degree of liberation of values, as well as the presence or absence of values in certain mill products, and to detect the existence of value-bearing minerals. Examples of such applications of microradiography are presented including studies of lead-zinc sulphide ores, a lead oxide and carbonate ore, a tin-tungsten ore and a finely disseminated pyritic gold ore.

INTRODUCTION

The preparation and concentration of ores is attaining ever increasing importance due to the gradual depletion of high grade deposits and expansion of the use of metals and minerals which are 1are in the earth's crust and occur naturally only in very small concentrations. The mineral dresser is thus concerned with liberating finely disseminated and dispersed minerals from the enclosing barren rock constituents and with concentrating the minority values to grades which are technically and commercially acceptable. To do this efficiently he must be able to control each stage of a process consisting of crushing and grinding, followed by concentration using physical or chemical methods, together with ancillary operations such as sizing or dewatering. In particular, he must have means for assessing the feed, products and wastes of milling operations so that causes of defective treatment may be localised speedily and eliminated.

For this purpose, methods of microscopic inspection have been widely used because of their speed and accuracy in providing mineralogical information that is often not attainable by chemical and other methods. However, microscopic techniques also have their limitations. A stereoscopic microscope is excellent for examining surface features of granular material but it will provide little or no information on internal details of grains. Polarising microscopes will fill this gap to some extent and will also permit very accurate identification of many minerals, but they necessitate elaborate and tedious preparation of mounted specimens. In particular opaque minerals which are important constituents of metalliferous ore deposits are studied in reflected polarised light and specimens have to be cut and polished to high perfection.

References p. 148

The most important defect common to all types of microscopical inspection is the failure to provide reliable evidence of the distribution of heavy metals in samples where the metal content of minerals is variable or in the presence of unknown or unidentifiable carriers of values. This also applies to ores or mill products in which very small particles containing valuable metals are totally enclosed in barren minerals. For example there is great difficulty in the identification of small particles of the lead minerals, anglesite and cerussite, and in distinguishing them from transparent gangue minerals. Another instance is the problem of the occurrence of gold particles a few microns in diameter inside crystals of pyrite or other sulphides. A polished surface will either miss or obliterate them thus preventing recognition of their presence in tailing products as a source of losses.

TECHNIQUES

The above problems are similar in principle to those solved by radiography on a macroscopic scale in other fields and this consideration led to the development of thin section microradiography. The technique was originally evolved for work on iron ores[1-4], other methods having failed to provide the information necessary to assess the exact distribution of iron in certain ores, sinters and slags.

In brief, a specimen of the material, 30 to 50 μ thick, was mounted on a thin cover glass for support. The second surface of the specimen was left bare and placed in contact with the emulsion of an ultra-fine grained photographic plate. X-rays of selected wavelength were then passed through the specimen onto the photographic plate. Differential absorption of the radiation by the various constituent elements of the minerals in the sample resulted in a shadow photograph which could be studied under a microscope with magnifications up to 500 diameters. The X-radiation was selected so as to be absorbed heavily by one particular element in the sample. In the case of iron ores the $K\alpha$ emissions of copper or nickel were used as they lie on the short wavelength side of the absorption edge of iron where absorption by the latter is at its strongest. The distribution of iron in the sample was thus plainly displayed in the radiograph, regardless of the metal's state of combination and independent of the optical properties of the iron-bearing minerals or their location within the sample. Details will be found in the papers quoted above.

The investigations on iron ores were confined to thin sections of solid specimens and, when microradiography was subsequently extended to the study of mill products of other ores, new techniques had to be evolved for dealing with granular materials. Preliminary experiments showed that particles 100 μ in diameter or smaller yield good radiographs without grinding or preparatory treatment other than mounting on a carrier glass. Close sizing of the particles was found to facilitate assessment of the radiographs. A single layer of particles was mounted on a thin cover glass with Canada Balsam. An ordinary slide-glass is not suitable as carrier because of its excessive absorption of X-rays. The absorption by cover glasses is still considerable but does not unduly lengthen exposure times while support for the samples is adequate. With a thermostatically controlled hot plate mounting of the powder is completed within five minutes.

The specimens thus produced have a sufficiently flat upper surface to be mounted without further treatment against the emulsion of the photographic plate. The latter, Kodak M. R. plate, is cut into pieces approximately 1 inch square, and two small pellets

References p. 148

of plasticine are used to secure immobile contact between the plate and the specimen. Contact photographs are necessitated by the fact that the X-rays are emitted from an extended source so that even a small separation between sample and plate would result in obliteration of boundaries and fine detail.

X-rays throughout the work are obtained from a "Raymax 60" unit. The $K\alpha$ emission (1.5418 Å) of a copper target is used, with a target spot 10 × 1 mm, at a potential of 30 kV and tube current of 15 mA. The cassette containing the plate and the specimen is located in an adjustable holder at a fixed distance of 23.5 cm from the tube window to ensure a uniform beam intensity over the whole area of the sample. Exposure time is standardised at 7 min (exceptions will be referred to below) and development time of the plates at $2\frac{1}{2}$ min.

For close comparison the specimen and the radiograph are set up on two microscopes side-by-side. Both are orientated and corresponding positions are located so that each particle can be accounted for to ensure the fullest assessment of all features of the sample. It is invariably noted that the radiograph provides a much clearer impression of locked values (intergrowths of valuable and gangue minerals) visible in the specimen but, in addition, it shows up locked values which are not exposed or visible on particle surfaces and which could not be detected by normal microscopical methods. This is especially valuable when dealing with fine disseminations and inclusions of a material present in very small quantity as is the case with gold in sulphides.

In this context it may be noted that the skill, care and time needed to prepare the grain mount and the radiograph are very much less than would be required to polish specimens for optical work. If minute gold particles are exposed on the surface of a grain they are easily rubbed off or covered with smears of other minerals. In addition, a polished surface shows, at best, the occurrence of gold particles at an arbitrary surface, while the radiograph shows all the gold throughout the sample. The chances of detection and correct diagnosis of small tailings losses is thus greatly enhanced, especially as the lower size limit of resolution of microradiography is the same as that of optical microscopy.

EXAMPLES OF APPLICATION

To illustrate mineral dressing applications of microradiography a number of photomicrographs and radiographs of identical areas on selected specimens have been reproduced. Shortcomings in the photographic technique together with a loss of detail and definition inherent in the methods of reproduction have made these examples appear far less informative than when they are seen by direct microscopic inspection in normal practice. In these reproductions, strongly absorbing grains appear white and weakly absorbing minerals in shades of grey against a black background of non-absorbing material. Some of the thinner grains of low absorption are barely differentiated from the background and any gradual shading of particles, with some particular exceptions, is due to changing thickness.

Materials containing one heavy element

As an example of material containing only one heavy element, a lead concentrate has been selected from the re-treatment of an old tailings dump in Persia. The material has a particle size of less than 74 μ, consisting of fine transparent or translucent

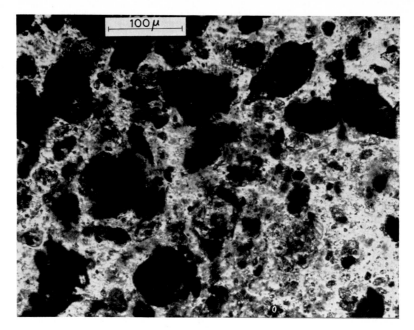

Fig. 1. Photomicrograph. Lead concentrate; tailing dump, Persia.

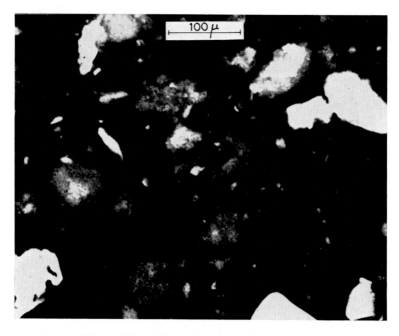

Fig. 2. Microradiograph corresponding to Fig. 1.

References p. 148

mineral grains which are all more or less heavily iron-stained. The valuable constituents are cerussite and mimetite and these are almost indistinguishable from gangue minerals such as calcite and other carbonates, quartz, etc. because of the fine grain size, the iron staining and the general weathered condition of the material. The normal appearance under the microscope is shown in Fig. 1.

Fig. 2 presents a radiograph of approximately the same area. The lead-rich grains stand out very prominently (white), ranging from coarse to very fine sizes. Approximate assaying by particle counting was fairly easy with the radiograph but quite impossible directly on the sample. A large irregular grain near the centre of the field in the photomicrograph appears to be quite uniform.

Reference to Fig. 2 shows that this grain consists of almost equal halves of value and gangue.

Materials containing two or more heavy elements

Presence of more than one heavy element sets some limitations on the diagnostic use of radiographs, but the latter still retain considerable advantages. This is illustrated in Figs. 3 and 4 which show a bulk concentrate of a lead-zinc ore from S.W. Africa. The heavy constituents in this material are the sulphides of lead (galena), zinc (sphalerite) and iron (pyrite). Among the grains shown in the radiograph in Fig. 3 are two typical particles of galena characterised by rectilinear outlines which result from a perfect cubic cleavage. Near the middle of the top edge lies a piece of sphalerite and in the top left-hand corner a grain of pyrite. Absorption intensity of the three minerals appears almost the same, pyrite and sphalerite are not differentiated and galena is distinguished from them only by shape.

Some of the other particles in this field are typical middlings, consisting of gangue minerals with inclusions of sulphides. These could be any or all of the three sulphide minerals named above since galena will not show cleavage faces on unbroken grains enclosed in other minerals. In this particular case direct visual recognition under the microscope is not possible because the inclusions consist of aggregates of very small crystals. A polished specimen would be needed for inspection in reflected light and that would only permit recognition of locked particles which happened to lie in the polished surface.

Figs. 5 and 6 show another area of the same sample. A grain of sphalerite lies in the lower left-hand corner, to the left of a typical cleavage fragment of galena. Near the top margin are two middlings, the one on the right containing discrete crystals of sulphides, the one on the left fine disseminations. Further liberation of the former by grinding appears doutbful but possible, while the latter must be accepted as being locked beyond the possibility of physical treatment. This type of information is provided more readily by radiography than by any other method, particularly with fine disseminations of heavy minerals which are likely to be overlooked by ordinary optical inspection.

Certain mineral species sometimes contain an unwanted heavy element in addition to the valuable metal and this may affect the behaviour of the minerals during concentration as well as lower the assay grade of the final product. Advance knowledge of such association may permit modification of the method of treatment or at least obviate futile efforts to improve a product in which the unwanted metal must be accepted because of its physical or chemical association with the values.

References p. 148

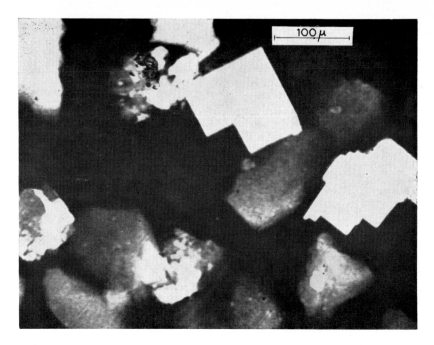

Fig. 3. Microradiograph. Lead-zinc ore; S. W. Africa.

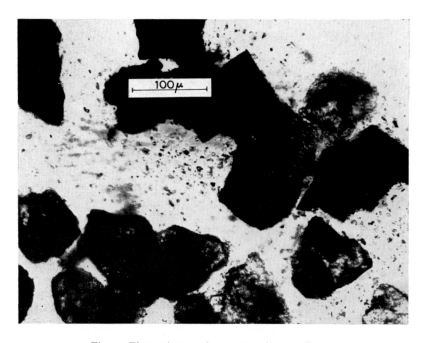

Fig. 4. Photomicrograph corresponding to Fig. 3.

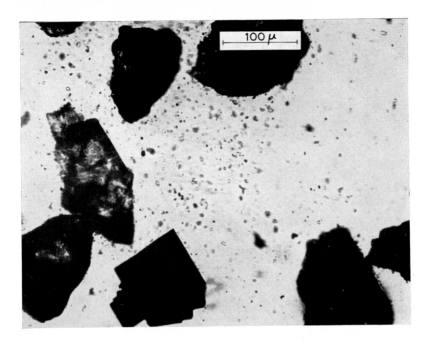

Fig. 5. Photomicrograph of another area of the specimen shown in Figs. 3 and 4.

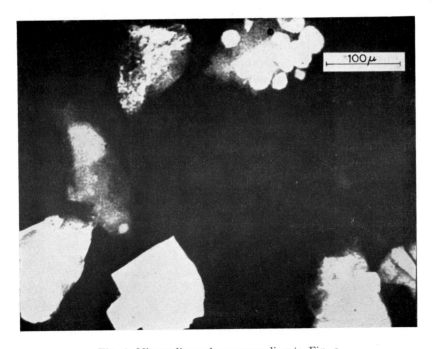

Fig. 6. Microradiograph corresponding to Fig. 5.

References p. 148

This problem is exemplified by two radiographs of a niobium ore from Norway (Figs. 7 and 8). Concentrates of the mineral columbite from this ore showed an unexpectedly high iron content and steps were contemplated to attain a more efficient rejection of iron oxide minerals. However, radiographs showed that the columbite crystals had outer rims rich in iron. The zonal structure may be seen in the rhomb-shaped columbite crystals in Figs. 7 and 8 in which higher absorption of the iron-rich outer zones makes them appear much whiter than the light grey cores. An efficient physical removal of this surplus iron is technically impracticable. The radiographs also show grains of magnetite which illustrate the difference in intensity of absorption.

Iron oxide coatings

Thin coatings of iron oxides on other minerals are a considerable nuisance in mineral dressing. They may occur indiscriminately on gangue and values alike and, by altering the surface properties or density of the coated grain, defeat the separation process. In addition, even very thin coatings are often sufficiently opaque to obscure the identity of their carriers under normal optical inspection. This is the case in Fig. 9 which represents a photomicrograph of a sand tailing from the gravity concentration of a tungsten ore from S.W. Africa. The dark grains are either wolframite or they are quartz and other gangue minerals with iron oxide coatings. It must be admitted that this illustration is less informative than the real sample under a stereoscopic microscope, due to the loss of colour and general surface features of the grains. Nevertheless it was not possible to assess by microscopic inspection whether the grains were of one kind or another. Fig. 10 shows a radiograph of the same area as Fig. 9. Grains of wolframite are white and iron-coated gangue is now almost invisible. An example of the latter kind is the grain marked "X" in Fig. 9. This grain is almost black in Fig. 10. Above it is a locked middling particle of wolframite and gangue with some iron staining, and the topmost grain in this group is almost pure wolframite. Comparison of other grains in the two illustrations yields similar evidence, and reference to Figs. 11 and 12 shows that the same circumstances prevail in the slime tailings. The dark grain near the right end of the upper margin of Fig. 11 is shown by Fig. 12 to be an iron-coated gangue particle. The dark grain on the left consists of wolframite locked with gangue, the whole being coated with iron oxides. Lower down in Fig. 11 a dark cluster appears which is clearly resolved on the radiograph in Fig. 12. It may be deduced that this particular milling operation could bear some improvement, but optical inspection alone does not give a clear picture of the true nature of the tailings losses.

Gold ores

Microradiography is particularly suitable for assessing the occurrence and distribution of gold in ores and in the products of milling operations because of the very high absorption of X-rays by the precious metal compared with most other elements which are normally present in these materials. For example the linear absorption coefficient of gold for copper $K\alpha$ radiation is 4130 while that of most of the associated iron sulphides is less than 1400. With cobalt $K\alpha$ radiation the conditions would be even more favourable since the absorption coefficient of gold is 6220 and that of pyrrhotite, for example, is only 410. However, the cobalt emission is very strongly absorbed by the thin carrier glass and this prevents the attainment of adequate radiographic contrast.

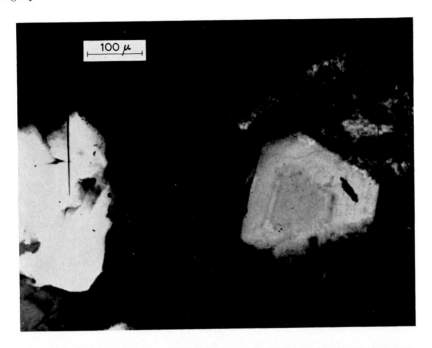

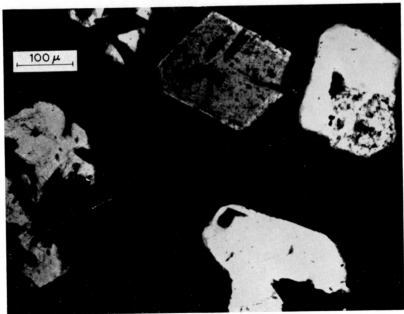

Figs. 7 and 8. Microradiographs of a Columbite ore; Norway.

If the normal exposure time for distinction between heavy and light elements is employed with samples containing light gangue, sulphides and gold, the contrast between gold and sulphides will be small, particularly if the former is present in

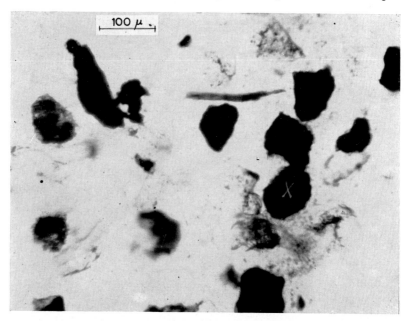

Fig. 9. Photomicrograph. Sand tailing from tungsten ore; S.W. Africa.

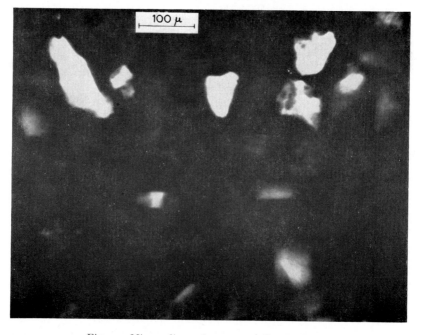

Fig. 10. Microradiograph corresponding to Fig. 9.

small grains and thin flakes while the latter occur in crystals of much larger bulk. Under such conditions photomicrographs taken in transmitted light and radiographs will show great similarity and will appear as negative images of each other.

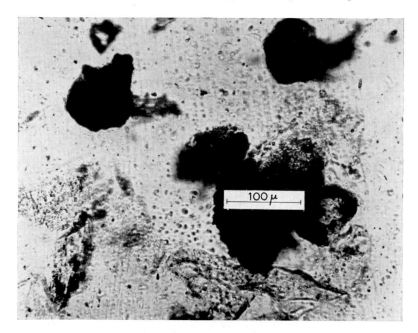

Fig. 11. Photomicrograph. Slime tailings from tungsten ore; S.W. Africa.

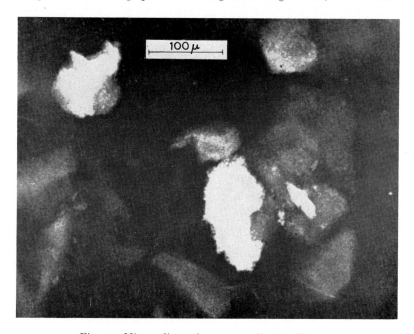

Fig. 12. Microradiograph corresponding to Fig. 11.

A typical example is shown in Figs. 13 and 14, presenting a photomicrograph and corresponding radiograph of the tailings of a gold ore from Tanganyika. The material contains quartz, pyrite and a small amount of gold (0.9 pennyweights per ton).

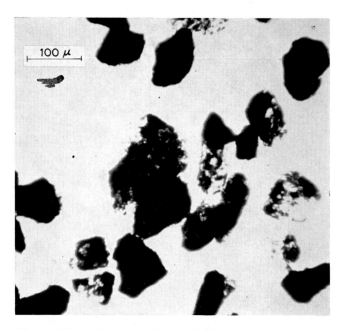

Fig. 13. Photomicrograph. Tailing from gold ore; Tanganyika.

Fig. 14. Microradiograph corresponding to Fig. 13.

Gold is not visible in either of the two illustrations nor can it be seen in the actual sample. Good crystals and fine disseminations of pyrite show up well in the radiograph and the distribution of this mineral is much better appreciated than in the photomicrograph because the latter is considerably obscured by iron staining.

Exposure times of the order of 20 min are necessary for the radiographic distinction between gold and pyrite shown in Fig. 15. Light gangue constituents such as quartz are now invisible, pyrite appears faintly absorbing and small inclusions and

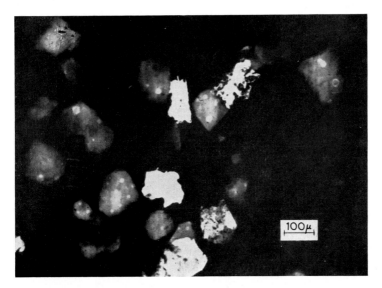

Fig. 15. Microradiograph. Auriferous pyrite concentrate.

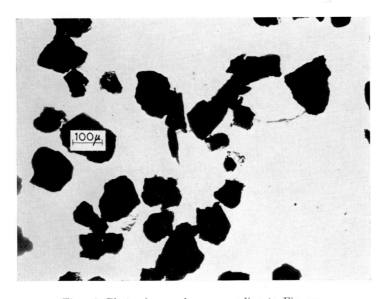

Fig. 16. Photomicrograph corresponding to Fig. 15.

fine disseminations of gold become visible as light markings inside their grey-coloured hosts. Larger particles of gold appear white. Fig. 16 shows a photomicrograph of the same area in transmitted light. Oblique illumination under a stereoscopic microscope provides more information than the photomicrograph in Fig. 16, but photography is difficult under these conditions and, although the surface picture may be clear, fine inclusions and particles below the surface can only be exposed by the radiographic technique.

The distribution of gold shown in Fig. 15 is in fact three-dimensional and this may be further emphasized by comparative presentation of a polished specimen and a corresponding radiograph. For this purpose a polished thin section was used but this technique is not recommended for ordinary routine work because of difficulties in preparation. In order to present the specimen to the X-rays with the same orientation as for reflected light photography, it was necessary to mount the polished surface against the carrier glass. This ruled out normal incident illumination which would have been reflected only by the topmost glass surface. Dark ground illumination, therefore, had to be used, causing the peculiar dark appearance of pyrite particles in Fig. 17. Most of the pyrite grains show light only along boundaries or in spots and lines left on their surfaces by imperfect polishing. The gold particles appear white, *i.e.*, highly reflecting under dark ground illumination, due to their irregular surfaces and the fact that they have been gauged and eroded below the general surface level of the specimen. The rich golden colour of these particles makes them easily recognisable under the microscope. Fig. 18 shows a radiograph of the same area, with pyrite appearing dark grey, and gold white. At first sight it is difficult to correlate the two illustrations because the radiograph shows several particles which are not visible in the photomicrograph, *i.e.* are not at the polished surface. Furthermore all gold particles now show their entire shape compared with their partial areas exposed in Fig. 17. The specimen, with a relative abundance of gold, demonstrates that radiography is capable of accounting for all such particles regardless of their position in the sample. This offers a much better chance than any other method of catching the odd grain or fine disseminations which are often responsible for tailings losses.

CONCLUSIONS

Microradiography offers considerable advantages over other methods in facilitating recognition of fine inclusions and disseminations of heavy elements in mill products. The diagnostic value is limited when more than one heavy element is present. Distinction between heavy elements is possible only in cases where a considerable difference in absorption intensity can be contrived by selection of a suitable radiation. It is unlikely that distinction between different sulphide minerals will ever be possible, but it is relatively simple to obtain excellent contrast between sulphides and gold.

The study of occurrence and losses of gold particles in mill products offers a most promising field for microradiography because of the method's reliability in detecting any small hidden particles of the precious metal. Similar advantages should apply with platinum ores. In fact, the technique deserves consideration in any milling problem where chemical assaying or optical inspection fails to trace the location of heavy metal-bearing minerals which are minority constituents or which are obscured in any way. Optical ambiguities caused by iron oxide coatings are

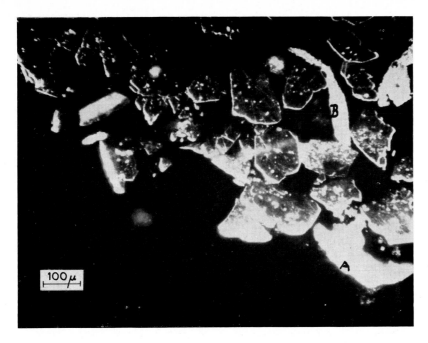

Fig. 17. Photomicrograph. Auriferous pyrite concentrate. Polished section. Dark ground illumination.

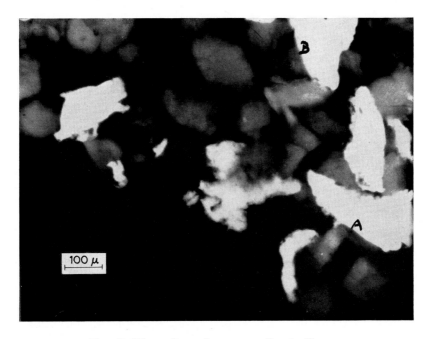

Fig. 18. Microradiograph corresponding to Fig. 17.

readily resolved by microradiography and the method often provides a clearer appreciation of the proportions and distribution of values in a sample than direct microscopic inspection. The technique requires no special skill or training and normally half an hour will suffice for sample preparation, X-ray work and inspection of the radiograph.

ACKNOWLEDGEMENTS

The authors wish to thank their colleagues in the Department of Mineral Dressing at the Royal School of Mines for considerable assistance during the work and in preparing this paper.

REFERENCES

[1] H. KIRCHBERG and H. MOLLER, *Mitt. Kaiser-Wilhelm-Inst. Eisenforsch, Düsseldorf*, 23 (1941) 309.
[2] E. COHEN, *Metallurgia*, 41 (1950) 227.
[3] E. COHEN, The Nature of Silicates and Carbonates of Iron in the Northampton Sand Ironstone of Central England. *Symposium sur les Gisements de Fer du Monde, 19th International Geological Congress, Algiers*, 1952.
[4] E. COHEN, *J. Iron Steel Inst. London*, 175 (1953) 160.

UTILISATION DES RAYONNEMENTS DE FLUORESCENCE EN MICRORADIOGRAPHIE DE CONTACT SES APPLICATIONS EN MINÉRALOGIE ET PÉTROGRAPHIE

S. GOLDSZTAUB et J. SCHMITT

Laboratoire de Minéralogie et Pétrographie, Université de Strasbourg (France)

ABSTRACT

USE OF FLUORESCENCE RADIATION IN CONTACT MICRORADIOGRAPHY
ITS APPLICATION IN MINERALOGY AND PETROGRAPHY

In order to apply a wide range of wavelengths, and appliance was designed consisting of a demountable X-ray tube equipped with interchangeable radiating surfaces, which, like the preparation being examined, are enclosed in vacuum.

Examples of the application of the technique to mineralogical and petrographic problems are presented.

L'objet de cette communication est de décrire l'appareillage de microradiographie de contact par fluorescence que nous avons réalisé et mis au point au Laboratoire de Minéralogie de l'Université de Strasbourg.

Nous nous sommes servis comme source de rayons X primaires d'un tube Beaudouin démontable qui est très répandu en France. Le tube est muni d'une anticathode présentant 4 faces qui, par rotation, peuvent être amenées successivement devant le faisceau d'électrons. On peut recouvrir ces différentes faces d'un dépôt électrolytique de différents métaux et changer ainsi commodément la nature de l'anticathode sans démontage. Ce tube est muni de deux fenêtres en aluminium de 1/100ème de mm d'épaisseur.

Sur les porte-fenêtres de ce tube, nous avons boulonné une pièce représentée sur la Fig. 1 et qui porte trois ouvertures:

une pour faire le vide
une deuxième pour le radiateur de rayons X secondaires
la troisième étant destinée à la chambre porte-objet.

L'objet, constitué par une lame mince, est en général collé sur une rondelle de laiton. Des ressorts appliquent la rondelle contre la plaque photographique disposée sur le porte-plaque qui vient obturer l'orifice de la chambre porte-objet. Des joints en perbunan assurent l'étanchéité de l'ensemble qui est relié au vide primaire du tube à rayons X.

Le vide dans le tube à rayons X est réalisé au moyen d'une pompe à diffusion d'huile Edwards 203, précédée d'une pompe à palettes Beaudouin.

Les radiateurs sont fixés sur des bouchons en aluminium et peuvent être facilement changés.

La Fig. 2 représente une vue de l'appareil.

Grâce à ce système on peut pratiquement exciter la fluorescence de tous les corps simples à l'exception des gaz rares.

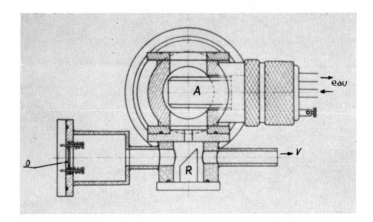

Fig. 1. Dessin du tube à fluorescence. A, anticathode; O, objet; R, radiateur; V, canalisation de vide.

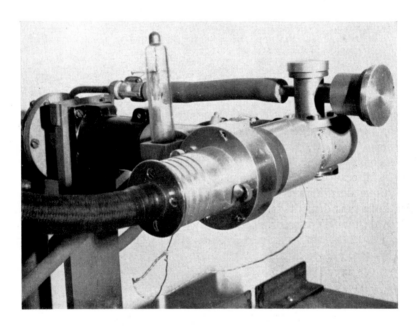

Fig. 2. Vue d'ensemble du tube.

C'est ainsi que nous nous servons couramment du rayonnement du chlore obtenu à partir d'un radiateur formé d'un cristal de chlorure d'ammonium.

La liste des radiateurs réalisés comprend:

Mg, Al, Si, P, S, Cl (ClNa, ClNH$_4$), Ca (Co$_3$Ca), Sc, Ti, V, Cr, Mn, Fe, Co, Cu, Zn, As, Se, Br (BrNH$_4$).

En disposant le porte-objet à la place du radiateur on peut faire des micro-radiographies avec le rayonnement direct du tube. L'ensemble réalisé est destiné à fonctionner avec les rayonnements de longueur d'onde moyenne émis par les éléments dont les numéros sont compris entre 13 et 42.

Une autre installation destinée à produire les rayons X très mous nécessaires aux applications biologiques a été également réalisée. Elle utilise le rayonnement continu d'une anticathode de cuivre. M. Dietrich de l'Institut de Botanique de l'Université de Strasbourg l'utilise et la décrira dans sa communication. Elle permet en particulier de travailler avec des tensions de 800 V.

Nous nous proposons d'utiliser un tube Philips 100 kV, PW 1551 avec anticathode de tungstène pour produire le rayonnement de fluorescence des éléments lourds.

Je n'insisterai pas sur l'intérêt considérable que présente la méthode de microradiographie de contact pour la minéralogie et la pétrographie. Elle permet de mettre en évidence d'une part, les textures invisibles au microscope ordinaire et d'autre part, de déterminer la nature des éléments chimiques qui composent la préparation.

Les photographies suivantes ont été obtenues avec l'ilménite.

Dans certains échantillons d'ilménite (dont la formule théorique est $FeTiO_3$) il y a démixtion de Fe_2O_3 sous forme de minces lamelles d'oligiste. L'ilménite se trouve d'autre part fréquemment associée à la magnétite Fe_3O_4.

La lame de 75 μ d'épaisseur taillée dans une ilménite d'Egersund (Norvège) présente ces particularités.

La photographie (Fig. 3) a été prise avec le rayonnement du cobalt (anticathode Cu 40 kV, 20 mA) temps d'exposition 1 h 30. Le rayonnement de cobalt est plus absorbé par le titane que par le fer. Les parties riches en fer (Fe_2O_3 et Fe_3O_4) sont donc sombres sur la photo.

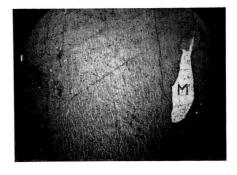

Fig. 3. Microradiographie au rayonnement de Co de l'ilménite. M magnétite (Fe_3O_4). G = 7.5 ×.

Fig. 4. Microradiographie au rayonnement de Ti de l'ilménite. M magnétite. G = 7.5 ×

La deuxième photo (Fig. 4) faite avec la radiation du titane présente un contraste inversé, les parties riches en fer apparaissent en clair.

La méthode utilisée ne permet pas de distinguer Fe_2O_3 de Fe_3O_4, nous avons cependant pu montrer que les plages observées en M étaient magnétiques puisqu'elles attiraient un petit aimant de 2 mm. Elles étaient donc composées de magnétite.

Nous pensons appliquer cette méthode à l'étude de la répartition des alcalins dans les feldspaths.

La photographie (Fig. 5) a été obtenue avec une orthose de 40 μ d'épaisseur et le rayonnement du chlore.

Ces résultats ne constituent que des essais préliminaires. Certainement l'appareillage peut être perfectionné. Il importe d'augmenter l'intensité du rayonnement tout en conservant sa pureté. La fluorescence présente sous ce dernier point un avantage.

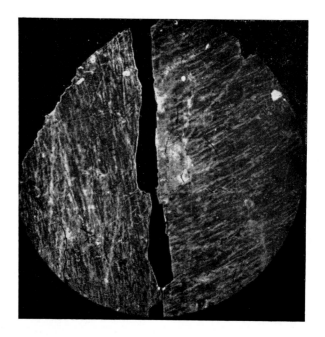

Fig. 5. Microradiographie au rayonnement Cl d'une orthose. G = 10 ×.

Des progrès doivent également être accomplis dans la connaissance des coefficients d'absorption des différents éléments pour les longueurs d'ondes des éléments légers Na–Ca.

Dans la limite de son emploi, la sonde de CASTAING permettant de déterminer la longueur d'onde d'émission pourrait constituer un moyen de contrôle rapide des coefficients d'absorption.

RÉSUMÉ

Afin de pouvoir utiliser une gamme étendue de longueurs d'ondes, on a réalisé un dispositif comprenant un tube à rayons X démontable muni de radiateurs interchangeables contenus, ainsi que la préparation, dans une enceinte évacuée.

Quelques applications à des problèmes de minéralogie et de pétrographie sont indiqués.

PROJECTION MICRORADIOGRAPHY OF METALS

A. W. RUFF, JR. and L. M. KUSHNER

Metal Physics Section, National Bureau of Standards, Washington, D.C. (U.S.A.)

ABSTRACT

The application of projection microradiography to the examination of a number of metallurgical specimens is described. Radiographs of iron dendrites in magnesium and of carbon flakes in a gray cast iron are shown. Particular emphasis is placed on the examination of alloys of copper in aluminum. Constitutional segregation and the dendritic growth process are clearly evident in radiographs of these alloys. In overaged specimens, precipitation results in the formation of needle-like $CuAl_2$ particles showing local orientation. Radiographs showing grain boundary precipitation and the effects of different ageing treatments are presented.

INTRODUCTION

The recent development, utilizing focussed electron beams, of "point" X-ray sources having dimensions of the order of 1—10 μ has stimulated considerable interest in projection microradiography[1]. The most important feature of this technique is that it permits the examination of the internal structure of small volumes of opaque specimens with primary magnifications of the order of several hundreds. The point-projection technique involves reasonably simple sample preparation and operating procedures as compared with X-ray contact microradiography. It has the advantages over electron-microscopy of greater sample penetration and of specimen location external to the vacuum system. In resolving power however, it falls far short of that attainable with the electron microscope.

To date, most of the applications of projection X-radiography to structure studies have concerned biological materials. Very few have dealt with metals[2,3]. This paper presents the results of examinations of a number of alloys using projection microradiography. In particular, some aluminum–copper alloy specimens were examined with the objective of observing decorated dislocations in well-annealed single crystal samples.

Other investigations[4–6] on well-annealed pure aluminum and dilute aluminum alloy crystals indicate a mean dislocation spacing of about 3 to 10 μ in such crystals. Projection microradiography with a resolution of about 1 μ should then be a satisfactory observational technique if the dislocations can be properly decorated. Using electron microscopy, WILSDORF and KUHLMANN-WILSDORF[7] have shown that during the decomposition of dilute aluminum–copper solid solutions, selective nucleation of the θ-phase occurs along dislocations. It was hoped in this work that by proper thermal treatments, the further development of the θ-phase particles would result in a decorated dislocation network whose form and extent in the crystals could be studied by projection microradiography.

Although a number of interesting features of the θ-phase particles have been observed, it has not yet been possible to relate them to the dislocation structure of the crystals. Nevertheless because of the aforementioned recent interest in projection microradiography and because of the lack of literature on the application of the technique to metals, it is desirable to present, at this time, an account of this work.

EXPERIMENTAL

A. *Description of instrument*

A number of descriptions of instruments for projection microradiography have appeared in the literature[8],[9]. The instrument used for this work was a commercial model whose electron optical system embodies the use of electrostatic lenses[10]. Accelerating voltages of 15—20 kV with beam currents of 30—40 μA were ordinarily used. The electron beam is focussed as a spot nominally 1 μ in diameter on a thin tungsten target. The resulting X-rays emerge from the vacuum chamber through a beryllium window which is also the mechanical support for the tungsten film. A platinum plate containing aperture holes 1, 0.5, 0.25 and 0.10 mm in diameter is included between the condenser and objective lens. Use of the smaller apertures results in a more precisely defined electron spot by reducing the effects of lens aberrations and hence one obtains more nearly a "point" source of X-rays. However, this is accompanied by a decrease in the beam intensity. It was found that for the work reported here, the 0.5 mm aperture gave adequate definition coupled with convenient exposure times.

External to the vacuum system, the divergent beam of X-rays passes through the specimen and casts a magnified shadow image on a photographic film. The source-specimen-film geometry is shown in Fig. 1.

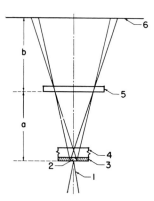

Fig. 1. Source-specimen-film geometry; (1) incident electron beam; (2) X-ray source volume; (3) tungsten film; (4) beryllium window of vacuum chamber; (5) specimen; (6) film.

The X-ray source size is actually somewhat larger than the electron beam spot because of the penetration and subsequent scattering of the electrons in the target material. In the case of a tungsten target and electrons accelerated by 20 kV, an X-ray source approximately 2 μ in diameter should result from an electron beam spot 1 μ in diameter[11]. The best resolution which was obtained with the instrument is consistent with a source size of 1—2 μ.

References p. 161

The specimen holder allows translation of the specimen in three mutually perpendicular directions. Two are in the plane normal to the beam axis so that the specimen can be scanned or precisely translated for taking stereo-pairs of exposures. Movement in the third direction results in a change in magnification in accordance with the simple relationship $M = (b + a)/a$. The resolving power of this instrument is determined primarily by the source size. Diffraction effects become important only for much smaller sources. Letting S be the source diameter, the penumbral blur of the image on the film plane is $S^* = S(M-1)$. Thus with a 1-μ source, one would not expect to resolve two objects in the specimen which were closer together than 1μ. This neglects the problem of obtaining sufficient contrast for resolution.

B. *Sample preparation*

Most of the work herein reported was done with aluminum–copper alloys prepared from aluminum and copper of 99.995 and 99.8 % purity, respectively. Compositions are given as weight per cent of copper in aluminum. Ingots of $4\frac{1}{2}$ % Al–Cu and $3\frac{1}{2}$ % Al–Cu alloys were prepared by vacuum fusion. In order to obtain large grained samples, they were subsequently remelted in pointed carbon crucibles and permitted to solidify as the crucible was lowered slowly through a temperature gradient. In both cases dendritic growth occurred resulting in copper-enriched inter-dendritic regions and numerous internal cavities.

The half-thickness of aluminum for X-radiation of wavelength 0.7 Å, a figure which approximates the peak intensity wavelength of the continuous tungsten spectrum obtained, is about 0.5 mm. In order to obtain wafers of the $3\frac{1}{2}$ and $4\frac{1}{2}$ % Al–Cu alloys of this thickness, the cylindrical ingots were cut transversely using an abrasive wheel. The sections were then repeatedly polished and etched to remove most of the cold worked material. The final polish with 400 grit paper left scratches which were not observed in the subsequent X-ray micrographs. The wafers were then given appropriate thermal treatments as described under RESULTS.

A 2 % Al–Cu alloy was prepared in air in an induction furnace and then remelted in vacuum. In order to obtain large single-crystal regions, the strain–anneal method was used. The alloy rod was rolled to a sheet 0.5 mm thick, with numerous annealing treatments during the reduction. The annealed sheet was cut into strips which were then strained 1—3 % and annealed at 530° C for 2—6 h. This treatment produced numerous grains with diameters of 3—5 mm. The geometry of the target plate limits the sample size to a 3 mm diameter when the maximum magnifications are desired, so there was no need to produce larger grains. The problem of removing these grains from the strips without severely working the material was solved by coating the strips with beeswax, scribing lines through the wax around the desired grain, and immersing the strip in aqua-regia. The grain would drop out after etching at room temperature had proceeded about 1 h. It was then cleaned and given the desired thermal treatments. To avoid distorting them, no surface polishing was employed with these grains and hence occasionally the etched surface features could be observed in the X-ray micrographs.

All of the heat treatments were carried out in a ceramic dish, in contact with the atmosphere, inside a tubular furnace. The temperatures given are probably accurate to $\pm 2°$ C. In all cases, the samples were allowed to cool in the furnace from the solution-treatment temperature to the ageing temperature. This took about ten minutes in a typical case. At the end of the ageing period, the samples were removed from the furnace and allowed to air-cool to room temperature.

C. *Procedures*

After the thermal treatments were completed, the samples were mounted on the specimen holder of the X-ray projection microscope. Small samples could be brought into contact with the target plate giving a maximum magnification of about × 200. If the largest lateral sample dimension exceeded 3 mm, the maximum magnification obtainable was about × 40. A fixed film-to-source distance of 35 mm was chosen which resulted in exposure times of the order of 10—20 min. While the contrast obtained was usually satisfactory, for purposes of reproduction in this paper, the negatives were copied once and then printed with dodging. This technique improves the contrast somewhat and results in heavily absorbing regions appearing white in the accompanying photographs. The film used was Eastman Kodak Contrast Process Ortho which permits secondary enlargements up to × 5. The negatives were generally overdeveloped to enhance the contrast.

Magnifications can be estimated in two ways. One can measure the shift on the film of some feature in the specimen when the specimen is translated a known distance, or, alternately, a standard grid (1000 mesh) can be placed on top of the specimen and an exposure taken. One must then correct for the sample thickness. Clearly, for any finite specimen thickness, the magnification of an object within a specimen depends on the object's position *i.e.* its vertical distance from the source. The effect is particularly important at high magnifications when the specimen is close to the source. The magnifications indicated are estimates for an object situated halfway through the specimen.

When stereo-viewing was desired, two exposures were made between which the specimen was translated a known distance. The distance it was translated depended on the magnification being used and on the stereo-angle desired.

RESULTS

A. *High contrast specimens*

Figs. 2 and 3 represent extreme cases of the two situations which give rise to contrast in X-ray micrographs; heavy particles in a light matrix and light particles in a heavily absorbing matrix. In Fig. 2 are shown dendritic particles of iron in a magnesium matrix. The magnesium had been melted in an iron crucible at 1000° C. On cooling, dissolved iron was precipitated yielding the structure shown. Detailed analysis of contact microradiographs[12] indicates that the dendrites grew in the dodecahedral directions leading to a three-dimensional figure with twelve radial spokes. Where projections of more than one spoke are superimposed on the film plane, this is evident by a different X-ray absorption suggesting a different apparent spoke thickness. The mass-absorption coefficients of iron and magnesium for 0.710 Å X-radiation are 38.5 and 4.30 respectively.

Fig. 3 is a projection radiograph through a 0.001 inch thick specimen of polycrystalline gray cast iron. The dark areas are carbon. The mass-absorption coefficients of carbon and iron for 0.710 Å X-radiation are 0.598 and 38.5 respectively. From stereo-viewing, it is evident that the carbon particles are flakes. Excellent contrast is

References p. 161

obtained in this photograph because of the extreme thinness of the specimen and relatively thick carbon particles.

Fig. 2. Iron dendrites in magnesium.

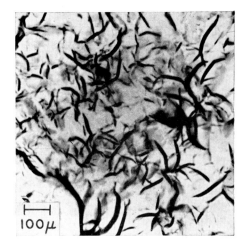

Fig. 3. Gray cast iron. Dark flakes are carbon. Sample thickness 0.001 inch.

B. *Aluminum–copper alloys*

Fig. 4a is a radiograph through a thin section of a $4\frac{1}{2}$ % Al–Cu alloy. The specimen was in the as-grown condition showing large grains and a dendritic structure. The white network in the photograph is the copper-rich interdendritic region which was the last material to solidify. The network of fine dark lines is believed to be a network of voids created in the interdendritic region as the last of the molten material solidified.

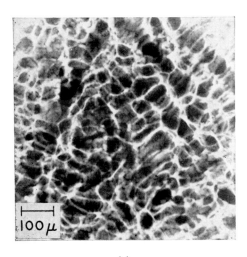

(a)

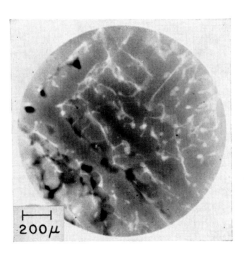

(b)

Fig. 4. Sections of as-grown Al–Cu polycrystals. (a) $4\frac{1}{2}$ % copper; (b) $3\frac{1}{2}$ % copper. Light areas are copper-rich regions.

References p. 161

Fig. 4b shows a $3\frac{1}{2}$ % Al–Cu sample in the as-grown condition. In this case too, there is a dendritic structure with crystallographic coherence over large regions. The dark regions are voids. Differences between Fig. 4a and 4b can be attributed not only to the difference in copper concentration but also to slightly different growth conditions. After the $3\frac{1}{2}$ % Al–Cu specimen was solution-treated for 11 days at 530° C, all of the copper-rich interdendritic material had dissolved leaving a specimen of uniform X-ray absorption.

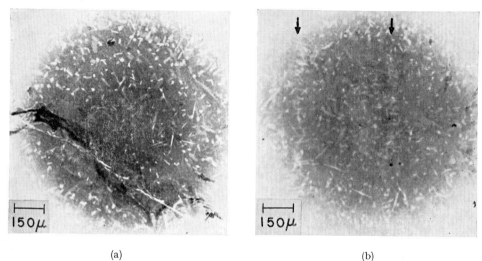

(a)   (b)

Fig. 5. Sections of over-aged $3\frac{1}{2}$ % Al–Cu polycrystals, aged 90 h at 441° C. (a) Dark region is a large cavity; (b) arrows indicate two lines of precipitate particles.

The sample shown in Fig. 5a was cut from a solution-treated $3\frac{1}{2}$ % Al–Cu block using an abrasive wheel and then mechanically polished down to 0.020 inch. It was solution-treated for 16 h at 532° C, cooled in the furnace in 15 min to 441° C and aged at that temperature for 90 h. At equilibrium, the composition of the precipitate is approximately $CuAl_2$ for which the mass-absorption coefficient is about 29.4 as compared to 6.2 for the matrix material. The predominant form of the large precipitate particles which are not associated with macroscopic faults, is needle-like. Some are plates. The shape of the smaller particles, even when examined in stereo is uncertain. Dark regions are once again cavities. Running diagonally across the lower portion of the figure is a white line illustrating the enhanced precipitation which is associated with gross faults in the crystal. A small, nearly circular, region in the upper part of the illustration, which represents a void, is seen to be delineated by precipitate. An interesting feature, evident upon close inspection, is the existence of irregularly curved needle-like particles. In Fig. 5b are shown two "lines" of particles running vertically. Each line of particles appears to be associated with a surface running through the crystal. From examination of stereo-pairs of radiographs, it is evident that the precipitate particles do not extend through the entire thickness of the specimen although the surfaces they are on may do so. As will be seen in subsequent figures, the precipitation that had occurred on these surfaces is not suggestive of that on large angle boundaries.

References p. 161

Fig. 6a is of a 2 % Al–Cu specimen cut from a strain-annealed strip 0.020 inches thick using the acid technique. The specimen was solution-treated for 7 h at 532° C and then furnace-cooled to 372° C in 12 min at which temperature it was permitted

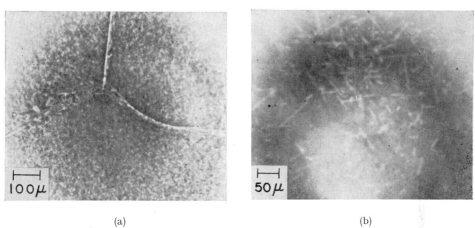

(a)   (b)

Fig. 6. Strain-annealed 2 % Al–Cu specimen. (a) Aged 72 h at 372° C, three-grain region; (b) aged 136 h at 392° C. Note alignment of precipitates. Single-grain region.

to age for 72 h. This treatment resulted in a high density of small particles. Their indistinct nature is taken as indicating that the diffusion process involved in the particle growth had not been completed. Advanced precipitation on the grain boundaries is evident. Neither in this nor other photographs that have been obtained is there any significant change in the character or density of boundary precipitate particles as a function of the boundary angle. When the ageing temperature is higher, 392° C, and the time longer, 136 h, the structure shown in Fig. 6b results. It is characterized by a low density of large, well formed particles. There are regions in the specimen (*i.e.* the upper part of the photograph) in which particle alignment is quite apparent. Such alignment is common in a number of alloys[13]. In age-hardened copper–aluminum alloys, however, the form of the individual particles is a platelet rather than a rod as observed in these over-aged alloys.

In Fig. 7 is shown a stereo-pair of radiographs of a specimen aged for 136 h at 392° C. The grain boundary precipitation is the striking feature. Over-ageing has resulted in the formation of very large particles in the grain boundaries and the virtual absence of any precipitate in a region, estimated to be approximately 48 μ thick, on either side of the boundary. The extent of this region agrees quite well with the mean diffusing distance of copper in aluminum as calculated for these ageing conditions. Some of the structures observed suggest that the large plates found in the boundary are formed from an originally ring-like array of particles by filling in the center.

In order to assess the effect of deformation on the morphology of the over-aged precipitate, the following experiment was performed. A specimen of the 2 % Al–Cu alloy, 0.018 inches thick, was prepared as previously described and solution-treated for 21 h at 525° C. The sample was removed from the furnace, air-cooled to room temperature and three hemispherical indentations, 28, 56, and 74 μ in depth, were made in it. The indenting operations took approximately 15 sec. The sample was then reinserted in the furnace at 525° C and immediately furnace-cooled to 393° C. It was permitted to age 95 h at this temperature. Around each of the indentations, recrystallization occurred. Fig. 8a shows a photomicrograph of the polished and etched

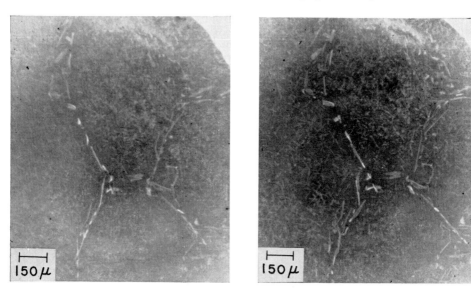

Fig. 7. 2 % Al–Cu strain-annealed specimen. Stereo-pair of radiographs shows advanced precipitation on grain boundaries.

surface surrounding the deepest indentation. Fig. 8b is a microradiograph of the same portion of the specimen. In both, the indented region is evident. In the photomicrograph, etching brings out the new grain. In the radiograph one sees the very large precipitates which have been formed on the surface of the new grain. By the

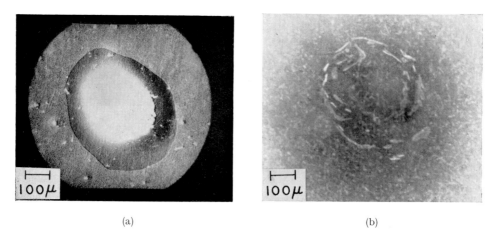

(a)   (b)

Fig. 8. Single-grain region of strain-annealed 2 % Al–Cu specimen. Surface indented prior to ageing at 393° C for 95 h. (a) Surface micrograph of indent and new grain after etching. (b) X-ray micrograph of same area.

Laue back-reflection method it was determined that the misorientation between the parent grain and the new one was large. The particles inside the new grain and those in the grain surrounding it show a tendency similar to that illustrated in Fig. 6b to lie in certain directions. It is not possible to determine these directions solely from the X-ray micrographs, since a distortion in the angular relationships results from this technique. One sample which exhibited this alignment of precipitate particles was mechanically polished so that the surface was within about 2° of {111}. Subsequent etching revealed a number of needle-like precipitates lying in the surface. These particles exhibited three preferred directions which corresponded to the <112> directions in that surface. The same sample was then polished to within about 3° of a {110} surface and etched. In this orientation there are two <112> directions in the surface, and a number of the particles revealed had these directions.

The conclusion from this work is that those particles which exhibit alignment lie in the <112> directions. However, in the same sample, certain regions contain needle-like precipitates which do not appear to lie in a discrete set of directions.

Two possibilities arise when attempting to explain the choice of growth directions. First the dislocation structure of the crystal may determine the shape and orientation of the precipitate particles. Alternatively the surface and strain interactions between the precipitate and the matrix may be most significant. Although we feel dislocations are involved in the nucleation process, we favor the second possibility for the particle growth. However, the details of the effect of the matrix on the growth process are not well understood.

C. *Kossel lines*

Kossel lines were occasionally observed in some of the radiographs obtained. The origin and utility of these lines have been discussed by other authors[14] and need not be gone into here. Nevertheless, they may be an important feature of future investigations utilizing projection microradiography.

REFERENCES

1 V. E. COSSLETT, A. ENGSTRÖM and H. H. PATTEE JR., *X-ray Microscopy and Microradiography*, Academic Press, Inc., New York, 1957.
2 C. K. JACKSON, *Ibid.*, p. 623.
3 F. W. VON BATCHELDER, *Trans. AIME*, 212 (1958) 798.
4 T. S. NOGGLE and J. S. KOEHLER, *Acta Met.*, 3 (1955) 260.
5 T. SUZUKI and T. IMURA, *Report of the Conference on Defects in Crystalline Solids, University of Bristol, 1954*, The Physical Society, London, 1955, p. 347.
6 G. K. WILLIAMSON and R. E. SMALLMAN, *Phil. Mag.*, 1 (1956) 34.
7 H. WILSDORF and D. KUHLMANN-WILSDORF, *Report of the Conference on Defects in Crystalline Solids, University of Bristol, 1954*, The Physical Society, London, 1955, p. 175.
8 P. KIRKPATRICK and H. H. PATTEE JR., in *Handbuch der Physik*, Vol. 30, Springer Verl., Berlin-Wien-München, 1957, p. 305.
9 W. C. NIXON, in V. E. COSSLETT, A. ENGSTRÖM and H. H. PATTEE JR., *X-ray Microscopy and Microradiography*, Academic Press, Inc., New York, 1957, p. 34.
10 S. P. NEWBERRY and S. E. SUMMERS, *ibid.*, p. 116.
11 L. L. MARTON, *Natl. Bur. Standards (U.S.) Circ. 527, Electron Physics*, (1954) 265.
12 H. C. BURNETT JR. and H. C. VACHER, *J. Research NBS*, 44 (1950) 443.
13 R. F. MEHL, C. S. BARRETT and F. N. RHINES, *Trans. AIME*, 99 (1932) 203.
14 T. IMURA, *Bull. Univ. Osaka Prefect. Ser. A*, 5 (1957) 99.

X-RAY MICROSCOPIC STUDY OF ZIRCONIUM AND ITS ALLOYS

GUNJI SHINODA, YOSHITSUGU AMANO, TERUICHI TOMURA and RYUICHI SHIMIZU

Faculty of Engineering, Osaka University, Higashinoda, Osaka (Japan)

ABSTRACT

We have constructed an X-ray microscope of the point-projection type having two electromagnetic lenses. The focus of the electron beam was about $1\ \mu$ in diameter. In the microradiograph of a recrystallized foil, the different crystals are visible because the path of the diffracted rays in the foil varies from crystal to crystal. From the observation of the photographic densities corresponding to each crystal, certain regularities in orientation of the crystal grains in recrystallized specimens were found.

The X-ray microscope used is, as already reported[1], an ordinary two magnetic lens type, but the high voltage source has been improved. In the circuit no special parts were used. As a high voltage coil we used a fly-back coil from a television receiving set. The D.C. source is stabilized by a feed-back circuit using a differential amplifier.

X-RAY MICROSCOPIC STUDY OF A WELDED PORTION OF ZIRCONIUM METAL*

Although our X-ray microscope has two lenses, we used only the objective lens, because as shown in Fig. 1 it gave sufficiently good definition. Fig. 1 is a photograph

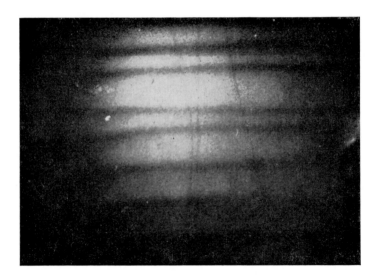

Fig. 1. Projection microradiograph of silver wire (0.08 mm dia.) and tungsten wire (0.02 mm dia.). × 56.

* Kindly supplied by Nippon Kinzoku-Kogyo Co. Ltd.

References p. 168

of a silver wire and a tungsten wire, whose diameters were 0.08 mm and 0.02 mm. The anticathode was copper foil 0.02 mm thick.

A plate of the Reactor-grade zirconium was bent and the seam was arc-welded in an argon atmosphere, so as to form a tube. Studies were made of the bead of (a) the welded zone, (b) the zone affected by heat and (c) the zone which was not affected by heat due to welding (base metal).

The samples were cut and etched by hydrofluoric acid to 0.02 mm thickness. Fig. 2 is the X-ray micrograph, white and black patterns of the type shown by VOTAVA et al.[2] being obtained. The boundaries of black and white spots, which corre-

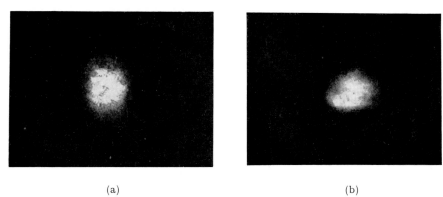

(a)   (b)

Fig. 2. Projection microradiograph of welded Zirconium. × 36. (a) Welded portion; (b) Base metal.

spond to individual grains, are sharp in the welded portion. The grain size is somewhat larger in the welded portion than in the base metal, but the difference is not great. Usually the size lies between 80 and 100 μ.

For comparison an ordinary optical microscopic study was made (Fig. 3). The bead in the welded portion shows acicular structure, but, as in dendrites of cast metals, these groups of acicular needles correspond to a single grain, the size of which nearly coincided with that determined by X-ray microscopic study. The base metal shows rather fine grains, though their boundaries are not so clear.

Therefore we must conclude that the several small grains discriminated by optical microscopy form a crystalline aggregate and this appears as one grain in the X-ray microscope. Thus the orientation of these crystallites may be nearly the same. But the diffuseness of the boundaries of grains may indicate that the orientation of each crystallite is not quite the same, as is shown in the X-ray micrograph. This suggests some kind of internal strain due to cold working of the base metal (Zirconium plate).

X-RAY DIFFRACTOMETRIC STUDY

Fig. 4 shows the diffractograms for each region. The diffractometer used was designed in our laboratory and constructed by Shimazu Seisakusho, Ltd., Kyoto.

In the base metal plate, in addition to the preferred orientation we can observe broadening of the lines. This is especially noticeable in the (112) and (201) lines, as these lines correspond to diffraction at large glancing angles. The lines due to the

(a)

(b)

Fig. 3. Microstructures of welded Zirconium, etched by 5 % hydrofluoric acid. (a) Welded portion, × 180; (b) Welded portion, × 84;

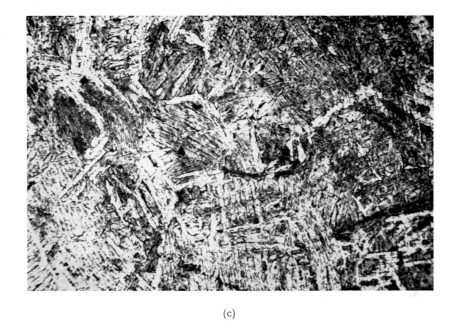

(c)

(d)

Fig. 3. (c) Heat-affected portion, × 180; (d) Base metal, × 180.

beads of the welded portion are quite sharp. Therefore we cannot expect any internal strains, and the grain boundaries should be clear in the X-ray micrograph.

On the contrary, as there is much internal strain in the base metal, the crystal-

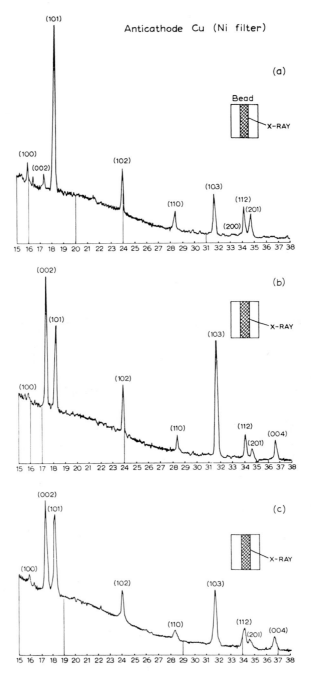

Fig. 4. Diffractogram of welded Zirconium: (a) bead; (b) heat-affected zone; (c) unaffected zone.

(a)   (b)

Fig. 5. Transmission Laue photograph of welded Zirconium, Mo radiation (a) Welded portion;
(b) Base metal.

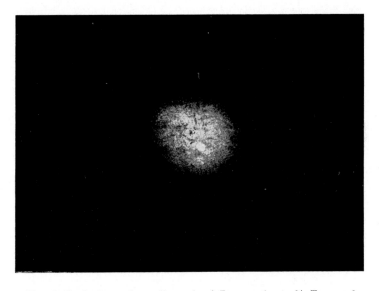

Fig. 6. Projection microradiograph of Zr – 0.016 wt. % Te. × 36.

lites which form a grain have nearly the same orientations, but they are not exactly the same. This will be the effect of cold rolling, and the boundaries become indistinct. The diffractogram for this region shows increased intensity of the (002) line, showing that the grains have hexagonal axes which nearly coincide with the normal to the plate.

Fig. 5 is a transmission Laue photograph. For the bead, crystal orientations are

References p. 168

at random, but for the base metal somewhat regular orientations about the axis perpendicular to the plate are indicated. But judging from the photograph, the regularities in the crystallites due to cold work are not so pronounced as in cold rolled zinc or cadmium. Also the initial orientation of each crystal grain is not so much influenced by cold working.

Figs. 6 and 7 are X-ray and optical microphotographs of Zr – 0.016% Te alloys, an oxidation-resistant alloy*. Thin needles of about 50μ in breadth can be seen, which are compounds of Zr and Te.

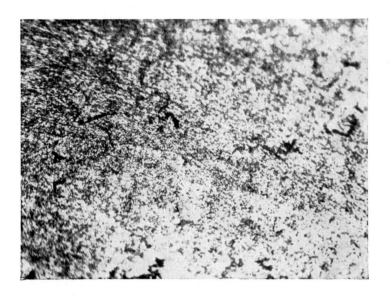

Fig. 7. Microstructure of Zr – 0.016 wt. % Te. × 180.

REFERENCES

[1] Y. Kato, S. Yamanaka and G. Shinoda, *Technol. Repts. Osaka University*, 3, No. 56 (1953).
[2] E. Votava, A. Berghezan and R. H. Gillette, in *X-ray Microscopy and Microradiography*, Academic Press, Inc., New York, 1957, p. 603.

* Kindly supplied by Professor T. Sano, Nuclear Engineering Department.

G. BIOLOGICAL APPLICATIONS — 1. HARD TISSUES

THE PREPARATION OF PLANE PARALLEL SECTIONS OF DESIRED THICKNESS OF MINERALIZED TISSUES

OLLE HALLÉN and HANS RÖCKERT

Department of Histology and Department of Otolaryngology, University of Gothenburg (Sweden)

ABSTRACT

By utilizing principles of modern mechanical ultra-precision work, a method has been designed for producing plane parallel sections of mineralized tissues under continuous thickness control.

The method comprises the following main procedure. Embedded tissue is sawn into slices about 1.5 mm thick. By grinding and lapping, one of the surfaces is given a very good planarity and surface finish. This surface is glued on one of the end surfaces of a cylindrical steel fixture. The free surface of the specimen is then ground by hand against a conventional grinding wheel down to a thickness of 1 mm. The same surface is then ground against a rotating grinding disc. By means of a V-block, the fixture with the specimen is adjusted perpendicular to the grinding plane. As there is very little vibration in the rotating disc, this step allows grinding down to the desired thickness.

Finally the fixture with the specimen is placed between two plane parallel surfaces, and the free surface of the specimen is lapped plane parallel to its bottom surface.

With this method it is possible to obtain sections thinner than 10 μ.

INTRODUCTION

Several quantitative methods with high resolution for cytochemical analysis of mineralized tissues have been developed during the last decade, *e.g.* X-ray microscopy, autoradiography and interference microscopy. Investigations with the aid of these methods have already given valuable information about such tissues. Increasing sensitivity of the methods makes great demands upon the preparation of the specimens. In order to obtain information about absolute amounts of certain substances, the thickness of the specimen has to be known very accurately. Some of the analytical methods requires for optimum conditions thin sections within the region of 5—20 μ. Consequently the preparation of mineralized specimens is very important.

Several attempts have been made in order to develop ideal methods for the preparation of mineralized tissues. Essentially two methods have been followed: (1) sections were prepared by sawing with the aid of thin saw-blades[1-7]; (2) a grinding technique was used[8-13]. Some authors described methods where both methods are combined[14-20].

The first of these methods has been improved by replacing the saw-blades by very thin wheels covered with carborundum or diamond particles. Consequently the loss of material has been reduced considerably. With this method it has been possible to produce sections in routine work with a thickness of about 100 μ. The main disadvantages of these methods are that they do not give plane parallel sections and that thinner sections than 100 μ can only be prepared by chance, and their surface finish will be bad.

The grinding methods are essentially carried out in three different ways: (1) grinding by hand against a fixed grinding surface, (2) grinding by hand against a rotating grinding surface and (3) grinding against a rotating grinding surface with the specimen mounted on a fixture. Apart from varying grinding speed, treatment of the material is the same in all these variations, therefore the results are comparable. The grinding methods allow a routine preparation of sections with a thickness of about 100 μ. A skilled operator might prepare sections considerably thinner. The main disadvantages of these methods are that they do not give plane parallel sections and that by preparing sections thinner than 100 μ, many of them will be lost.

All methods at present used make the sections more or less wedge shaped. Hence thickness determination must either be carried out at the areas to be analyzed in the section, or a complete topographical mapping of the entire section will be necessary. Both ways are difficult, time-consuming and introduce errors. Thus the ideal solution would be to prepare plane parallel sections.

OWN METHOD

By applying the principles which are used in ultra-precision work in mechanical industry, a new method has been developed for preparing plane parallel sections. The method consists of the following steps.
1. Embedding and coarse cutting.
2. Plane preparation of one surface of the specimen.
3. Mounting on fixture.
4. Grinding to thickness region 1000 μ.
5. Grinding to desired thickness.
6. Plane parallel lapping.
7. Final thickness control and demounting from fixture.

1. *Embedding and coarse cutting*

In order to possess all the qualifications for good cutting results, an ideal embedding material must have good penetrating capacity, good binding effect and the same hardness as the specimen. Nowadays methyl methacrylate is the embedding material commonly used. Its penetrating capacity and binding effect are pre-eminent. Its hardness however is not quite ideal. Micro hardness tests of teeth embedded in methyl methacrylate showed a hardness of the enamel of 90—100 Vickers units and a hardness of the methacrylate of about 20 Vickers units. Unfortunately no other embedding material that would be better in this respect is available. Therefore the material used in our tests was embedded in methyl methacrylate.

After embedding, the material is sawn into slices of a suitable thickness (*e.g.* about 1.5 mm). In order to avoid overheating, the saw must be sharp and the sawing procedure performed under cooling.

2. *Plane preparation of one surface of the specimen*

The purpose of this step is the final preparation of one of the surfaces of the section. Great demands upon planarity and surface finish have to be satisfied. In order to save time, several sections are ground and lapped simultaneously. With the aid of double sticky tape, the sawn discs are mounted close to each other on a plastic fixture with a plane surface (Fig. 1). The free surface of the specimens is ground first against a coarse and then against a finer rotating grinding disc to be described later.

References p. 176

Using diamond abrasive (Hyprez No. W-47) lapping by hand is then performed against a cast iron lapping disc (Fig. 2). Planarity and surface finish are checked with the aid of interference glass and incident light microscopy respectively.

Fig. 1. By means of double sticky tape the specimen slices are attached to the plastic fixture.

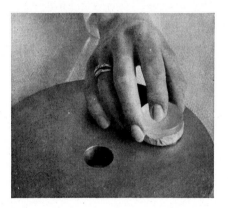

Fig. 2. The polished surfaces are lapped against a cast iron lapping disc with diamond abrasive.

3. Mounting on fixture

In order to make further treatment possible, it is necessary to mount each specimen on a fixture which enables a plane parallel grinding and lapping, continuous thickness control and convenient handling. The fixture is a steel cylinder (Fig. 3) whose both end surfaces are lapped plane parallel to each other and perpendicular to the axis of the cylinder. A square-ruled area ($100 \ \mu^2$) is etched on one of the plane surfaces. The width of the grooves is about $25 \ \mu$ and their depth about $5 \ \mu$. The plane surface of the specimen is glued on the square-ruled area of the cylinder with the aid of a glass glue (methacrylate). The glue between the specimen and the cylinder is worked out to a thin film with light pressure on the specimen and small rotating movements. When the resistance to the rotating movement is increasing, the procedure is stopped. Repeated tests showed that the glue film at this moment has a thickness of less than

0.3 μ. The square-ruled area increases the contact surface and prevents displacements between the glue and the steel. Under light pressure, the glue is allowed to dry over at least 4 h. For different sizes of specimen, different fixtures are available with

Fig. 3. The steel fixture bearing the specimen.

diameters varying from 25, 35 up to 60 mm. The length of the cylinders is the same as their diameter. For each size, there are 5—10 fixtures.

4. *Grinding to thickness region of* 1000 μ

Rapid coarse grinding without making demands upon planarity and surface finish is the purpose of this step. The fixture with the specimen is held against a rotating emery disc and ground down to a thickness of about 1 mm.

5. *Grinding to desired thickness*

Fairly rapid grinding down to desired thickness is performed in this step. At the same time, the section is made almost plane parallel, with reasonable planarity and surface finish. In order to avoid cracking or loosening of the specimen, grinding has to be performed *without vibration*.

The specimen is ground against a silicon carbide paper (type: "Wetordry Tri-M-ite No. 120"). The paper is glued on one of the surfaces of a plane parallel cast iron disc. The maximal deviation from plane parallelity is less than 0.5 μ. The disc has a diameter of 220 mm, a thickness of 23 mm and a central hole with a diameter of 26 mm.

The disc is fastened to the chuck of a precision lathe with the aid of a flange holder (Fig. 4). One of its axle journals is built as an expander and fits in the hole of the disc. With the aid of the expander, the non-papered side of the disc is attached to the flange surface of the holder. The other axle journal of the flange holder is attached to the lathe chuck. The jaws of the chuck are provided with adjustable screws reaching the free surface of the flange holder. With the aid of these screws the rotating axis of the holder can be adjusted to coincide with the axis of the spindle of the lathe. To allow this, soft steel jaws are used. The axis of the fixture is adjusted

Fig. 4. Grinding disc fastened to the chuck with the aid of a flange holder.

perpendicular to the plane of the grinding paper with the aid of a V-block. This stands on a flat sided block of diabase which is placed on the bed of the lathe.

The installation is made in the following way. The flange holder is attached to the lathe chuck. The screws are adjusted to come in contact with the flange holder. A plane parallel disc without grinding paper is attached to the flange holder. The flat sided block of diabase is placed on the bed of the lathe. With the aid of an indicator, the axial movements of the disc are registered. By adjusting the screws, these movements can be reduced to a minimum. In order to obtain good results of the grinding, the axial movements of the peripheral parts of the disc must not exceed 5 μ. On the lathe used by us (Schaublin SA Nr. 120 VM), the axial movements can be reduced to 1 or 2 μ. Due to the plane parallel shape of the grinding discs, it is possible to change discs without repeating the adjustment of the axial movement.

The V-block is rectangular. (Size 75 $\times$ 115 $\times$ 100 mm. Weight 5 kg). Due to its weight, it rests firmly in place on the diabase block without any fixing arrangements. The V-block can be easily set perpendicular to the grinding disc by placing a thin paper (0.1 mm) on the disc, and gently pressing the V-block against it. The grinding disc is rotated by hand. As the paper is removed, a plane parallel gap of about 0.1 mm will thus appear between the V-block and the grinding disc. If the V-block appears to be moving during grinding, it can be glued on to the diabase plane and its desired orientation can be obtained by moving the flat sided block of diabase on the lathe bed. The gluing of the papers is performed with a contact glue (Bostik A3). The glue is worked out to an even film. When it is almost dry, the paper is put on top of it and an evenly distributed pressure is applied to the entire surface of the disc with the aid of a metal plane.

When grinding the specimen, the fixture is placed in the V-block (Fig. 5). The feeding is done by gentle pressure of the hand and rotating movements. The disc is rotated with a speed of 285 rev./min. Continuous thickness control is performed

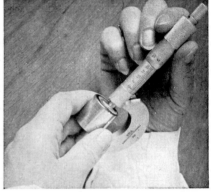

Fig. 5. Steel fixture in V-block.   Fig. 6. Thickness control with the aid of
                                              a micrometer.

with the aid of a micrometer (Fig. 6). Then the distance between the free surface of the specimen and the cylinder is measured. As the thickness of the glue can be ignored, and as the length of the fixture is known, the thickness of the specimen is obtained. Grinding down to about 100 μ will take 1—2 min. Thereafter feeding must be done carefully down to the thickness region of around 50 μ.

For grinding from 50 μ down to the desired thickness, a finer grinding paper is used (No. 600 A). A suitable speed of the disc at this stage is 120 rev./min. Feeding requires great cautiousness at this step, which lasts about 5 min and is terminated by polishing against a disc with polishing paper (Emery polishing paper 4/0).

6. *Plane parallel lapping*

This step is carried out as a controlled lapping in order to obtain good planarity, good surface finish, and plane parallel sections. The equipment consists of commercial parts of a cylindrical stand for Mikrokator measuring. (The parts are manufactured by C. E. Johansson, Eskilstuna, Sweden) (Fig. 7). Two measuring tables facing each other are mounted on two arms attached to the cylindrical stand. The lower table consists of a special fixture and a measuring plane. This fixture is adjustable in order to set the top surface of the measuring table plane parallel to the corresponding surface of the other table. The top surface of the lower table is made as an edge plane. The upper table is mounted in a similar fixture and has a lapping plane made of cast iron. The lower table can be moved vertically with the aid of a screw on the stand. Thus the gap between the two tables can be altered by about 0.2 mm without affecting their plane parallel position. The plane parallel adjustment is done with the aid of a steel fixture without a mounted specimen.

References p. 176

When lapping against the lapping plane, the same diamond abrasive as mentioned above (step 2) is used. The fixture with the specimen is put in position with its free surface gliding along the edge plane. Then by means of the screw, the top

Fig. 7. Equipment for plane parallel lapping.   Fig. 8. Mikrokator measurement of the section thickness.

surface of the specimen is brought lightly into contact with the lapping plane. The free surface of the specimen is then gently lapped by small movements in different directions. The planarity of the specimen is checked with the aid of an interference glass. When sufficient planarity is obtained, the section is also plane parallel and lapping can be stopped if the surface finish is satisfactory.

7. Final thickness control and demounting from fixture

Thickness determination of the sections in routine work is performed in two ways. Average thickness can be measured with the micrometer as described above. This method has an accuracy of 5μ. If more accurate measuring is desired, the sections can be measured with the aid of a Mikrokator. These measurements are then performed in an apparatus similar to the one used in step 6 with the difference that the top table is replaced by the Mikrokator (Fig. 8). A plane lapped circular measuring point is applied to the Mikrokator in order to avoid damage of the specimen. This method allows measurements with an accuracy of one tenth of a μ.

References p. 176

The section is demounted by placing the fixture in acetone. The glue as well as the embedding material will then be removed. In spite of this the sections will not fall to pieces even if their thickness is only about 10 μ.*

TESTS OF THE METHOD

In order to test the method, a series of 18 tooth sections embedded in methyl methacrylate has been prepared within the thickness region of 7—20 μ. The thickness of each section has been measured at 10 evenly distributed points with the aid of an optical mechanical method[21]. This allows measurements down to 0.1 μ without pressure and with the same lateral resolution as an ordinary light microscope.

The results show that the standard deviation for the variation in the top surface of the sections is equal to $\pm$ 0.2 μ. The same deviation can be expected in the bottom surface of the section. The relative error for a 20 μ thick section can therefore be calculated to about 1.5 %. Variations in the thickness of the glue film can increase this error to a maximum of 3 %.

Thus, with the method described it is possible to prepare plane parallel sections of desired thickness.

Sections down to a thickness of 30 μ can be prepared in routine work without any loss. In order to prepare thinner sections, increased attention and care are necessary.

In spite of the fact that the method involves 7 steps, it is not time-consuming. This is due to the shape of the fixtures which allow serial preparation.

As far as possible, commercially available parts were used in the apparatus in order to keep the price within reasonable limits.

ACKNOWLEDGEMENT

We want to express our sincere gratitude to civil ing. ERIK GISSLÉN for his unfailing interest and generous support.

REFERENCES

[1] M. T. JANSEN, *J. Dental Research*, 25 (1946) 355.
[2] H. F. ATKINSON, *Brit. Dental J.*, 84 (1948) 260.
[3] H. F. ATKINSON, *Brit. Dental J.*, 88 (1950) 29.
[4] M. T. JANSEN, *J. Dental Research*, 29 (1950) 401.
[5] H. M. MYERS, E. JENNINGS and H. BECKS, *J. Dental Research*, 31 (1952) 416.
[6] S. M. CLARK and J. IBALL, *J. Sci. Instr.*, 32 (1955) 367.
[7] E. HAMMARLUND-ESSLER and G. BERGMAN, *Trans. Royal Schools of Dentistry, Stockholm and Umeå*, 4 (1958).
[8] W. MEYER, *Vierteljahresschr. Zahnheilk.*, 41 (1925) 111.
[9] E. WELANDER, *Odontologiska Föreningens Tidsskr.*, July (1946) 351.
[10] G. GUSTAFSON and Ö. KLING, *Odontologisk Tidsskr.*, 56 (1948) 23.
[11] C. P. LEBLOND, G. W. WILKINSON, L. F. BELANGER and J. ROBICHON, *Am. J. Anat.*, 86 (1950) 289.
[12] TOR ØRVIG, *Arkiv Zool.*, 2 (1951) 321.
[13] E. HAMMARLUND-ESSLER, *Acta Odontol. Scand.*, 13 (1955) 167.
[14] B. M. PATTEN and S. W. CHASE, *Anat. Record*, 30 (1925) 123.
[15] C. F. BÖDECKER, *Dental Cosmos*, 68 (1926) 860.
[16] W. LEFKOWITZ, *J. Dental Research*, 20 (1941) 77.
[17] R. SOGNAES, *Anat. Record*, 99 (1947) 133.
[18] P. P. LAUDE, R. G. JANES and J. D. BOYD, *Anat. Record*, 104 (1949) 11.
[19] E. KLEIN, O. R. TRAUTZ, H. K. ADDELSTON and J. FANKUCHEN, *J. Dental Research*, 30 (1951) 439.
[20] G. FOSSE, *J. Dental Research*, 33 (1954) 139.
[21] O. HALLÉN, *Acta Anatom., Suppl.* 25 (1956).

---

*   By using ethanol the embedding material will be saved and only the glue film is solved.

A NEW APPARATUS FOR THE PREPARATION OF VERY THIN GROUND SECTIONS FOR HIGH RESOLUTION MICRORADIOGRAPHY

I. MOLENAAR

Department of Histology, Utrecht University (The Netherlands)

ABSTRACT

Methyl methacrylate-embedded tissue is sawn into sections of $50-100\ \mu$; subsequently the sections are embedded by polymerization in a thin plastic layer which may be stretched tightly on the surface of a steel object carrier. A tight fit is ensured because the object carrier serves as the mould when polymerizing the layer. The layer can be easily removed from its holder for measuring the progress of the grinding procedure and can be accurately replaced afterwards. Grinding is performed on a disc that has been ground even by means of a diamond tool temporarily fastened to the object-carrying arm of the apparatus. The surface of the object carrier in its turn is ground flat on the disc thus prepared. The grinding force is supplied by steel springs, the excursions of which are controlled by means of a micrometer screw. Thus, grinding may be stopped at any predetermined section thickness down to $10\ \mu$ or less.

If high resolution and quantitative results are to be obtained in microradiography, thin plane-parallel sections are required. In this respect, the investigation of objects containing both hard and soft tissues presents special difficulties, for they can neither be sectioned nor ground with the usual techniques.

The method by which good results on such tissues were obtained is as follows: After fixation, the tissue is embedded in methyl methacrylate and sawn into slices of $50-100\ \mu$ with the aid of a sawing machine designed by M. T. JANSEN. Every sawed section is polished on one side. Next, a part of the section is selected, cut out, and its thickness is measured by means of a sensitive micrometer gauge.

In the usual grinding techniques the next step involves the glueing of the section unto an object carrier or polymerizing it into the surface of a small block of plastic. This is done for two reasons: first, of course, to enable the manipulation of the section during the grinding process and second, to provide a support for it. Canada balsam as well as glue and plastic polymerized *in situ* meet this second requirement very well as they support the section down to the very smallest irregularities of its surface.

On the other hand, it must be possible to measure the thickness of the section in the course of the grinding process. It would therefore be of great advantage to be able to detach the section from the object carrier and refasten it again in an easy, rapid and safe manner.

In our method this was realized as follows: The section is embedded in the centre of a dish-shaped methacrylate carrier which, except for its centre, is much thicker than the section itself. The centre part of the dish is occupied by the section, so that the latter, for all practical purposes, is connected to the carrier along its circumference only (Fig. 1). Of course, the section is not strong enough to resist the forces of the grinding process, unless it is supported by an accurately fitting base, over which it is stretched. The perfect fit of the section to this base is ensured by using the latter as the mould during the polymerization process (Figs. 2 and 3).

Fig. 1. Pieces of the mould in which object carrier and section are polymerized together. The product is shown in the centre below. ($^3/_4$ real size.)

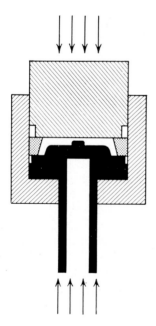

Fig. 2. The situation during the polymerization process: the section lies on top of the part of the mould drawn in black. ($1^1/_2 \times$ real size.)

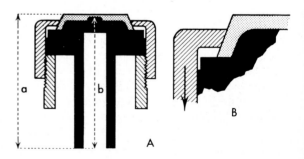

Fig. 3. The way the plastic object carrier (and the section polymerized in it) is stretched over the steel mould.

Reference p. 183

The technique hinges on the fact that during grinding, the plastic carrier can be removed from its steel base in a few seconds for measuring the thickness of the section by means of a sensitive micrometer gauge. Afterwards it can be easily replaced to its base in exactly the same position as before.

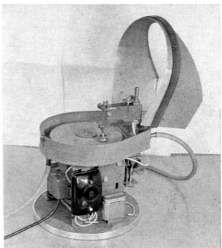

Fig. 4. The grinding apparatus. ($^1/_8$th real size.)

Fig. 5.

Fig. 7. The arm with two springs that moves the object carrier to and fro over the grinding disc. The adjustable stop is shown in two positions. In the photograph below the grinding process will proceed until screw A touches stop B.

Reference p. 183

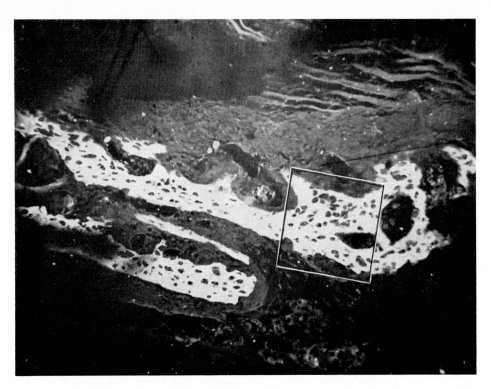

Fig. 8. Alveolar bone of newborn cat, 7 μ thick section, 130 ×. Exposure: 3 kV, 3 mA, 180 sec.

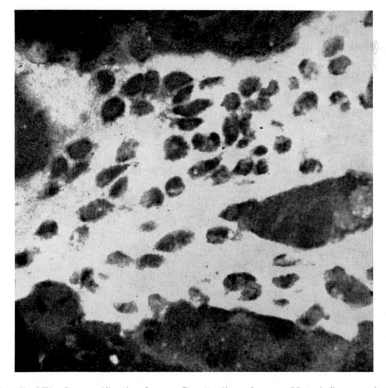

Fig. 9. Detail of Fig. 8, magnification 800 ×. Canaliculi can be seen. Note influence of thickness compared to 15 μ section.

Reference p. 183

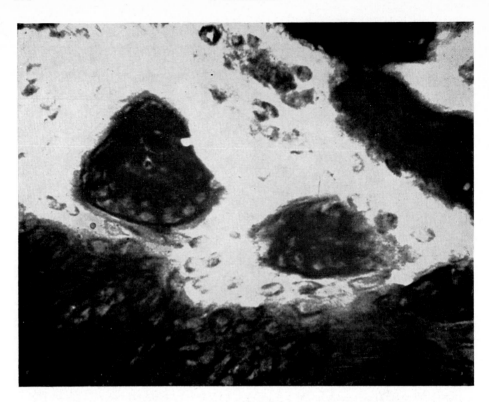

Fig. 10. Alveolar bone of newborn cat, 15 μ thick section, 800 ×. Osteoblasts and osteocytes. See influence of thickness compared to 7 μ section. Exposure: 3 kV, 3 mA, 240 sec.

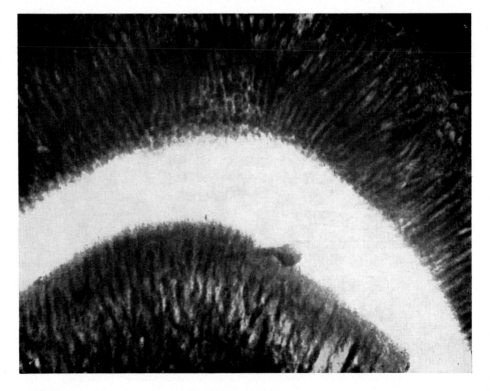

Fig. 11. Top of very young growing incisor, 15 μ thick section, 800 ×. See ameloblasts, odonto-blasts and predentin.

The grinding machine proper consists of a horizontally rotating grinding wheel, against which the object carrier is pressed by means of springs (Figs. 4 and 5). An adjustable stop cuts off the force of the springs at any desired distance from a zero setting, that is after a predetermined amount of material has been ground away (Figs. 6 and 7). Moreover a warning signal is actuated as soon as the stop is reached. The grinding speed can be controlled to a large extent by varying the water supply.

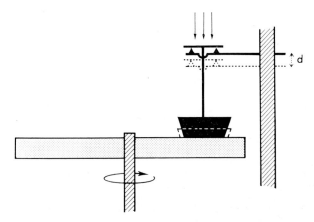

Fig. 6. The principle of grinding a section down to a predetermined thickness. Before the grinding process starts the situation is depicted by the dotted lines; then the adjustable stop is moved over a desired distance d μ and fastened again; the grinding force can exert its influence now and will be eliminated; when the stop is reached again the object will be thinner by an amount of d μ.

During grinding, the object is moved to and fro over the surface of the grinding disc. In view of this and also in order to obtain plane-parallelism of the sections, it is imperative that the disc first be made perfectly smooth and level. This can be achieved by grinding the disc itself by means of a diamond inserted into the holder instead of the object carrier. Finally the steel mould that supports the section is ground flat before use on the same machine so as to ensure an even thickness of the sections.

If all precautions are observed and provided the machine is sufficiently stable, the technique allows the grinding of sections containing both hard and soft tissues down to a thickness of 10 μ or less[1]. The minimum thickness reached was 6 μ. Some results are shown in Figs. 8, 9, 10, 11. Contact microradiographs were taken with a Philips CMR 5 apparatus.

Many thanks are due to MR. KERSSEN for his technical assistance.

REFERENCE

M. T. JANSEN, *J. Dental Research*, 29 (1950) 401.

---

* For discussion on this subject see remarks in the paper by K. HOOPER, p. 216 this volume.

MICRORADIOGRAPHIC INVESTIGATIONS ON BONES IN OSTEOMALACIA AND RICKETS

H. BOHR and E. DOLLERUP

Orthopedic Hospital and Medical Department C of the Municipal Hospital, Aarhus (Denmark)

ABSTRACT

Specimens of bones with osteomalacia and rickets have been examined with microradiography and autoradiography (after *in vitro* labelling with [45]Ca), in combination with a histological investigation of the decalcified tissue, and with an analysis of the content of calcium, phosphorus and nitrogen of the bone. It was found that the characteristic microradiographic picture of osteomalacia and rickets was consistent with a low content of calcium and phosphorus as compared with nitrogen, differing significantly from normal and osteoporotic bones as well as from other bone diseases.

Among 46 cases, mainly with osteoporosis, examined at the Orthopedic Hospital in Aarhus during the last two years, 2 cases of osteomalacia occurred and a report of these is given.

Through microradiographic investigations it was shown by AMPRINO and ENGSTRÖM that the normal lamellar bone presents different degrees of mineralization. Some of the Haversian canals are surrounded by bone-lamellae, which are less mineralized than other parts of the bone, and according to ENGSTRÖM and collaborators[1] they represent young bone tissue under development. Experiments on the uptake of radioactive calcium and phosphate in the living animal support this view, showing that the less mineralized lamellae take up more radioactive isotopes than those which are already fully mineralized. This offers a possibility of evaluating the degree of rebuilding or new growth in the bone. Besides such information, microradiographic investigation gives important evidence as regards the pathological processes in bone diseases among others in osteopetrosis, Paget's disease, osteogenesis imperfecta and rickets or osteomalacia.

The present report concerning osteomalacia is part of an investigation carried out on patients with roentgenographically identified osteoporosis, at the Orthopedic Hospital in Aarhus, during the last two years. Biopsies were taken from the iliac crest, and on these bone specimens microradiographic investigations were performed along with ordinary histopathological studies and an analysis of the contents of calcium, phosphorus and nitrogen in the bone. For comparison, normal bone specimens were obtained from the Pathological Department of the Municipal Hospital, deriving from dissection in cases of fatal accidents or sudden death.

The method of microradiography had been studied in the department of Professor ENGSTRÖM, and the technique used there had been adopted. After fixation and dehydration, the bone specimen was embedded in polymerized methylmethacrylate. Sections were cut with a circular saw and ground to a thickness of 50—100 μ. The microradiographic picture was produced with a Machlett O.E.G. X-ray tube at

14 kV and 8 mA, with 20 min exposure time and 16 cm focal distance. Eastman Kodak Spectroscopic plates 649 were used. Analysis of the contents of calcium, phosphorus and nitrogen was carried out after cleansing the bone of soft tissue by mechanical rinsing in water and drying to constant weight. Nitrogen was determined by the method of Kjeldahl, and calcium and phosphorus, after ashing, by the modified method of BIEDERMANN and SCHWARZENBACH and by the method of Fiske and Subbarow respectively.

A microradiographic picture from a normal male person, 35 years old, is shown in Fig. 1. The well-known pattern of Haversian systems with varying degrees of mineralization is observed.

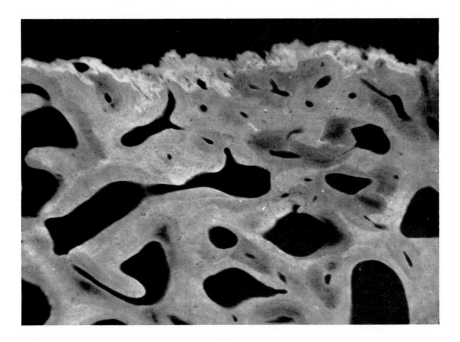

Fig. 1. Microradiographic picture from the iliac crest of a normal male person, aged 35.

It was shown by ENGFELT and ZETTERSTRÖM[2] that the microradiographic picture of experimental rickets in puppy dogs differs characteristically from the normal by an almost complete lack of mineralization in the osteoid tissue around the Haversian canals, and a high rate of mineralization in the remaining part of the bone. In the present investigation 2 of the 46 patients studied for osteoporosis proved to have osteomalacia.

The first case was a 44 year old woman, who had had several attacks of pyelonephritis and during the last 7 years had suffered from pains in the low back and in the ribs. X-ray photographs showed Milkman's syndrome with osteoporosis and ribbon-like zones in the pelvis and some of the ribs. Serum calcium was 8.6 mg %, serum inorganic phosphate was 2.5 mg % and serum alkaline phosphatase 26 KA units. The urine clearance was reduced to 20 %. Histopathological investigations showed an increased amount of osteoid tissue, indicating osteomalacia. The relation

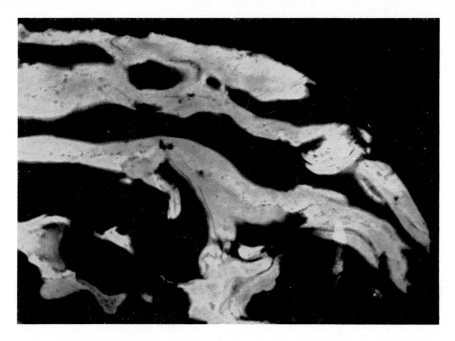

Fig. 2. Microradiographic picture from the iliac crest of a patient with osteomalacia, case 1.

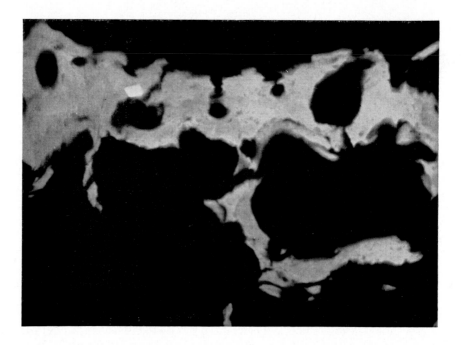

Fig. 3. Microradiographic picture from the iliac crest of a patient with osteomalacia, case 2.

References p. 190

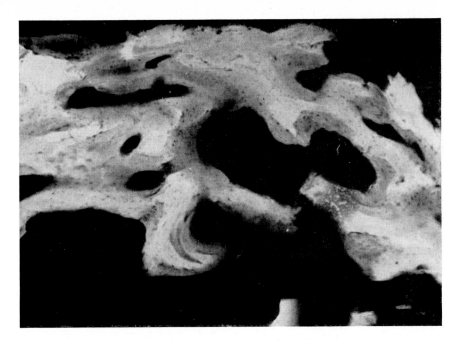

Fig. 4. Microradiographic picture from the iliac crest of case 2 after vitamin D treatment.

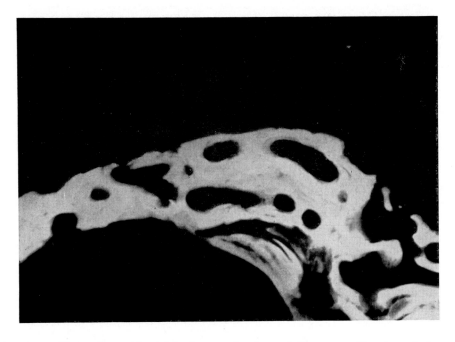

Fig. 5. Microradiographic picture from a rib of an adult person with osteomalacia.

References p. 190

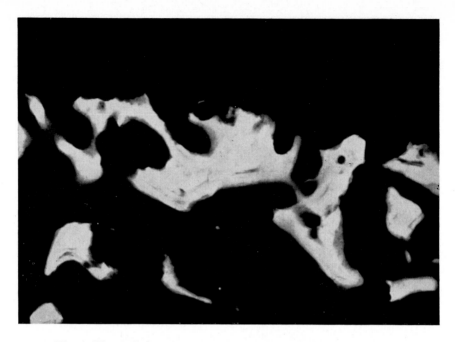

Fig. 6. Microradiographic picture from a rib of a child with rickets.

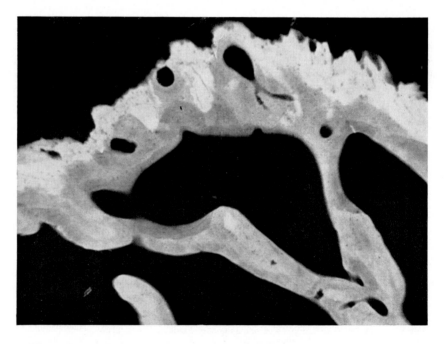

Fig. 7. Microradiographic picture from the iliac crest of 56 year old woman with ordinary osteoporosis.

References p. 190

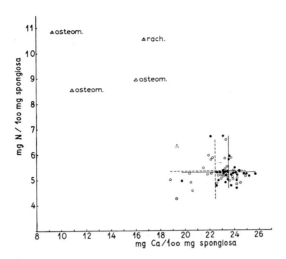

Fig. 8. The amount of nitrogen and calcium in the bone of normal and osteoporotic cases as well as cases with osteomalacia and rickets $_{o\bullet o}^{o\bullet o}$ = the values of case 2 after Vitamin D treatment. • = normal, o = osteoporosis.

between the amount of nitrogen to calcium in the bone was 0.79 and that of nitrogen to phosphorus was 1.65. These are distinctly higher ratios than found in the normal bone, where the average values were 0.23 and 0.50 respectively. The microradiographic picture is seen in Fig. 2, and a striking difference from the normal picture will be observed. There is a uniformly high mineralization without any less mineralized rings around the Haversian canals, and the structure of the bone is irregular.

The second case was a woman, 62 years old, who had suffered from increasing pains in the bones during the last two years. X-ray photographs showed osteoporosis of the entire skeleton and Milkman's syndrome with ribbon-like zones in different bones. Serum calcium was 8.0 mg %, serum inorganic phosphate 3.7 mg % and serum alkaline phosphatase 10 Bodansky units. The histopathological investigation of a bone specimen showed an increased amount of osteoid tissue, indicating osteomalacia. The microradiographic picture is shown in Fig. 3, presenting the same characteristic appearance as Fig. 2.

While the first patient, a case of nephrogen osteopathy, was treated with methylandrosterone, and not with vitamin D, to avoid any further reduction of the renal function, the second patient, a case of vitamin D deficiency, was treated with vitamin D, starting with 300,000 units and gradually reducing the dose to 10,000 units. During this treatment the pains in the bones rapidly disappeared, and X-ray photographs showed that the ribbon-like zones had vanished. A second biopsy from the iliac crest was taken half a year after treatment had been started, and the microradiographic picture is shown in Fig. 4. The difference compared with Fig. 3 is obvious: there is mineralization in the osteoid tissue, and less mineralized rings around the Haversian canals are observed, like in the normal bone. Correspondingly the relation of nitrogen to calcium and phosphorus showed values of 0.33 and 0.69 respectively, which is within the normal range.

Microradiographic pictures of ribs from typical cases of osteomalacia and rickets are seen in Figs. 5 and 6, which show the same characteristic appearance as Figs. 2 and 3.

For comparison, a typical microradiographic picture from a patient with ordinary osteoporosis is shown in Fig. 7. This was taken from a 56 year old woman with general osteoporosis, where clinical examination, including histopathological investigations, revealed nothing abnormal. It is seen that the bone structure, except for being more open, is essentially similar to the normal one. The analysis of calcium, phosphorus and nitrogen in the bone showed no essential difference from normal. In Fig. 8, the amounts of nitrogen and calcium in the bone are shown in normal and osteoporotic cases as well as in cases of osteomalacia and rickets.

In conclusion, it should be emphasized that the microradiographic picture of osteomalacia has a characteristic appearance showing absence of the less mineralized lamellar structures which are seen around the Haversian canals in normal as well as in ordinary osteoporotic bones. In combination with a high ratio of nitrogen to calcium and phosphorus in the bone, this offers a clue in cases where clinical observations do not lead to a diagnosis.

REFERENCES

[1] R. AMPRINO and A. ENGSTRÖM, *Acta Anat.*, 15 (1959) 1.
[2] B. ENGFELDT and R. ZETTERSTRÖM, *A.M.A. Arch. Pathol.*, 59 (1955) 321.

MICRORADIOGRAPHIE ET MICROSCOPIE D'UN MENINGIOME DE LA VOÛTE*

M. JUSTER, H. FISCHGOLD et J. METZGER

Laboratoire de Microradiographie, Paris (France)

ABSTRACT

MICRORADIOGRAPHY AND MICROSCOPY OF A MENINGIOMA OF THE CRANIAL DOME

The normal and pathological cranial dome was studied by radiography, using 2–3 mm thick bone sections embedded in a plastic material, by which means the bone structure can be examined. After thinning down the section to 100–200 μ, the micro-structure of the two tables and the diploë can be revealed by microradiography.

A 2–3 mm thick slice under the ordinary microscope, in transmitted light, shows the same structure as that revealed by microradiography. The controls show that light rays only reveal the structure of the surface layer of a preparation, which is of the same order of magnitude as the sections used for microradiography.

The two techniques were used to investigate two meningiomas of different type and morphology.

In the first case, radiographic examination of the thick slice was complemented by making microradiograms of the fine section. In the second case, the same slice (approx. 2 mm thick) was used to obtain information about the bone structure, by means of radiography, and about the structure of the various elements by microscopic examination of the surface layer.

Les méningiomes développés au voisinage de l'endocrâne ne modifient pas toujours les os de la voûte ou de la base; mais d'une façon générale, l'os subit des transformations importantes.

Si l'étude clinique et radiologique des méningiomes a donné lieu à des travaux remarquables, la lésion osseuse a été moins étudiée. Dans les lignes qui suivent on insiste sur l'étude des lésions osseuses. En conjuguant deux techniques différentes on a essayé de pénétrer le mécanisme des modifications osseuses.

OBSERVATION CLINIQUE

Madame M.G., 30 ans, est hospitalisée en 1957 pour un syndrome d'hypertension intracranienne avec baisse de l'acuité visuelle, oedème papillaire bilatéral, céphalées et vomissements. Elle revient à l'hôpital en 1958 avec une symptomatologie aggravée en acceptant cette fois-ci l'intervention chirurgicale.

Le diagnostic clinique de méningiome est confirmé par l'acte opératoire: l'on constate une énorme tumeur du 1/3 moyen de la faux envahissant le sinus longitudinal supérieur et infiltrant l'os.

Le volet enlevé dans la salle d'opération nous a permis d'effectuer la micro-

---

* Travail du Centre d'Etudes Scientifiques de l'Homme du C.N.R.S., Paris, 41, rue Gay Lussac (Professeur C. SOULA).

Effectué avec l'aide de la Sécurité Sociale et de l'Institut National d'Hygiène.

radiographie et l'étude microscopique de l'os sus-jacent au méningiome globuleux.

La radiographie de profil (Fig. 1) et l'image tangentielle de la bosse (Fig. 2) sont comparées à la radiographie du volet (Fig. 3).

Ce dernier est ensuite inclus dans une matière plastique et découpé en tranches sagittales de 3 mm environ. Une de ces tranches est radiographiée (Fig. 4) et amincie jusqu'à 0,03 mm. Chemin faisant des radiographies ont été effectuées à l'épaisseur de 1 mm et 0,3 mm (Fig. 5).

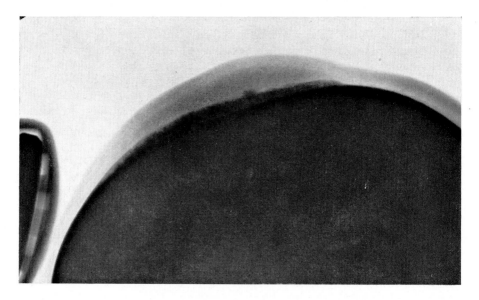

Fig. 1. Profil tiré au Logetron. Table interne hypertrophiée et dense en avant et en arrière de la suture coronaire. Clarté diploïque diminuée ou disparue. Table externe épaissie, irrégulière. Frontal et pariétal: aspect moucheté en marge du sinus longitudinal supérieur.

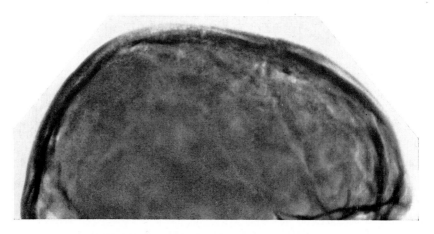

Fig. 2. Image de profil sous-exposée avec rayons de faible pénétration (tirage au Logetron) mettant en évidence: la bosse recouverte par la peau; l'hyperostose en spicules au bregma, avec une fine ligne de clivage par rapport à la table externe.

Bibliographie p. 198

La tranche épaisse de 3 mm (Fig. 4) donne une vue d'ensemble de l'architecture de l'os et de l'état de chacun de ses éléments: tables, diploë et néoformations osseuses. Avec l'amincissement, la morphologie se précise, les détails augmentent en nombre et définition.

Le supplément d'informations apparu pour chaque amincissement peut être suivi sur les Figs. 4, 5 et 6.

Mais la microradiographie ne renseigne que sur les parties minéralisées de l'os et reste de ce fait incomplète.

La microscopie des tranches osseuses épaisses, non colorées ou colorées en surface, remplit cette lacune.

L'examen par la lumière transmise, d'une tranche fine d'os, dans le but d'étudier sa structure, est bien connu depuis HAVERS. Il est moins classique d'examiner, de la même manière, *des tranches plus épaisses* de l'ordre de plusieurs millimètres.

Pourtant, si l'on regarde au microscope une tranche d'os frais de 1 mm—3 mm d'épaisseur, elle fournit un nombre de renseignements.

La même tranche, soumise à certaines préparations (imprégnation plastique, coloration en surface, etc.) deviendra une source plus riche d'informations; de plus, elle se gardera indéfiniment.

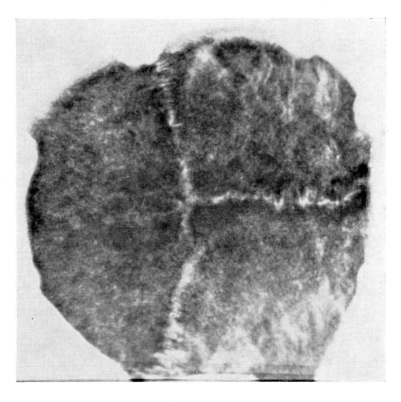

Fig. 3. Radiographie du volet opératoire: l'hyperostose respecte les sutures et accentue la densité des rebords osseux autour du bregma.

Bibliographie p. 198

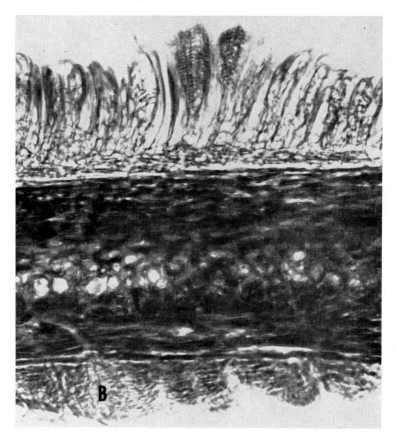

Fig. 4. Tranche sagittale de pariétal normal (A) et du volet opératoire (B). Épaisseur: 3 mm. Grossissement × 6. A. Voûte normale. La table externe en haut et la table interne en bas, se présentent sous forme de deux bandes denses, non homogènes. Le diploë est composé de mailles arrondies ou polygonales, séparées par des cloisons d'épaisseur inégale et à bords nets.
B. Tranche du volet opératoire. Les tables interne et externe s'hypertrophient au détriment du diploë; elles s'uniformisent et sont parcourues de fins canalicules à section horizontale. Sur la table externe; apposition spongieuse à mailles fines et spicules perpendiculaires en ,,plumes d'oiseau''. Sur la table interne: appositions spongieuses denses. Persistance de la suture coronaire.

On trouve ailleurs l'ensemble de ces techniques[2-5]; ci-dessous leurs applications à l'étude microscopique de la lésion osseuse provoquée par le méningiome.

Une tranche sagittale du volet opératoire longue de 8 mm et épaisse de 3 mm est radiographiée: ceci permet d'avoir une vue d'ensemble. Elle est ensuite découpée en 8 parties (de 1 cm de longueur), l'épaisseur de chaque segment restant toujours 3 mm. Chaque segment est coloré *en surface* différemment. Les Figs. 8 et 9 rapportent deux de ces essais.

Fig. 7: coloration hématéine – Bleu d'Aniline.

Les images suggèrent une destruction *locale* de la travée osseuse: pas d'ostéolyse partielle, pas de débris de travée. La morphologie de la destruction pourrait être résumée dans l'expression imagée de ,,morsures à la pince gouge''.

Fig. 8: coloration Giemsa.

Le colorant a agi et sur la travée osseuse et sur les éléments cellulaires. Le processus pathologique sera plus facilement suivi sur la Fig. 9 (schéma de la Fig. 8).

La surface hachurée marque une zone d'ostéolyse; celle-ci est limitée, à droite et à gauche, par des travées osseuses partiellement détruites. La direction des systèmes lamellaire et cellulaire de ces travées laisse présumer une continuité qui a

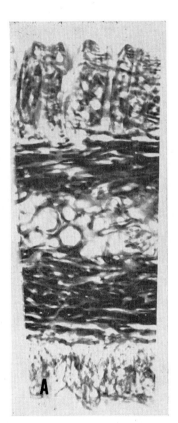
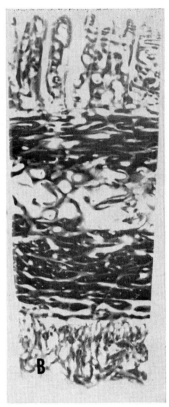

Fig .5. Tranche sagittale du volet opératoire. Grossissement × 6; A.Épaisseur: 1 mm; B.Épaisseur: 0,35 mm. L'amincissement multiplie les détails et augmente la définition.

Bibliographie p. 198

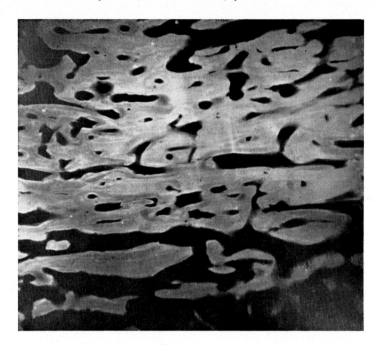

Fig. 6. Table interne du volet opératoire. Épaisseur 3 mm. Grossissement × 21. Dissociation du système lamellaire dans le sens horizontal. Dans les travées osseuses, l'existence de nombreux orifices, dont la morphologie et l'orientation fait penser à des canaux vasculaires.

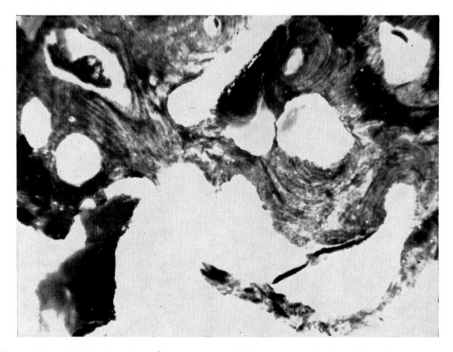

Fig 7. Examen microscopique. Épaisseur 3 mm. Grossissement × 85. Coloration en surface: Hématéine - Bleu d'Aniline. Tranche sagittale du volet opératoire, examinée à la lumière transmise. Le colorant a agi sur les travées osseuses: celles-ci, partiellement détruites, paraissent comme ,,mordues à la pince gouge''.

Bibliographie p. 198

Fig. 8. Examen microscopique. Épaisseur 3 mm. Grossissement × 85. Coloration en surface: Giemsa. Tranche sagittale du volet opératoire, épaisse de 3 mm, examinée à la lumière transmise. Le colorant agit, et sur la travée osseuse, et sur l'élément cellulaire.

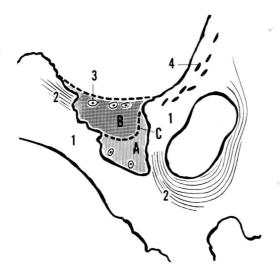

Fig. 9. Schéma de la Fig. 8. 1, Travées osseuses; 2, lamelles interrompues par la destruction de la travée; 3, grosses cellules (vraisemblablement ostéoclasiques) semées à la périphérie de la zone ostéolytique; 4, Cytoblastes; A, zone d'ostéolyse plus récente — morphologie rapprochée de celle de la travée osseuse qui l'entoure; B, zone d'ostéolyse et d'infiltration tumorale plus avancée que A; C, liséré blanc qui sépare les deux zones (A et B).

Bibliographie p. 198

été interrompue par le processus d'ostéolyse. La zone ostéolytique, à bords irréguliers, est bordée par une série de grosses cellules, auxquelles incombe, très vraisemblablement, l'ostéoclasie de la travée.

On remarque aussi que cette zone est divisée par un liséré (C) en deux parties d'aspect différent: le côté inférieur A garde partiellement l'aspect des travées osseuses environnantes; par contre, la partie supérieure présente un remaniement profond et tranche nettement avec l'os qui l'entoure. Ceci permet de penser que l'ostéolyse s'est accomplie par étapes, la zone B étant la première en date.

CONCLUSIONS

L'emploi de ces nouvelles techniques a permis de compléter les renseignements fournis par les méthodes classiques.

Les radiographies des tranches épaisses et minces précisent la morphologie de la lésion.

La microscopie des tranches épaisses d'os non déminéralisé permet de mieux comprendre la pathogénie de la lésion.

RÉSUMÉ

La voûte cranienne normale et pathologique est étudiée à l'aide des tranches osseuses épaisses de 2 à 3 mm, incluses dans une matière plastique. La radiographie de ces tranches renseigne sur l'architecture de l'os. La tranche est ensuite amincie jusqu'à 100–200 μ; à cette épaisseur la microradiographie peut nous révéler la structure microscopique des deux tables et du diploë.

En soumettant au microscope ordinaire une préparation de 2–3 mm d'épaisseur on retrouve en lumière transparente la même structure que celle révélée en microradiographie. Les contrôles prouvent que l'examen d'une préparation par le rayon lumineux dégage uniquement la structure de la couche superficielle; celle-ci est de l'ordre des préparations utilisées en microradiographie.

Les deux techniques ont été utilisées pour étudier deux méningiomes de type et de morphologie différente.

Dans le premier cas, l'étude radiographique de la tranche épaisse à été complétée par les images microradiographiques de la tranche fine. Dans le deuxième cas, la même tranche épaisse de 2 mm environ renseigne sur l'architecture de l'os grâce à la microscopie de la couche superficielle.

BIBLIOGRAPHIE

[1] H. FISCHGOLD, M. JUSTER et J. ECOIFFIER, *J. radiol. et électrol.*, 38 (1957) 1069.
[2] M. JUSTER, *Arch. anat. pathol., Semaine hôp.*, 7 (1959) 179.
[3] M. JUSTER, *Arch. anat. pathol., Semaine hôp.*, 7 (1959) 180.
[4] M. JUSTER, *Bull. microscop. appl.*, 9 (1959) No. 2.
[5] M. JUSTER, Sur l'examen des tranches osseuses épaisses et colorées en surface; A paraître dans *Compte Rendu de l'Association des Anatomistes*.
[6] M. JUSTER et H. FISCHGOLD, Comparaisons entre les images microradiographiques et microscopiques de la même tranche osseuse épaisse, *Presse méd.*, á paraître.
[7] M. JUSTER, H. FISCHGOLD et J. ECOIFFIER, Microradiography of Bone Metastases; dans V. COSSLETT, A. ENGSTRÖM et H. PATTEE, *X-ray Microscopy and Microradiography*, Academic Press, Inc., New York, 1957.
[8] P. LACROIX, *L'organisation des os*, Editions Derver, Liège, 1950 (voir bibliographie).
[9] E. E. TAMBOISE, *Thèse*, Paris, 1956, T. 128, No. 271 (voir bibliographie).

QUANTITATIVE MICRORADIOGRAPHY OF BONE TISSUE

H. A. SISSONS, J. JOWSEY and L. STEWART

Institute of Orthopaedics, London (Great Britain)

ABSTRACT

Quantitative microradiography of bone involves the preparation of a section of undecalcified bone of accurately known thickness, and the determination in a microradiograph of the densities of particular microscopic areas by means of microphotometry. From the literature, it appears that two rather different methods have been used for the photometric determinations. One method utilizes the comparison of the bone specimen with an aluminium reference system included in the microradiograph. The other dispenses with this reference system and involves the direct assessment of the ratio of incident to transmitted X-rays as shown by the microradiograph. The reasons which have lead us to prefer the first method using the aluminium reference system are given: the technical procedures used in the work described in the paper "The Microradiographic Appearance of Normal Bone Tissue at Various Ages" are described.

INTRODUCTION

Microradiography has been in use for some years as a technique for the study of the structure and composition of biological material, and a number of interesting and important findings have been made. In the study of bone, microradiography was first used[1,2] to indicate the outlines of calcified structures in microscopic and semi-microscopic tissue preparations. In recent years, following the work of ENGSTRÖM and AMPRINO[3] it has provided important information on the distribution of the bone mineral within such calcified structures (see[4] for recent review). The uneven distribution of bone mineral revealed by this method of examination makes it a most convenient one for the descriptive study of certain aspects of bone structure: microradiography can also be used to obtain quantitative information regarding the mineral (*i.e.* hydroxyapatite) content of different areas of bone in various preparations.

We are using microradiography in a survey of human bone structure at different ages, and the aim of the present paper is to summarise the theoretical background of our methods.

THEORY OF X-RAY ABSORPTION

The use of microradiography for the study of the distribution of hydroxyapatite in bone depends on the selective absorption of X-rays by this material. This is shown in Fig. 1, where the mass absorption coefficients of hydroxyapatite, protein and water have been calculated from empirical data[5,6]. Between 0.5 and 3.0 Å, X-rays are absorbed primarily by the mineral component, and over the greater portion of this range the values for hydroxyapatite are at least 10 times those of the other components.

References p. 205

Two methods have been described for quantitative determinations of the hydroxyapatite content of bone. One of these, used by AMPRINO[7], by LINDSTRÖM[8], and by OWEN[9] and more recently by ROWLAND, JOWSEY and MARSHALL[10], involves

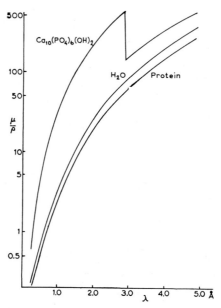

Fig. 1. Mass absorption coefficients of hydroxyapatite, protein and water calculated from empirical data.

the comparison of the bone section with a reference system of known composition and thickness. Most workers using this method have employed a continuous X-ray spectrum, and have adopted aluminium as a reference material. Aluminium is obtained in pure form as a thin foil, and the ratio of its mass absorption coefficient to that of hydroxyapatite is reasonably constant over the range of wave lengths used. The other method, developed by WALLGREN[11] and HOLMSTRAND[12], dispenses with the reference system, and directly determines the ratio of incident to transmitted X-rays by the degree of blackening of the photographic emulsion produced. These workers have used a monochromatic X-ray beam for their studies. The absence of a reference system means that it is necessary to restrict the density of microradiographs to the range for which there is a linear relationship between X-ray intensity and photographic response: for the particular type of photographic emulsions used in microradiography this corresponds to a maximum (*i.e.* background) density of less than 0.7. Under these conditions the microradiograph of a bone section of 100 μ, or even 50 μ, appears extremely under-exposed, and it is not possible, under the microscope, to distinguish the various structural units making up the bone tissue. In our work this restriction of optical density makes such a method unsuitable as we wish to make measurements on specifically identified areas of bone tissue. Section densities from 0.8 to 1.3 are desirable: they correspond to very high background densities, and make the use of a reference system necessary.

The ideal X-ray conditions for this type of quantitative microradiography of bone are that the absorption by hydroxyapatite is high compared with that of other components, and that the ratio between the mass absorption coefficients of the reference material and hydroxyapatite can be specified with accuracy. Fig. 2 shows

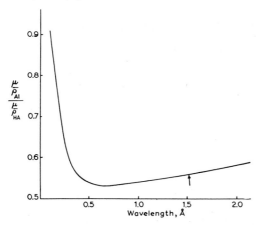

Fig. 2. Ratio of the mass-absorption coefficients of aluminium and hydroxyapatite. The arrow indicates the ratio at 1.54Å.

that with an aluminium reference system this ratio is wave-length dependent: by using a monochromatic X-ray beam the ratio at the wave length used is known. We have followed WALLGREN and HOLMSTRAND in using the K_α line radiation of copper ($\lambda = 1.54$ Å), for which the ratio of the mass-absorption coefficients of aluminium to hydroxyapatite is 0.561. Our work has been carried out with a Raymax 60 unit operated at 20 kV, with a copper target and a 20 μ nickel filter. We understand from WALLGREN's work that under these conditions the X-ray beam is effectively monochromatic.

The general equation for the absorption of X-rays is

$$(1) \qquad I = I_0 e^{-\frac{\mu}{\rho} \cdot m}$$

where
I = the intensity of the beam after passing through the specimen,
I_0 = the original intensity of the beam,
$\frac{\mu}{\rho}$ = the mass absorption coefficient (cm²/g)
m = the mass of absorbing material per unit area (g/cm²)
[$m = \rho d$, where ρ is the density (g/cm³) and d the thickness (cm)].

By including an aluminium step wedge of known thickness in the microradiograph with the bone section, the absorption of any area of bone is expressed in terms of an equivalent thickness of aluminium: by measuring the thickness of the section the mass per unit volume is obtained and expressed as hydroxyapatite.

From the general equation, the absorption in the bone section is given by

$$(2) \qquad I = I_0 e^{-\left(\frac{\mu}{\rho} \cdot m\right)_{HA}}$$

and that in the aluminium reference system by

$$(3) \qquad I = I_0 e^{-\left(\frac{\mu}{\rho} \cdot m\right)_{AL}}$$

References p. 205

For areas of corresponding optical density in the same microradiograph, $\dfrac{I}{I_0}$ has the same value, and it follows that

(4)
$$\left(\frac{\mu}{\rho}\,m\right)_{HA} = \left(\frac{\mu}{\rho}\,m\right)_{AL}$$

For the wave length used

$$\left(\frac{\mu}{\rho}\right)_{AL} = 0.561\left(\frac{\mu}{\rho}\right)_{AH}$$

Substituting in eqn. (4)

$$m_{HA} = 0.561\,m_{AL}$$

$$i.e. \qquad \rho d_{HA} = 0.561\,\rho d_{AL}$$

(5)
$$\text{or} \qquad \rho_{HA} = \frac{0.561\,\rho d_{AL}}{d_{HA}}$$

and this equation can be used to determine the hydroxyapatite content (ρ_{HA}) of selected areas of the section.

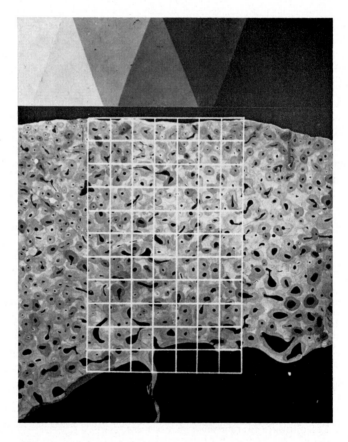

Fig. 3. Microradiograph of a section of cortical bone together with an aluminium stepwedge. A superimposed grid indicates the points at which measurements of thickness were made.

References p. 205

TECHNICAL PROCEDURES

In our microradiographic survey of normal bone structure, specimens of cortical bone from the mid-femoral shaft are embedded in methyl methacrylate after fixation in neutralised 10 % formol saline. Sections of approximately 100 μ thickness are cut with a milling machine[13]: their thickness is adjusted by gentle grinding between roughened glass plates, and contact microradiographs of the section together with a step wedge of 12 μ aluminium foil are prepared. The X-ray conditions have already been specified: in order to obtain an even X-ray field and a high image resolution, we have used a target-film distance of 20 cm for our quantitative work. The photographic material used is Kodak maximum resolution plate, and this is developed for $2\frac{1}{2}$ min in D. 178.

Measurements of optical density are made with a photomultiplier photometer using a highly stabilised light source. A number of readings are made on each osteone in a selected area of the microradiograph, and at a number of points on each step of

Fig. 4. Instrument used to measure thickness of sections.

the aluminium wedge. Each reading corresponds to a spot 25 μ in diameter on the microradiograph.

The thickness of the section is measured at intervals of 500 μ over the area concerned, as shown by the grid superimposed on the microradiograph in Fig. 3. To do this, we use a dial gauge, the foot of which consists of a sphere of radius < 0.8 mm: the section is fixed to a stage which can be moved in relation to the fixed gauge by two micrometer screws (see Fig. 4).

RESULTS

The area of cortical bone analysed corresponds roughly to the area covered by the grid (in Fig. 3) and such a sample contains approximately 150 to 250 osteones. The results can best be shown in the form of a distribution diagram where the proportion of osteones is shown for each range of hydroxyapatite content. The results for 3 individuals, aged 20, 65 and 84 years respectively, are shown in Fig. 5.

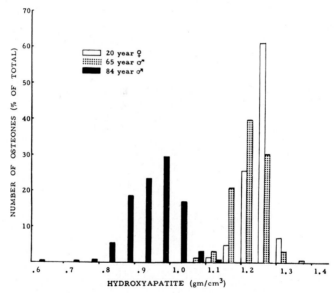

Fig. 5. Distribution diagram showing the amount of hydroxyapatite present in the osteones of the cortical bone of the mid-femoral shaft in 3 normal individuals.

In each case, determinations on interstitial bone in the same area showed a hydroxy-apatite content slightly greater than that of the most highly calcified osteones.

The range of values we have found for the two individuals aged 20 and 65 years corresponds closely to the values already reported[10]. Values for the 84 year old individual are much lower: this observation appears to be confirmed by the results of chemical analysis of samples of femoral cortical bone from 2 of these cases: the calcium content in the 20 year old individual was 25.5 % of dry weight while in the 84 year old it was 20.3 %. As in the microradiographic results, this figure is approximately 20 % lower than that for the younger individual.

Since the introduction of the technique of microradiography it has been suggested by many authors that the growth and development of an osteone is accompanied by a progressive increase in its mineral content. Such a proposition merits more detailed investigation, but it is reasonable to assume that in any area of bone tissue the least mineralised osteones, which also show the greatest uptake of radioactive isotopes such as ^{45}Ca and ^{90}Sr are the youngest[14]: their relative numbers may consequently provide information on the rate of formation of osteones and thus on the rate of turnover of the bone tissue which they make up. We are planning to collect this information on a larger number of normal individuals.

REFERENCES

1 G. CLARK, Radiology, 49 (1947) 483.
2 H. A. SISSONS, Brit. J. Radiol., 23 (1950) 2.
3 A. ENGSTRÖM and R. AMPRINO, Experientia, 6 (1950) 267.
4 A. ENGSTRÖM, in V. E. COSSLETT et al., X-ray Microscopy and Microradiography, Academic Press Inc., 1957, p. 24.
5 R. H. MORGAN, Handbook of Radiology, Year Book Publ. Inc., Chicago, 1955, p. 90.
6 K.-Å. OMNELL, Acta Radiol., Suppl. 148 (1957).
7 R. AMPRINO, Arch. Chir. Organi Mov. Putti, 2 (1952) 173.
8 B. LINDSTRÖM, Acta Radiol., Suppl. 125 (1955).
9 M. OWEN, J. Bone and Joint Surg., 38B (1956) 762.
10 R. E. ROWLAND, J. JOWSEY and J. H. MARSHALL, Radiation Research, 10 (1959) 234.
11 G. WALLGREN, Acta Paed., Suppl. 113 (1957).
12 K. HOLMSTRAND, Acta Orthopaed. Scand., Suppl. 26 (1957).
13 J. JOWSEY, J. Sci. Instr., 32 (1955) 159.
14 J. JOWSEY, Atompraxis, in II. Internationale Atomkonferenz, Geneva, 4 (1958) 291.

THE MICRORADIOGRAPHIC APPEARANCE OF NORMAL BONE TISSUE AT VARIOUS AGES

H. A. SISSONS, J. JOWSEY and L. STEWART

Institute of Orthopaedics, London (Great Britain)

ABSTRACT

Information on normal bone structure is needed for the recognition and assessment of the abnormalities encountered in skeletal diseases, and in order to aid our understanding of the processes of "turnover" of skeletal tissue in health and disease.

Tissue from a number of skeletal sites, from individuals dying from accident or acute illness, is being studied by means of histological, chemical and microradiographic methods. Information is available from 17 individuals whose ages range from $2\frac{1}{2}$ to 93 years, and the present preliminary account describes the microscopic structure of the cortical bone of the mid-shaft of the femur in these individuals. Results include microradiographic indications of bone formation and bone destruction, the number of "less than $\frac{3}{4}$ closed" osteones, and the presence of "plugged Haversian canals" and "filled osteocyte lacunae".

INTRODUCTION

There are two good reasons for wishing to have further information on bone structure. In the first place, the range of the normal at various ages must be determined in order to provide a base-line for the recognition of skeletal diseases such as osteoporosis: in the second place certain aspects of bone structure are of interest in connection with the assessment of the local rates of renewal of bone tissue. The relationship between bone structure and the rate of turnover of bone tissue was recently discussed by one of us[1], and the need for quantitative information on the morphological indications of bone formation and bone resorption under both normal and abnormal conditions was stressed. For any part of the skeleton it is of interest to know the areas of the available bone surface which are concerned with these two processes. Such information does not enable us to specify the actual rates at which bone formation and bone resorption are proceeding, but any increase or decrease in the proportion of the available surface occupied by one or other of these processes might be expected to indicate a change in their relative activities.

We are at present engaged on a study of normal bone structure at various ages, in an attempt to obtain information of this sort: we are making considerable use of microradiography, and the aim of the present communication is to give a preliminary account of the methods used and the results obtained so far.

References p. 215

MATERIALS AND METHODS

We are collecting and studying normal bone material from a number of parts of the skeleton in individuals where death has occurred suddenly, either as a result of accident or acute illness. In the first instance we have chosen to study the cortical bone of the mid-shaft of the femur, and for the present report we have included material from 17 individuals aged from $2\frac{1}{2}$ to 93 years. Variations of structure have been studied in relation to age, but so far no analysis of sex differences has been attempted. Specimens are fixed in 10 % formol–saline neutralised with calcium carbonate, and material from adjacent slices of bone tissue is used for conventional histological study (after decalcification), for microradiography, and for chemical analysis. In the present report we are concentrating on the results of microradiography.

The specimen for microradiography, a transverse slice of femoral cortex about 0.5 cm thick, is divided into quadrants: these are embedded in methyl methacrylate and sections approximately 100 μ in thickness are cut with a circular toothed saw[2]. Contact microradiographs are made as described in the previous communication[3]. In order to get a comparable and representative sample of cortical bone from each case, the microradiographs are photographed and prints made at a magnification of approximately 30 diameters: on the prints a wedge-shaped sample is outlined (see Fig. 1) to include one third of the area of each quadrant, and it is on this sample that our measurements have been made.

The unit of bone structure concerned in the remodelling activities of cortical bone is the Haversian system or osteone, which is formed by the deposition of

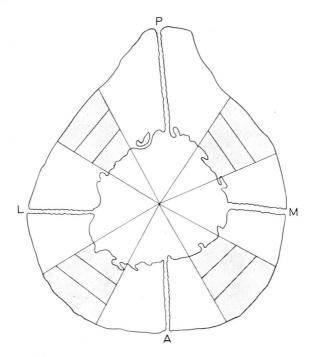

Fig. 1. Diagram of femur cross-section showing the sample areas used for the survey.

concentric lamellae of bone on the wall of a resorption cavity. Initially, the developing bone tissue consists of a narrow rim: as deposition of bone continues the cavity becomes narrowed until only a small central canal remains. The appearance of the surface of the central Haversian space is thought to give an indication of the dynamic state of the osteone: bone formation is recognised in a microradiograph when this surface consists of low-density bone (see Fig. 2). Such surfaces appear to correspond

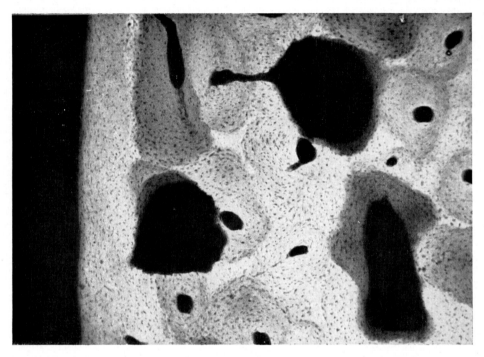

Fig. 2. (× 70) 2½ year-old male. Microradiograph showing 3 osteones where bone formation is in progress, as indicated by the low density of the layer of bone making up the inner surface of the central space.

with those which in decalcified and stained preparations are covered by osteoid borders and osteoblasts: in microradiographs they contrast with what is presumed to be the inactive part of the bone surface where the superficial layer of bone is of somewhat higher density. We have taken the fraction of the available bone surface where the superficial layer consists of low-density bone as an indication of bone formation: this has been measured, and is shown as "amount of bone formation" in Fig. 9.

In any microradiograph of bone, osteones of varying degrees of mineralisation are present, those that are the least mineralized presumably being the most recently formed. In our work, the number of these osteones of particularly low mineralisation has been determined. We have counted osteones which, on visual examination, show an obvious contrast with the fully mineralised interstitial bone adjacent to them (see Fig. 3): the result is expressed as a percentage of the total number of osteones in the area concerned, and shown as "Haversian bone of low density" in Fig. 9. This method of visual identification of low-density osteones appears to correspond to approximately 75 % of complete mineralisation: one reason for our interest in quantitative microradiography is to give greater precision to the definition of low-density osteones and their practical identification.

Bone resorption is recognised in a microradiograph by the presence of a crenated

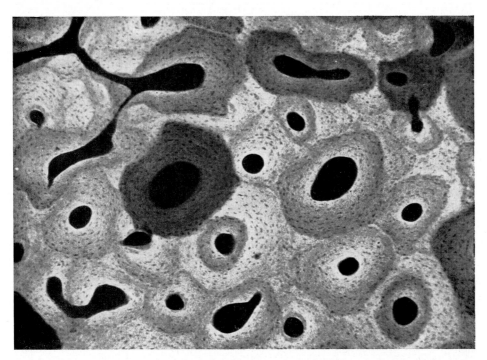

Fig. 3. (× 70) 54 year-old female. Microradiograph showing an osteone of low density: it is in the upper part of the field, and appears dark grey in comparison with other structures. Several osteones in the field are less than ¾ closed. Some rather grey osteones to the right show a surface layer of somewhat higher density bone, indicating an inactive (*i.e.* non-growing) surface.

surface of high-density bone. In cortical bone such a surface outlines a resorption cavity (Fig. 4), or constitutes a localised area of resorption in an osteone where the remainder of the surface is quiescent or at a stage of formation (Fig. 5). We have measured the areas of resorption, and expressed the result as a fraction of the available bone surface: this is shown as "amount of bone resorption" in Fig. 8. The resorption surfaces seen in microradiographs correspond with the similar surfaces in decalcified and stained preparations: the latter are sometimes known as "Howship's lacunae", and some of them are occupied by osteoclasts.

Some idea of the porosity of the bone has been obtained by counting the number of osteones in which the central canal occupies more than a quarter of the total diameter. These less than ¾ closed osteones (see Figs. 3, 5) include resorption cavities, some osteones in the course of formation, and others where this process has been arrested at a stage of incomplete closure. An example of this last type is seen in the lower part of Fig. 5, where a wide central canal is bounded by a narrow superficial zone of higher density than the surrounding tissue. The number of less than ¾ closed osteones is expressed as a percentage of the total number of osteones in the area concerned (see Fig. 9).

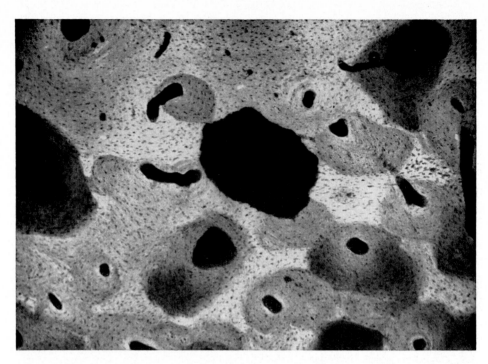

Fig. 4. (× 70) 2½ year old male. Microradiograph showing a resorption cavity with a crenated surface of high-density bone.

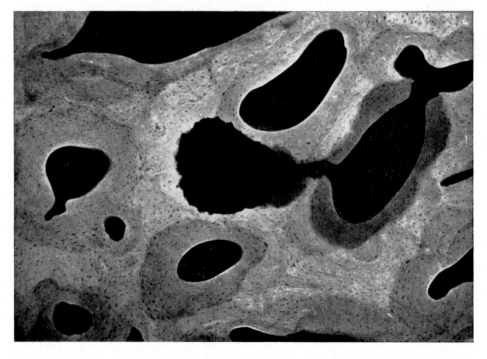

Fig. 5. (× 70) 65 year-old male. Microradiograph showing an osteone with a large area of resorption and a small area where the low density of the surface layer of bone indicates bone formation.

References p. 215

Our results demonstrate the great structural variation that is seen in the cortical bone of the femoral shaft at different ages, and which has been commented on from different points of view by such workers as AMPRINO and BAIRATI[4] and KNESE[5].

Under 10 years of age (see Fig. 6), a high proportion of the bone surface is occupied by bone formation and bone resorption, and as a result a large number of low-density osteones and less than ¾ closed osteones are present.

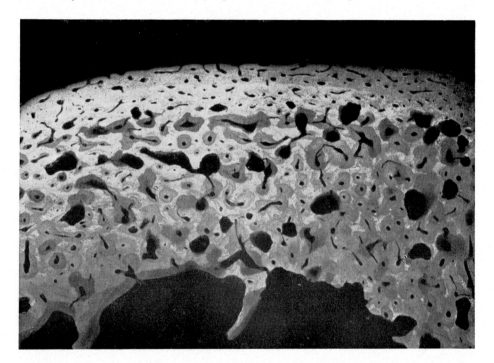

Fig. 6. (× 22) 2½ year-old male. General view of cortical bone of mid-femoral shaft, showing conspicuous bone formation and bone resorption.

After 10 years of age, the areas of bone surface involved by bone formation and bone resorption drop, until by 20 years of age these processes are quite inconspicuous (see Fig. 7) and there are few low-density or less than ¾ closed osteones. The bone consequently has a compact appearance.

After 50 years of age, there is a definite increase in the area of available bone surface occupied by resorption, although there appears to be little change in the amount of bone formation or the number of low-density osteones. Fig. 8 shows the increase in the number of less than ¾ closed osteones in an individual aged 65 years, and this now gives the cortical bone — particularly its inner half — a rather porous appearance.

Fig. 9 summarises information from the 17 individuals making up the present survey. The results can be very simply interpreted as indicating a high rate of bone formation and resorption (*i.e.* of bone turnover) in early life. This is followed by a period of remarkable inactivity from approximately 20—40 years of age. In later life,

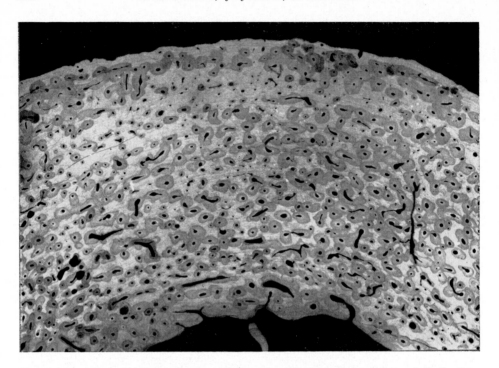

Fig. 7. (× 24) 20 year-old female. General view of cortical bone of mid-femoral shaft: there is little evidence of bone formation or bone resorption.

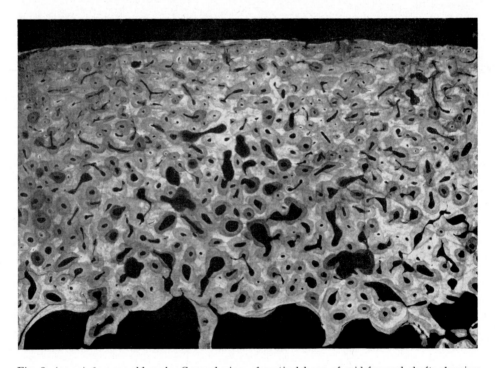

Fig. 8. (× 22) 65 year-old male. General view of cortical bone of mid-femoral shaft, showing an increased number of less than $\frac{3}{4}$ closed systems.

although the indications of bone formation appear to remain at a low level, the evidence of resorption becomes more conspicuous. There is a progressive increase in the porosity of the bone, as shown by the number of less than $\frac{3}{4}$ closed osteones.

Two other features of bone structure deserve mention. In older individuals we have encountered osteones where the central canal has become completely occluded by calcified tissue, which appears in a microradiograph as a high-density plug (Fig. 10). Similarly, certain of the lacunae in the bone, normally occupied by osteocytes and appearing in microradiographs as dark spaces, become filled with bone mineral and appear instead as dense spots — "filled lacunae" (Fig. 10). Osteones

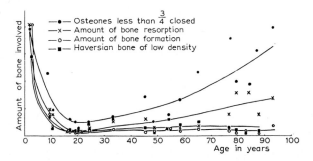

Fig. 9. Structural variations in bone tissue at various ages as seen in the Haversian bone of the mid-shaft of the femur.

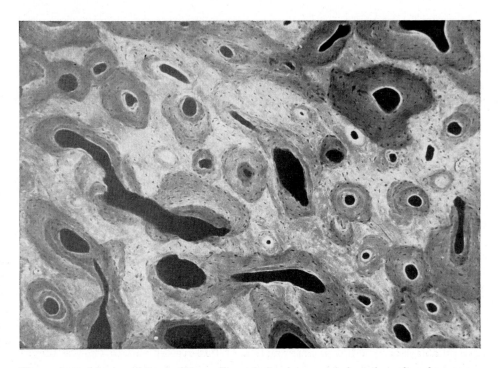

Fig. 10. ($\times$ 70) 84 year-old male. Microradiograph showing several plugged canals and numerous filled lacunae.

References p. 215

with plugged canals can also be identified in decalcified and stained preparations by the presence of amorphous basophilic material in their central canals, and by the absence of any central blood vessel (Fig. 11). Death of osteocytes has clearly occurred in the filled lacunae, and it is of interest that conspicuous areas of acellular bone are present in the decalcified and stained sections of bone from cases where they occur (Fig. 11).

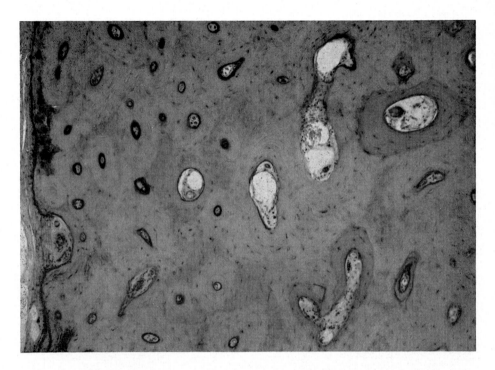

Fig. 11. (× 70) 84 year-old male. Decalcified celloidin section stained with haematoxylin and eosin. The central canals of several osteones are occupied by amorphous basophilic material. Conspicuous areas of acellular bone are also present.

The areas of acellular bone are more extensive than the patches of filled lacunae, and it appears that not all dead osteocytes have reached the stage of calcification. While a few plugged canals and calcified lacunae are found at 20 years of age, their incidence does not show much increase until late in life.

CONCLUSION

This preliminary attempt at a quantitative estimate of bone renewal and other features of bone structure has demonstrated important variations in the structure of the cortical bone of the mid-femoral shaft at different ages. During childhood there is evidence of rapid turnover of growing bone tissue. In young adults there is a remarkable lack of either bone formation or bone resorption. In old age there is evidence of extensive bone resorption with little indication of increased bone formation.

References p. 215

REFERENCES

H. A. Sissons, Osteoporosis of Cushing's syndrome, in *Proceedings of Lankenau Conference on "Bone as a Tissue"*, Blakiston Co., New York (in course of publication).

2 J. Jowsey, *J. Sci. Instr.*, 32 (1955) 159.

3 H. A. Sissons, J. Jowsey and L. Stewart, this volume, p. 32

4 R. Amprino and A. Bairati, *Z. Zellforsch. u. mikroskop. Anat.*, 24 (1936) 439.

5 K. H. Knese, *Knochenstruktur als Verbundbau*, Georg Thieme Verlag, Stuttgart, 1958.

DISCUSSION

B. Lindström (*Dept. of Medical Physics, Karolinska Institute*):

In the application of microradiographic methods to mineralized tissues the main interest has been focused on the inorganic fraction, mainly due to the favourable absorption conditions of hydroxyapatite. However, the organic fraction must be as important, but it is more difficult to investigate. Recently we have analysed the two main components in mineralized tissues by a new microradiographic method. Sections of mineralized objects, about 20 μ thick, are microradiographed with strictly mono-chromatic X-rays, one wavelength being situated on the short wavelength side of the K absorption edge of calcium (chromium $K\alpha_{1,2}$ radiation), and the other on the long wavelength side of the K absorption edge of phosphorus (zirconium $L\beta_1$ radiation). For chromium $K\alpha_{1,2}$ radiation the mass absorption coefficient of organic material is small compared with that of the inorganic fraction, and for zirconium $L\beta_1$ radiation the ratio between the mass absorption coefficients for the organic and the inorganic fraction has a relative maximum, as neither calcium nor phosphorus have any K absorption at this wavelength. Utilizing this method we can analyse the two main fractions in mineralized tissues quantitatively in a non-destructive way, but until now we have only obtained preliminary biological results.

I. Molenaar (*Dept. of Histology, State University, Utrecht*):

I think Dr. Lindström is very right, and I would like to use this opportunity for stressing the importance of another part of organic matter, the soft tissue around the bone proper, *i.e.* that region in which osteoblasts and osteoclasts are lying. If ever we want to see something and say something about this region, we cannot do so using thick or rather thick sections; even 50 μ is far too thick. One has to make the specimen much thinner, down to 5—10 μ, for two reasons. Firstly, to see details in the soft tissue one has to use soft radiation; secondly, only in very thin sections will the resolution be in the order we want. In view of this we developed the apparatus for making very thin sections. Further, we tried also to look for the organic matrix of the bone proper, not by using special, on phosphorus directed radiation like Dr. Lind-ström did, but by decalcifying very carefully and using polychromatic radiation. Then one sees very clearly that the organic matrix is not distributed evenly but that the bone-spicules are lined with a high-X-ray-absorbing zone; this zone can also be seen around the lacunae, in which the osteocytes lie. We have good reasons for thinking that these zones contain acid and neutral mucopolysaccharides in a highly polymerized state. We suggest that this layer of condensed material can have a function in forming a barrier between the bone material proper (the mixture of collagen, mucopolysaccharides and apatite crystals) and all the cellular elements plus tissue fluid.

MICRORADIOGRAPHY IN QUANTITATIVE MICROPALAEONTOLOGY: TECHNIQUES

KENNETH HOOPER

Carleton University, Ottawa, Ont. (Canada)

ABSTRACT

Projection microradiography (PMR) and contact microradiography (CMR) produce microradiographs from which internal structure measurements are taken for large samples of fossil foraminifera populations.

For CMR, errors of penumbral blurring, emulsion grain size, resolution limits, photomicrography and projection are less than 5 %. Total percentage errors vary inversely with size of structure measured. A comparison of CMR with the conventional sectioning method shows errors of ±7%.

Microradiographic methods are considered nondestructive, faster and more accurate than sectioning methods and are suitable for some quantitative population studies in the foraminifera.

INTRODUCTION

The 'new palaeontology' is concerned with quantitative studies of fossil populations. Microfossils are especially important because; (a) many hundreds, even thousands, may be contained in 1 cm³ of rock, and (b) many have great value in correlation of rock strata. Conventional methods for measuring internal structures of individual microfossils depend upon sectioning techniques which are destructive, tedious and inaccurate. This paper outlines, in briefest detail, two microradiographic techniques which have been applied to the biometrical and statistical study of the foraminiferal genus *Operculina*[1], and are nondestructive, fast, and more accurate than conventional methods.

TECHNIQUES

CONTACT MICRORADIOGRAPHY (CMR) [2,3]

The ordinary X-ray diffraction equipment of the University of Cambridge, Department of Mineralogy, was used; two simple brass cylindrical cameras were made to hold the specimens and the maximum-resolution plates.

The apparatus consisted of a continuously evacuated demountable X-ray tube, a straight line tungsten filament focussed by bias, a copper target, (water cooled) and a beryllium window, diameter 5 mm. The 1 mm² spot was line-focussed; the take-off angle of X-rays was 5° and the distance from spot to window, 25 mm. It was operated at 30 kV, 18 mA.

To hold the specimen and plates, two cameras were cut from 2 inch diameter, ⅛ inch thick walled brass tubing so that the total plate–spot distance was 40 cm (Fig. 1a). A series of baffle rings was inserted in the tubes to give an image diameter of 4 cm and to prevent X-rays, reflected from the brass tube walls, reaching the photographic plate. A thin piece of black paper in the aperture prevented light

intrusion. The specimen holder comprised an adhesive "sellotape" sheet fixed to a
cardboard annulus of interior diameter 4 cm, exterior diameter 6 cm. This was fixed
to a brass ring of depth 0.5 cm, diameter 6 cm, with the adhesive surface upwards as

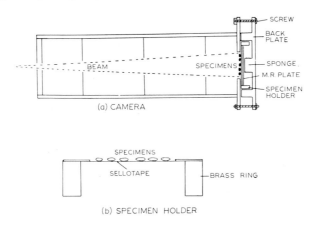

(a) CAMERA

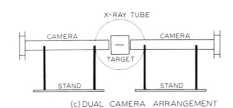

(b) SPECIMEN HOLDER

(c) DUAL CAMERA ARRANGEMENT

Fig. 1. Contact microradiography.

shown in the diagram (Fig. 1b.). The foraminifera were placed upon the adhesive
surface of the "sellotape" in a plane spiral. The holder was held in position by a brass
plate screwed on the rear of the camera tube, as shown in the Fig. 1a.

The procedure followed was to take previously numbered specimens from the
population sample according to the sequence given for random numbers in ref.[4].
Each specimen was measured for thickness at the centre, by micrometer screw gauge.
A description of its external features was made and in the case of strongly umbonate
or lenticular forms, which tended to lie at an oblique angle, the central ornament was
removed to ensure a horizontal position and a clearer microradiograph. The specimen
was then pressed upon the adhesive surface of the "sellotape". The specimens were
carefully checked for horizontality.

The position of the cameras with respect to the X-ray beam was arranged by
resting them upon stands (see Fig. 1c). Only the central portion of the beam was
utilised so that at a distance of 40 cm and an image diameter of 4 cm, for all practical
purposes the X-rays may be regarded as parallel. The cameras were loaded under
"safe light" conditions; Kodak Maximum Resolution Plate being cut to size and
placed, emulsion to non-adhesive side of the "sellotape", in the specimen holder.
The holder was then placed in position with the specimen-bearing (adhesive) surface

forwards. The brass back plate was screwed into position and the cameras were placed upon their stands with protective lead linings in position. The X-ray beam was switched on.

Exposure times were 5 h at 18 mA 30 kV for thin specimens and 7 h at 18 mA 30 kV for thick specimens. The long exposure times necessary using this method were compensated for by the large number (200 max.) of specimens that could be handled per exposure per camera; in addition two cameras could be operated from one X-ray tube concurrently. The processed plate (the negative) was not suitable for direct enlargement because of density variations from image to image over the plate area. It was necessary to photocopy the image of each specimen separately.

Photomicrography of contact microradiographs

Ordinary microscopes with the usual ocular–objective combinations were not suitable for photomicrography of the individual specimen images because the small diameter of the microscope tube gives a small field of view, and variation in size of *Operculina* is large. Thus, frequently it was not possible to photograph the entire specimen in one frame. The following apparatus was constructed to avoid the difficulty (Fig. 2).

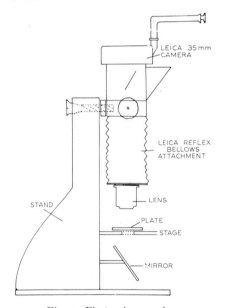

Fig. 2. Photomicrography.

A heavy metal bracketpiece was modified to form a stand for a 35 mm Leica camera (lens removed) with a Leica reflex bellows attachment. A series of holes drilled in the stand allowed the vertical position of the camera and attachment, and the stage to be varied by adjusting a screw. The reflex attachment was modified to take interchangeable lenses, checked for maximum flatness of field to reduce distortion of the image by the maximum. The contact microradiograph was placed emulsion upwards upon the stage over a previously drilled 1 cm diameter hole in line vertically with the lens. To accommodate the full range of size variation of *Operculina*, adjustments were made to lens, bellows and camera height to give optimum magnification of individual specimen image. Two lenses and two positions of the camera relative to the stage (*i.e.* film to microradiograph plate distance) were necessary. Thus two series of exposures were required, the apparatus being focussed upon a graticule of known size at the beginning of each film roll or when the magnification was changed. Later this graticule frame was used to obtain 100 times total enlargement by projection (see "Projecting and Viewing Apparatus").

METHOD OF MAKING MEASUREMENTS

Projection

The apparatus comprised; (a) a Leitz Prado 150 watt projector with a Hektor f-8.5 cm lens, (b) a portable viewer, (c) a tape recorder, (d) translucent graph paper lined in mm, (e) transparent ruler and protractor.

The viewer was essentially a collapsible wooden "box" with one side removed and a lid of good quality ⅛ inch plate glass 32 cm square, set in a wooden frame (Fig. 3). A good quality plate glass mirror was set in the "box" at an angle of 45°.

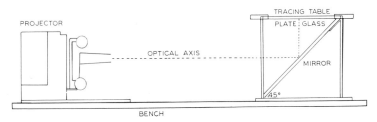

Fig. 3. Projecting and viewing apparatus.

The viewer was placed upon a bench and tilted forward, so that the glass lid formed a tracing table, with the surface inclined slightly towards the operator for convenience of drawing. Translucent graph paper was placed upon the glass surface and made fast with "sellotape".

Arrangement of the apparatus

The projector was set up facing the open end of the viewer with its axis parallel to the bench and at right angles to the viewer. The graticule (first frame of the film strip) was projected, the projector to viewer distance being adjusted to give 100 times total enlargement of the graticule upon the tracing paper. The projector was then securely fixed in position.

Distortion test

A series of comparative measurements over sections of the projected graticule image was made. It was found that the distortion between the centre and the perimeter was less than 2 %. Because the graticule is photographed with the photomicrographic apparatus described, the total distortion (optical and photographic), from apparatus, projector and viewer, is included in this figure.

References p. 223

Measurement

The image of an operculine was projected upon the graph tracing paper, and the lines of structures to be measured were strengthened, with a sharp H.B. pencil. Eyestrain was reduced by inserting a green filter in the projector. Measurements were made with a ruler and protractor in the same sequence as their headings appeared upon the raw data sheets and were called in the same sequence into the tape recorder. Later, the tape was played back and the measurements were written onto the raw data sheets. It was estimated that the time taken to make the 14,000 measurements recorded, was reduced 50 % by using the tape recorder in this way. Details of the internal structures measured are not given here, but may be found in the literature[1].

Discussion of accuracy

Penumbral blurring. NIXON[5] has discussed the limitation imposed upon contact microradiography by penumbral unsharpness. This is given by the formula,

$$\frac{f}{p} = \frac{d}{t}$$

where f is focal spot size
p is penumbral blurring
d is distance of specimen from spot
t is thickness of specimen

$$\therefore p = \frac{ft}{d}$$

Substituting the values used in this work, we have, (assuming average thickness of specimen to be 0.5 mm — a rather high estimate)

$$p = \frac{1 \times 0.5 \text{ mm}}{400} = \frac{1}{800} \text{ mm}$$

penumbra blurring $= 1.25\ \mu$.

Thus we cannot have complete depth sharpness in the CMR method. This is important in stereomicroradiography[1,6,7].

Limitation due to grain size and granularity of the photographic emulsion. The properties of fine grained photographic emulsions used in microradiography are stated by ENGSTRÖM and LINDSTRÖM[7-9]. In the present work, Kodak Maximum Resolution Plates were used, for which the makers claim a resolving power of 1000 lines per mm. The contraction or elongation of the emulsion was less than 0.1 %.

Resolution. In discussing the resolution obtainable using CMR, NIXON[5] has illustrated a 3 μ triangular metal grid, (1) contact microradiographed, (2) photo-micrographed, for comparison. The triangular bars of the grid are thinner in the former image than the latter. This is due to the excessive X-ray penetration at the edges of the bar. Thus it is necessary to distinguish between the resolution limit and the contrast. Therefore, correct exposure and development of the photographic plates for the structures of particular interest is important. From these considerations it is apparent that the resolution limit is in the order of 1.25 μ for this work.

The effect of the shape of the internal structures. From NIXON's comparative images measurement of curved structures, such as the proloculus wall, might be seriously in error if the wall is very thin or the radius of curvature very small. It has been calculated that as the thinnest wall in the foraminifera used here is 10 μ, and it has a radius of curvature 30 μ, then, the loss of resolution of the outer edge is less than 0.5 μ, or 5 % of wall thickness. This is an extreme case, for the vast majority of specimens it must be considerably less. This could be a serious disadvantage for measurement of marginal and septal canals, pores and other very small foraminiferal structures.

Errors due to photomicrography, projector and viewer. These have already been discussed on page 5 and estimated at 2 %. However, this figure does not include pencil and ruler errors.

Pencil error. The thickness of a fine line upon tracing graph paper, drawn by a sharp H.B. pencil was estimated as 0.2 mm. Comparing this to the minimum proloculus wall thickness, 10 μ, which enlarged 100 times became 1 mm on the image we have,

$$\frac{0.2 \text{ mm}}{100} = \frac{1}{5} = 20\%$$

Thus, the maximum possible error for the extreme case is 20 % of the wall thickness. However, this structure has not been used as a character. In the case of the minimum proloculus radius, a character that has been used, the largest error is 10 % of the radius. This is the greatest error possible in this work and it occurs in this extreme case. All other errors must be less than it.

Comparative test with the sectioning method. It seemed advisable to compare measurements obtained by contact microradiography with those of the conventional sectioning methods. Ideally, all the specimens microradiographed, or a random sample of them, should be sectioned and measurements compared; to have done this would have destroyed the specimens which were required for further study. Therefore one large, one medium and one small specimen was sectioned giving an approximate estimate of comparative measurements, the average error being $\pm$ 7 %.

PROJECTION MICRORADIOGRAPHY (PMR)

The COSSLETT and NIXON projection X-ray microscope, as described in the literature[5,10], equipped with a 9 μ copper foil target, was also used to produce microradiographs of foraminifera. Very fine-grained emulsions were not essential because some magnification of image is inherent in projection X-ray microscopy. Thus it was possible to use pan F film. The camera described below is suitable for handling 20 5 mm diameter specimens per exposure. Foraminifera are usually smaller than this, however, and a greater number may be radiographed per exposure if desired.

The brass camera in which a series of detachable slotted brass arcs act as object holders, carries a 35 mm film strip (Fig. 4). The arc-shaped holders are fitted to

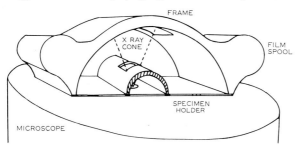

Fig. 4. Projection X-ray microscope camera.

calculated point-source to object distances. The fossils are placed upon adhesive "sellotape" fixed over a cut-out area (the window of the holder), so that they are each normal to the X-rays which emerge from the point-source to form a 60° solid angle cone. This radial arrangement reduces distortion of the image from parallax, which, because the fossil has an average thickness of approx. 0.5 mm, could be serious at short distances from the normal ray (Fig. 5b). In the width direction the holder

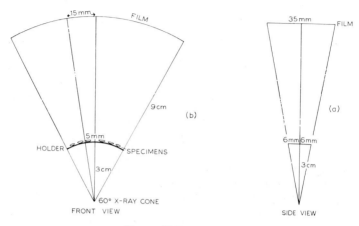

Fig. 5. X-Ray cone.

is not curved (Fig. 5a), and it has been calculated that in order to avoid more than $2\frac{1}{2}$ % distortion of image due to specimen thickness, a maximum distance of 6 mm from the normal is required. Thus two rows of six 5 mm diameter specimens could be accommodated at a holder distance 3 mm from the source (*i.e.* radius of curvature 3 mm) giving a magnification approx. 3 times with the film 9 cm from the source and an exposure time approx. 100 min. By increasing the radius of curvature of the holder, more specimens could be accommodated, but magnification would be lower. However, exposure time would not be affected. After processing, the film strip may be placed in a projector and measurements taken as described above (p. 219). A typical microradiograph, at × 26, is shown in Fig. 6.

PMR AND CMR COMPARED

Stereomicroradiography should be possible by PMR because of the greater depth of focus which is theoretically possible.

In PMR, film strip microradiographs are produced directly, the photomicrographic stage is unnecessary. On the other hand, with CMR, a greater number of specimens may be handled per exposure, and X-ray diffraction apparatus is commonly available whereas microfocus apparatus is rare.

Future work

The development of stereomicroradiography[6, 7, 11, 12] on a quantitative basis should increase the number and kind of internal structure measurements that can be made. Microradiographic techniques should make the rapid examination of many foraminifera populations a practical proposition for micropalaeontologists.

References p. 223

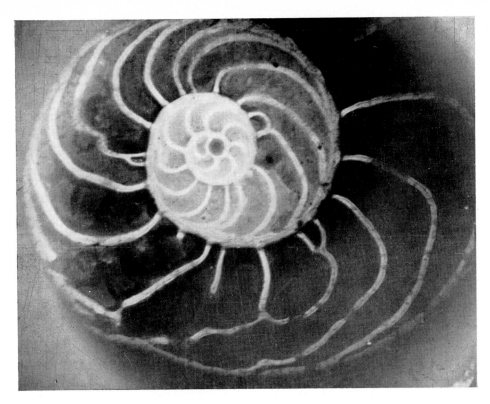

Fig. 6. Typical microradiograph of an operculine, × 26.

ACKNOWLEDGEMETS

Thanks are due to Drs. COSSLETT, NIXON and LONG of the Cavendish Laboratory, University of Cambridge, for facilities and helpful encouragement.

REFERENCES

1 K. HOOPER, *Studies in Operculina: M. Sc. Thesis*, University of London, 1958.
2 R. H. HEDLEY, *Micropalaeontology*, 3, No. 1 (1957) 19.
3 R. A. M. SCHMIDT, *Science*, 115 (1952), 94.
4 FISHER and YATES, *Statistical tables for Biological, Agricultural and Medical Research*, Oliver and Boyd, Edinburgh and London, 1957, p. 126.
5 W. C. NIXON and A. V. BAEZ, *Lectures on the X-ray Microscope: University of Redlands, Calif.*, 1956.
6 SVEN BELLMAN, *Acta Radiol., Suppl.* 102 (1953).
7 A. ENGSTRÖM, in G. OSTLER, *Physical Techniques in Biological Research*, Vol. III, Academic Press, Inc., New York, 1957, p. 503.
8 A. ENGSTRÖM and LINDSTRÖM, *Acta Radiol.*, 35 (1951) 33.
9 A. ENGSTRÖM, *Acta Radiol., Suppl.* 63 (1946).
10 V. E. COSSLETT and W. C. NIXON, *J. Appl. Phys.*, 24 (1953) 616.
11 A. E. BARCLAY, *Micro-arteriography*, Blackwell Scientific Publications, Oxford, 1951.
12 P. BURKHARDT and J. G. HELMCKE, in *Proc. Intern. Conf. Electron Microscopy*, Royal Microscopical Soc., London, 1954, p. 651.

2. VASCULAR STRUCTURES

MICRORADIOGRAPHIC TECHNIQUES USED TO STUDY THE LIVER VESSELS IN RATS

J. R. BLICKMAN
Radiological Institute, State University, Groningen

P. J. KLOPPER
Surgical University Clinic, Amsterdam

A. RECOURT
Physical Technical X-ray Laboratory of Philips' Gloeilampenfabrieken, Eindhoven
(The Netherlands)

ABSTRACT

The preparation technique used to study the vascular pattern in the liver is described. It is followed by a report on the preparation of the material, the micro-angiography of the fixed liver lobes and of thin sections of these lobes. The results obtained by using this technique are described separately.

To study the hepatic vascular bed we made use of radiographic techniques after injecting radiopaque substances. For these studies adult rats were used. A laparatomy was performed under ether anaesthesia. In the cases of portal vein injection a plastic cannula was tied in the portal vein. The thorax was opened, and the aorta clamped. The injection was administered slowly, until even distribution of the contrast substance in the hepatic lobes could be observed.

The contrast medium we used was Micropaque (Damancy and Co.) in 25 % saline solution. According to the manufacturers 0.5 μ average particle size may be expected. On completion of the injection the animal was dead. The cannula was removed and the animal submerged in 10 % formaline for at least 48 h, after which the liver was removed. For injection into the hepatic artery the same general procedure was followed, except that the cannula was tied into the abdominal aorta, the aorta being clamped at the level of the diaphragm. Injection of the hepatic vein bed was obtained by tying the cannula in the inferior vena cava.

The portal vein was opened prior to making the injection and after clamping the lower vena cava below the renal veins.

The lobes of the fixed livers were in the first place radiographed separately with an X-ray diffraction unit. In most cases a tube with Mo target was used. The technical data are: 25—30 kV, 20 mA, focus–film distance 40 cm. The film emulsion used was a Gevaert fine-grain film type No. 053. This emulsion permits an enlargement of 25 to 30 times. In a later stage a small Philips diffraction unit (PW 1008) was available, this having a microfocus diffraction tube (400 μ) with Cu anode. With this apparatus it is possible to use the tube in 2 positions with the X-rays in the vertical or in the horizontal direction. An advantage of this instrument is that it is very easy to do stereographic work with the standard apparatus. The pictures obtained by using the diffraction unit provide a clear image of the vascular system down to a diameter of approx. 0.3 mm. As far as the portal system is concerned, this means that all of the contributing vein system is visible; the distributing veins and sinusoids are, however, not shown clearly. For identifying the finer details we made use of micro-radiography. The microradiographic apparatus used was the type CMR 5, made by Philips.

As we used 25 μ-thick frozen sections (thinner sections do not give sufficient information) it can be calculated that the geometric blurring at a focus–film distance of 24 mm is about 0.3 μ.

Many difficulties arise from the need to make the specimens sufficiently flat to do microradiographic work. The relatively thick sections come off the supporting film during the drying period or, in other cases, the supporting films crack. It has been shown that formvar films made from 4 % solution in chloroform give far better results, *i.e.* they are much freer from the above faults than collodion films or formvar films made of lower concentrations. The 4 % films are relatively thick, but this proved to be no disadvantage, because of the rather thick sections used. Mounting the section with an intermediate film directly on the photographic emulsions did not give any better results. This technique provides excellent pictures with thin sections, but thicker ones are also liable to come off the emulsion. The use of celloidin as an embedding medium has likewise given only negative results. The dried preparations are microradiographed on Eastman Kodak spectroscopic emulsion 649-0. The technical data are: W-anode; 5 kV, 2 mA.

For our own use we have made a film cassette designed to allow a section with a diameter of about 12 mm to be radiographed. In addition, we rotate the camera about its vertical axis during the exposure. This is done to make sure that dirt on the tube window does not spoil part of the image. Any inhomogeneity is then spread over a larger area.

MICRORADIOGRAPHIC INVESTIGATION OF THE ACTION OF VASOCONSTRICTOR DRUGS ON THE LIVER VESSELS IN RATS

J. R. BLICKMAN
Radiological Institute, State University, Groningen
P. J. KLOPPER
Surgical University Clinic, Amsterdam
A. RECOURT
Philips Gloeilampenfabrieken, Eindhoven
(The Netherlands)

ABSTRACT

By means of microradiography, the authors studied the influence of vaso-constrictor drugs on the liver vessels of rats. The drugs (epinephrine and norepinephrine) were given by way of the portal and hepatic vein and by the hepatic artery.

In slides, a distinct contraction of the liver vessels and sinusoids could be shown.

From the results it can be concluded that in the liver, not only the vessels but also the sinusoids contract under the influence of vasocon-strictor drugs.

The action of vasoconstrictor drugs on the portal area is a fascinating physiological and pharmacological problem. The portal area with its twofold supply of blood: a venous supply from the mesenteric and splenic veins, an arterial supply from the hepatic artery, has only the hepatic veins for an efferent blood flow.

We can give only a comprehensive description of the pertinent data. The knowledge on the anatomy of the liver tissue has made great progress since the investigations by ELIAS have shown the exact relationship between liver vessels and liver cells.

Injection studies on the normal anatomy of the three vascular systems in the rat liver have been published previously by us[1] (Figs 1—3). These normal anatomic vascular conditions have been found to be reproducible in normal rats.

The influence of vasopressor drugs on the portal circulation has been studied extensively, however with conflicting results. Most authors are in agreement on the following effects of these drugs:

a. rise of portal vein pressure
b. changes in hepatic blood flow
c. decrease of liver volume.

Increased portal vein pressure occurs both after administration of vasopressor drugs in the general circulation and in the portal vein area. Although the pattern of this pressure rise shows distinct differences, the time of response shows that a direct liver action must be held, perhaps partly, responsible.

From this follows that changes must occur in the hepatic blood flow. Portography performed in animals before and after administration of vasopressor substances

References p. 232

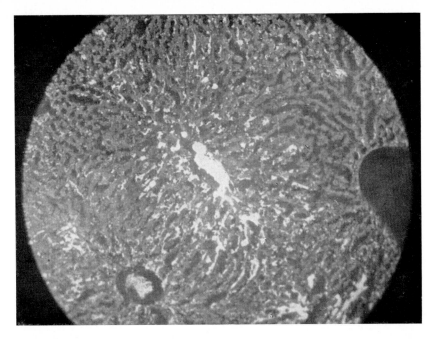

Fig. 1. Portal vein injection shows the typical structure of the portal space with the distributing veins running towards the portal side of the sinusoids.

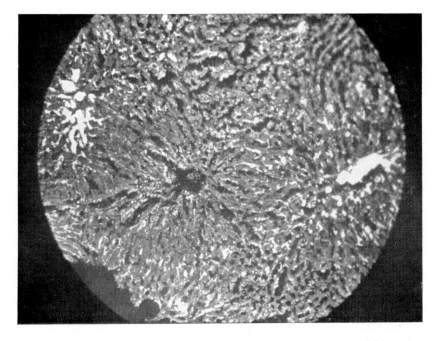

Fig. 2. The normal aspect of the hepatic artery after injection shows the arterial branches, with contrast substance present in the portal area; hepatic vein and hepatic sinusoids do not contain contrast substance.

References p. 232

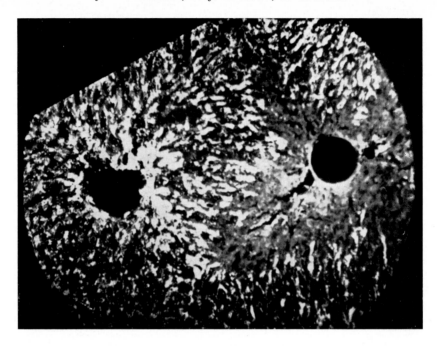

Fig. 3. Retrograde injection of the hepatic vein shows filling of the straight hepatic sinusoids without backflow into the portal vein area.

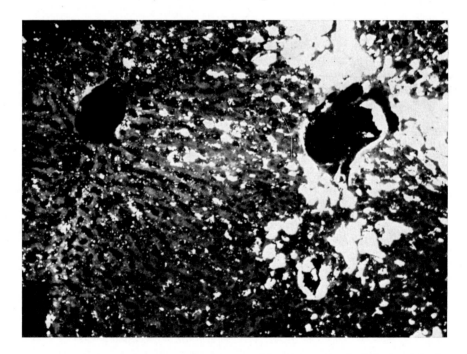

Fig. 4. Injection of contrast substance (micropaque) in the portal vein following injection of 0.2 μg of adrenaline the same vein. The portal side of the sinusoidal system is overfilled. The distributing veins are obviously blocked, as practically no contrast substance is visible in the central sinusoids. These show distinct narrowing (Fig. 5).

References p. 232

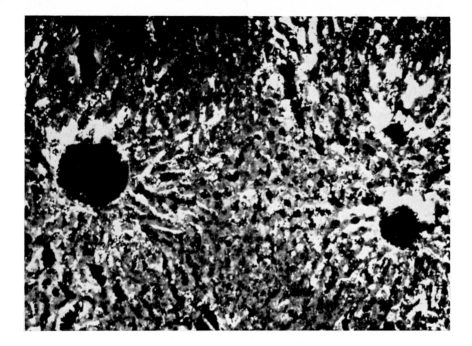

Fig. 5a.

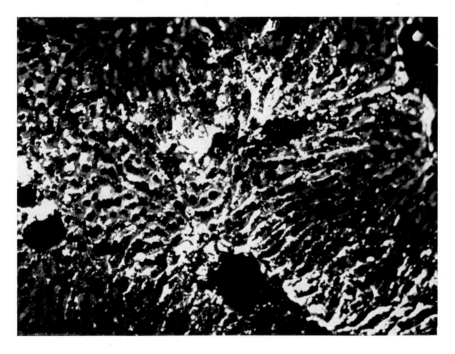

Fig. 5b. Injection of contrast substance in the portal vein following injection of 0.2 μg of adrenaline in the tibial vein.

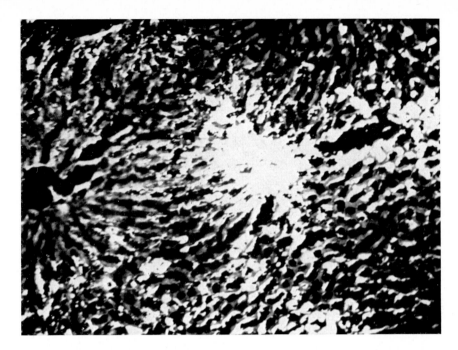

Fig. 6. Generalized filling of all sinusoids after intraportal administration of adrenaline. Both the portal and the central sinusoids are full.

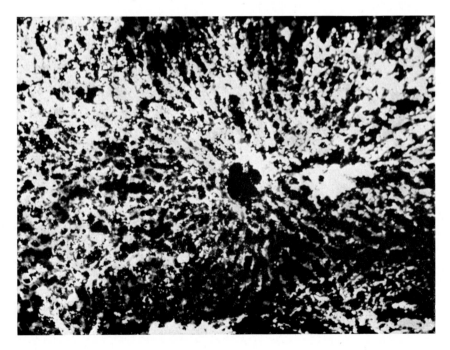

Fig. 7. The same overall picture, with filling of the entire sinusoid, but to a lesser degree. In this case noradrenaline was administered intraportally.

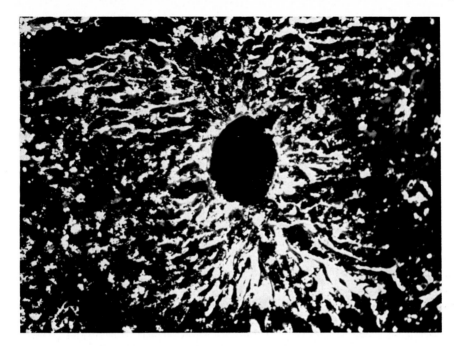

Fig. 8. Narrowing of the central part of the sinusoids, without reflux into the portal side.

Fig. 9. The same impression of narrowing of the central sinusoids.

shows a general narrowing of the branches of the portal vein. This can be interpreted as a direct action of muscular elements in the portal vein wall or can be due to an active decrease in liver volume. The first mode of action has been advocated on grounds of sphincter-like muscular elements found in the hepatic veins of dogs.

Much attention has been given to the action of the liver sinusoids since the transillumination method has made the study of the liver tissue *in vivo* possible.

Several authors[2-4] described the regulating action of the sinusoidal system by shunting blood from one contributing system to another. The possibility of drawing on the large amount of "resting" sinusoids must be borne in mind.

Transillumination studies of the sinusoids give subjective information. We therefore used microradioangiography as means for the study of sinusoidal behaviour after administration of vasopressor drugs.

The vasopressor drugs can be administered in two different ways: into the general circulation or into the portal circulation. At the moment of maximal effect, the contrast substance can be injected into one of the three vascular systems.

Generally, death follows immediately upon completion of the injection. After fixation of the animal in formalin, frozen sections are made of the liver tissue. Microradioangiography is performed, using the technique described by RECOURT in the previous paper[5]. The results will be shown in the Figs. 4–9.

Fig. 5a shows essentially the same picture as Fig. 4. Obviously there is an impeded flow towards the central sinusoids. Another picture from the same liver, Fig. 5b, shows that the impediment may be overcome. Whether this must be considered as an artifact is not certain. The next two figures show the result of injection of contrast substance in the hepatic artery (Figs. 6 and 7).

Retrograde injection of the hepatic vein with contrast substance was performed in the last two animals, one following injection in the tibial vein (Figs. 8 and 9).

The results from these experiments may be interpreted as follows: The action of vasopressor drugs on the liver parenchyma, known to result in elevation of the portal pressure, produces changes in the hepatic blood flow and in liver volume which result in a generalized narrowing of the central sinusoids.

The distributing veins are not clearly influenced, there seems to be a sharp borderline. The hepatic artery contributes to a much larger degree to the filling of both the hepatic and portal sinusoidal area.

In conclusion, we may state that microradioangiography must be considered as a valuable adjunct in the study of the complex action of the liver blood-vessels.

REFERENCES

[1] J. R. BLICKMAN, A. RECOURT and P. J. KLOPPER, *J. belge radiol.*, 41 (1959) 452.
[2] W. ANDREWS, *Brit. Med. Bull.*, 13 (1957) 82.
[3] C. G. CHILD, *The Hepatic Circulation and Portal Hypertension*, Saunders, Philadelphia, 1954.
[4] H. D. GREEN, L. S. HALL, J. SEXTON and C. P. DEAL, *Am. J. Physiol.*, 196 (1959) 196.
[5] J. R. BLIKMAN, P. KLOPPER and A. RECOURT, this volume, p. 224.

ÉTUDE PHYSIO-ANATOMIQUE DE L'OPACIFICATION DE LA LAME CRIBLÉE PAR MICRORADIOGRAPHIE

G. F. LEROUX, J. FRANÇOIS, J. M. COLLETTE et A. NEETENS

Laboratoire de Radiodiagnostic de l'Université de Liége, Hôpital de Bavière, Liége et Clinique ophtalmologique de l'Université de Gand (Belgique)

ABSTRACT

PHYSIO-ANATOMICAL STUDY OF THE OPAQUENESS OF THE LAMINA CRIBROSA SCLERAE BY MICRORADIOGRAPHY

On perfusion of the ophthalmic artery under a pressure of at least 350 mm Hg, with simultaneous injection of thorotrast into one of the short posterior ciliary artery under a pressure of 200 mm Hg, the eyeball becomes hard, and microradiography reveals that thorotrast is absent at the level of the lamina cribrosa sclerae.

If the anterior chamber of the eye is punctured, or the pressure of perfusion in the ophthalmic artery diminished, or the pressure of injection into the short posterior ciliary artery increased, microradiography shows that the vascular system of the lamina cribrosa is well filled with thorotrast.

If the pressure of injection into the short posterior ciliary artery is diminished while the pressure of perfusion of the ophthalmic artery is maintained at 350 mm Hg, no thorotrast is found in the lamina cribrosa sclerae.

Après avoir trépané le canal optique, nous enlevons tout le contenu orbitaire en même temps qu'une partie du contenu intracranien, comprenant l'artère ophtalmique et le segment correspondant de la carotide interne. Le contenu orbitaire est enlevé en bloc après avoir détaché le périoste le long des quatre parois osseuses. Comme les paupières sont laissées en place, nous suturons la conjonctive des culs de sac au périoste. Les orifices veineux au niveau de la fissure orbitaire supérieure sont laissés ouverts. Mais à partir de l'artère ophtalmique, on perfuse tout le réseau vasculaire à l'aide d'une solution aqueuse colorée (bleu de Paton ou bleu de méthylène), de façon à pouvoir placer une ligature au niveau de tous les points de ,,leakage''.

Après avoir ainsi préparé notre matériel d'expérimentation, nous perfusons l'artère ophtalmique pendant 10 à 15 minutes, à l'aide de thorotrast sous une pression d'environ 350 mm Hg, qui est de temps à autre augmentée jusqu'à 450 ou 500 mm Hg. Nous pouvons alors constater que:

1. le système vasculaire de l'uvée est très bien rempli, mais la tête du nerf optique (lame criblée) et la rétine sont tout à fait vides.

2. En même temps, le globe oculaire devient dur et le diaphragme irido-cristallinien se déplace en avant. Une ponction décompressive de la chambre antérieure permet le remplissage de la tête du nerf optique et de la rétine.

Si l'on perfuse l'artère ophtalmique pendant un temps plus long, 45 à 60 min, sous une pression constante de 350 à 500 mm Hg, ce que nous avons fait dans deux expériences, on observe qu'assez brusquement, au bout de 30 à 45 min, la tension oculaire baisse, en même temps que le diaphragme irido-cristallinien se remet en place.

Le but de ces expériences étant avant tout de nous rendre compte de ce qui se passe au niveau de la tête du nerf optique, nous avons perfusé l'artère ophtalmique avec du serum physiologique légèrement coloré, et injecté en même temps du thorotrast dans une artère ciliaire postérieure brève, que nous isolons après incision du périoste enveloppant le contenu orbitaire et dissection de ce dernier jusqu'au niveau du nerf optique juxtabulbaire, tout en prenant évidemment soin d'éviter le moindre vaisseau important et de suturer les fuites éventuelles.

Nous plaçons une ligature sur l'artère ciliaire postérieure brève, que nous intubons ensuite à l'aide d'une fine aiguille, maintenue par une suture. Cette aiguille est raccordée soit à un système manométrique, soit à une seringue, munie d'un manomètre à ressort. Si l'on utilise le système manométrique, la pression est gardée constante; si l'on utilise la seringue elle peut varier.

Nous avons adopté comme pressions ,,normales'' 350 mm Hg pour la pression de perfusion de l'artère ophtalmique (P_1) et 200 mm Hg pour la pression d'injection de l'artère ciliaire postérieure brève (P_2). Ces valeurs ont été déterminées d'une façon empirique, nos expériences antérieures sur la vascularisation du globe oculaire et des voies optiques nous ayant montré que c'est avec ces pressions que nous obtenions le meilleur remplissage du système vasculaire.

Ces pressions doivent être constamment adaptées, si nous voulons les maintenir constantes; elles ont en effet, surtout au début de l'expérience, tendance à diminuer. Nos expériences n'ont d'autre part jamais été prolongées au delà de 10 à 15 min. Après ce temps, certaines modifications difficilement contrôlables peuvent intervenir.

Le Tableau I résume les résultats de nos expériences. Le nombre de ces dernières est actuellement de huit, mais dans deux cas, nous avons obtenu des résultats, qu'il est impossible d'interpréter par suite des mauvaises conditions d'expérimentation.

TABLEAU I

No.	Nombre d'expériences	Art. ophtalmique P_1 (mm Hg)	Art. cil. post. brève P_2 (mm Hg)	Remplissage du système vasculaire de la lame criblée
1	2	450	200	nul ou presque nul
2	1	250	200	parfait
3	2	350	> 200	parfait
4	1	350	< 200	nul ou presque nul

Dans aucune de nos expériences, nous n'avons fait varier les deux pressions.

Dans l'expérience du type 1, nous constatons que le globe oculaire devient plus dur et que le diaphragme irido-cristallinien se déplace en avant de façon à réduire la profondeur de la chambre antérieure.

Dans l'expérience du type 2, la tension du globe oculaire et la profondeur de la chambre antérieure ne sont pas modifiées. Le thorotrast au niveau de la papille optique est très marqué, comme s'il n'était presque pas dilué.

Dans les expériences du type 3 et du type 4, la tension du globe oculaire et la profondeur de la chambre antérieure ne sont pas modifiées non plus.

MICRORADIOGRAPHIES DE LA LAME CRIBLÉE

Expérience du type 1 (Fig. 1)

On ne voit pas de capillaires ni de grands vaisseaux au niveau de la papille optique. Un peu plus en arrière, on observe par contre quelques capillaires et des plus grands vaisseaux, qui regorgent de thorotrast, celui-ci ayant même diffusé à travers leur paroi.

Expérience du type 2 (Fig. 2)

Le réseau de la lame criblée est bien rempli. En arrière, le système vasculaire est normalement marqué. Une partie de la choroïde est également marquée.

Expérience du type 3 (Figs. 3 et 4)

Le réseau de la lame criblée est bien rempli, mais le thorotrast marque cependant moins, comme s'il était dilué par le serum physiologique, ce qui explique que l'image est moins contrastée.

Il faut remarquer que le cercle de Zinn-Haller est presque complètement rempli, alors que la lame criblée ne l'est qu'en regard de l'artère ciliaire postérieure brève qui a été injectée.

La Fig. 3 montre au centre une branche de la veine centrale de la rétine. Ce fait montre la possibilité d'une anastomose entre l'artère ciliaire postérieure brève et la veine rétinienne.

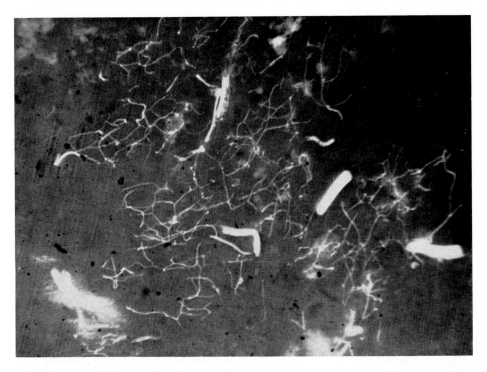

Fig. 1. *Expérience du type* 1. P_1 élevée, P_2 normale. Vue transversale du nerf optique, à 1 mm derrière la pupille (agrandissement 37.5 ×).

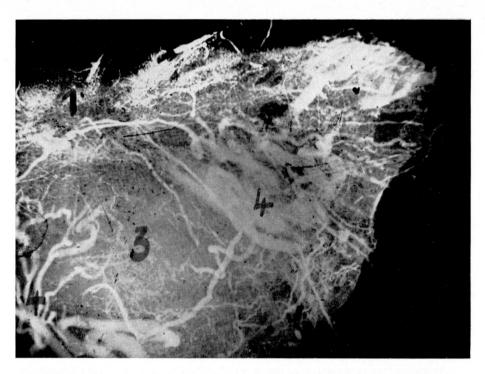

Fig. 2. *Expérience du type* 2. P_1 basse, P_2 normale. 1. Papille; 2. Choroïde; 3. Nerf optique; 4. Anneau de Zinn-Haller. (Agrandissement 15 ×.)

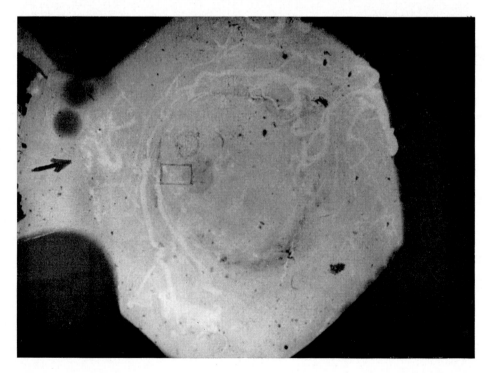

Fig. 3. *Expérience du type* 3. P_1 normale, P_2 élevée. La → indique la région de l'artère ciliaire brève injectée. (Agrandissement 15 ×.)

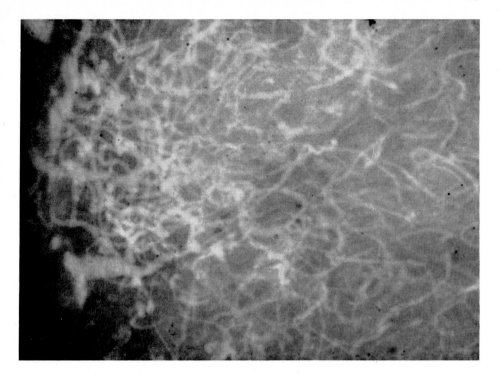

Fig. 4. *Expérience du type* 3. Agrandissement de la région papillaire opacifiée (152 ×).

Expérience du type 4

On voit au niveau du cercle de Zinn-Haller quelques grands vaisseaux à contraste peu marqué. La lame criblée elle-même est dépourvue de capillaires.

DISCUSSION ET CONCLUSIONS

1. Lorsqu'on injecte du Thorotrast dans une seule artère ciliaire postérieure brève et que le globe oculaire présente une tension normale ou diminuée, tout le système vasculaire de la lame criblée est pratiquement rempli. On obtient non seulement un remplissage parfait du réseau de Zinn-Haller et d'une partie de la papille optique, mais aussi du réseau choroïdien. Ce remplissage est d'autant meilleur que la tension du globe oculaire est moindre ou que la pression dans l'artère ciliaire postérieure brève est plus forte.

2. Lorsqu'on injecte du thorotrast dans une seule artère ciliaire postérieure brève et que le globe oculaire présente une tension exagérée, le système vasculaire de la lame criblée n'est pas rempli.

Une hypertension du système vasculaire uvéal, s'accompagnant d'une hypertension oculaire expérimentale, ischémie la lame criblée sur le plan capillaire, bien que les grands vaisseaux soient remplis de thorotrast. Les vaisseaux rétiniens sont également vides, ce qui prouve qu'il n'y a pas de communication avec l'artère centrale de la rétine et de ses branches.

En d'autres mots, dans un globe oculaire hypertendu le moindre déficit vasculaire

d'une artère ciliaire postérieure brève peut avoir de graves conséquences fonction-
nelles, tandis que, dans un œil à tension normale, l'intégrité d'une ou de deux
artères ciliaires brèves suffit à maintenir une fonction normale.

Dans le glaucome, même lorsque la circulation est intacte, l'hypertension oculaire
suffit à empêcher la circulation normale de la lame criblée.

3. Une hypertension isolée de l'artère ophtalmique, même en l'absence d'hypertension oculaire, empêche le remplissage du réseau vasculaire de la lame criblée et
par le fait même la nutrition du disque optique.

RÉSUMÉ

Si l'on perfuse l'artère ophtalmique sous une pression d'au moins 350 mm Hg et si
l'on injecte en même temps du thorotrast dans une artère ciliaire postérieure brève
sous une pression de 200 mm Hg, le globe oculaire devient dur et la microradiographie
montre l'absence de Thorotrast au niveau de la lame criblée.

Si l'on ponctionne la chambre antérieure, si l'on diminue la pression de perfusion
de l'artère ophtalmique, ou si l'on augmente la pression d'injection dans l'artère
ciliaire postérieure brève, la microradiographie montre que le système vasculaire de
la lame criblée est bien rempli de thorotrast.

Si l'on diminue la pression d'injection dans l'artère ciliaire postérieure brève
en maintenant la pression de perfusion de l'artère ophtalmique à 350 mm Hg, on ne
retrouve pas de thorotrast dans la lame criblée.

RÉSEAU CANALICULAIRE DE L'IRIS RÉVÉLÉ PAR LA MICRORADIOGRAPHIE

G. F. LEROUX, J. FRANÇOIS, J. M. COLLETTE et A. NEETENS

Laboratoire de Radio-diagnostic de l'Université de Liége, Hôpital de Bavière, Liége et Clinique ophtalmologique de l'Université de Gand (Belgique)

ABSTRACT

THE CANALICULAR NETWORK OF THE IRIS REVEALED BY MICRORADIOGRAPHY

Microradiographic study of the human iris, after perfusion of the anterior chamber with thorotrast, reveals the presence of a canalicular system from the vascular network. It is characterized by radial channels in the central area, and circular ones in the peripheral region of the iris.

Plus personne ne peut nier l'importance de l'angle irido-cornéen dans l'écoulement de l'humeur aqueuse; il suffit, sur le plan expérimental, de se rappeler que la perfusion *in vitro* de la chambre antérieure, sous une pression physiologique, montre l'apparition presque instantanée du liquide au niveau du limbe.

Il reste cependant des problèmes à résoudre et c'est un de ceux-ci que nous voulons étudier aujourd'hui.

Pour éviter que le liquide, introduit dans la chambre antérieure et s'écoulant à travers le trabeculum et le canal de Schlemm, ne pénètre dans des vaisseaux intra-scléreux, nous faisons, après avoir débarrassé le globe oculaire de toute trace de conjonctive et de tissu épiscléral, autour du limbe, une résection sclérale lamellaire et annulaire de 3 à 4 mm de largeur et pénétrant en profondeur jusque tout près du canal de Schlemm, dont le repérage est facilité par l'injection préalable de bleu de méthylène.

Nous perfusons ensuite les yeux ainsi préparés, pendant 10 min, à l'aide de thorotrast, introduit dans la chambre antérieure sous une pression physiologique (27 cm eau).

Nous examinons enfin l'iris à l'aide de la microradiographie. Cet examen nous révèle, à côté de taches superficielles irrégulières dues à l'imprégnation de la face antérieure et des cryptes de l'iris, un réseau canaliculaire inconnu, qui est situé dans le feuillet mésodermique de l'iris et qui présente deux parties; une partie péripupillaire à traits radiaires et une partie périphérique à traits circulaires (Fig. 1).

Les traits radiaires sont parallèles, mais de largeur irrégulière. Du côté pupillaire, ils dépassent le tissu mésodermique de l'iris, et se terminent soit par une anse, qui rejoint un trait voisin, soit par un point, qui constitue la jonction de deux traits radiaires.

Au niveau de la partie médiane de l'iris, ils sont reliés entre eux par des traits circulaires (Fig. 3, zone intermédiaire entre la partie péripupillaire et la partie périphérique); ils peuvent aussi s'y terminer par une formation annulaire ou ovalaire complète ou incomplète, à l'intérieur de laquelle il n'y a pas de thorotrast.

Bibliographie p. 243

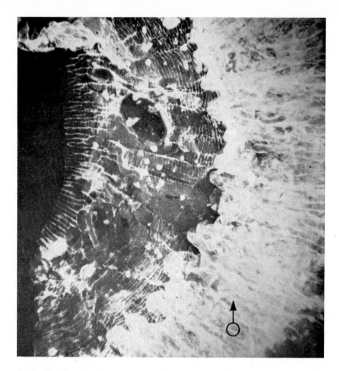

Fig. 1. Vue générale de l'iris et des procès ciliaires après imprégnation à partir de la chambre antérieure de l'œil. Le réseau canaliculaire est bien visible avec sa disposition radiaire péripupillaire et sa disposition circulaire périphérique. (En ♂: procès ciliaires; agrandissement 15 ×.)

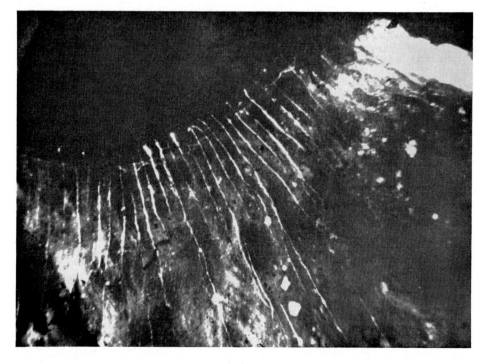

Fig. 2. Vue en agrandissement (39 ×) du réseau péripupillaire.

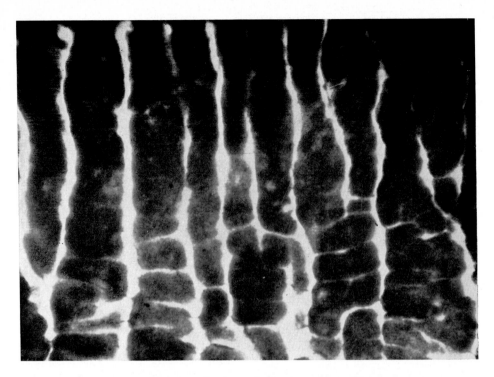

Fig. 3. Vue agrandie (150 ×) du réseau intermédiaire.

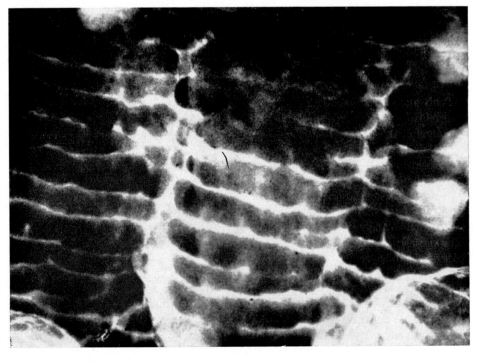

Fig. 4. Vue agrandie (150 ×) du réseau circulaire périphérique.

Au niveau de la partie périphérique de l'iris (Fig. 4) c'est une structure circulaire qui prédomine: les traits, toujours parallèles, assez rapprochés et onduleux, dessinent un réseau circulaire, entrecoupé par des traits radiaires non continus, situés à des distances plus ou moins régulières; les traits circulaires semblent converger vers ces traits radiaires, en décrivant une ligne concave vers l'intérieur.

Ce réseau régulier, qui est tout à fait différent du réseau vasculaire de l'iris et qui paraît bien canaliculaire, se retrouve dans tout iris jeune et normal.

Par contre, nous n'arrivons pas à le mettre en évidence lorsque nous perfusons la chambre antérieure sous une forte pression, de 100 cm d'eau par exemple.

Si d'autre part, nous isolons l'iris et le plaçons simplement dans du thorotrast, si nous le rinçons ensuite dans le serum physiologique et le fixons, nous retrouvons le même réseau, ce qui permet de supposer que le remplissage se fait instantanément et par capillarité.

Si nous faisons la même expérience avec un iris dépourvu de son feuillet pigmentaire, nous retrouvons encore le même réseau, ce qui permet de le localiser dans le feuillet mésodermique.

OBSERVATIONS FAITES

Que voyons-nous au cours de ces expériences de perfusion au thorotrast, sur les microradiographies du corps ciliaire et de la pars plana?

A côté des images d'imprégnation, qui constituent une belle réplique de la surface tourmentée des procès ciliaires, on peut obtenir des images plus intéressantes en enlevant ces procès ciliaires. Dans ces conditions on ne voit pas de vaisseaux, mais une ombre plus ou moins régulière, qui se continue vers la pars plana par des traits toujours dédoublés, entre lesquels s'observe également une ombre discrète caractérisant le thorotrast périvasculaire.

Déjà au niveau de la pars plana, mais d'une façon plus évidente au niveau de la choroïde, on voit ensuite apparaître au milieu des ombres périvasculaires, une structure réellement vasculaire.

DISCUSSION

Il faut se demander s'il existe au niveau de la face antérieure de l'iris de petites ouvertures, au niveau desquelles l'endothelium est absent et qui pourraient constituer les embouchures du réseau canaliculaire. ZIMMERMAN[1] (Armed Forces Institute of Pathology, Washington) a pu observer, sur des coupes d'iris humain, colorées d'après la méthode de Wilder, qu'il existe apparemment une discontinuité dans la couche cellulaire antérieure et qu'au niveau de ces interruptions il y a une accumulation de fibrilles de réticuline.

FINE ET TOUSIMIS du même Institut ont également montré, par des examens au microscope électronique, que les cellules de la face antérieure de l'iris ne forment pas une couche ininterrompue, mais qu'il existe de nombreuses ouvertures, au niveau desquelles on trouve des fibrilles dont la périodicité est caractéristique du collagène (650 Å).

GREGERSEN a perfusé *in vivo* des yeux humains à l'aide d'une solution de dextrose et procédé à l'énucléation 6 à 15 min plus tard. L'examen histologique de l'iris montre la présence de dextrose non seulement au niveau de la couche superficielle, mais à n'importe quel endroit de la couche mésodermique.

Bibliographie p. 243

CONCLUSIONS

Quelle est la nature, la signification et la raison d'être du réseau canaliculaire, que nous venons de décrire? Il est actuellement impossible de donner une réponse satisfaisante à cette question.

Nous devons pour le moment nous contenter de constater son existence. Nous ne pouvons pas, sans autre preuve, admettre qu'il s'agit d'une autre voie d'écoulement pour l'humeur aqueuse.

Tout au plus pouvons-nous émettre l'hypothèse que ce réseau est en rapport avec le plexus veineux du corps ciliaire, de la pars plana et de la choroïde.

RÉSUMÉ

L'examen microradiographique de l'iris humain après perfusion de la chambre antérieure au thorotrast met en évidence un réseau canaliculaire, différent du réseau vasculaire et caractérisé par des pertuis radiaires au niveau de la partie centrale et circulaires au niveau de la partie périphérique de l'iris.

BIBLIOGRAPHIE

[1] L. ZIMMERMAN, communication personnelle, 1958.
[2] B. S. FINE et A. J. TOUSIMIS, communication personnelle, 1958.
[3] E. GREGERSEN, *Acta Ophtalmol.*, 36 (1958) 522.

MICROANGIOGRAPHY OF THE BRAIN AND SPINAL CORD

R. L. DE C. H. SAUNDERS

Anatomy Department, Dalhousie University, Halifax, Nova Scotia (Canada)

ABSTRACT

The deeply placed and microscopic vessels within the human brain and spinal cord have been studied by contact and projection X-ray microscopy using contrast media of colloidal dimensions. Contact microradiography was used for survey purposes and a COSSLETT-NIXON X-ray projection microscope for magnification and examination of fine detail. Owing to its penetration and depth of field, this microscope is particularly suited to such vascular studies, since the course, connections, and volume pattern of intracerebral vessels can be readily determined and imaged stereoscopically. Interesting morphological features of the cortical, transcerebral, and central vessels of the cerebral microcirculation have been recorded, as well as certain capillary beds. Vessels contributing to the intraspinal circulation, such as the radicular, peripheral and central arteries of the spinal cord have similarly been recorded.

The deeply placed and microscopic vessels within the human brain and spinal cord can be studied by contact and projection X-ray microscopy using contrast media of colloidal dimensions. These methods demonstrate the minute arrangements and distribution of such vessels with striking clarity, and make it possible to record their volume pattern stereographically. Microangiography may be expected to make important contributions to the understanding of the developmental and topographic anatomy of the intracerebral and intraspinal vessels, and provide a more satisfactory basis for cerebro-vascular physiology and pathology.

A recent bibliography[1] on the anatomy and physiology of the cerebral vessels (covering the period 1938—'48) contains more than four thousand titles, yet most of the studies devoted to cerebral angiography deal mainly with the larger vessels, and but few with capillarization of the human brain. The present study was prompted by earlier radiographic studies[2,3] of the autopsy brain, and previous experience of the microcirculatory detail[4,5] obtainable with a point source of X-rays. No previous work on cerebral or spinal microangiography by X-ray projection microscopy has been reported. This is understandable since the COSSLETT-NIXON X-ray projection microscope[6] is a recent development.

In an earlier study[7] of the cerebral vascular pattern by the contact method, the authors unfortunately drew upon PFEIFER's findings, apparently unaware that he had mistaken arteries for veins. Correct designation is obviously important and the criteria of distinction established by CAMPBELL[8] and SCHARRER[9] can be confirmed by separate injection of arteries and veins, or the simple expedient of tracing vessels to or from parent trunks of irrefutable identity. Their criteria are essential to vascular differentiation and hence to the interpretation of cerebral microangiograms, since they can be confirmed by X-ray microscopy.

References p. 255

METHODS

Preliminary injection studies of the cerebral capillaries were carried out on the rabbit, it being the only common laboratory animal in which the circulus arteriosus (Willis) is mainly supplied by the internal carotid arteries[10]. Complete filling of cerebral capillaries can be obtained in both the rabbit and human brain with 25 % Micropaque (Damancy), which is a fine barium suspension of colloidal proportions with a particle size of $0.1-0.5 \mu$. This injectant is highly suited to microangiography since the vessels appear white under both the dissecting and X-ray microscope, and the tissue can be fixed in formalin for further study.

The blood vessels of the foetal and adult human brain and spinal cord were injected with a warm solution (40° C) of 25 % Micropaque made up in either saline or 10 % formalin. Since the eye is part of the brain, a dissecting microscope was used to study the flow of the injectant into its iridial capillaries, and so gauge the degree of capillary filling (Fig. 1).

To ensure filling of the vessels of both the brain and spinal cord, (a) foetal injections were made *via* the aortic arch, following ligation of both the ductus arteriosus and the abdominal aorta near its bifurcation, to eliminate leakage by vessels of the foetal circulation; and (b) adult injections were made into the common carotid and vertebral arteries, and retrogressively into the femoral arteries. On removal the brain and spinal cord were fixed either in 10 % formalin or aqueous Bouin's solution; the latter gives better fixation of the pulpy foetal brain. Material from eight foetuses ranging between the fourth and seventh month (C.R. 11—25 cm), and three adult brains (age range 59, 65, 95 years) have so far been studied; also the pituitary gland from a hydrocephalic female infant (age 9 months).

After fixation, one cerebral hemisphere was sectioned coronally, and the other either horizontally or sagittally, for study purposes. Thick serial sections, 5—10 mm in thickness, gave the best picture of the volume pattern of the blood vessels. Microtome sections 200—400 μ in thickness, were cut from these on a freezing microtome, to determine capillary detail.

The general distribution of the vessels within the brain sections was recorded on large lantern slides ($3\frac{1}{4} \times 4\frac{1}{4}$ in. Ilford Medium) by contact microradiography. The sections were mounted on thin plastic film (1/1000 in. I.C.I. Melinex) to protect the emulsion. The X-ray source was a Philips diffraction tube possessing a copper target, beryllium port, and focal spot of 1.0×1.2 mm, operated at 28 kV 35 mA. A target–specimen distance of 35 cm was used, exposure times averaging $1\frac{1}{2}$ min depending on specimen thickness.

Vascular detail was studied with a COSSLETT-NIXON X-ray microscope (Mark II, E.R. 3) which operates on the principle of point projection. Brain sections, supported when necessary by a thin Melinex sheet, were placed approx. 6 mm from the target, with a plate distance of 2.3 cm. Accelerating voltages of 15 to 20 kV were used with a copper foil target (5—12 μ thick). Exposure times, as dictated by section thickness, ranged between 2 and 8 min for Ilford Contrasty plates. The above camera length gave a wide field of view of 8 cm diameter. The plates were processed in Kodak Dektol (dil. 1:1) 2 min (20° C), transferred to a stop bath, and fixed with Amfix.

References p. 255

ANATOMICAL BACKGROUND

The brain is supplied by the paired anterior, middle and posterior cerebral arteries which course over the surface of the cerebral cortex. These arteries divide into smaller and smaller branches, which freely anastomose, and then sink into and supply particular areas of the brain. Basal or central branches enter the brain base to supply the interior of the cerebral hemisphere. The cortical arteries on the brain surface break up into short or long branches which penetrate and supply the cortex and its subjacent white matter. It is commonly stated that no direct anastomotic connection of any practical significance exists between the cortical and basal system of vessels, and that in fact these branches are end arteries.

The venous drainage of the brain surface is accomplished by superficial cerebral veins which course over the hemisphere and receive tributaries from the cortex and underlying white matter. Venous channels within the brain substance converge upon the lateral ventricle and drain into the thalamo-striate or other deep veins (*e.g.* striate). SCHLESINGER[11] and KAPLAN[12] described intracerebral connexions between the superficial and deep venous systems of the brain.

The brain stem and cerebellum are supplied by the vertebral and basilar arteries. The spinal cord is supplied by a single anterior spinal artery and paired posterior spinal arteries derived from the vertebral arteries, and reinforced by small radicular arteries which arrive by way of the spinal nerve roots. Central and peripheral branches arise from the spinal arteries to supply the interior and surface of the spinal cord.

The spinal cord is drained by a number of longitudinal venous trunks or spinal veins, united by a venous plexus, and the radicular veins which communicate with both the vertebral venous plexuses and body wall veins.

Knowledge of the smallest intracerebral and intraspinal vessels in the human brain and spinal cord is understandably limited, neither dissection nor histological means lending themselves to the tracing of the arterial tree in its entirety.

RESULTS

Examples of the results are shown in Figs. 2 through 12. These X-ray micrographs depict the microscopic vessels in which blood flows from the arteries to the veins over the brain surface, as well as through the brain surface, from the cortex towards the ventricular cavity within the cerebral hemisphere. The vessels of the microcirculation in and about the spinal cord and spinal nerve roots are also shown.

Fig. 2 shows the blood vessels ramifying within the pia-arachnoid membrane stripped from over the frontal area of the foetal cerebrum. The pial arteries and veins form an anastomosing network within which lies a complex lace-like capillary bed. The network formed by the pial arteries and capillaries both here, and in Fig. 3, shows numerous small club-like projections; these represent the commencement of the small cortical and transcerebral arteries which descend vertically into, and supply, the grey and white substance of the brain. The long transcerebral course of some of these arteries is shown in Fig. 3, 4 and 5. A constriction at the origin of these small arteries and arterioles is a common feature (Fig. 3). The pial veins for the most part lie under the arteries (Fig. 2), are angular, and lack the graceful lines of the arteries. The largest vein in this field was 2 mm in diameter at its termination. No arterio-venous anastomoses as commonly understood have as yet been observed, but arterio-venous bridges or preferred channels of short transit distance are common.

References p. 255

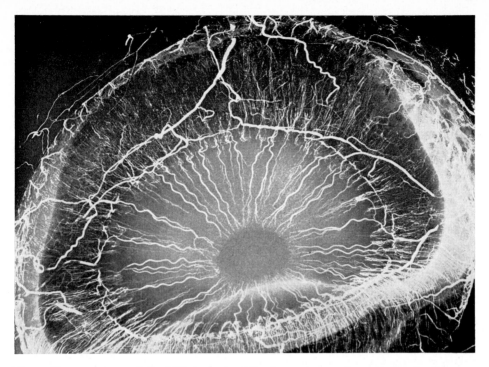

Fig. 1. The appearance of the iridial vessels of the human eye used as an index of satisfactory injection of the cerebral vessels. The vessels of the iris, ciliary body, and choroid have been recorded by contact microradiography. (Female, aged 9 months.) Mag. × 6.75.

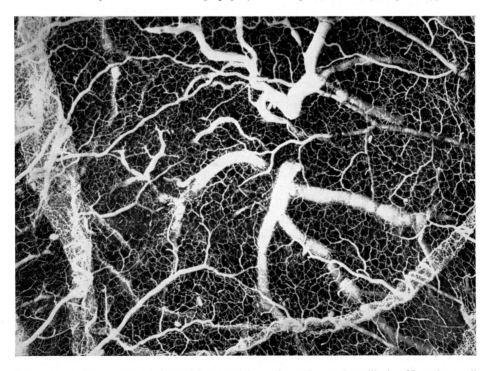

Fig. 2. The complex network formed by the pial arteries, veins, and capillaries. Note the small club-like projections marking the origin of the cortical and transcerebral arteries (cf. Fig. 3). Projection micrograph. Mag. × 8.2.

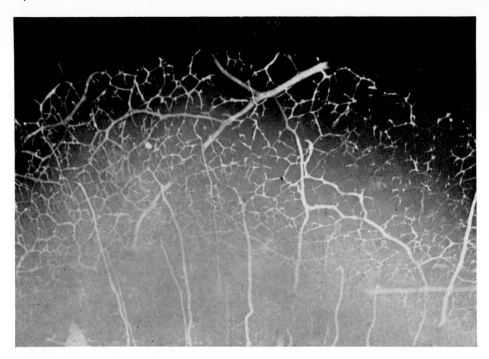

Fig. 3. Short cortical and long transcerebral arteries arising from the pial network; the pial net and part of an underlying gyrus are seen three dimensionally. Note the club-like projections also seen in the preceding figure. Projection micrograph. Mag. × 16.4.

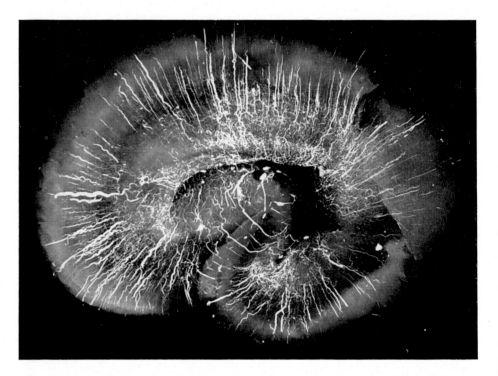

Fig. 4. Parasagittal section showing long transcerebral arteries passing from brain surface to periventricular capillary bed. (Human foetus C. R. 14.5 cm.) Projection micrograph. Mag. × 8.2.

References p. 255

Fig. 4 represents a parasagittal section of the left cerebral hemisphere of a five month human foetus (C.R. 14.5 cm; section 2 mm in thickness). This microangiogram shows the transcerebral blood vessels passing from the cortical surface of the brain, through the entire thickness of the cerebral hemisphere, to end in a subependymal capillary plexus about the lateral ventricle. The convergence of these numerous transcerebral arteries upon the lateral ventricle might be termed a vascular corona radiata since it appears to coincide directionally with the fibre pattern of the main projection systems. Centrally within the curve of the lateral ventricle lies a portion of the striatum and its vascular plexus. Most of the transcerebral vessels here seen are arteries, little contrast medium having passed over into the veins. The peripheral constriction of the arteries is ascribed to greater cortical fixation. The deeply placed, somewhat abrupt, localised dilatations seen in some of these arteries have been noted in both foetal and adult material. The cortical vascular bed has been disturbed, owing to the unavoidable stripping of the pia-arachnoid membrane during sectioning. A dense subependymal capillary plexus extends around and adjacent to the lateral ventricle.

A higher power view (Fig. 5) reveals that these transcerebral arteries have a long and graceful course, giving off relatively few collateral branches prior to their terminal arborisation about the lateral ventricle. Viewed with Fig. 3, this plate provides an overall picture of the origin and termination of these vessels. Drainage of the dense subependymal capillary plexus takes place near the lateral ventricular angle by venules which pass either into deep cerebral veins (*e.g.* thalamo-striate or striate), or else into transcerebral veins which radiate outwards to the brain surface.

Micrographs of sagittal and coronal sections of the foetal brain (Figs. 6 and 7) support the impression that these numerous transcerebral arteries follow the fibre pattern of the corona radiata and are influenced by its intersection with the fibre pattern of the corpus callosum (Fig. 5). A sagittal section (Fig. 6) of the cerebrum shows the varied changes in direction taken by the transcerebral vessels; the fore-shortened vessels seen here course almost perpendicular to the plane of the plate. Since inspection of a flat plate can be misleading, this illustrates the importance of using stereomicrographs to determine the true direction of a leash of vessels. A coronal section (Fig. 7) of the frontal lobe also shows the radiation of the transcerebral arteries, and their convergence upon the anterior horn of the lateral ventricle and the ovoid corpus striatum.

The large number of transcerebral arteries which pass inward from the pial network to join the periventricular or subependymal capillary plexus is again shown in a more posterior coronal section (Fig. 8). This micrograph depicts the lateral ventricle and thalamo-striatal area of the developing cerebral hemisphere, and depression of the sylvian fossa. It shows the transcerebral vascular radiation, and the arborescent vascular pattern within the caudate nucleus. Numerous basal or striate arteries ascend into the thalamo-striate area from the region of the middle cerebral artery. A number of contrast "haemorrhages" can be seen.

The transcerebral arteries can also be seen in the adult brain (Fig. 9). This contact micrograph shows a horizontal section of a right cerebral hemisphere at the level of the widest part of the lentiform nucleus. Apart from the short cortical arteries that supply the grey matter of the occipito-temporal gyri, transcerebral arteries which pass inward through the white matter toward the posterior horn of the lateral

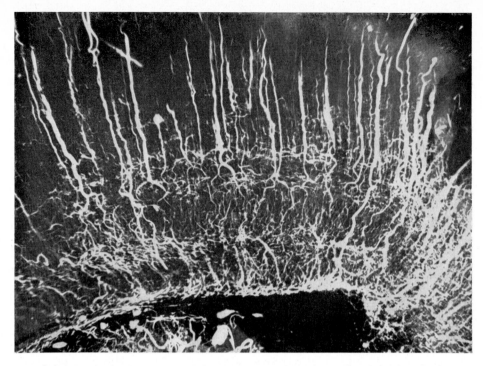

Fig. 5. High power view showing termination of long transcerebral arteries in periventricular capillary bed (*cf*. Fig. 4). Projection micrograph. Mag. × 25.5.

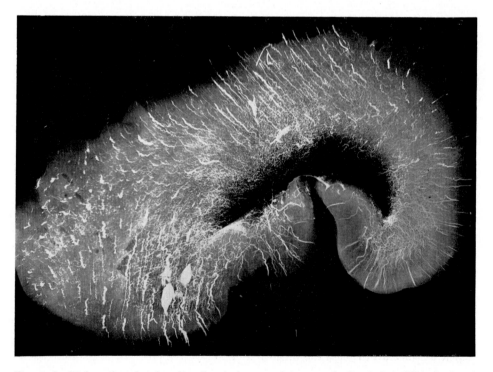

Fig. 6. Sagittal section showing directional changes of transcerebral arteries visible in foetal brain. Projection micrograph. Mag. × 6.

References p. 255

Fig. 7. Coronal section of foetal brain showing convergence of transcerebral arteries upon ventricle and corpus striatum. Projection micrograph. Mag. × 8.2.

Fig. 8. Blood supply of thalamo-striatal area as seen in section of foetal brain. The transcerebral arteries are again evident. Projection micrograph. Mag. × 6.75.

References p. 255

ventricle can be seen. The transcerebral arteries here seen were of the order of 2.1—
3 cm in length and 75 to 150 μ calibre, as measured on the plate. Some of the larger
cortical branches of the middle and posterior cerebral arteries also can be identified
on this plate, as well as the vascular pattern of the choroid plexus and striate arteries
of the thalamo-lenticular region. Projection micrographs revealed the capillary detail
in the cortical and subependymal regions of this brain.

Coronal and horizontal sections of the adult brain both show the same general
arrangement of the short cortical arteries within the grey matter, and the course of
the long transcerebral arteries through the subcortical white matter. In this high
power view (Fig. 10) of a section through the parietal region, parts of the pial vascular
net are visible between the sectioned gyri since the intervening cortex and its covering
have remained undisturbed. The long transcerebral arteries, depending on their
calibre, are seen to arise either from the large cortical arteries or the pial net on the
brain surface (cf. Figs. 3 and 10). They give off infrequent collaterals throughout their
long and graceful course, and terminate adjacent to the cavity of the ventricle, where
portion of the ependymal capillary bed can be seen.

Turning to the blood supply of the spinal cord, Fig. 11 provides a longitudinal
view of the intraspinal vascular pattern as observed in a human foetus of the fifth
month (C.R. 19 cm). Essential features of the intraspinal microcirculation such
as the peripheral and central system of vessels are revealed by this projection micrograph. The anterior spinal artery, really a longitudinal anastomotic chain[13] formed by
ascending and descending branches of the radicular arteries, can be seen in the
midline. The central branches of the anterior spinal artery are readily identified since
they pass to both right and left of the midline. Each central artery appears somewhat
"brush-like" since it divides into ascending, transverse, and descending branches to
supply higher and lower levels of the cord. Depending on the region, as many as four
or five central arteries may be counted between the attachment of one spinal nerve
and the next.

The spinal cord is surrounded by a longitudinally directed and irregularly looped
anastomotic network, formed by branches from both spinal and radicular arteries.
The posterior spinal artery appears as an irregular and incomplete anastomotic chain
near the nerve roots. From this complex network of peripheral arteries in the pia,
many small arteries penetrate into the white matter of the spinal cord.

Projection micrographs of cross sections of the spinal cord show that the central
arteries arise either independently or by a short common trunk from the anterior
spinal artery. Within the anterior median fissure the central arteries pass right and
left to supply the grey matter of the anterior and lateral horns, and the base of the
posterior horn. Numerous small "central" or intramedullary arteries also arise from
the peripheral net enveloping the cord, and penetrate all three white columns to
supply the anterior, lateral and posterior horns of grey matter. Precapillary branches
corresponding to the chief nerve cell groups in the grey matter of the spinal cord can
be identified. Micrographs demonstrate that the peripheral and central system of
arteries are not separate, since their intramedullary branches are essentially similar
in purpose, both supplying and meeting in the continuous capillary network in the
grey matter.

Micrographs of foetal, neonatal and adult pituitary glands have been taken,
permitting the study of the blood supply of the whole pituitary complex in both the

References p. 255

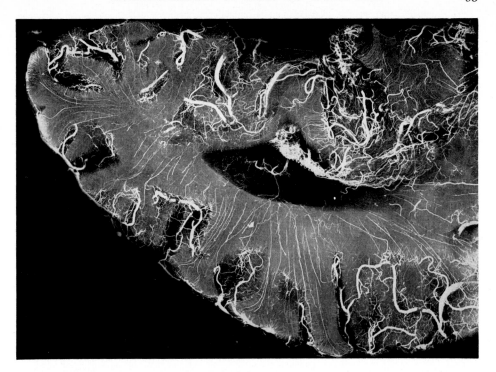

Fig. 9. Horizontal section of adult brain showing transcerebral arteries converging upon posterior horn of lateral ventricle. Contact microradiograph. Mag. × 1.4.

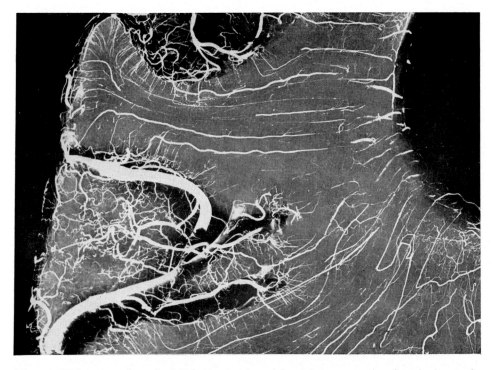

Fig. 10. High power view of adult brain showing pial net between sectioned gyri, also mode of origin and termination of transcerebral arteries. Portion of the lateral ventricle and sub-ependymal capillary bed is evident. Contact microradiograph. Mag. × 3.5.

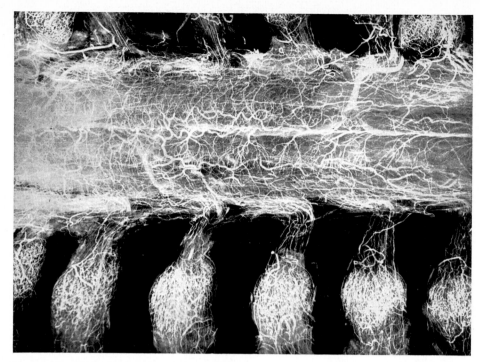

Fig. 11. Longitudinal view of spinal cord showing the peripheral system of blood vessels surrounding the cord. The brush-like central arteries are visible in the midline. Note the radicular vessels and capillary bed in the spinal root ganglia (Human foetus C.R. 19 cm.) Projection micrograph. Mag. × 7.5

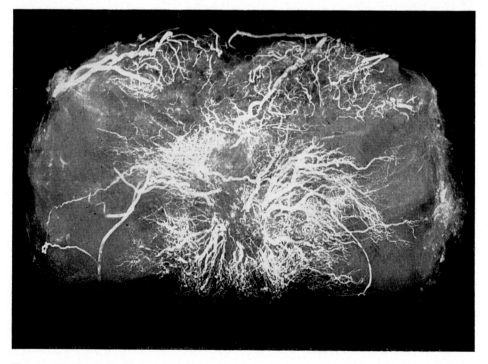

Fig. 12. Blood supply of the pituitary gland. Parts of the superior and inferior hypophyseal arterial systems are visible as well as the rich capillary bed. (Infant. F. 9 months.) Projection micrograph. Mag. × 22.

References p. 255

intact and sectioned gland. A micrograph (Fig. 12) of a child's pituitary (F.; age 9 months) seen as though from above shows the site of the pituitary stalk and the rich blood supply of both lobes. Parts of the inferior hypophyseal arterial circle which roughly demarcates the two lobes can be identified, also the plexus formed by the superior hypophyseal vessels, and the rich intra-glandular capillary network.

CONCLUSIONS

These observations, although of a preliminary nature, show that a considerable amount can be learned by X-ray microscopy concerning the arrangement and connections of the deeply placed and microscopic vessels within the human brain and spinal cord. A strikingly detailed record of their internal vascular pattern can be obtained by both the contact and projection method.

The intricate meningeal network formed by the pial vessels, and mode of origin of the short cortical and long transcerebral arteries, clearly suggest a haemodynamic mechanism concerned with cortical distribution or subcortical diversion. The transcerebral arteries apparently provide an anatomical basis for the physiological observation that circulatory changes in the subcortical centres accompany cortical stimulation; for example increased blood flow within the caudate only follows stimulation of the frontal pole or motor cortex[14] (cf. Fig. 7).

The complex capillary beds related to the cortical and ventricular surfaces of the cerebrum, interconnected by the transcerebral vessels, call for further study, X-ray or otherwise, of these deep vessels and the role of the subcortical circulation. Interestingly enough, autoradiographic studies recently showed[15] that radioactive protein from the cerebro-spinal fluid courses through the capillaries within and subjacent to the cerebral pia and ventricular ependyma (cf. Figs. 3 and 5). The demonstration of the transcerebral arteries, and also the nature of the cerebral and spinal microcirculation, recalls KETY's observation[16] that the cerebral blood flow depends essentially upon the pressure gradient across the brain or the resistance which the blood meets within the brain.

X-ray microscopy has opened the way to the study of the smallest vessels within the brain, since sections opaque to light can be viewed from different projections with a wide field of view, and where necessary can be analysed stereoscopically.

ACKNOWLEDGEMENTS

The project of which this work is part was supported by a grant from the James Picker Foundation.

The author wishes to thank Mr. H. ELLIS for his assistance with specimen preparation and injection; Mr. M. BRZAK and Mr. L. VAN DER ZWAN for help with contact and projection X-ray microscopy; and Dr. F. W. FYFE for photographic assistance.

REFERENCES

1 R. KENK and M. B. NALL, Physiol. Revs., 32 (1952) 1.
2 EGAS MONIZ, Amatus Lusitanus, 3 (1944) 506.
3 A. R. ELVIDGE, Proc. Assoc. Research Nervous Mental Disease, 18 (1937) 110.
4 R. L. DE C. H. SAUNDERS, Nature, 180 (1957) 1353.
5 R. L. DE C. H. SAUNDERS and R. M. FRYE, Microscopy Symposium, 1958, McCrone Associates, Chicago.

[6] V. E. COSSLETT and W. C. NIXON, *Proc. Roy. Soc. (London), B* 140 (1952) 422.

[7] I. MESCHAN et al., *J Radiol.,* 65 (1955) 770.

[8] A. C. P. CAMPBELL, *Proc. Assoc. Research Nervous Mental Disease,* 18 (1937) 69.

[9] E. SCHARRER, *Anat. Record,* 78 (1940) 173.

[10] C. F. SCHMIDT, *The Cerebral Circulation in Health and Disease,* C. C. Thomas, Springfield, Ill., 1950.

[11] B. SCHLESINGER, *Brain,* 62 (1939) 274.

[12] H. A. KAPLAN, *Proc. Am. Assoc. Anatomists, Anat. Record,* 130 (1958) 323.

[13] D. H. M. WOOLLAM and J. W. MILLEN, *J. Neurol. Neurosurg. Psychiat.,* 18 (1955) 97.

[14] K. VON SANTHA and A. CIPRIANI, *Proc. Assoc. Research Nervous Mental Disease,* 18 (1938) 346.

[15] D. BOWSHER, *Anat. Record,* 128 (1957) 23.

[16] S. S. KETY, *Med. Sci. Publ. Army Med. Serv. Grad. School, Walter Reed Army Med. Center,* No. 3 (1954) 180.

MICROANGIOGRAPHY *IN VIVO**

SVEN BELLMAN, HOWARD A. FRANK, PETER B. LAMBERT, BO ODÈN
and JOHN A. WILLIAMS

Department for Medical Physics, Karolinska Institute, and the Department of Surgery,
Serafimerlasarettet, Stockholm (Sweden)
Kirstein and Yamins Laboratories for Surgical Research, Beth Israel Hospital, and the Department
of Surgery, Harvard Medical School, Boston, Mass. (U.S.A.)

ABSTRACT

Single exposure microangiography *in vivo* using the rabbit ear is a very
versatile technique applicable to a wide variety of problems concerned with the
development, regression, and re-arrangement of vascular beds, permitting
repeated examination of the local vascular system over any selected period
of time with little interference with the tissue. The newly-developed technique
of cine-microangiography makes it possible to study the dynamics of the
distribution of X-ray contrast media in small blood vessels and lymphatics.
The cine method is not designed for long-term experiments because of the
heavy X-ray doses involved.

Microangiography *in vivo* as developed in our laboratories using the rabbit's ear[1]
and employed in studies of various types of vascular transformation[2-5] is demonstrated.
The method employs the injection of X-ray contrast medium into the local vascular
system after cannulation of the middle one of the three anastomosing branches of
the posterior auricular artery. The contrast medium is injected by hand using pressure
high enough to displace temporarily the circulating blood in the ear; at this moment
a microradiogram is taken using a microradiography tube and a fine-grain photographic film or plate in close contact with the ear. One microangiogram is taken per
injection of contrast medium; repeated pictures can be taken with new contrast
injections during one cannulation. For later microangiograms the artery is re-
cannulated; this can be done at any time after the initial experiment. The number
of experiments that can be performed on one ear is limited by the progressive
shortening of the middle branch of the posterior auricular artery by repeated can-
nulations and, most importantly, by the X-ray dose imposed on the tissue. In general,
no more than ten exposures are taken of an ear. Macroscopic and histologic signs of
radiation injury have not been observed under these conditions.

In the present experiments a Machlett AEG-50 A microradiography tube was
used. The exposure data were 45 to 50 kV, 20 to 22 mA, a focus-to-film distance
of 25 cm, and exposure times ranging between 0.1 and 0.3 sec Gevaert Duplo Ortho
Microfilm served as photographic material. Development was in Eastman Kodak
D 19 developer at room temperature for 2 to 3 minutes. The unit-scale primary
microangiograms were enlarged using standard photographic technique.

The normal vascular pattern of the rabbit ear demonstrable by microangiography

---

* This investigation was supported by grants from the National Institutes of Health, Public
Health Service (H-1984), the Life Insurance Medical Research Fund (G-56-8), and Karolinska
Institutets reservationsanslag.

References p. 262

in vivo is shown (Fig. 1). Vessels down to small arterioles and venules are clearly visible. The capillary system is seen as a diffuse shadow in most of the ear; at the margin individual capillary loops can usually be distinguished (Fig. 1B). Numerous

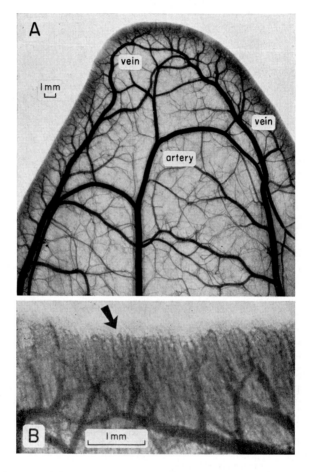

Fig. 1. Microangiograms. (A) shows the typical vascular arrangement in the distal part of the rabbit's ear with three major arteries connected *via* two large arcades, and numerous smaller anastomoses. The veins collect to venous trunks, one at each margin of the ear and with direct end continuity at the tip of the ear. (B) shows a higher magnification of the vasculature at the margin of the ear. Numerous capillary loops can be distinguished, one of which is indicated by an arrow.

arterio-venous shunts can normally be seen. Most form short connections between secondary or tertiary arterial and venous arborizations in the ear. Occasional a—v shunts come off the main ear vessels. The open shunts have a caliber of 0.05 to 0.1 mm and are 0.5 to 1 mm long. There is a considerable variation in shape: some form quite complicated patterns, many have a rather simple loop-shape, and some just form a moderately tortuous or corkscrew-shaped channel (Fig. 2A and B). Contrast-rich streamers can usually be seen in the vein near an arterio-venous shunt (Fig. 2C).

References p. 262

As examples of the use of the microangiographic single exposure technique are shown illustrations from studies of the development and subsidence of an inflammatory vascular reaction about a firmly tied stitch in the tissue, and the transformation of collaterals about a site of arterial obstruction (Fig. 3).

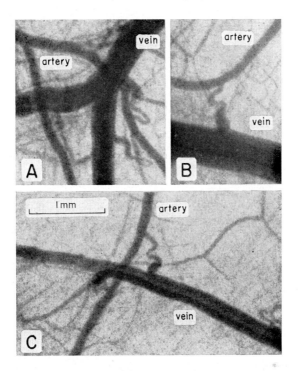

Fig. 2. Microangiograms showing arterio-venous shunts. (A) shows several loop-shaped shunts in a region where an artery and a vein arborize. In (B) is a moderately tortuous a—v shunt. (C) shows two a—v shunts at a crossing of an artery and a vein, and contrast-rich streamers in the vein.

The method of introducing X-ray contrast material into lymphatics by sub-cutaneous injection is used for microangiographic demonstration of lymphatics in the rabbit ear. The microradiographic technique is quite similar to that used for the study of blood vessels, except that the slow flow and long persistence of contrast medium in the lymphatics permit longer exposures at lower kilovoltages. Most micro-lymphangiograms of the rabbit ear are taken at about 25 kV. Thorotrast (Testagar Co.) has been found to be the most advantageous contrast medium for most types of micro-lymphangiographic animal experiments. Occasionally 45 % Hypaque (Winthrop Laboratories) has been employed.

The normal lymph vessel patterns demonstrable with this method are shown in Fig. 4. By injecting air bubbles together with the contrast medium it is shown that there apparently is direct wide passage from the subcutaneous contrast depot into the lymphatics, presumably *via* lacerations caused by the puncture and the injection.

As an application of the micro-lymphangiographique technique are shown illustrations from a study of surgically divided lymphatics: the stoppage of contrast medium at first at the line of incision, the establishment of circumventing pathways *via* pre-existing lymphatics whose valves have been rendered incompetent (Fig. 5), and the development of bridging lymphatics across the wound and scar.

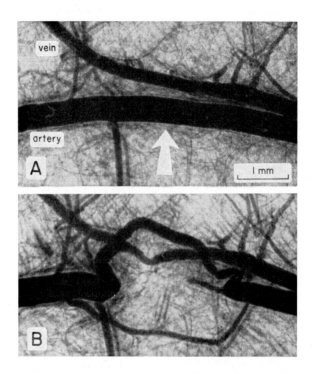

Fig. 3. Microangiograms taken before (A) and 6 weeks after (B) ligation of an arterial arcade. The point of ligation is marked with an arrow in (A). Two newly-appeared vessels bridge the interruption just around the scar at the site of ligation.

In addition to the single exposure technique for microangiography *in vivo* a newly-developed method for cine-microangiography is shown here for the first time. In the set-up used, the photographic film is replaced by a fine-grain fluorescent screen in close contact with the rabbit ear, and a cine camera records the image formed on the screen. The same microradiography tube is used, with a focus-to-screen distance of 10 to 15 cm which gives a large enough field even for overall images of the ear. The fine-grain screen is made with a commercially available phosphor* (silver-activated zinc sulphide made by Du Pont) as described by KOLLER[6]. It is placed with the grain side against the ear, with black paper interposed. The black paper increases the contrast in the image by reducing the back-reflexion of light. The camera is focused on the grain of the screen through its lucite base. An Eastman Kodak Cine Special II 16 mm film camera was used with Cine Ektar objectives ranging in focal length from 25 to 65 mm. With suitable spacers for the lenses the field of view was reduced down to about 3 cm². Using Eastman Kodak Tri-X negative

---

* The screens were made for us by Mr. H. KRANER of M.I.T., Cambridge, Mass.

References p. 262

film, the microradiography tube could be run at 25 kV and 16 mA. Normally the film was taken at 24 frames per second.

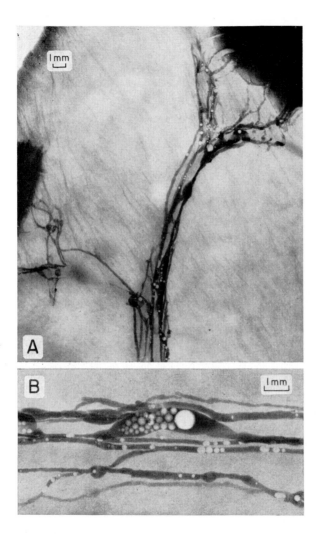

Fig. 4. Micro-lymphangiograms of a normal rabbit ear. (A) shows the main drainage channels along the middle branch of the posterior auricular artery, injected from two subcutaneous reservoirs of Thorotrast, seen at the upper right corner and the middle of the left side. (B) shows a higher magnification of these lymphatics after the injection of Thorotrast with air bubbles.

With the cine technique the rapid and extensive penetration of intra-arterially injected Hypaque throughout the vascular system of the ear is shown at varying magnifications. Cine-micro-lymphangiography demonstrates the instantaneous migration of Thorotrast throughout the central draining lymphatics of the ear as the subcutaneous depot is formed (Fig. 6). Using high power, the rate of flow of injected bubbles can be measured.

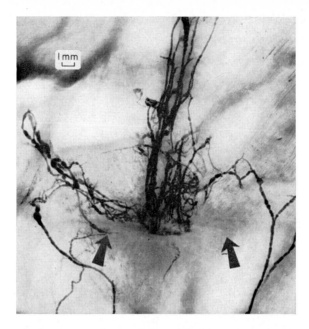

Fig. 5. Micro-lymphangiogram showing by-pass established *via* pre-existing lymphatics around a several weeks old incision. The ends of the incision are indicated by arrows. One small lymph vessel has established passage through the scar.

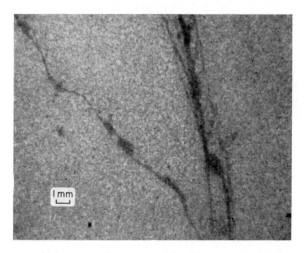

Fig. 6. Cine-micro-lymphangiogram from a normal ear showing the lymphatics around the middle branch of the posterior auricular artery, to the right, and one large tributary to the left. This frame was exposed within one second of the commencement of the subcutaneous injection of contrast medium.

REFERENCES

[1] S. BELLMAN, *Acta Radiol., Suppl.*, 102 (1953).
[2] S. BELLMAN and J. ADAMS-RAY, *Angiology*, 7 (1956) 339.
[3] S. BELLMAN and E. VELANDER, *Brit. J. Plastic Surg.*, 12 (1959) 1.
[4] S. BELLMAN, H. A. FRANK, P. B. LAMBERT and A. J. ROY, *Angiology*, 10 (1959) 214.
[5] S. BELLMAN and B. ODÉN, *Acta Chir. Scand.*, 116 (1958/1959) 99.
[6] L. R. KOLLER, *J. Optical Soc. Am.*, 43 (1953) 620.

3. SOFT TISSUES

TROCKENGEWICHTSBESTIMMUNGEN OHNE REFERENZSYSTEM MIT DEM PHILIPS HISTORADIOGRAPHEN CMR 5

D. MÜLLER und W. SANDRITTER*

Pathologisches Institut der Universität, Frankfurt am Main (Deutschland)

ABSTRACT

DRY WEIGHT DETERMINATIONS WITHOUT A REFERENCE SYSTEM USING A PHILIPS CMR 5 MICRORADIOGRAPHIC APPARATUS

Reproducible dry weight determinations were achieved by means of a simple Philips CMR 5 instrument that has hitherto only been used for qualitative tests. The routine use of a reference system which is difficult to fix alongside the object in the small illuminated field could be dispensed with.

The results were achieved by (1) keeping the X-ray spectrum incident on the preparation constant, and (2) by experimentally establishing the density curve and the fluctuation range of the MR-emulsion used. With the Gevaert developer G 209 A the proportionality of D and I is guaranteed up to $D \leqq 0.8$. Therefore the X-ray absorption of the object can be calculated from the blackening of the film. The mass absorption coefficient of the object was determined by comparison with reference systems as well as by calculation. The reproducibility of the results was checked with biologically homogeneous material. The results agreed with those obtained with interference microscopy.

Die Röntgenhistoradiographie[1, 2] hat sich in den letzten Jahren immer mehr zu einer wertvollen und unentbehrlichen Bereicherung quantitativer histochemischer Methoden entwickelt[3]. Allein der erforderliche umfangreiche apparative Aufwand stand einer weiteren Ausbreitung entgegen und beschränkt ihre Anwendung immer noch auf wenige Speziallaboratorien. Deshalb wurde das Röntgenhistoradiographiegerät CMR 5 entwickelt[4, 5], das klein und einfach zu bedienen ist. Es fand aber bisher in der Regel nur für qualitative Untersuchungen Verwendung, da das kleine ausgeleuchtete Feld es kaum ermöglicht, zusammen mit dem Präparat noch ein Referenzsystem zu belichten, das als Gewichtsäquivalent für quantitative Trockengewichtsbestimmungen dienen könnte.

Wir haben deshalb versucht, Trockengewichtsbestimmungen ohne routinemässige Verwendung eines Referenzsystems mit diesem Gerät durchzuführen[6]. Werden nämlich alle Präparate mit dem gleichen Röntgenspektrum belichtet, das peinlich konstant gehalten wird, kann man einen einmal festgelegten Gewichtsäquivalenten für alle Untersuchungen einsetzen. Durch genaue Analyse der Zeitschwärzungskurve für die verwandte Emulsion, die für Röntgenstrahlen keinen Schwellenwert besitzt, ist es dann möglich, die Röntgenabsorption des auf dem Film abgebildeten Gewebes aus der Filmschwärzung zu bestimmen und mit Hilfe des Gewichtsäquivalenten das Trockengewicht zu berechnen.

---

* Mit Unterstützung der Deutschen Forschungsgemeinschaft.

Literatur S. 267

Hierfür wurde dem Historadiographen CMR 5 ein Stabilisator (Philips Typ PE 4222/01) vorgeschaltet. Nach halbstündiger Vorstabilisierung bleibt die Hochspannung konstant. Wir arbeiten bei 1,52 kV, entsprechend einer Grenzwellenlänge von 8 Å. Zum Einlegen des Filmes wird die Hochspannung getrennt abgeschaltet, wozu die Schaltung geringfügig geändert werden musste. Nach dem Wiedereinstellen ist die Spannung in weniger als einer halben Minute wieder auf dem Nennwert und wird während der Belichtung mit einem Voltmeter kontrolliert, das einen Messbereich von 0,9—1,8 kV besitzt und noch gestattet, Spannungsschwankungen von ± 5 V abzulesen.

Trotz Stabilisierung noch auftretende Spannungsschwankungen können mit Hilfe der Röhrenstromfeineinstellung exakt kompensiert werden, da Zunahme des Röhrenstroms zu einem Spannungsabfall führt. Eine noch erfassbare Energieänderung des Spektrums von ± 5 V führt eine Änderung der Gewebsabsorption um nur ± 1,3 % herbei und zieht den gleichen Fehler bei der Trockengewichtsbestimmung nach sich.

Beim Durchtritt durch das 50 μ Berylliumfenster der Röntgenröhre erleidet das von der Anode emittierte Röntgenspektrum eine berechenbare Absorption. Eine Zunahme durch Wolframniederschläge von der Glühkathode haben wir in jetzt zweijähriger Betriebszeit nicht feststellen können. Zur Ausschaltung der Luftabsorption in der Filmkassette evakuieren wir auf ein Vakuum besser als 0,1 Torr mit einer Pfeiffer-Vakuumpumpe. Dann liegt auch bei einer Wellenlänge von 15 Å die Luftabsorption noch unter 1 %. Dadurch ist es möglich, die Belichtung von Film und Präparat mit einem konstanten Spektrum durchzuführen mit einem Fehler für die Trockengewichtsbestimmung von weniger als ± 1,5 %.

Die durch das Präparat auf den Film einfallende Röntgenstrahlung bewirkt hier eine Schwärzung gemäss dem Bunsen-Roscoe'schen Gesetz

$$D = f(I\, t^P)$$

Der Schwarzschildexponent liegt in Übereinstimmung mit vielen Untersuchern um 1[7-9]. Da es im Gegensatz zum sichtbaren Licht keinen Schwellenwert gibt, findet sich bis zu einer bestimmten Schwärzung ein Bereich, in dem die Density proportional der einfallenden Strahlungsintensität ist [10]. Wir haben eine Schwärzungskurve für die von uns verwandte Kodak Maximum Resolution Emulsion für eine Röntgenstrahlung von 1,5 kV aufgestellt. Dabei zeigte sich mit dem Entwickler D 19 b ein linearer Anstieg etwa bis $D = 0,3$, während mit dem Entwickler G 209 A bei 18° und 6 min Entwicklungszeit ein linearer Anstieg der Schwärzung mit $I \cdot t$ bis zu einer Density von 0,8 vorliegt und auch darüber die Kurve nur sehr langsam von einer Geraden abweicht. Damit lässt sich bis zu einer Density von 0,8 aus dem Grad der Schwärzung einer abgebildeten Struktur die prozentual durchgefallene Strahlungsintensität und damit die Gewebsabsorption unter dem einfallenden Röntgenspektrum berechnen. Da sich das auf das Gewebe einwirkende kontinuierliche Spektrum — wie oben gezeigt — sehr konstant halten lässt, kann nach einmaliger Festlegung des Massenabsorptionskoeffizienten das Gewicht pro Flächeneinheit

Gewebe gemessen werden. Aus dem Absorptionsgesetz

$$I_{(\lambda)} = I_{0(\lambda)} \cdot e^{-\frac{\mu}{\varrho}m}$$

folgt

$$m = \frac{\ln \frac{I_0}{I(\lambda)}}{\frac{\mu}{\varrho(\lambda)}}$$

und da $D : D_0 = I : I_0$ für $D, D_0 \leqq 0.8$

$$m = \frac{\ln \frac{D_0}{D}}{\frac{\mu}{\varrho(\lambda)}} \; ; D, D_0 \leqq 0.8$$

wobei I, I_0 die durchfallende bzw. einfallende Strahlungsintensität D, D_0 die korrespondierende Filmschwärzung

$\frac{\mu}{\varrho} = $ der Massenabsorptionskoeffizient und

$m = $ das Gewicht pro Fläche ist.

Zur Bestimmung des Massenabsorptionskoeffizienten untersuchten wir dreistufige Referenzsysteme, die in der von LINDSTRÖM[10] angegeben Weise aus Nitrozellulose hergestellt und gewogen wurden. Der für unsere späteren Messungen verwandte Gewichtsäquivalent ist der Mittelwert aus 30 Stepwedge-Untersuchungen. Diesen Wert haben wir mit einer guten Übereinstimmung auch rein rechnerisch festlegen können[6]. Die Schwärzung der Mikroradiogramme wurde mit einem Cytophotometer mit einem Messfeld bis $5 \, \mu^2$ gemessen. Um die Reproduzierbarkeit unserer Methodik zu überprüfen, untersuchten wir getrennt Fehlerquellen, die auftreten

1. bei der Densitometrie; dazu wurde das gleiche Radiogramm mehrfach densitometriert.

2. bei der Aufnahme des gleichen Objekts auf verschiedenen Radiogrammen, (a) bei gleichem, (b) bei wechselndem Röhrenstrom und Belichtungszeit. Dazu wurden die gleichen Objektstrukturen auf den einzelnen Radiogrammen getrennt ausgewertet und miteinander verglichen. Diese vergleichenden Untersuchungen wurden durchgeführt

(a) an Referenzsystemen, deren Gewicht pro Fläche vorher mit einer Mikrowaage bestimmt war,

(b) an verschiedenen Ausstrichen kleiner relativ homogener Zellen, deren Trockengewicht gleichzeitig mit dem Bakerschen Interferenzmikroskop gemessen wurde.

Abb. 1 zeigt die mittels Densitometrie berechnete Röntgenabsorption der 3 Stufen eines Referenzsystems. Die Kreise entsprechen Werten von zwei gleich belichteten Mikroradiogrammen, die Quadrate stammen von einem dritten mit doppelter Belichtungszeit aufgenommenen Radiogramm des gleichen Referenzsystems, die Dreiecke endlich wurden von einer Kontrolldensitometrie des gleichen Radiogramms gewonnen. Die Abbildung lehrt, dass der durch die spezielle Technik bedingte Fehler in der Reproduzierbarkeit innerhalb des reinen Densitometriefehlers liegt. In Tabelle I sind das Trockengewicht von Froscherythrocyten berechnet aus zwei getrennt belichteten Radiogrammen gegenübergestellt. Hier geht zusätzlich die Zellplanimetrie als Fehlerquelle ein. Man sieht, dass der mittlere Fehler für eine hier willkürlich herausgegriffene Gruppe von 18 Zellen trotzdem nur 7,7 % beträgt.

Literatur S. 267

In der entsprechenden Weise wurden Bullenthymuslymphocyten und Bullenspermien untersucht, wobei wir ebenfalls eine gute Reproduzierbarkeit feststellen konnten. Die Ergebnisse wurden gleichzeitig mit dem Baker'schen Interferenzmikroskop überprüft, wie in Tabelle II zusammengestellt[11].

Die einfache von uns angewandte Technik ermöglicht also gut reproduzierbare Trockengewichtsbestimmungen auch mit dem kleinen Mikroradiographiegerät CMR 5, die in ihrer Genauigkeit kaum hinter anderen Methoden zurückstehen dürften. Ihr Nachteil liegt allein darin, dass das Röntgenspektrum nur schwer geändert und unterschiedlichen Versuchsbedingungen angepasst werden kann. Für Trockengewichtsbestimmungen an Zellausstrichen oder 5 μ-Schnitten dürfte das aber kaum notwendig werden.

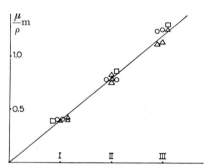

Abb. 1. Daten eines Referenzsystems von 0,27 mg/cm² Gewicht. Untersuchungen bei 1,52 kV. $\frac{\mu}{\rho} m$ Werte, berechnet aus 3 Kontrolldensitometrien des gleichen Radiogramms = $\triangle$; aus 2 gleich belichteten Radiogrammen des gleichen Referenzsystems = $\bigcirc$; aus einem mit doppelter Belichtungszeit aufgenommenen Radiogramms des gleichen Referenzsystems = $\square$.

TABELLE I

REPRODUZIERBARKEIT VON RÖNTGENHISTORADIOGRAPHISCHEN TROCKENGEWICHTSBESTIMMUNGEN

| Zell-Nr. | Trockengewicht (10⁻¹² g) | | | |
	Versuch 1	Versuch 2	Mittelwert	Abweichung %
1	15,5	16,9	16,2	4,3
2	16,3	19,5	17,9	8,9
3	25,2	20,5	22,8	10,1
4	17,2	16,7	17,0	1,2
5	22,9	25,7	24,3	5,7
6	18,0	18,0	18,0	0,0
7	22,5	29,0	25,8	12,4
8	27,0	20,4	23,7	13,9
9	18,8	23,6	21,2	11,3
10	20,6	19,8	20,2	2,0
11	25,2	30,6	27,9	9,7
12	20,9	20,0	20,5	1,9
13	21,3	17,5	19,4	9,8
14	20,0	24,5	22,3	9,8
15	20,2	23,3	21,8	6,8
16	20,0	29,3	24,7	18,6
17	24,9	20,9	22,9	8,7
18	22,5	20,7	21,6	4,1

Das aus 2 getrennt belichteten Radiogrammen berechnete Trockengewicht von Froscherythrocyten ergibt für 18 Zellen einen mittleren Fehler von 7,7 %.

Literatur S. 267

TABELLE II

VERGLEICHENDE RÖNTGENHISTORADIOGRAPHISCHE UND INTERFERENZMIKROSKOPISCHE
TROCKENGEWICHTSBESTIMMUNGEN

Zellart	Röntgenhistoradiographische Messungen		Interferenzmikroskopische Messungen	
	Zellzahl	Trockengewicht in 10^{-12} g	Zellzahl	Trockengewicht in 10^{-12} g
Bullenspermien	16	7,87 ± 0,46	162	8,94 ± 1,17
Bullenthymuslymphocyten	26	15,05 ± 0,53	96	14,40 ± 1,58
Froscherythrocyten				
Kern	49	24,00 ± 0,69	26	21,55 ± 0,84
Kern	18	21,29 ± 0,78	6	20,00 ± 0,72
Plasma	29	89,24 ± 5,40	—	— —

Mit Hilfe der beschriebenen Technik haben wir bereits quantitative Untersuchungen an Inselzellen des Pankreas [12, 13], an Carcinomen und Metaplasien des Bronchialsystems (noch nicht publiziert) und an Epithelkörperchen unter verschiedenen Funktionszuständen (unpubl.) durchführen können.

ZUSAMMENFASSUNG

Mit dem bisher für qualitative Untersuchungen verwandten einfachen Philips Gerät CMR 5 konnten wir reproduzierbare Trockengewichtsbestimmungen ohne routinemässige Verwendung eines Referenzsystems durchführen, das sich bei dem kleinen ausgeleuchteten Gesichtsfeld nur schwer neben dem Objekt anbringen lässt. Das gelang uns (1) durch Konstanthaltung des auf das Präparat einfallenden Röntgenspektrums und (2) durch Austestung der Density-Kurve und ihrer Schwankungsbreite der verwandten MR-Emulsion. Mit dem Gevaert-Entwickler G 209A ist eine Proportionalität von D/I bis $D \leq 0,8$ gewährleistet. Dadurch lässt sich aus der Filmschwärzung die Röntgenabsorption des Objekts berechnen. Sein Massenabsorptionskoeffizient wurde sowohl durch vergleichende Untersuchungen mit Referenzsystemen als auch rechnerisch bestimmt. An biologisch homogenen Objekten wurde die Reproduzierbarkeit der Ergebnisse überprüft. Vergleichende interferenzmikroskopische Untersuchungen zeigten übereinstimmende Resultate.

LITERATUR

[1] A. ENGSTRÖM und B. LINDSTRÖM, Nature, 163 (1949) 563.
[2] A. ENGSTRÖM und B. LINDSTRÖM, Biochim. Biophys. Acta, 4 (1950) 351.
[3] A. ENGSTRÖM, Contact microradiography, General Survey, in V. E. COSSLETT, A. ENGSTRÖM and H. H. PATTEE JR., X-ray Microscopy and Microradiography, Academic Press, Inc., New York, 1957.
[4] B. COMBÉE und A. ENGSTRÖM, Biochim. Biophys. Acta, 14 (1954) 432.
[5] B. COMBÉE, J. HOUTMAN und A. RECOURT, Brit. J. Radiol., 28 (1955) 537.
[6] D. MÜLLER, W. SANDRITTER und G. SCHWAIGER, Histochemie, 1 (1959) 420.
[7] R. GLOCKER und W. TRAUB, Physik. Z., 22 (1921) 345.
[8] A. BOUWERS, Z. Physik, 14 (1923) 374.
[9] E. MÜLBACH, Z. wiss. Phot., 36 (1937) 269.
[10] B. LINDSTRÖM, Acta Radiol., Suppl., 125 (1955).
[11] W. SANDRITTER und D. MÜLLER, Experientia, 15 (1959) 158.
[12] D. MÜLLER und W. SANDRITTER, Exptl. Cell Research, 15 (1958) 441.
[13] W. SANDRITTER, U. BECKER, D. MÜLLER und E. F. PFEIFFER, Endokrinologie, 37 (1959) 193.

PROJECTION X-RAY MICROSCOPY AND MICROANALYSIS OF BIOLOGICAL MATERIALS USING VERY SOFT RADIATION

AN EVALUATION OF AN ELECTROSTATIC FOCUS SYSTEM FOR OBTAINING HIGH RESOLUTION MICRORADIOGRAMS WITH PRIMARY MAGNIFICATION

THORNE J. BUTLER, GUNTER F. BAHR*, LEON I. TAFT and ROBERT B. JENNINGS

Department of Pathology, Northwestern University Medical School, Chicago, Ill. (U.S.A.)

ABSTRACT

The technique and application of the General Electric projection X-ray microscope for studying soft tissues is discussed.

The following is a report on our experience with projection X-ray microscopy of soft tissue.

APPARATUS

The instrument used in this study utilizes an electrostatic focus system to obtain an electron beam spot of approximately $1\ \mu$ in diameter. The equipment is built by the General Electric Company who have been most generous in the redesign and loan of the apparatus. The tube consists of an electron gun, condenser lens, objective lens, and apertures located between the condenser and objective. The target is $6\ \mu$ of aluminum foil which acts also as a window for the produced X-rays.

The target and camera system are seen in Fig. 1. In the center you see the camera chamber attached to the vacuum pump. A fluorescent screen lies above the camera chamber and a simple 10 × lens is used to view the screen. Within the camera there are disc holders for both the specimen and the film plate. For tissue work the specimen is mounted 7—8 mm from the window and the plate is mounted 18 mm from the window. The plate–window distance is easily varied by using Bakelite rings of different thicknesses.

The background shows the control panel and meters for measuring tube vacuum, beam current, and accelerating voltage. The cylindrical control projecting from the right side of the tube is for the aperture having four settings of 10, 25, 50, and 100 μ in diameter.

The centering controls for the condenser and electron gun are located beneath the table and are not seen in this picture.

On the right portion of the table there is a target plate to which is glued 6 μ-thick aluminum foil target. The target is freshly prepared for each operation. The window measures 2 mm in diameter. The aluminum foil readily supports the pressure difference between the window surface and target surface.

---

* Present address: Karolinska Institutet, Institution för almän Patologi, Sabbatsberg, Stockholm, Sweden.

METHOD

The microscope is aligned and brought into focus by evaluating the appearance of a 1500 mesh silver screen. The screen is viewed under direct X-ray magnification of 50 ×. Because of the grain of the screen, the focus is checked by taking a series of exposures at different objective settings. Fig. 2 shows a typical grid photograph on Eastman Contrast Lantern Slide Plate with an X-ray magnification of 25 ×. The lantern slide has a photographic magnification of 22 ×. As you can see the screen is distinct and even small particles of dust are easily seen.

The accelerating voltage used to make this and the following pictures is 3.5 kV. The exposure of the plates for grid pictures is one minute. Development is done in Eastman Dektol for 3 min.

We have evaluated the photon energy pattern being emitted by the target. The following technique is used:

a) Expose a series of plates at a factor of 2 apart in time with a step-wedge of 5 thicknesses of 6 μ Mylar Sheet.

b) Measure the optical density (O.D.) of the film at each exposure and plot optical density vs. log time by joining points of any given thickness of Mylar into a curve.

c) Plot log relative X-ray intensity vs. thickness of Mylar. At any given optical density from (b) measure ratio of time between 0—1 thicknesses, 1—2 thicknesses, 2—3 thicknesses of Mylar, and to completion. These ratios are equivalent to intensity ratios since reciprocity holds for X-ray.

The plot of log relative X-ray intensity vs. Mylar thickness at several different optical densities is a straight line up to 18 μ of Mylar. At 5 kV accelerating voltage the linearity falls off at 12 μ of Mylar. At operating voltages of 3.5 kV the effective photon energy consists of approximately 95 % $K\alpha$ radiation of aluminum.

For soft tissue studies, the tissue (formalin fixed and paraffin embedded) is mounted 6—8 mm from the window. The sections are cut 2—3 μ thick. The film is mounted at either 18 mm or 36 mm from the window. The field size is such that the difference in intensity from the center to the edge of a field is 3 %.

RESULTS

In this laboratory we are interested in renal disease and the work with the X-ray microscope is being directed toward studying kidney material.

Fig. 3 shows a section of kidney, 2 μ thick and observed at an X-ray magnification of 6 ×. The photographic magnification is 22 ×, yielding a total manification of 132 ×. The plate is Eastman Contrast Lantern Slide exposed for 15 min. Development is for 5 min in Eastman Detkol. Many renal structures are readily recognizable. In the upper right a distinct glomerular tuft is seen adjacent to a vessel. Both tubular and glomerular basement membranes are seen in the center portion. However, nuclear patterns are not easily seen. Lantern slide has large grain and tends to reduce resolution.

Fig. 4 shows the same section photographed with X-ray magnification of 3 × upon Eastman film C3—34, 067. The exposure time is 4 h and the film developed in Dektol for 10 min. The fine grain of this film does allow superior resolution for densitometer studies. Again glomerular tufts, tubular cells, tubular lumens, and basement membranes are clearly distinguishable.

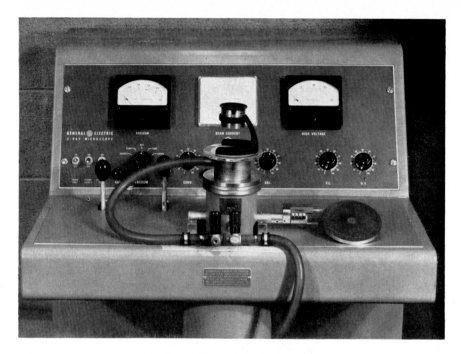

Fig. 1. Picture of apparatus.

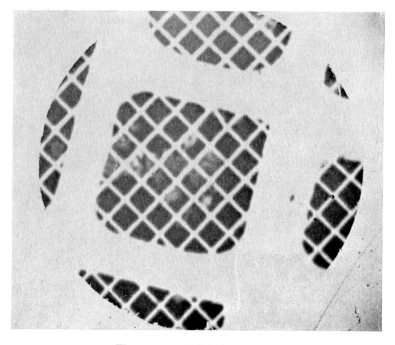

Fig. 2. 1500 mesh screen, 25 ×.

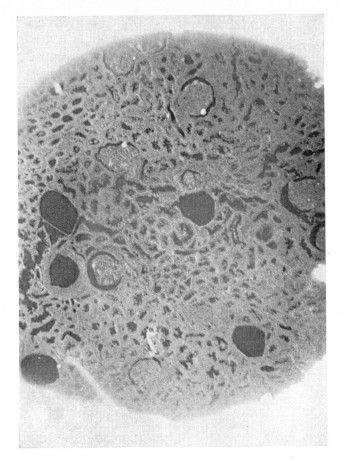

Fig. 3. Kidney section, 2 μ thick, 6 $\times$ X-ray magnification.

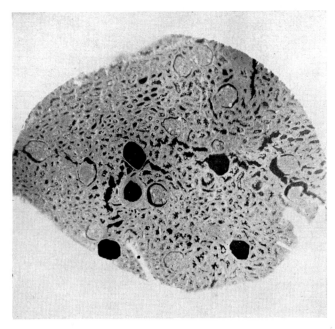

Fig. 4. Kidney section, 2 μ thick, 3 $\times$ X-ray magnification.

Generally, we feel that this type of projection X-ray microscopy is practical and readily adaptable to quantitative determinations of mass in biological material. We are now undertaking a study of material deposited in renal glomeruli in several pathological conditions.

ACKNOWLEDGEMENTS

This work was supported by General Electric Company, Kidney Disease Foundation of Illinois, and grant H 1815 from the National Heart Institute of the United States Public Health Service.

General Electric Company and particularly Messrs. BIGELOW AND MASSAPUST deserve much credit for their help and ideas in redesigning the original apparatus.

APPLICATION OF HIGH RESOLUTION MICRORADIOGRAPHY TO QUALITATIVE EXPERIMENTAL MORPHOLOGY

RICHARD C. GREULICH

*Department of Anatomy, University of California Medical Center,
Los Angeles, Calif. (U. S. A.)*

ABSTRACT

A polychromatic X-ray spectrum has been utilized in high resolution contact microradiographic studies of cellular and tissue components. The qualitative distribution of organic mass in parenchymatous organs, connective tissues, single cells and cell organelles will be described. Emphasis in the presentation will be placed on the attainment of a high degree of structural resolution, and its potential value to experimental morphology. Examples from a variety of experimental circumstances will be shown to illustrate the scope and utility of the method. The ultra-soft microradiographic camera will also be described.

INTRODUCTION

Over forty years have passed since the pioneer microradiographic studies of GOBY[1] and of BARNARD[2] on the capacity of X-rays to demonstrate the internal structure of opaque biological objects possessing semimicroscopic or microscopic dimensions.* Even with the primitive instrumentation and crude photographic emulsions which were available to these investigators at the time, their microradiograms were of remarkably good quality (Fig. 1).

Although primarily an optical physicist, BARNARD was a capable microscopist who maintained an active interest in the development of physical-optical methods for biological research. With respect to the present-day field of X-ray microscopy and microanalysis, I believe that he deserves particular credit for his visionary statement in the summary of his 1915 paper:

"... the possibility of using X-rays ... as a source of energy for microscopic work is not merely a possibility, but is a problem the solution to which is a reasonable certainty."

It would seem virtually certain that BARNARD was not then in a position to appreciate the extent to which micromethods involving X-rays might develop during the ensuing years. Probably he was later most gratified at the progress which was made in certain areas, for example the field of X-ray microcrystallography. He may

---

* It is not the purpose of this presentation to trace the evolution of the microradiographic technique in biology since the time of GOBY and BARNARD. It seems fitting, however, to cite in this connection the first systematic qualitative histological application of the method by LA-MARQUE and TURCHINI over twenty years ago[3, 4]. During the last decade, impetus toward the development and refinement of microradiography, both in qualitative and quantitative terms, has to a large extent been provided by the Stockholm group, led by our host and colleague, ARNE ENGSTRÖM. Several of those of us participating in this meeting owe to Professor ENGSTRÖM their introduction to and enthusiasm for the microradiographic technique.

References p. 287

have been somewhat disappointed, on the other hand, to find that the application of X-rays in biological microscopy did not rapidly become a routine procedure. However, his prediction has been borne out by the fact that the potentialities of the micro-radiographic and projection microscopic techniques are now beginning to attract widespread attention in biology. Such is attested to by the relatively large number of biologically-oriented papers which are being presented in this international symposium.

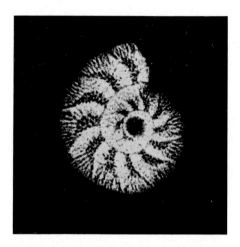

Fig. 1. Microradiogram of the carbonaceous foraminiferan *Cyclammina cancellata*, prepared by BARNARD[2] in 1914. × 25. The labrynthic wall structure is clearly defined. (Reproduced from the Journal of the Royal Microscopical Society.)

The intention of this paper is to stimulate yet further interest in the utilization of microradiography* among biological micromorphologists. It will be the thesis of my presentation that the microradiographic method can be utilized on a qualitative basis — circumspectly, and within certain rather strict limits — as a most profitable adjunct to the methods which the micromorphologist might normally be expected to employ in pursuit of a problem involving fine structure in animal or plant tissues. The circumspection and limitations to which I allude take origin in the physical principles which underlie the microradiographic technique; for without an under-standing of the physical rationale of the method, even qualitative interpretation of results would be fraught with potential error (see below). However, it appears to me that a carefully planned qualitative approach to microradiography is entirely justi-fied, since present techniques of quantitation are not only tedious, but they require complex and expensive instrumentation — and may even then suffer from con-siderable error.

Frequently, too, problems of structural-functional relationships in animal or

---

* Microradiography may be defined as a technique in which an image of a microsample is obtained on photographic emulsion at unity magnification by means of exposure to radiant energy, the wavelength(s) of which lie in the X-ray range of the electromagnetic spectrum. The fact that images are produced at unity magnification differentiates the method from pro-jection X-ray microscopy, in which primary image magnification is obtained. The ultra-soft range of X-rays has been defined as that whose shortest wavelength is 10 Å.

plant microscopy do not necessarily depend for their solution on quantitatively ex-pressed data. Those experienced in the descriptive morphological fields can cite many examples of experimental alterations in structure in which a quantitative knowledge of the degree of alteration is relatively superfluous; often, only the fact that the change has occurred has been of pertinence to the development of valuable new concepts and hypotheses.

By no means do I intend to minimize the tremendous value of quantitative techniques, and their ultimate necessity in biological research; but one should not, I feel, fail to remember that accurate qualitative observations (even of a descriptive character) usually point the way toward the most efficient and rewarding route for application of available quantitative techniques.

Fortunately, as many of the presentations at this symposium suggest, techniques of microradiographic quantitation are becoming progressively more refined. It seems very likely that they will ultimately be perfected to the point that their use will be as routine and general as I propose that qualitative methods should be at the present time.

APPARATUS FOR QUALITATIVE MICRORADIOGRAPHY

The results which will be reported below have been obtained by the use of a *poly-chromatic* X-ray spectrum, and therefore pertain only to *relative mass distribution* in the samples rather than to their elementary chemical composition. One need not review here the physical principles of X-ray absorption in microsamples, since detailed expositions on this subject are already available in the literature[5,6]. It has also been noted previously[7,8] that sufficient image contrast for high resolution structural analysis in microradiograms of samples consisting of organic materials (*i.e.*, histological tissue sections) can be obtained only by the use of low-voltage X-radiation, *i.e.*, the longer or ultra-soft X-ray wavelengths. The microradiographic apparatus (Fig. 2) which has been constructed in my laboratory for qualitative mass analysis of histological material is of an extremely simple design[9] and, until recently, incorporated the ultra-soft X-ray tube constructed by ENGSTRÖM and LUNDBERG[10]. Lately, I have been testing a new tube, based on a design by HENKE[11], which includes a movable vacuum seal separating the sample chamber from the filament-target area of the tube. This design obviates the principal disadvantage of the ENGSTRÖM–LUNDBERG tube, namely that of the filament and target being open to the atmosphere with each change of sample. This situation leads to problems of target contamination, outgassing, and shortened filament life. All of the microradiograms which are il-lustrated here, however, were made with the ENGSTRÖM–LUNDBERG tube, which in general has given excellent service, and which during these studies utilized a copper target.

The apparatus has been designed with the intention of making its operation as simple and straightforward as possible. The vacuum system is mounted within the console, and includes mechanical forepump, oil diffusion pump, appropriate high vacuum valving, and a Pirani-type vacuum probe. The diffusion pump and X-ray tube are cooled by constantly circulating water from a 5-gallon fibreglass reservoir mounted on the floor of the console. Water pressure sufficient for the system is provided by a small peristaltic pump. The coolant also passes through a coiled copper radiator, 32 feet in length, mounted on the inner surface of the access door at the rear of the console. A small fan, which is also mounted on the access door, serves to dissipate the heat generated by the diffusion pump heater and by the radiator.

Fig. 2. Views of the ultrasoft polychromatic microradiographic apparatus constructed in the author's laboratory. See text for description of components.

As a precaution against damage to the vacuum system, a thermal relay has been installed which shuts down the diffusion pump heater, should the water temperature in the reservoir exceed 125° F. Recently, a pressure relay of the diaphragm type has also been added which shuts down the pump heater if the flow of coolant is in any way impeded. Flexible connections in the cooling system are made by means of "Tygon" tubing. As an extra convenience, aluminum "quick-connectors", of the type utilized in compressed air systems, have been used at the water input and output orifices of the X-ray tube. This greatly facilitates removal of the X-ray tube, when the vacuum system is utilized for other purposes, as, for example, in metal evaporation[12].

The control panel of the console includes, besides the valving required for high vacuum operation, a main power switch, which provides current to the forepump, the water pump, the fan, and to a pilot light. Separate switches and pilot lights are provided for the diffusion pump heater (in connection with the relays described above), for the power supply main, for the power supply high voltage transformer, and for a 110 V AC accessory plug at the side of the unit (usually utilized for vacuum gauge and safelight). The panel controls are completed by an electric 60-min interval timer and by-pass switch connected to the power supply main. Thus, once the exposure of a sample is begun, and the by-pass is in the "off" position, the power supply will shut down after a predetermined interval without further attention.

Entry to the X-ray tube sample chamber is made from the top of the console. Electrical connections for power supply, vacuum gauge, accessories and line input are placed together at one side of the console. The power supply, the vacuum gauge and a safelight are placed on the top of the unit. The instrument may be wheeled to any convenient working location. In operation it weighs 360 lb., and draws a maximum of 8 amperes from the 110 V AC line.

The power supply is also of a very simple design and permits variable high voltage outputs of 100—3000 V at currents of up to 2 mA. Under ordinary conditions, exposures are made in the range of 1.5 to 2.0 kV at 1 mA. Only slight and infrequent fluctuations of tube current have been noted during routine 30 to 45 min exposures.

In practice, the unit has been in semi-continuous operation for over a year, often being run continuously for many successive working days without difficulty. Its design and safety features enable it to be operated by students and technicians without prior experience, after only a brief instruction period, and with little risk to themselves or to the successful completion of the experiment in progress.

SAMPLE PREPARATION FOR HIGH RESOLUTION MICRORADIOGRAPHY

A method for preparing histological sections for high resolution microradiography has been described elsewhere[13], but the technique used for the present studies differs in certain rather important respects, and so shall be described in full in the following paragraphs.

Paraffin sections, usually of formalin-fixed tissues, in a range of thickness from 2—8 μ are spread on warm water, and under a Wratten 1A (light red) safelight are picked up on the emulsion surface of a bit of Eastman Kodak Spectroscopic Plate, No. 649-GH or No. 649-0. The latter is cut from stock 2″ by 10″ plates and is of a size appropriate to the apparatus sample chamber ($\frac{3}{4}$″ square in my instrument). The emulsion face of the small plate has previously been "subbed" by dipping into a 1 % solution of nitrocellulose (Parlodion) in ether–ethanol. The nitrocellulose film over the emulsion protects it to a certain extent from abrasion, and facilitates the ultimate removal of the specimen after X-ray exposure. After drying for at least 4 hours, the combined section–emulsion–plate complex is deparaffinized according to the following schedule:

1) Benzol	2 changes of 5 min each
2) Absolute ethanol	1 change, 1 min
3) 95 % Ethanol	1 change, 1 min
4) 80 % Ethanol	1 change, 1 min
5) 70 % Ethanol	1 change, 1 min
6) Distilled water	1 change, at least 10 min
7) 70 % Ethanol	1 change, 30 sec
8) 80 % Ethanol	1 change, 30 sec
9) 95 % Ethanol	1 change, 30 sec
10) Absolute ethanol	1 change, 1 min
11) Benzol	1 change, 1 min or longer.

References p. 287

Experience with various methods of deparaffination has indicated that paraffins of the type used ordinarily for histological work contain a benzol-insoluble fraction, which has been found to be water-soluble. Failure to utilize the water step in the schedule set forth above often leads to the production of an X-ray image of the crystalline water-soluble residue superimposed on the sample image. Usually, the water treatment eliminates this hazard. The section–emulsion–plate complex is finally removed from benzol, is allowed to dry, and then is placed in the X-ray tube.

Following exposure, the complex is placed in absolute acetone, in which the nitrocellulose "subbing" is readily soluble. Commonly, the sample (section) floats free of the emulsion of its own accord after a minute's exposure to acetone. Often, however, it is helpful to use a sable brush, or the tip of one finger moistened well with acetone to clear the section from the emulsion. After 2 min in acetone, and after ascertaining that the sample has been completely removed, the bit of plate is then placed directly into developer (Kodak D-19b, full strength, 5 min at 20° C), whereupon routine photographic procedures prevail. Care is exercised to prevent any drying of the emulsion during the acetone step, since the rapid cooling effect of acetone evaporation is very apt to cause wrinkling and distortion of the emulsion.

After development, fixation and washing, the microradiogram is dried, is covered with a microscope coverslip under balsam, and is mounted with balsam on a clean 1 × 3″ microscope slide. The original tissue sample, especially one which has floated free of the emulsion of its own accord, may then be mounted from the acetone bath in which it is floating onto an albuminized microscope slide for subsequent staining and comparison to the microradiogram. It is often convenient to mount the finished microradiogram on the same slide as the stained section, since comparison in the microscope may then be carried out without changing from one slide to another (Fig. 4 and 5).

Exposure of the emulsion to such a wide variety of solvents in the course of this technique may cause some misgivings as to possible deleterious effects upon emulsion response and sensitivity. Tests run in my laboratory, however, have indicated that no such effects can be detected. The presence of the nitrocellulose membrane over the emulsion causes a reduction in its ultimate response to a given exposure as compared to the uncoated plate, but this factor is, of course, kept reasonably constant at all times.

APPLICATION OF THE METHOD

Using the apparatus and method of sample preparation described above, ultrasoft microradiography has been utilized in the study of fine structure in a variety of histological samples taken from animal tissues. Some of these will be described in the following paragraphs. In pursuance of my thesis regarding the general utility of the method and its potential for adding new information, I should like to divide the results into three categories. The divisions are admittedly arbitrary. They tend to overlap to some extent, but are based on the following criteria:

1. Are there details of fine structure which are seen equally well by microradiography and by other available histological methods, but in which a concept of relative mass distribution adds information that other techniques do not provide?

2. Are there details of fine structure which are made more readily appreciable by microradiography than by other methods?

3. Are there details of fine structure which are seen *only* in the microradiographic image, to the exclusion of other methods?

We shall now examine, in order, selected examples of structural detail which satisfy the respective criteria.

Criterion 1. Can microradiography add a new dimension to previously established concepts of structure and function?

Fig. 3 illustrates a sector through the wall of a small artery from the mesentery of a rat, fixed in formalin, and microradiographed in the polychromatic spectrum of the apparatus described above (1.5 kV, 1.0 mA, 30 min). Immediately obvious is the marked radiopacity of the internal elastic lamella. One may also detect in the figure

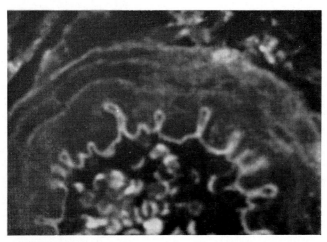

Fig. 3. Photomicrograph ($\times$ 960) of contact microradiogram showing a sector of the wall of a small artery in rat mesentary. Section fixed in formalin and sectioned at 4 μ. See text for description.

more peripherally placed lamellae of elastic tissue which are somewhat less absorptive, and therefore presumably contain a smaller concentration (mass per unit area) of elastin protein than does the internal lamella.

The fine structural details of elastic lamellae in blood vessels have been examined previously on many occasions by means of electron microscopy, or by appropriate histological staining techniques. Neither technique, however, brings out the significant fact that the elastic tissue is comprised of a far greater concentration of protein than is the surrounding tissue.

It will also be noted in Fig. 3 that the erythrocytes which lie within the lumen of the vessel frequently appear to possess an annular pattern of mass distribution which results from their biconcave discoidal geometry. However, it is important to point out the fact that the central (thin) portion of the cell appears in the microradiogram to contain no mass, despite the fact that even in fixed erythrocytes the hemoglobin residue is known to extend throughout the full volume of the cell. This observation emphasizes one of the most critical limitations of the qualitative X-ray absorption technique, namely that for a given range of X-ray wavelengths in the polychromatic spectrum, a certain specific minimal amount of material must be present to provide the absorption signal.

References p. 287

Calculations pertaining to the optimal range of mass concentrations and X-ray wavelengths for a variety of biologically important elements and compounds are provided elsewhere[6] and need not be dealt with here. The important point in terms of this presentation is the realization that the lack of X-ray absorption by a biological sample in qualitative microradiography does not always indicate the absence of absorbing materials, but frequently only reflects the fact that insufficient material is present in the sample.

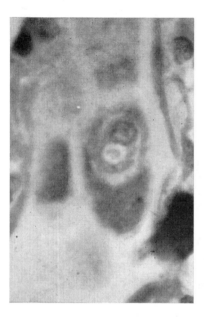

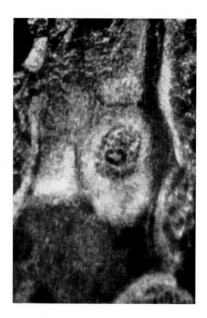

Fig. 4. Masson trichrome-stained section of an actively secreting osteoblast embedded in a subepiphyseal bone spicule from a young mouse. Formalin fixation, demineralized 6 μ paraffin section, × 860.

Fig. 5. Ultrasoft microradiogram of same area prepared at 1.5 kV and reproduced at the same magnification as for Fig. 4. Note the clarity with which increased dry mass of bone matrix is indicated in the microradiogram.

Fig. 4 and 5 provide still another example of the fulfillment of our first criterion. This pair of illustrations is respectively a photomicrograph of a Masson trichrome-stained, formalin-fixed, 6 μ demineralized section of mouse bone, together with a reproduction at the same magnification of the corresponding microradiogram. An actively secreting osteoblast is seen at the center of the figures, embedded in a spicule of cartilage, but surrounded by newly-formed bone matrix. Reference to the black-and-white reproduction of the stained specimen in Fig. 4 indicates that the tinctorial properties of the newly-formed matrix are different from those of the surrounding cartilage (respectively red and pale green in the stained slide). The microradiogram brings out the fact that the mass concentration within bone matrix is strikingly greater than that of the cartilage. Additionally, this microradiogram provides information with respect to the mass distribution and structure within the juxtanuclear vacuole of the osteoblast (Fig. 5), which may be difficult to appreciate by staining techniques.

References p. 287

Fig. 6 a–d is a final example of the first criterion, although in some respects it verges on the second criterion as well. In it are shown several microradiograms of skeletal muscle presented at various magnifications to bring out internal structural details. The muscle is taken from the rat (Figs. 6 a, b), mouse (c) and guinea pig (d). No attempt has been made to correlate these images with the physiological status of the specimen at the time of sacrifice (*i.e.*, its degree of contraction, stretching, etc.). The point which is emphasized here is that, since the internal structure of the muscle fiber can so easily be demonstrated, elucidation of structural-functional relationships may be greatly facilitated by the additional information regarding mass distribution which the technique provides.

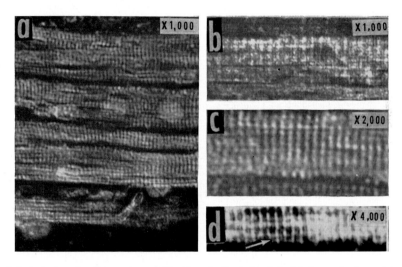

Fig. 6. Selected reproductions, at magnifications indicated, of skeletal muscle from:(a) and (b), rat; (c), mouse; (d), guinea pig. All tissues fixed in formalin and sectioned at 5 μ. Mass distribution in striped muscle may vary with species, body origin, and physiological status. See text for details.

It is also possible to observe and measure mass concentration of structures by the use of the interference microscope. The interference microscopic method has already made many significant contributions in biology, particularly by virtue of the fact that it can perform quantitative measurements on biological samples which are not amenable to microradiographic treatment (esp. living tissue). However, it, like the microradiographic method, possesses certain shortcomings[14], among which is the fact that it is limited in its capacity to deal with extremely small structures in which the distribution of mass varies gradually rather than suddenly. The microradiographic method, on the other hand, is particularly well-suited to this situation.

Moreover, one cannot overlook the fact that the microradiogram is, as it were, a permanent record in itself of mass distribution. Unless a photomicrographic recording of the interference microscopic field is made at the time of examination, the observations made by this method cannot be re-examined visually without carefully re-establishing the experimental conditions of specimen, lighting and optics. Finally, in this regard, it may be germane to point out that the financial investment in one commercially manufactured interference microscope will pay for the construction of two microradiographic apparatuses of the type described above.

Criterion 2.   Can microradiography reveal structures more clearly than other conventional methods?

Fig. 7 provides an excellent example of the second criterion. This is a microradiogram (1.5 kV, 1.0 mA, 30 min) of a formalin-fixed 8 μ section through the wall of the

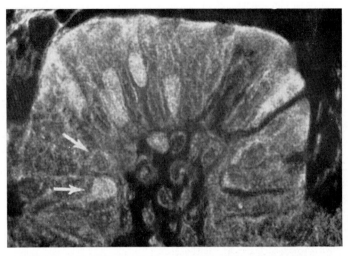

Fig. 7. Photomicrograph ($\times$ 1,000) of microradiogram prepared from 8 μ section of formalin-fixed rat jejunum. Differences in dry mass content of adjacent nuclei in surface cells are indicated (compare upper and lower arrows).

jejunum of a young rat. Attention is drawn to the fact that certain nuclei of the surface epithelium appear to contain a high concentration of dry mass. However, other nuclei in the epithelium, often closely adjacent to those possessing a high dry mass content, appear virtually empty of absorbing materials. The latter type of nucleus can be discerned only by the fact that its nuclear membrane exhibits a fairly well defined concentration of mass, and appears therefore as a ring-shaped structure in the microradiogram (compare nuclei indicated by arrows in Fig. 7). It is reasonably easy to distinguish goblet cells of the surface epithelium from surface epithelial cells proper, and I have concluded that the nuclei concerned in this phenomenon are those of the true surface cells. Moreover, since the section thickness is approximately equal to the diameter of these nuclei, and since the surface epithelial cells are arranged in very orderly rows, it does not seem likely that the variance in absorption pattern is caused by variations in the plane of section in relation to nuclear diameter. This absorption pattern has been noted frequently both at the surface of the intestine and in the intestinal crypts in a number of species. Some suggestion of nuclear staining differences has been noted by means of routine hematoxylin-eosin, or by the Feulgen method. However, the results of the latter methods are far less convincing, possibly because of the fact that visual distraction is minimized in the black-and-white image provided by the microradiogram. The functional significance of this finding remains obscure.

References p. 287

Fig. 8a and 8b illustrate another situation in which structures are selectively demonstrated in microradiograms, and in which conventional methods are less effective. Fig. 8a shows the terminal bar (terminal web) apparatus of an actively secreting ameloblastic epithelium in the rat incisor[15], microradiographed at 1.25 kV, 0.5 mA, 45 min. The figure demonstrates clearly the presence of aggregations of highly-absorptive material (protein) between the tips of adjacent ameloblasts.

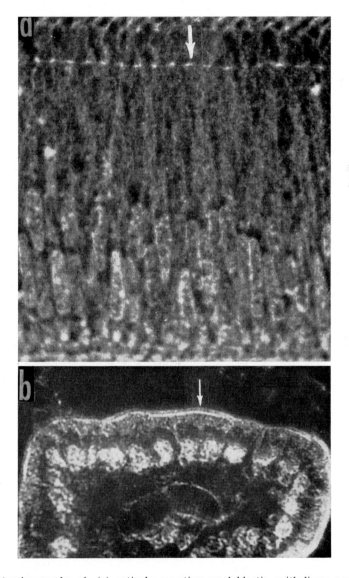

Fig. 8. Photomicrographs of: (a) actively secreting ameloblastic epithelium; and (b) cross-section of duodenal villus from a newborn rat. Microradiograms (1.25 kV) prepared from 6 μ formalin-fixed paraffin sections, reproduced at × 1,000. The terminal bar apparatus (a) and striated border (b) are clearly defined by their opacity to the ultrasoft X-ray beam. It is assumed that these structures consist of protein aggregates.

References p. 287

Similarly, in Fig. 8b, the striated border of the intestinal epithelium of a young rat is shown to be comprised of a high concentration of structural protein. As in the case of striations in muscle, no attempt has been made as yet to assign physiological functional significance to these qualities of the terminal bar apparatus, or of the striated border. The fact that they are so easily rendered accessible to examination by the microradiographic technique, however, may encourage further investigation of their function in the organism.

Criterion 3. Can microradiography reveal structural details which have not previously been described by the use of conventional methods?

Two examples of this facet of qualitative microradiography will be described briefly. Both pertain to the structure and physiology of mineralized tissue. Fig. 9a and 9b are

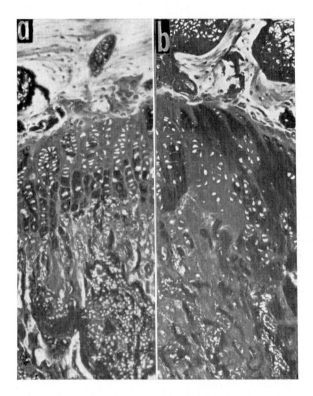

Fig. 9. (a) Microradiogram (× 130) of sector through demineralized proximal humeral epiphysis of a normal guinea pig. (b) Similar sector (× 130) from humerus of ascorbic acid-deficient guinea pig (21 days on diet). Note the loss of dry mass from cartilage in (b) resulting from the vitamin deficiency. See text for details.

respectively microradiograms of the formalin-fixed and demineralized proximal epiphyseal cartilage plates from the humeri of guinea pigs. That illustrated in Fig. 9a is from a normal animal, while that in Fig. 9b is from an animal suffering from acute ascorbic acid deficiency[16].

The normal structural orientation of the epiphysis is readily apparent in Fig. 9a.

References p. 287

It will be noted that the coatings of bone matrix about the subepiphyseal spicules are clearly differentiated from the underlying cartilage matrix by virtue of their increased absorption (see also Fig. 5). Also apparent in the normal bone is the presence of an absorptive fibrillar component of cartilage matrix, which outlines the chondrocyte lacunae, and which also tends to separate adjacent cartilage cell columns. Reference to Fig. 9b reveals that in scurvy these fibrillar constituents are no longer present. To my knowledge, this deficiency of structural elements in scorbutic cartilage has not been demonstrated previously. It is also worthwhile to note the clarity with which the microgram in Fig. 9b demonstrates that no new bone matrix has been formed in the subepiphyseal region during the vitamin-deficient period.

A more striking example of the utility of microradiography in demonstrating new structural features is provided in Fig. 10a and 10b. These are respectively the Masson trichrome-stained section and corresponding microradiogram of a spicule of bone which is undergoing osteoclastic resorption. The section is from a formalin-fixed normal mouse femur, and has been demineralized.

The role of the osteoclast in bone resorption has never been completely explained, primarily because it has not been possible to ascribe definitely to this cell any specific enzymic or other chemical activity which might account for its apparent lysing effect on bone[17].

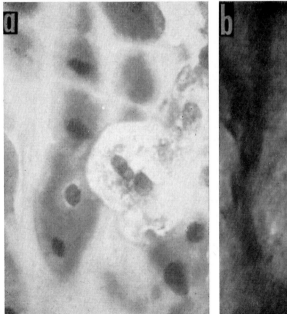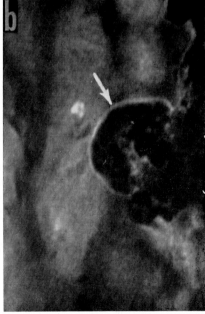

Fig. 10. (a) Masson trichrome-stained section ($\times$ 960) of a demineralized subepiphyseal bone spicule from a young mouse, fixed in formalin and sectioned at 6 μ; (b) photomicrograph of ultrasoft microradiogram (1.5 kV) of the same area as (a), also reproduced at $\times$ 960. In the center of both figures is a large osteoclast. Histological and microradiographic details of osteoclast structure may be compared. Note that the microradiogram in (b) indicates the presence of a thin area of increased dry mass at the junction of the osteoclast cytoplasm with the bone matrix (arrow).

References p. 287

Examination of the microradiogram, however, reveals that at the junction of the cell cytoplasm and the bone matrix, there is a sharply delimited, narrow rim or "rind" of material possessing a high mass density (Fig. 10b, arrow). Close examination of this and other comparable preparations suggests that the region of increased mass actually lies within the bone matrix rather than in the osteoclast cytoplasm. Staining reactions of this region are equivocal; for example, in the Masson stain, only a slight increase in avidity for the Fast Green component is noted. It is significant to note that this area has been described by others[17,18] as the site of the so-called "brush border," a structure which has been attributed to the presence therein of strands of collagen extending from the bone to the osteoclast. Interpretation of this structure has depended on the concept that the lytic action of the osteoclast on collagen is less rapid than that upon the mineral and ground-substance constituents of bone. Consequently, collagen fibers may remain relatively intact for some time after the other components of bone have disappeared.

The possible physiological significance of this rim or "rind" of increased microradiographic density has been discussed elsewhere[19]. It is sufficient here to suggest that since the absorption of the adjacent intact bone matrix, which is known to consist almost entirely of collagen protein, is *less* than that of the "rind", it is hardly likely that collagen content alone is responsible for its increased capacity for absorption. The most reasonable explanation, it seems to me, is that additional material (probably protein) is present at the junctional zone. Possibly this material may play an active role in the resorption process.

CONCLUDING COMMENTS

It may be apparent from the foregoing that while results obtained by the qualitative microradiographic method are in themselves of considerable value, their full significance cannot be appreciated unless other, complementary methods are also utilized. Examples of the value of the multi-methodological approach in this connection are numerous. To cite but a few, the excellence of the correlated studies by the group led by HYDÉN and BRATTGARD on mass, structure and chemistry of neurons under a variety of experimental conditions stands out clearly[20, 21]. Recent work in collaboration with FRIBERG[16] has shown some interesting correlations between alterations in the mass distribution of collagenous tissues in scurvy and the autoradiographic pattern of sulfomucopolysaccharide metabolism. Similarly, the significance of certain staining reactions in selected tissues may be elucidated, at least partially, by simultaneous application of microradiography[15].

In conclusion, therefore, it seems to me entirely reasonable on theoretical and practical grounds to recommend a wider application of qualitative polychromatic microradiography as a worthy adjunct to the methods already available to the histologist and to the plant or animal pathologist. The fact that such applications of the method may be entirely qualitative in approach need not detract from its usefulness, provided that extreme care is exercised in interpreting results, and provided that the reproducibility of the latter is unequivocal.

With continuing progress in the development of precise methods for quantitation of organic mass content, and ultimately, of elementary chemical composition, we may hopefully assume that it will be but a very short time until the prediction made by BARNARD has achieved a complete reality in biological microscopy.

References p. 287

ACKNOWLEDGEMENTS

The work reported here was supported by a research grant (D-635) from the National Institutes of Health, D.H.E.W. The author takes pleasure in gratefully acknowledging the talented assistance of Mr. NICHOLAS A. DODICH in all phases of the study.

REFERENCES

1 P. GOBY, Compt. rend., 156 (1913) 686.
2 J. E. BARNARD, J, Roy. Microscop. Soc., Transactions (1915) 1.
3 P. LAMARQUE, Radiology, 27 (1936) 563.
4 J. TURCHINI, Bull. histol. appl. et tech. microscop., 14 (1937) 17.
5 A. ENGSTRÖM, in G. OSTER and A. POLISTER, Physical Methods in Biological Research, Academic Press, Inc., New York, 1956, Vol. 3, Chapt. 10.
6 B. LINDSTRÖM, Acta Radiol., Suppl. 125 (1955).
7 A. ENGSTRÖM and R. C. GREULICH, J. Appl. Phys., 27 (1956) 758.
8 A. ENGSTRÖM, R. C. GREULICH, B. L. HENKE and B. LUNDBERG, in V. COSSLETT, A. ENGSTRÖM and H. PATTEE, X-ray Microscopy and Microradiography, Academic Press, Inc., New York, 1957, pp. 218 et seq.
9 R. C. GREULICH, in preparation.
10 A. ENGSTRÖM and B. LUNDBERG, Exptl. Cell Research, 12 (1957) 198.
11 B. L. HENKE, personal communication.
12 A. ENGSTRÖM, B. LUNDBERG and G. BERGENDAHL, J. Ultrastructure Research, 1 (1957) 147.
13 R. C. GREULICH and A. ENGSTRÖM, Exptl. Cell Research, 10 (1956) 251.
14 A. J. HALE, The Interference Microscope in Biological Research, E. and S. Livingstone, Ltd., Edinburgh, 1958.
15 R. C. GREULICH, Arch. Oral Biol., in the press.
16 R. C. GREULICH and U. FRIBERG, in preparation.
17 N. J. HANCOX, in G. BOURNE, Biochemistry and Physiology of Bone, Academic Press, Inc., New York, 1956, Chapter 8.
18 A. W. HAM, J. Bone and Joint Surg., 34A (1952) 701.
19 R. C. GREULICH, Science, in preparation.
20 S.-O. BRATTGARD, J. E. EDSTRÖM and H. HYDÉN, Exptl. Cell Research, Suppl. 5 (1958) 185.
21 S.-O. BRATTGARD and H. HYDÉN, Acta Radiol., Suppl. 94 (1952).

AN EVALUATION OF QUANTITATIVE MICRORADIOGRAPHIC PROCEDURES APPLIED TO BIOLOGICAL AND MEDICAL RESEARCH

B. LINDSTROM

Department of Medical Physics, Karolinska Institute, Stockholm (Sweden)

ABSTRACT

Contact microradiography and point projection microradiography applied to biological and medical problems are evaluated from the practical point of view. For several reasons, contact microradiography is at present to be preferred for quantitative analyses on a cellular level.

From the technical point of view contact microradiography and point projection microradiography have both advantages and disadvantages. In contact microradiography the main advantages are the relatively simple apparatus, the possibility of obtaining a large field with a uniform X-ray intensity, and the possibility of utilizing ultrasoft X-rays and strictly monochromatic radiation, preferable in quantitative analyses. However, the resolving power in contact microradiography is limited mainly by the granularity of the photographic emulsion, though it is better than 1μ for the best fine-grained emulsions. Point projection microradiography has the outstanding advantage of primary magnification, which reduces the influence of the photographic material considerably. The equipment is, however, rather complicated, and it is difficult to obtain uniform intensity across larger areas in the specimen. Furthermore, strictly monochromatic X-rays and radiation in the ultrasoft wavelength range cannot be utilized in this procedure.

The objects to be analysed are also very important for the choice of the most suitable microradiographic procedure. In biological and medical investigations the preparation of the specimens for microradiographic analysis is the most difficult problem, since the object should be as unmodified as possible, compared to the *in vivo* state. For material from solid soft tissues freeze-sectioning combined with freeze-drying is the best method to preserve the structure. Specimens which are only frozen-fixed and then freeze-dried, must generally be embedded in paraffin before microtome sectioning. The embedding medium must be removed before the exposure to X-rays, and the different cellular components may be dissolved. If routine fixatives are used, such as formalin or ethanol, a dissolution may occur also during the fixation procedure. Different shrinkage effects may introduce serious artefacts in the specimens, sometimes invalidating quantitative cytochemical analyses.

In microradiograms of well preserved specimens from solid tissues the differences in X-ray absorption in different cellular structures are generally rather small, contrary to the case for *e.g.* specimens fixed in formalin. It may therefore be extremely difficult to identify the cellular structure to be analysed. Thus it is often necessary to utilize additional methods, mainly histological staining procedures, in order to obtain valid microradiographic measurements. Consequently, a detecting system for direct recording of X-ray intensities is often inferior to the fine-grained photographic emulsion.

In biological and medical investigations utilizing microradiography it is often necessary to register an X-ray absorption image of a relatively large area in a tissue section in order to select structures suitable for quantitative analyses. A large field with a uniform X-ray intensity may therefore be very important.

The absorption of the X-rays in the biological object implies a further limitation concerning the choice of method for microradiography. The mass absorption coefficient of dry soft tissues is of the same order as that of nitrogen, and for a resolving power better than 1μ the thickness of the specimen ought to be between 2 and 5 μ. Consequently, sufficient contrast in the absorption image of the tissue section is only obtained when very soft X-rays are used.

When polychromatic X-rays are utilized in quantitative analyses, filtration effects and the quantum efficiency of the photographic emulsion may sometimes influence the results. Therefore, monochromatic X-rays are advantageous to use in many investigations, since they give more accurate analyses.

Evaluating the different error factors in quantitative microradiography applied to biological and medical problems, it is found that the main sources of variation lie in the material itself and in the pretreatment of the specimens. Direct recording of the X-ray intensity may be more accurate than photographic procedures, but increased accuracy of the detecting system has but little influence on the total error. If, however, more refined methods of specimen preparation can be introduced, the total variation will decrease considerably.

Summing up, contact microradiography is at present found to be more suitable for the analysis of biological and medical problems than point projection microradiography. The two methods have approximately the same practical resolving power, but regarding the area of uniform X-ray intensity, the useful range of wavelengths, and monochromaticity, contact microradiography has several advantages, particularly important in biological and medical applications.

LUNG STRUCTURE STUDIED BY MICRORADIOGRAPHY

CHARLES P. ODERR

Veterans Administration Hospital, New Orleans, La. (U.S.A.)

ABSTRACT

The study of intact alveoli, alveolar ducts, and small vessel patterns does not lend itself well to the classical methods of histology.

The greater depth of focus available by microradiography has potential contributions to this field. Some of these have been partially realized, especially with regard to vascular pattern. A projection-type instrument is being designed for the 500 to 2,500 volt range with which it is hoped that intact alveolar ducts and associated alveoli can be demonstrated.

We have been using *contact* microradiography in the study of lung slices ($\frac{1}{2}$ to 5 mm in thickness) and are preparing to use a *projection* technique. Working with un-injected inflation-dried lungs, we have visualized arterioles and venules and occasionally capillaries, but details of the finer air passages have been difficult to

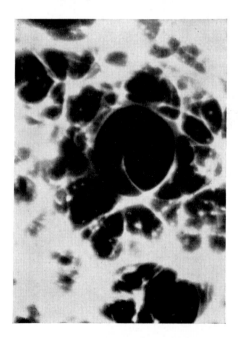 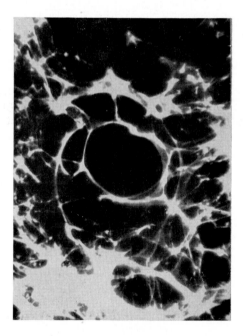

Fig. 1. Microradiograph of portion of alveolar duct. × 70. From Kodak High Resolution Plate (1600 V, 2.5 mA., 0.05 μ Hg vac., 40 min, 6 cm distance). Case 131, age 62. From an area of early emphysema.

Fig. 2. Microradiograph of alveolar duct showing alcove-like arrangement of alveoli. × 70. Case 131, age 62, WM. Same technique as Fig. 1.

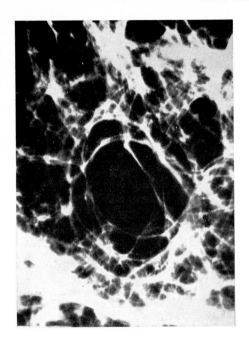

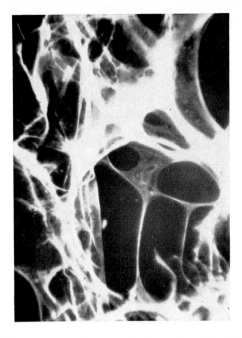

Fig. 3. Microradiograph of alveolar duct from area of early emphysema, × 70. (1600 V, 2.5 mA, 0.05 μ Hg vac., 40 min, 6 cm distance). Case 130, age 40, WM.

Fig. 4. 45 × enlargement of area from Kodak High Resolution Plate (1600 V, 2.5 mA, 0.05 μ Hg vac., 40 min, 6 cm distance). Locally advanced emphysema.

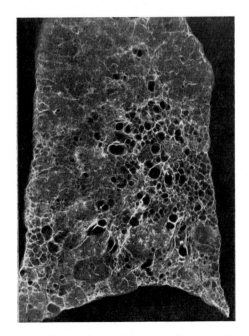

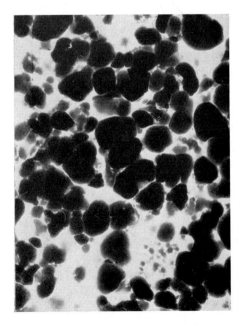

Fig. 5. Human lung with areas of destruction and interstitial fibrosis. Dried in inflation. Cut 2 mm thick. (Case 68, age 61). Technique: 12 kV, 3 mA, 3 min. Dist: 10 in. Tube: 0.08 in. Be with 0.7 mm focal spot. Film: Fine Grain Positive. Dev.: Kodak Dektrol. Reduced × 0.7.

Fig. 6. Lung with islands of normal tissue surrounded by destruction and interstitial fibrosis. Farmer and roofer. (Case 68). Technique: 0.5 mm slice in contact with Fine Grain Positive Film inside cassette with front (Radelin TD) screen. 120 kV, 10 mA, 12 sec 40″, 0.3 mm focal spot. Photoenlargement × 7.

delineate. We would like to show the results we have obtained with the Philips CMR unit and invite your comments, concerning the problems at hand.

We produced films delineating considerable detail of the secondary lobule structure in the lung with 3 kV at 13 cm. Early emphysema lesions and their positions within the secondary lobule were well shown. We demonstrated that almost all of the dilated air sacs had abnormal fenestrations. To study the latter in greater detail we needed longer rays, which lead us to construct a 6 cm camera. Using 1600 V X-rays through fairly high vacuum (0.05 μ Hg), radiographs suitable for up to 200 magnification were obtained.

We have two anatomical-pathologic problems in mind at this juncture. One is the further delineation of cells, connective tissue structures, and embedded dust in the interalveolar septa. These septa are perhaps 10—20 μ in thickness and they do not lie in a plane parallel with the film. The other problem is delineation of intact alveolar ducts. This will require a focal-depth-equivalent of a few hundred microns, and a field size of at least several millimeters in diameter*. Sufficient soft tissue differentiation to bring out muscle structure would be highly desirable.

---

* The depth of field for 200 magnification through light microscope varies from about 2 μ (8 mm objective with numerical aperture 0.50 and $\times$ 10 eye piece) to 8 μ (16 mm objective with numerical aperture 0.25 and $\times$ 20 eye piece).

EXPLORATORY STUDIES OF TISSUE BY X-RAY PROJECTION MICROSCOPY

R. L. DE C. H. SAUNDERS and L. VAN DER ZWAN

*Anatomy and Physics Departments, Dalhousie University,
Halifax, Nova Scotia (Canada)*

ABSTRACT

The present study is to determine how the COSSLETT-NIXON type of X-ray projection microscope may be applied to histological studies. Various unstained animal and human tissues are being examined, *e.g.*, hair, sebaceous gland, kidney, etc. Tissue preparation techniques such as freeze drying or substitution, and the problems of floatation, are considered important in X-ray projection microscopy in order to minimise morphological changes and solution losses from the cells. The operating and recording techniques used with this X-ray microscope are described including the methods of utilising the primary magnified images. Remarkably contrasty and detailed projection micrographs of both soft and mineralised tissues can be obtained rapidly ($\frac{1}{2}$—4 min), with varying primary magnification, and with fewer tissue manipulations than required by many contact techniques, so that the section can be subsequently stained histologically.

The present study has sought to determine ways of applying X-ray projection microscopy to the histology of unstained animal and human tissues. Its object has been to ascertain which tissues lend themselves to the technique, and whether useful information might be obtained regarding unstained cell structure and its densities, with the hope of applying primary magnification of the X-ray projection microscope to tissue microanalysis.

Contact microradiography has long been available to biologists and recently techniques[1, 2] have been elaborated whereby quantitative cytochemical analysis can be so determined. Point-projection X-ray microscopy as developed by COSSLETT and NIXON[3] at Cambridge University is the newest of the three methods of X-ray microscopy. Its value in comparative entomology[4], metallurgy[5], medical and dental microangiography[6, 7] has been indicated.

Plant cells were the first examined with the X-ray projection microscope, recalling the development of the optical microscope and HOOKE's description (*Micrographia*, 1665) of the cells in cork. The cellular detail obtainable by the projection method in botanical specimens is interesting but does not yet exceed that of the optical microscope. In *Allium cepa*, nucleus and nucleolus can be clearly imaged within the cell cytoplasm (Fig. 2), and stages of mitosis have been recorded. The marked absorption of the cell walls produces striking cell patterns, as of phloem and xylem in Helianthus, and it is perhaps here that the penetration and stereographic recording of X-ray microscopy may find an application in connection with the problem of circulation or translocation in plants.

Animal cells with their complexities of form and composition present X-ray microscopy with problems of tissue preparation, examination, and interpretation,

References p. 305

for much remains to be learned concerning the varying radio-densities of soft and mineralised tissues. Before X-ray projection microscopy becomes a well established method of microscopical investigation, attention must be paid to the improvement of focussing, especially at lower kilovoltages, and betterment of resolution. This study shows that some insight has already been gained as to the type of tissue and preparation best suited to the projection method.

METHODS

A COSSLETT-NIXON X-ray projection microscope (Mark 11 E.R. 3) was used. In this instrument two successive electro-magnetic lenses are employed to focus an electron beam upon a thin metal foil serving both as tube window and X-ray target, thereby producing an X-ray point source of less than 1 μ in diameter. The projection method of X-ray microscopy depends essentially on the X-ray point source casting an enlarged image of a nearby object on to a distant screen or photographic plate. Since the magnification depends on the ratio of the target–plate to the target–object distance, both of which are variable, high primary magnification ($\times$ 200) is possible. The kilovoltage is variable (5—30 kV) hence a voltage giving maximum penetration and contrast can be selected.

The present studies were carried out at approx. 7 kV, using a beam current of 4—100 μA, with a thin aluminium target of 4—10 μ, and a tungsten filament of 0.004 in. diameter. Exposure times ranged between $\frac{1}{2}$—4 min, and a primary magnification of approx. $\times$ 2 was used in the interests of exposure time, intensity, and ease of photographic recording. On occasion a primary magnification of $\times$ 7 was employed. A target–plate distance of 1.6—5.6 cm was generally used. Preliminary focussing of the projection microscope was carried out with a piece of 1500 mesh silver grid (3 μ bars and 17 μ spaces) as a test object placed upon the target foil, using a fluorescent screen.

Initially, histological sections (7—10 μ in thickness) were mounted directly on terylene or melinex plastic film and examined under atmospheric conditions. Strikingly contrasty low-power projection micrographs were obtained on standard lantern-slide emulsion (Ilford Contrasty plates) with both soft and mineralised tissues. Absorption by the plastic film and air column limited cellular definition, leading to the use of a vacuum camera.

The camera (Fig. 1) consisted of a brass funnel, whose smaller end was threaded

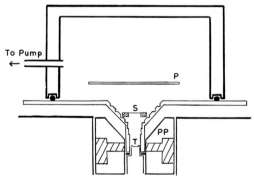

Fig. 1. Diagram of camera and camera base as used in X-ray projection microscope.

References p. 305

to engage and surround the target assembly of the X-ray microscope, while fitting within its pole piece. The interior of the brass funnel was machined to give circular tiers (depth 1 mm) at distances of 1, 3, 5, 7, 9, 11, and 13 mm from the target, and fitted with removable brass rings for the support of tissue sections, so giving a variable but known target–specimen distance. The larger end of the funnel was connected to an aluminium platform which supported a removable photographic plate chamber (4 cm high) evacuated by a vacuum pump.

Most of the tissue micrographs were taken on Kodak Maximum or High Resolution plates, Gevaert Lippmann being used on occasion. The plates were developed in Dektol (dil. 1:1) 2 min at 20° C), transferred to an acid bath, and fixed in Amfix (1 min). Secondary images were recorded on either Kodak Microfile or Adox (K.B. 14 or 17) 35 mm film, using a microphotographic unit (Leitz Aristophot) and printed out on Kodabromide paper with an enlarger (Leitz Focomat).

Ordinary fixation methods were used first, but later freeze-drying or substitution were adopted as giving the optimum results. Tissues were quenched in isopentane cooled to $-190°$ C in liquid air and freeze dried in an Edward's T.D. 2 at $-40°$ C for 96 h, or transferred to absolute alcohol at $-50°$ C and freeze substituted for a similar period.

Sections cut at 4 and 6 μ were mounted on brass rings bearing a formvar film, prepared by dipping the ring in a 0.25 % or 0.5 % solution of formvar in ethylene dichloride and allowing it to dry. Non-magnetic mounting rings proved essential since the section lies within the magnetic field of the pole piece.

The microtome sections were either "dry-mounted" or else "floated-out" over water or saline, to determine whether such procedures influenced cytological definition and contrast in X-ray microscopy. Recently it was reported[8] that floatation causes solution losses and marked changes in the appearance of the nuclei and cytoplasm such as vacuolation and the loss of certain cell inclusions. Control sections for optical microscopy were stained with haematoxylin and eosin.

RESULTS

Examples of the results obtained are shown in Figs. 3 through 10. They include X-ray micrographs of bone, kidney, thyroid, submaxillary gland, skin and its appendages, and are representative of a large number of tissues taken.

The structure of skin, hair and sebaceous glands are well demonstrated by X-ray microscopy. Certain internal details are revealed with clarity, possibly because keratin has a high sulphur content.

Fig. 3 shows an unstained section of epidermis. Keratinized strands are evident at the skin surface and contain occasional dark areas representative of nuclear remnants. The superficial cells of the Malphigian layer have undergone keratinization as shown by a marked band of absorption. Just below this layer of keratinization cell definition is lost, giving a fairly homogeneous zone. Beneath this again can be seen the polygonal cells of the stratum spinosum whose irregular intercellular boundaries appear as white areas indicative of X-ray absorption. Marked absorption is seen in the basal region adjacent to the dermis.

A cross section of human scalp showing hair follicles cut at various levels is seen in Fig. 4. On the left, the section passes through the lower third of a follicle, and demonstrates from without inwards the vitreous membrane and cells of the outer

References p. 305

epithelial root sheath, of which the former appears as a strikingly white ring of heavy absorption. Within the outer root sheath lies another white ring of high absorption corresponding to Henle's layer, and also the cells making up Huxley's layer, both of which constitute the inner epithelial root sheath. Centrally is seen the cortex

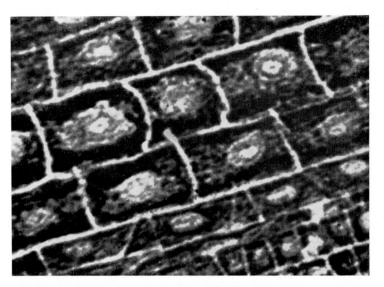

Fig. 2. Micrograph (P.M.R.) of onion root tip (*Allium cepa*) showing cell cytoplasm, nuclei, and nucleoli. Mag × 450.

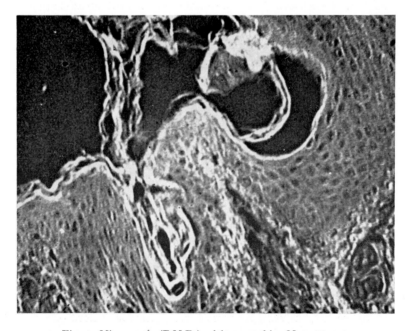

Fig. 3. Micrograph (P.M.R.) of human skin. Mag. × 275.

References p. 305

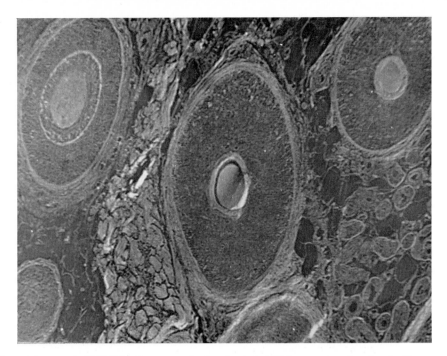

Fig. 4. Micrograph (P.M.R.) of human scalp showing hair follicles cut at various levels. Mag. × 275.

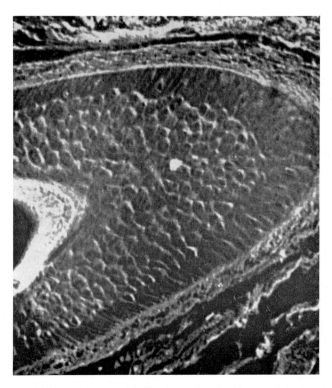

Fig. 5. Micrograph (P.M.R.) of outer epithelium root sheath of human hair follicle. Mag. × 562.

References p. 305

of the hair, which shows a degree of absorption that depends on the level of section. The connective tissue sheath surrounding the hair follicle can also be seen, as well as white absorption areas among the cells of the inner root sheath heralding their keratinization.

On the right, the hair follicle is sectioned in a region which is midway between epidermis and root papilla. The parts of the outer epithelial root sheath are again recognised, but at this level the inner root sheath differs in that it appears white owing to marked absorption, so giving evidence that its cells have undergone keratinization. Centrally, the cortex of the hair is also seen to be highly X-ray absorbent, no doubt due to its being composed of hard keratin and possessing a high sulphur content. Note that cell nuclei can be readily identified as dark radiolucent dots within the cells of the outer root sheath. Adjacent to the hair follicles can be identified a transected arrector pili muscle and sweat gland; both show some absorption, especially the basement membrane of the latter.

Fig. 5 shows the cells of the outer epithelial root sheath of a hair follicle at higher magnification. The outermost cells, adjacent to the connective tissue sheath, are seen to be tall and arranged in a row, forming the so-called stratum cylindricum. Within this lie polygonal cells which show varying degrees of X-ray absorption, sometimes so marked as to give the appearance of a white cell containing a dark black nucleus. The cells of the inner root sheath have undergone conversion to soft keratin and so give a white area of marked absorption containing nuclear remnants. The hair itself has been displaced from the center of the follicle which consequently records black.

Human sebaceous glands are strikingly demonstrated by X-ray microscopy. In Fig. 6 several sebaceous lobules, encapsulated by connective tissue, are shown adjacent to a hair follicle. The component cells contain dark radiolucent areas of a discrete or confluent type representative of lipid droplets (sebum) of various sizes. Some micrographs have revealed extreme lipid accumulation within the sebaceous cells; the uniformly black cytoplasm then contrasts strikingly with the "doughnut" appearance of the white (absorption) nucleus and its black nucleolus. As a rule the cells contain "doughnut" nuclei but some of the central cells contain nuclei which are markedly X-ray absorbent, presumably because they are pyknotic (dense mass). The cell membranes show heavy absorption and are distinctive except in the region of dying cells where they are broken down. Other micrographs have shown a group of sebaceous cells surrounded by cellular and nuclear debris; this debris appears mottled since it contains both fat and keratin. Duct structure has also been recorded (Fig. 7).

Human foetal tissue, such as the developing kidney, intestinal villi, and thyroid gland, yielded interesting results. Fig. 8 is a micrograph of foetal thyroid, which shows that the gland at this stage (C.R. 160 mm; 5 months) consists of numerous epithelial cords containing a small central lumen, and irregular (beaded) epithelial plates in which follicular cavities have begun to appear. Elsewhere are seen quite large thyroid follicles or acini (approx. $20-40 \mu$ in diameter), bounded by a markedly absorbent simple epithelium, whose cavities however contain no colloid. The inner margin of the follicular cells is highly absorbent; a feature possibly associated with future colloid formation. Foetuses of various ages are being examined by X-ray microscopy to determine the date of iodine appearance, since colloid begins to ac-

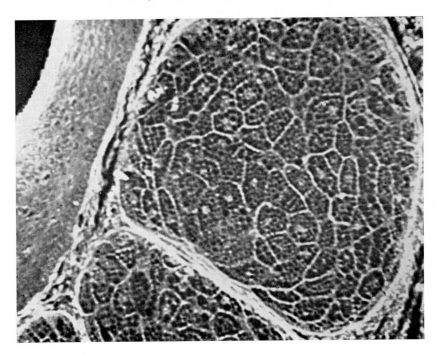

Fig. 6. Micrograph (P.M.R.) of human sebaceous gland. Mag. × 560.

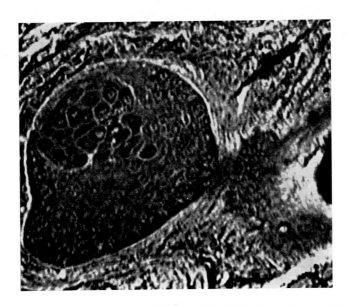

Fig. 7. Micrograph (P.M.R.) of human sebaceous gland showing cells, secretion, and duct. Mag. × 275.

References p. 305

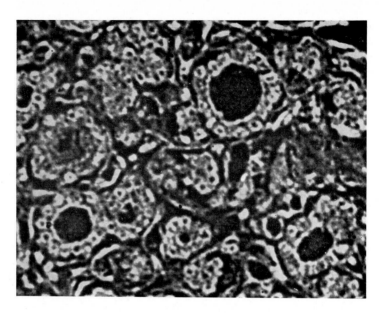

Fig. 8. Micrograph (P.M.R.) of developing thyroid gland (Human Foetus C.R. 160 mm). Mag. × 450.

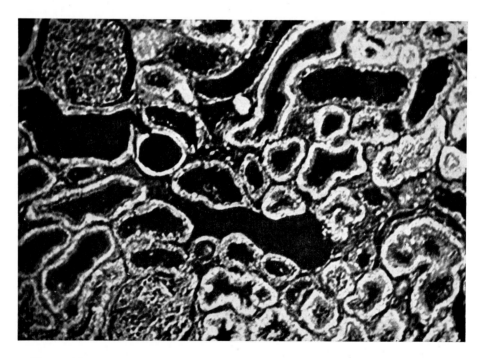

Fig. 9. Micrograph (P.M.R.) showing cortical labyrinth ot rat kidney. Mag. × 275.

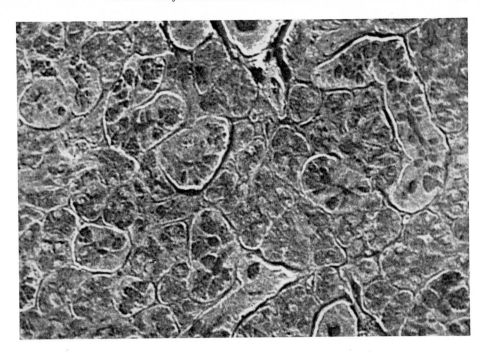

Fig. 10. Micrograph (P.M.R.) of terminal ramification in submaxillary gland of rat. Mag. × 275.

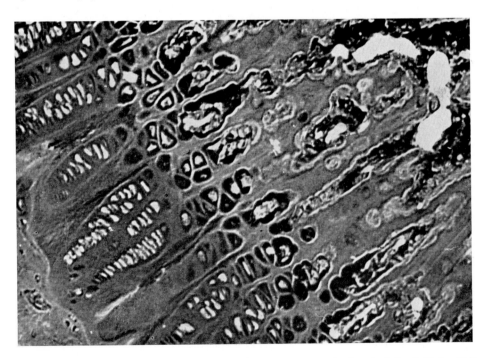

Fig. 11. Micrograph (P.M.R.) of epiphyseal growth zones at proximal end of decalcified rabbit tibia. Mag. × 275.

References p. 305

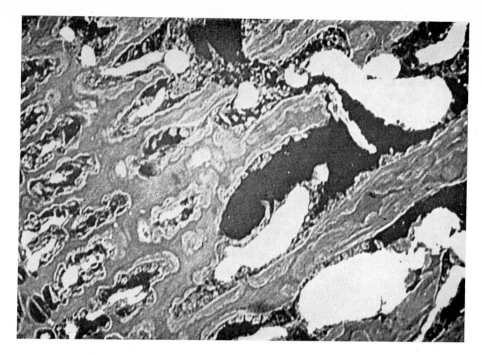

Fig. 12. Micrograph (P.M.R.) of proximal end of decalcified rabbit tibia showing trabecular formation, osteoblasts along marrow spaces, and blood vessels filled with contrast medium. Mag × 275.

cumulate in the cell nests during the 4th month of intrauterine life[9]. The high iodine content of adult thyroid epithelium and colloid gives a strikingly heavy X-ray absorption and consequently contrasty micrographs.

Animal studies of a survey nature have been carried out on the abdominal viscera of the rabbit and rat. Fig. 9 is a projection micrograph of unstained rat kidney which shows many details of the cortical labyrinth. From left to right, can be identified two renal corpuscles, numerous convoluted tubules, and a collecting tubule. The parietal layer of Bowman's capsule can be identified as well as the dark radiolucent nuclei of the glomerular epithelium. Proximal convoluted tubules are seen in both oblique and cross section, and are rendered conspicuous by the fact that the free surface of the cells lining the lumen exhibits a brush border. The junction of cytoplasm and brush border is marked by a layer of granules, more noticeable at higher magnification. Occasional dark nuclei are visible within the markedly absorbent cytoplasm of the proximal convoluted tubules, contrasting with the more numerous nuclei in the lower epithelium of the distal convoluted tubules. The collecting tubules are identified by their sharply outlined cuboidal cells and dark radiolucent nuclei, which appear to bulge into the lumen. In longitudinal section the collecting tubules present a strikingly multinucleated appearance, which characterises micrographs of the medullary region.

The appearance of glandular epithelium varied from organ to organ as expected. Fig. 10 reveals the terminal ramification of the submaxillary gland in the rat. Salivary and intercalated ducts are seen against a background of numerous acini. The seromucinous cells of the acini show indistinct cell boundaries and a rather homogeneous appearance. Closer study reveals a granular conglomeration within the cytoplasm, more evident in sections floated out on saline or water. The black radiolucent clefts and small dots visible in some acini may be interpreted as intercellular secretory canaliculi and secretory vacuoles respectively. Here and there dark areas contrast with the general background, representing the markedly radiolucent cells of the granular tubules. Other features that have been identified in projection micrographs of this gland, are the striations of the intralobular salivary ducts; also the epithelium and narrow lumen of the intercalated ducts, which are surrounded by a highly absorbent basement membrane.

As might be expected, mineralised tissues such as developing teeth, cartilage and bone provide contrasty projection micrographs even when decalcified by the usual methods. Such a micrograph is shown in Fig. 11, which represents a section through the epiphyseal growth zones of the proximal end of a decalcified rabbit tibia. The zone of young proliferating cartilage seen in the upper part of the plate shows columns of wedge shaped cartilage cells separated by bundles of collagen fibrils. The midfield shows the zone of maturing and calcifying cartilage, where the large cartilage cells undergoing dissolution are separated by partitions of calcified intercellular substance as evidenced by the variation in radiodensity. Here, and more especially in the next plate (Fig. 12), dark marrow spaces lined with osteoblasts can be identified, also bone newly laid down on the persisting cores of cartilage matrix in the process of trabecular formation. The more absorbent nature of osteoblasts, and young bone in particular, contrast with the calcified cartilage. The large white areas within the marrow spaces represent transected blood vessels filled with contrast medium (25 % Micropaque). Comparison micrographs taken of undecalcified sections at the same stage of bone growth show that the usual decalcification methods leave a considerable proportion of minerals especially at the sites of latest deposition.

CONCLUSIONS

Historadiography to date has been carried out almost exclusively by contact microradiography at unit magnification.

A certain primary magnification ($\times$ 2 $-$ $\times$ 10) of unstained animal and human tissues and cells, can be obtained by X-ray projection microscopy. The images so obtained exhibit much useful histological and cytological detail, and furthermore can provide a useful secondary magnification up to $\times$ 1100.

In projection microscopy, resolution depends upon the size of the X-ray source and hence also partly upon focussing accuracy. Focussing is unfortunately critical and difficult at the lower kilovoltages so essential to the production of reasonable contrast in tissue sections. A focussing aid[10] is desirable for biological purposes.

Other factors influencing sharpness of definition and contrast, are the choice, fixation, and preparation of the tissue. Tissues which undergo keratinisation (skin) or mineralisation (teeth, bone) give contrasty projection micrographs, as do those which accumulate chemical elements sufficiently to induce high X-ray absorption (thyroid). Most animal tissues are formed from elements of low atomic number, but curious and often unexplicable variations in cellular radiodensity occur. The chemical significance and interpretation of these microscopic areas of transparency and selective absorption await study.

References p. 305

Freeze drying or substitution provide the best tissue fixation for X-ray microscopy, as well as the best contrast, since they produce few or no chemical changes and remove only water. Contrast may be artificially produced and even enhanced, by methods of tissue preparation normally acceptable to optical microscopy. Hence attention must be paid to the cytological changes and solution losses now known to attend floatation, for density differences are readily detectable in comparison micrographs taken of serial sections either dry mounted, or "floated out" over water or saline. The latter may yield better pictures but are not representative of the tissue; this point must be considered in carrying out absorption analyses.

The structure of hair and its appendages can be well visualised by projection X-ray microscopy owing to the presence of hard and soft keratin, both of which contain sulphur. The process of keratinization within the hair follicle can be recorded, and also the accumulation of lipids within the cells of the sebaceous glands prior to their dissolution.

Many of the differences which occur in glandular epithelium from organ to organ and within the same organ can be detected by X-ray microscopy. For example the terminal ramifications and cytoplasmic differences in the submaxillary gland can be detected, as can the formation of the cell cords and follicles in the developing thyroid gland. General microscopic structure, such as the glomerular and tubular patterns of the kidney, are easily and quickly demonstrated by the projection method, revealing striking differences presumably related to changes coincident with functional activity. Projection microscopy reveals many cytological features in unstained sections, such as the distinctive cells of the collecting tubules and brush border of the proximal convoluted tubules. The cytoplasmic granules within the latter can perhaps be correlated with those already described on light microscopy[11].

The study of bone, under normal or experimental conditions, is particularly suited to projection X-ray microscopy. Low and high power views of ordinary or decalcified bone are easily recorded, while the penetration and three dimensional view obtainable give a decided advantage over optical methods. The mineralisation and cells connected with osteogenesis can be identified. Many interesting features in the region of the epiphyseal disk and developing trabeculae can be imaged with striking clarity, including the blood vessels and other contents of the marrow spaces. Fully formed and developing Haversian systems can be recorded. The projection method is also applicable to the study of normal and pressurized bone.

It should be recalled that the early results of electron microscopy were modest, but substantial improvements in resolving power and tissue preparation have brought about a new era in microscopy. Owing to the great penetration of X-rays and inherent possibility of a higher resolving power, the X-ray microscope may be expected to take its place beside the electron and optical microscope. The principles of X-ray microscopy promise significant contributions to the visualisation, spectrography and analysis of microscopic objects.

ACKNOWLEDGEMENTS

This investigation has been carried out under grants from the National Research Council of Canada.

We are indebted to Mrs. E. FRASER, Mr. D. CONYERS D'ARCY, and Dr. C. R. LEESON for assistance in specimen preparation, and Dr. F. W. FYFE for supplying bone sections from his pressure experiments.

References p. 305

REFERENCES

[1] A. ENGSTRÖM, *Use of Soft X-rays in Assay of Biological Material*, Ch. 7, Butterworth, London, 1950.

[2] S.-O. BRATTGARD and H. HYDÉN, *Acta Radiol., Suppl.* 94 (1952) 14.

[3] V. E. COSSLETT and W. C. NIXON, *Proc. Roy. Soc. (London)*, B 140 (1952) 422.

[4] D. S. SMITH, in V. E. COSSLETT et al., *X-ray Microscopy and Microradiography*, Academic Press, Inc., New York, 1957, pp. 492—503.

[5] P. DUNCUMB, *Ibid.*, pp. 617—622.

[6] R. L. DE C. H. SAUNDERS and R. M. FRYE, *Microscopy Symposium*, McCrone Associates, Chicago, 1958, pp. 67—75.

[7] R. L. DE C. H. SAUNDERS, *Nature*, 180 (1957) 1353.

[8] N. M. HANCOX, *Exptl. Cell Research*, 13 (1957) 263.

[9] B. M. PATTEN, *Human Embryology*, Ch. 17, Blakiston, New York, 1953.

[10] ONG SING POEN and J. B. LE POOLE, *J. Appl. Sci. Research*, B 7 (1958) 233.

[11] A. A. MAXIMOW and W. BLOOM, *A Textbook of Histology*, Ch. 28, W. B. Saunders, Philadelphia and London, 1957.

4. BOTANICAL MATERIAL

APPLICATION DE LA MICRORADIOGRAPHIE PAR CONTACT À L'ÉTUDE DE LA CELLULE VÉGÉTALE

J. DIETRICH

Laboratoires de Phytogénétique et Minéralogie, Faculté des Sciences, Strasbourg (France)

ABSTRACT

APPLICATION OF CONTACT MICRORADIOGRAPHY TO THE STUDY OF THE PLANT
CELL

Contact microradiography according to the method of Engström can be used to study the components of the plant cell, especially the nucleus. $2-5\,\mu$ sections of the anther, pasted directly on the emulsion, are removed after exposure, and stained by a conventional method (Feulgen). The findings can be interpreted by comparing each element of the stained cell with its corresponding radiographic image. The state of the membrane, the cytoplasm, the nucleus and the nucleolus during normal and pathological evolution of the plant cell can be more accurately followed by this method than by the usual cytological techniques.

Nous avons utilisé la microradiographie par contact selon la méthode de ENGSTRÖM[1] comme moyen d'investigation cytologique. L'image radiographique dûe à l'absorption différentielle d'un rayonnement pénétrant est susceptible d'apporter des informations complémentaires à la simple coloration, puisque la densité des ombres projetées, pour un rayonnement donné, est fonction à la fois de la nature chimique (nombre atomique Z) et de l'épaisseur des structures traversées. Cependant pour obtenir une résolution de l'image qui permette une analyse à l'échelle des constituants cellulaires, il faut tenir compte de tous les facteurs susceptibles de l'améliorer: caractères de l'émulsion, épaisseur des coupes et, plus spécialement, longueur d'onde du rayonnement.

TECHNIQUE

La préparation des échantillons a été faite suivant les indications techniques de GREULICH et ENGSTRÖM[2]: coupes collées directement sur l'émulsion et récupération du matériel radiographié pour une coloration de type banal (par exemple, Feulgen). L'émulsion utilisée est en général ,,Gevaert Lippmann" (5 E — 56); occasionnellement on s'est servi de ,,Kodak 649 — O" avec des résultats comparables. Les coupes ont été faites à $2-4\,\mu$ après fixation du matériel à l'alcool acétique (mélange 3 : 1) et inclusion dans la paraffine. Pour obtenir le maximum de résolution de l'image, l'utilisation des rayons X ultradoux était indispensable. Ils furent produits par une source fonctionnant sous des tensions d'anode de 700 à 1000 V, avec le tube expérimental, construit au Laboratoire de Minéralogie de la Faculté des Sciences de Strasbourg, sous la direction de Mr. le Professeur GOLDSZTAUB (Fig. 1).

Les microradiographies obtenues dans ces conditions peuvent être étudiées

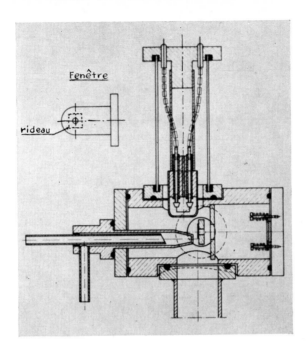

Fig. 1. Coupe du tube à RX: la préparation se trouve dans l'enceinte même du tube, protégée de la lumière du filament par une feuille d'aluminium de 1 μ d'épaisseur.

aux grossissements utiles de 800 à 900, et les images interprétées en comparant élément par élément, la cellule colorée (de la coupe récupérée) à sa propre image radiographique (Figs. 2 et 3).

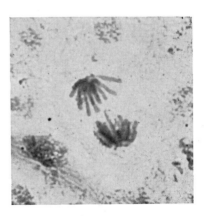

(a)   (b)

Fig. 2. *Paeonia sp.* Mitose dans le tissu d'anthère; (a) microradiographie, (b) coupe colorée correspondante (Feulgen). Grossissement optique. × 850.

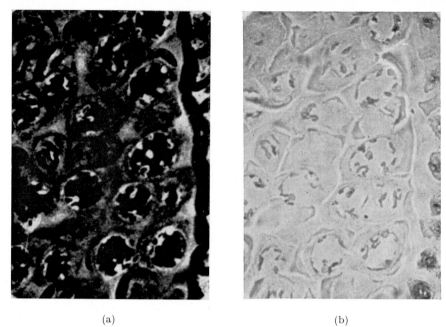

(a)   (b)

Fig. 3. *Listera ovata*. Cellules-mères de pollen en diacinèse; (a) microradiographie, (b) coupe colorée correspondante (Feulgen). Grossissement optique. × 650.

RÉSULTATS

Des observations faites avec différents matériels (surtout des anthères de plantes à fleur), nous présentons les plus nettes qui sont les suivantes:

La membrane cellulaire est toujours absorbante mais le degré d'opacité varie beaucoup: faible dans les tissus très jeunes, l'absorption devient importante dans les cellules différenciées et remarquablement élevée dans les cellules physiologiquement déficientes. Une évolution de la membrane au cours de la méiose dans les cellules-mères de pollen a pu être observée pour différentes espèces. Durant la prophase son absorption reste très faible, de même ordre que celle du cytoplasme de sorte que la membrane n'est généralement pas reconnaissable à ce stade. Vers la fin de la prophase l'opacité augmente, elle est forte en métaphase et très rapidement au moment de la formation des quatre noyaux de la jeune tétrade la coque de la cellule-mère devient impénétrable au rayonnement. Plus tard, au fur et à mesure que se prépare la libération des microspores, la perméabilité revient progressivement. À ces variations dans la perméabilité de la membrane des cellules-mères de pollen correspondent vraisemblablement des transformations biochimiques importantes que les techniques habituelles d'observation ne permettent pas de révéler.

Le cytoplasme est absorbant mais de manière très variable. En microradiographie, le protoplasme apparaît non homogène avec une structure qui peut être finement analysée. Les cellules pathologiques ou celles qui sont visiblement dégénérescentes sont toujours très absorbantes. Les plastes et les inclusions sont fortement opaques.

Le *fuseau* a fait l'objet d'une observation intéressante au cours de la méiose dans *Listera ovata* (Fig. 4). En métaphase, des fibres fusoriales apparaissent comme des stries, chacune d'elles reliée à un chromosome. Leur faisceau converge vers des zônes cytoplasmiques plus denses situées aux deux pôles de la cellule et dont elles semblent être des émanations. En anaphase, chaque fibre reste clairement différenciée sur le segment qui relie le chromosome au pôle, puis elle disparaît progressivement derrière lui au cours de l'ascension polaire. L'espace qui sépare les deux groupes anaphasiques est généralement très transparent, mais dès que les noyaux fils sont

Fig. 4. *Listera ovata*. Cellules-mères de pollen (début d'anaphase), microradiographie. Grossissement optique. × 850.

constitués il devient absorbant de manière uniforme, ce qui indique une redistribution de la masse au sein de la cellule-mère. Après la formation des quatre noyaux disposés en tétrade, tout le territoire cytoplasmique est très fortement opaque.

La substance fondamentale du *noyau* (caryolymphe) est toujours très transparente aux rayons X aussi bien à l'état quiescent qu'au cours des divisions, à tous les stades où la membrane nucléaire assure une séparation nette avec le cytoplasme (Fig. 2). Au point de vue de la microradiographie, la caryolymphe se présente à la fois comme le plus homogène et le moins absorbant des constituants de la cellule. Le matériel chromatique fait contraste par son opacité: durant toute la caryocinèse, tant qu'ils sont morphologiquement distincts, les chromosomes sont imperméables au rayonnement, mais leur opacité est d'intensité variée (Figs. 2, 3 et 4). L'analyse de cette variation est intéressante:

— les mêmes chromosomes qui sont en coloration au Feulgen uniformément colorés et d'épaisseur sensiblement égale sur toute leur longueur, en microradiographie, si la dureté du rayonnement est bien adaptée, se révèlent plus grêles et différenciés en zônes d'absorption inégale.

— Dans le cas d'agglutination chromatique, il a été possible de reconnaître des degrés d'altération que les techniques de coloration ne permettent pas de révéler.

Bibliographie p. 310

Des masses de matériel chromatique agglutiné sont perméables, alors que d'autres, de même densité de coloration au Feulgen, restent opaques au même rayonnement. À l'analyse radiographique, des masses apparemment astructurées laissent apparaître parfois en leur sein des élément chromosomiques, encore distincts, plus absorbants.

Le nucléole est remarquable par sa forte opacité: c'est l'élément le plus absorbant de la cellule au repos. Cependant, l'analyse le montre souvent structuré: par exemple, il peut être formé de granulations ovoïdes très absorbantes noyées dans une substance homogène à peine plus transparente. Le nombre et la taille de ces granules peut varier avec la taille relative du nucléole lui-même. Parfois, on distingue à leur place des masses absorbantes de taille et de forme plus irrégulières. En certains cas, au contraire, le nucléole paraît formé d'une substance périphérique très opaque entourant une masse centrale plus transparente d'aspect homogène.

CONCLUSIONS

Il ressort de l'ensemble de ces observations et de la confrontation des coupes colorées avec l'image microradiographique que la coloration seule ne permet généralement pas de soupçonner les structures révélées par la microradiographie.

Il paraît s'imposer d'exploiter plus largement cette méthode de microradiographie par contact. On peut envisager la confrontation des images avec du matériel traité par des colorations variées. Il serait surtout précieux d'utiliser cette méthode dans la recherche éventuelle de différenciations d'ordre chimique correspondant à l'analyse de structure, en particulier en ce qui concerne le matériel chromatique.

RÉSUMÉ

La microradiographie par contact utilisée selon la méthode de ENGSTRÖM peut être appliquée à l'étude des constituants mêmes de la cellule végétale, en particulier du noyau. Des coupes d'anthères à 2—5 μ collées directement sur l'émulsion sont récupérées après exposition. L'interprétation peut ensuite être faite en comparant, élément par élément, la cellule colorée (notamment au Feulgen) à sa propre image radiographique. Des informations plus précises que celles que fournissent les méthodes cytologiques habituelles peuvent être obtenues sur l'état de la membrane, du cytoplasme, du noyau et du nucléole au cours de l'évolution normale ou pathologique de la cellule végétale.

BIBLIOGRAPHIE
[1] A. ENGSTRÖM, *Acta Radiol., Suppl.*, 63 (1946).
[2] R. C. GREULICH et A. ENGSTRÖM, *Exptl. Cell Research, et Suppl.*, 10 (1956) 251.

DISCUSSION

JANINE SALMON: J'ai observé aussi chez *Lilium candidum* la résistance des tétrades polliniques au passage des rayons X, lorsqu'elles atteignent leur maturité. Si ce phénomène de radio-opacité est général, nous suggérons de voir s'il ne serait pas dû à une augmentation caractéristique des pectates de calcium au moment de la séparation des cellules-mères du pollen.

CONTRIBUTION À LA MICRORADIOGRAPHIE EN BIOLOGIE VÉGÉTALE

JANINE SALMON

Laboratoire de Biologie végétale I de la Sorbonne, Paris (France)

ABSTRACT

CONTRIBUTION TO THE APPLICATION OF MICRORADIOGRAPHY IN PLANT BIOLOGY

The progress achieved in this field is two-fold:

(1) A *technical improvement* obtained by the application of wavelengths sufficiently varied to offer a choice of contrasts useful for the study of plant tissue. Examples of the new technique are given and further improvements suggested.

(2) Recent results achieved in the investigation of plant tissue by *microradiography*. Examples are presented in the fields of phytopathology (study of experimental tumours), systematics (utilization of foliar and floral nervation), and cytology (detection of newly formed crystals in plant organs).

L'intérêt que nous portons à la microradiographie des tissus végétaux nous a incitée à rechercher l'amélioration de cette technique. Nous utilisions jusqu'à présent les rayons mous correspondant à des tensions de l'ordre de 15 à 20 kV. Nous employons maintenant aussi les tensions plus basses du générateur Philips (2 à 4 kV) dont les rayonnements produisent des contrastes plus élevés dans les tissus. La comparaison de microradiographies réalisées sur des coupes semblables d'écorces, rend compte de la différence des résultats obtenus avec 15 et 4 kV (Fig. 1) sur la tige de *Pelargonium zonale*: avec 15 kV on distingue particulièrement bien les structures cristallines des contenus cellulaires dont le faible contraste ne laisse pas percevoir les méats radio-opaques. Ceux-ci sont visibles avec le rayonnement de 4 kV, mais par contre les cristaux sont à peine discernables. Le choix des longueurs d'onde offre donc des ressources intéressantes, suivant le genre d'observations désiré; d'autres exemples les mettraient également en évidence. L'emploi de films nécessairement rapides pour des tensions de moins de 5 kV limite la définition des images. Le film Lipman, supérieur par sa qualité et la finesse de son grain, demanderait une pose de plusieurs heures pour des tensions inférieures à 2 kV, susceptibles de détailler davantage les contrastes cellulaires. L'emploi de telles tensions, pour des coupes à la fois épaisses de plusieurs dizaines de μ et sensibles à la dessiccation, nécessiterait soit l'inclusion de l'objet, soit sa réfrigération; cette solution d'avenir est assez délicate mais non impossible à réaliser.

Les clichés présentés maintenant concernent des recherches biologiques en cours dans le domaine végétal. La Fig. 2 montre des cristaux de weddellite, forme assez méconnue d'oxalate de calcium dans les organes végétaux; il s'agit d'un tissu tumoral de tige de *Pelargonium* dont les diagrammes de diffraction de Debye-Scherrer avaient signalé l'existence avant toute prospection à vision directe. Cet exemple précise l'intérêt complémentaire des deux méthodes de rayons X; il attire l'attention

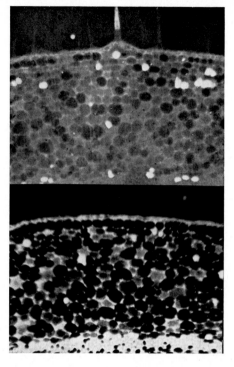

Fig. 1. Tige de *Pelargonium zonale:* haut: 15 kV, bas: 4 kV, × 45.

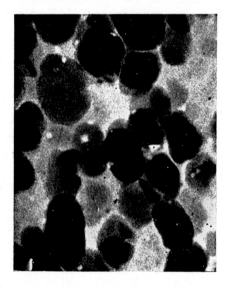

Fig. 2. Cristaux de weddellite du tissu tumoral de *Pelargonium zonale,* × 220.

sur la formation d'une cristallisation propre aux tissus tumoraux de cette plante, au cours des remaniements fonctionnels consécutifs à leur infection.

La Fig. 3 réunit quelques aspects différents de la cristallisation de l'oxalate de calcium chez une autre plante, la Vigne vierge (*Parthenocissus quinquefolia*): ses conditions d'habitat sont telles qu'une rupture de l'équilibre calcique s'est faite au profit de l'accumulation des sels de calcium par la plante. En voici quelques manifestations:

(a) production de cristaux extra-épidermiques; deux d'entre eux présentent à leur base un socle radio-opaque visible sur la microradiographie. Noter aussi la surcharge des méats corticaux en éléments lourds dans les assises sous-épidermiques.

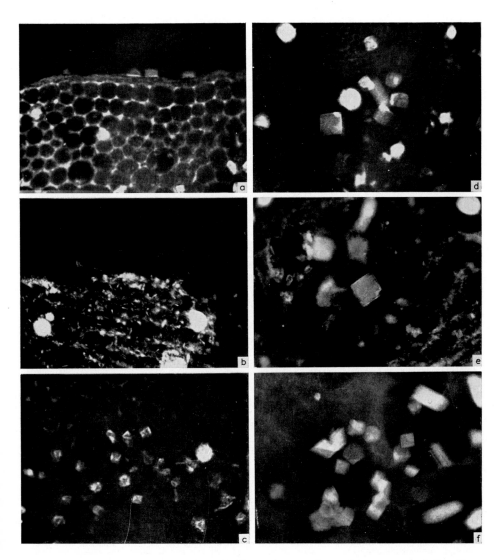

Fig. 3. Cristallisations diverses des tissus de Vigne vierge après une intense accumulation d'ions lourds: (a), (b) écorce, × 24; (c) moëlle, × 24; (d), (e), (f) moëlle, × 95.

(b) formation de très courts stylets cristallins dans les cellules d'une écorce riche en sels radio-opaques.

(c) coexistence de cristaux quadratiques, pouvant être de la weddellite en „enveloppes de lettres", avec les oursins habituels d'oxalate de calcium du tissu cortical.

Les photos (d), (e), (f) de la Fig. 3 offrent trois autres territoires cellulaires de la Vigne vierge précédente; on y remarque la présence de certains cristaux quadratiques, accompagnant les concrétions habituellement très opaques des oursins et des raphides. Le cristal central de (e) représente un carré imparfait dont les angles sont composites; les fins détails de la microradiographie suggèrent qu'il s'agit vraisemblablement de plans superposés analogues à ceux des spirales cristallines dont on commence à saisir le mécanisme de formation en cristallographie. La nature chimique de ces cristaux quadratiques n'est pas encore connue.

La Fig. 4 reproduit trois microradiographies intéressant toujours les tissus de Vigne vierge. Elles montrent avec encore plus d'évidence l'étonnante variété de formes cristallines issues de l'activité du tissu médullaire. La photo (b) représente une vacuole cellulaire contenant les styloïdes dispersés de l'oxalate de calcium dont les raphides classiques se trouvent tout à coté. Le groupe de cristaux enchevêtrés, visibles sur la photo (a), restent encore de nature chimique incertaine. Enfin les arborescences des multiples aiguilles cristallines qui forment les nombreux sphérites (c) de la moëlle étudiée, complètent le riche ensemble des substances concrétisées au cours des variations métaboliques de la plante.

Nous comparerons maintenant la microradiographie d'une feuille de Vigne vierge avec l'autoradiographie naturelle du même tissu (il s'agit de feuilles ayant

Fig. 4. Autres formes cristallines du tissu médullaire de Vigne vierge, × 90.

Fig. 5. Microradiographie (feuille de Vigne vierge), × 40.

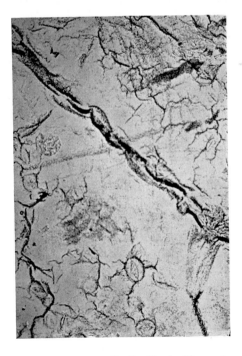

Fig. 6. Autoradiographie naturelle (feuille de Vigne vierge), × 130.

poussé près d'une source radioactive). La microradiographie met en évidence les nervures ponctuées de fins cristaux alignés (Fig. 5) ainsi que les nombreux raphides d'oxalate de calcium intracellulaires de la feuille; l'autoradiographie révèle un tout autre aspect de cet organe (Fig. 6), aspect essentiellement superficiel dont tous les éléments figurent le tissu épidermique avec ses stomates, ses nervures, ses poils épidermiques et le contour des membranes cellulaires de la surface foliaire. Cette confrontation est très instructive car les informations qu'elle apporte ne sont pas de même ordre dans les deux cas. De tels documents peuvent beaucoup éclairer les recherches biologiques actuelles et ne nécessitent pas un matériel trop onéreux.

Ne pouvant faire figurer ici toutes les projections présentées au Symposium, qu'il nous suffise d'attirer l'attention sur l'aide efficace de la microradiographie au cours des recherches histochimiques. Nous avons eu bien souvent recours à elle, plutôt avant l'intervention des réactifs ou des colorants. La comparaison de plusieurs techniques est toujours enrichissante, mais nous sommes particulièrement heureuse d'avoir déjà éprouvé la garantie du diagnostic apporté par la microradiographie, après avoir fréquemment reconnu l'utilité de son rôle de détection.

RÉSUMÉ

Les progrès réalisés peuvent être considérés sous deux aspects:

(1) une *amélioration technique,* acquise par l'emploi courant de longueurs d'ondes assez variées pour offrir un choix de contrastes utilisables en histologie végétale. Nous donnons quelques examples de ces nouvelles ressources et suggérons d'autres perfectionnements.

(2) les résultats récemment obtenus par l'*étude microradiographique des tissus végétaux,* au cours de recherches biologiques. Nous donnons des exemples en phyto-pathologie (étude des tumeurs expérimentales), en systématique (utilisation des nervations foliaire et florale) et en cytologie (détection de nouveaux cristaux dans les organes végétaux).

SECTION TWO

X-RAY MICROEMISSION

A. INTRODUCTION

V. E. COSSLETT

Cavendish Laboratory, The University, Cambridge (Great Britain)

Emission microanalysis is a direct development of the long-established method of X-ray spectrometry of macroscopic samples. The characteristic lines of the elements present may be excited either by electron bombardment or by a primary X-ray beam ("fluorescence"). The micromethods use direct excitation almost exclusively, the essential difference from the macrotechnique being in the size of the electron spot which is directed on to the sample. In an ordinary X-ray tube the focal spot may be several sq. mm. in area, whereas in the microanalyser it may be smaller than 1 sq. micron (10^{-6} sq. mm). By this means a volume of order 10^{-12} c.c. can be analysed, with an ultimate detection limit as low as 10^{-15} g, providing a higher degree of localisation than any other method.

The technique relies on the use of electron lenses to form the required ultra-fine focus, but otherwise the apparatus is no more than a specialised type of X-ray tube with provision for inserting a sample and a number of reference elements in quick succession. The initial exploration of the method was carried out by CASTAING[1] in 1949—51, and independently by BOROWSKY[2] soon after, using electrostatic and magnetic lenses respectively. The value in metallurgy of local microanalysis on this scale was at once appreciated, and a considerable amount of experience has been obtained since that time in both France and the U.S.S.R. It is now possible to estimate all elements from magnesium through the periodic table to uranium, with an accuracy that varies on either side of 1% according to the amount of the element concerned and the nature of the matrix in which it is embedded. Much is now known, especially from the recent work of PHILIBERT[3], about the corrections needed in particular circumstances for absorption and fluorescence losses. Commercial models of the X-ray emission microanalyser are now being produced in the United States and Great Britain[4] as well as in France and the U.S.S.R.

In all these instruments the electron spot is static and the sample is explored by mechanically moving it under the spot with a stage motion. By building a deflecting system into the apparatus, as used in television, the electron beam can be scanned across the sample and the X-ray output used to form an image on a cathode ray tube. In this way a direct display is obtained of the distribution over the sample surface of a particular element, in which brightness is determined by local concentration. By using a double-beam oscillograph and scanning along a line, variations in concentration can be directly measured. These methods greatly increase the speed and flexibility of emission microanalysis, especially with samples from which optical observation gives little or no indication as to the localisation of elements. They have been developed in Cambridge by COSSLETT, DUNCUMB[5] and LONG[6], and are now being incorporated in a commercial scanning microanalyser[7]. The applications have been mainly in metallurgy, but also to an increasing extent in mineralogy.

The 1956 X-ray Symposium included a few papers on the emission technique, but rapid progress has been made in several directions since then and the 1959 Symposium includes some 15 contributions on its principles and applications. The major problem remaining to be solved is that of the determination of the lighter elements, and of carbon, nitrogen and oxygen in particular. Promising progress, reported below[8], is being made. Once a solution is found, it should greatly extend the scope of emission microanalysis in ferrous metallurgy, and possibly also to certain types of biological material.

REFERENCES

[1] R. CASTAING and A. GUINIER, *Proc. Conf. Electron Microscopy, Delft*, 1949, Martin Nijhoff, Delft, 1950, p.60.
[2] I. B. BOROWSKY, *Collections of Problems in Metallurgy*, Moscow, 1953, p. 135.
[3] J. PHILIBERT and H. BIZOUARD, *Rev. mét.*, 53 (1959) 187; this volume, p. 416.
[4] R. S. PAGE and I. K. OPENSHAW, this volume, p. 385.
[5] P. DUNCUMB and V. E. COSSLETT, *X-ray Microscopy and Microradiography*, Academic Press, New York, 1957, p. 374.
[6] J. V. P. LONG, *Thesis*, Cambridge, 1959; S. O. AGRELL and J. V. P. LONG, this volume, p. 391.
[7] P. DUNCUMB and D. A. MELFORD, this volume, p. 358.
[8] R. M. DOLBY and V. E. COSSLETT, this volume, p. 351.

B. APPARATUS AND TECHNIQUES

RELIABILITY OF TRACE DETERMINATIONS BY X-RAY EMISSION SPECTROGRAPHY

HERMAN A. LIEBHAFSKY, HEINZ G. PFEIFFER and PAUL D. ZEMANY

General Electric Research Laboratory, Schenectady, N.Y. (U.S.A.)

ABSTRACT

Chemical analysis does not generally permit adequate verification of conclusions drawn from the theory of errors. For various reasons, modern X-ray emission spectrography is a unique exception to this rule. In determinations of major constituents, precision is the principal issue, and conclusions relating thereto have been corroborated in earlier work.

Trace determinations by X-ray emission spectrography fall into three regions, the boundaries of which occur at amounts that depend upon the element being determined and upon the experimental conditions. As experiments with cobalt show, the intensity of the analytical line is proportional to the amount present in the center region. Quantitative determinations are possible here and in the region of larger amounts, which is characterized by the appearance of a measurable absorption effect. In the third region, that of the smallest amount, fluctuations in the background assume overriding importance, and only qualitative observations are possible. The upper boundary of this erratic region may be systematically defined as the minimum amount guaranteed detectable.

The conclusions just given have been extensively tested and reasonably well confirmed for samples in the microgram range. The results show that trace determinations by X-ray emission spectrography rest upon a logical basis.

DISCUSSION OF TRACE DETERMINATIONS

The reliability of trace determinations by X-ray emission spectrography is best examined under simple conditions. For this reason, we shall confine ourselves to samples in which the traces are major constituents: to samples very low in weight. The complementary case, in which the traces are minor by weight and the sample must therefore be large, is more complex owing to the possibility that absorption and enhancement effects may enter [1]. Though these effects must always be compensated or allowed for if correct results are to be obtained, they do not affect reliability, which — as we shall use the word — is concerned with errors, not with effects predictable from the composition of the sample.

Fig. 1 was prepared to give a broad view of the trace determination problem. The experimental details will be given later. The range of sample sizes was chosen large enough so that the results could indicate that trace determinations by X-ray emission spectrography fall into the three broad regions indicated in Fig. 1 and in Table I. Though cobalt was used, the same three regions should be found with any other element accessible to X-ray emission spectrography. The sample weights that bound the regions will of course depend upon the conditions of the determination.

The results in Fig. 1 were obtained as follows. By counting for an interval Δt, N_T was obtained as the count at the peak of the analytical line (cobalt $K\alpha$).

This count was then reduced by N_B, the background independently estimated, to give $N_T - N_B$, which should be proportional under simple conditions to the amount of cobalt present. The regions of Fig. I can now be described as in Table I.

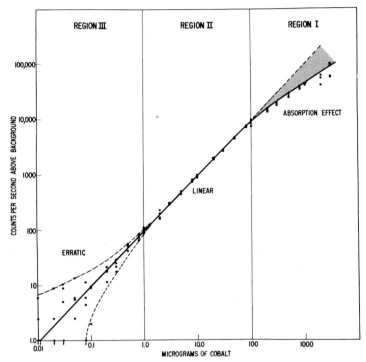

Fig. I. Cobalt determinations carried out to illustrate the occurrence of three regions in trace determinations by X-ray emission spectrography under simple conditions.

TABLE I

CHARACTERIZATION OF THREE REGIONS IN TRACE DETERMINATIONS

Region	Description	Relative Importance of N_B	Absorption effect[a]
I	Large-sample region	$N_T \gg N_B$	Present
II	Linear region	$N_T > N_B$	Absent
III	Erratic region	$N_T \approx N_B$	Absent

[a]Enhancement effects may be superimposed upon absorption effects, which are always present in Region I.

Region II, being the simplest, will be discussed first. Fluctuations in the background have no important influence on the results because N_T considerably exceeds N_B. The amount present of E (the element being determined; cobalt in Fig. I), and the amounts present of other elements are small enough so that each atom of E may be said to absorb and emit X-rays independently of all other atoms. For the two reasons stated,

(1) $$N_T - N_B = km$$

where k is the slope of the line in Region II when the units are counts for the ordinate and micrograms, m, for the abscissa. The existence of this linear region was appreciated by v. Hámos and Engström in 1944[2].

In Region I, the sample has become large enough so that the contribution by an atom of E to the intensity of the analytical line depends upon the other atoms in the sample. So long as E is the only element present that absorbs X-rays significantly, only a negative absorption effect will occur (Fig. 1). With more complex samples, other absorption effects will be superimposed upon this negative effect, and enhancement effects may eventually appear. We have already explained why these complications do not concern us here. The scattering of points in Region I, Fig. 1, is also a side issue. This scattering reflects uneven distribution of the residue from evaporation of the solution that contained the sample.

In Region III, the results are so erratic as to make eqn. (1) virtually useless. Three points (with arrows attached) near the bottom of the figure even represent negative values of $N_T - N_B$, an absurdity in light of eqn. (1). As one gathers from Table I, the fundamental reason for the erratic character of Region III is this: As m continues to decrease, N_T and N_B become indistinguishable with the result that fluctuations in the background overshadow the small contribution that element E makes to N_T. Region III is the region of trace detection — that is, the region in which only *qualitative* determinations are possible. The fact that the points in this region are virtually enclosed by the upper and lower curves indicates that a theoretical treatment of this region might succeed. This hope rests on the fact that the curves represent a divergence of 2 standard counting errors (see eqn. (2)) from the straight line.

Theoretical basis of trace determinations

Reliability is determined by precision and accuracy. Because X-ray emission spectrography usually rests upon the comparison of the unknown with a standard, questions of accuracy need not enter. In quantitative work, the unique position of X-ray emission spectrography as regards precision has been described elsewhere [3,4]. Later we shall show that reliable qualitative conclusions can be drawn in Region III if one proceeds from a theoretical basis that can be experimentally verified.

The theoretical basis is supplied by probability theory and by the law of errors. The contribution of probability theory defines the random fluctuations to be expected in N_T and N_B, and it was applied long ago to radioactive decay[3]. More recently, this contribution was proved applicable to X-ray emission spectrography under satisfactory operating conditions — more exactly, it was demonstrated that X-ray spectrograph systems are sufficiently reliable so that virtually all the fluctuations observed in a series of counts N_{1---n} are the unavoidable fluctuations that occur also in counts of radioactively decaying atoms[5].

For our purposes, the contribution of probability theory may be summarized as follows: In an X-ray spectrograph, successive counts (N_{1---n}) each taken over the same interval Δt under identical and satisfactory operating conditions will lie on the *unique* Gaussian of mean $\bar{N}$ and standard deviation $\sqrt{\bar{N}}$. Fig. 2 shows how this situation differs from that of the usual analytical method. Fig. 3 shows that the situation is realized in the simple case of negligible background[4].

In Region III, Fig. 1, the background is far from negligible. The means $\bar{N}_T$ and $\bar{N}_B$ are comparable, and each individual count is subject to fluctuations of the kind shown in Fig. 3. To assess the effect of these fluctuations on the difference $N_T - N_B$, one must have recourse to the law of combining errors. If values of N_T lie upon one Gaussian, and values of N_B upon another, the values of $N_T - N_B$ will lie upon a third related as follows to the others. The standard deviation S_c of this third Gaussian will be formed from the standard deviations of the other two according to the law for the standard error of a difference; that is,

(2)
$$S_c = \sqrt{\bar{N}_T + \bar{N}_B}$$

where each term under the radical is the square of the standard deviation for the Gaussian distribution concerned. Fig. 4 illustrates the argument just concluded.

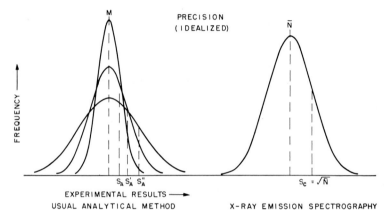

Fig. 2. Contrast between expected distributions of results for the usual analytical method (error curves) and for X-ray emission spectrography (unique fluctuation curve), both under idealized conditions.

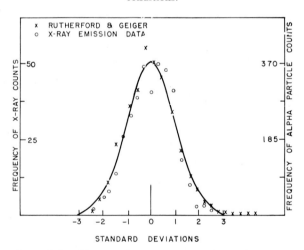

Fig. 3. Experimental proof that X-ray emission spectrography and radioactivity both conform to the unique Gaussian fluctuation curve based on $\bar{N}$ alone.

In cases where more than two kinds of counts are required to establish $N_T - N_B$, the expression for S_c will be more complex. Each additional kind of count increases S_c.

References p. 330

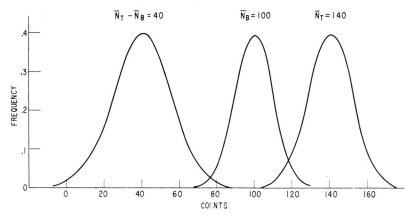

Fig. 4. Graphical illustration to show how the argument underlying Fig. 3 can be extended to more complex cases by use of the rules governing the combination of errors.

Experimental verification

Figs. 5 and 6, together with Fig. 3, provide extensive experimental evidence to show that the contributions made by probability theory and by the law of errors can be applied with confidence to estimate the reliability of X-ray emission spectrography. Such applications have proved successful for samples in Regions II and I, and in general analytical work as well. We shall now see what can be done in Region III — the region of trace detection — on the basis that Figs. 3, 5, and 6 establish the applicability to this region of the argument illustrated in Fig. 4.

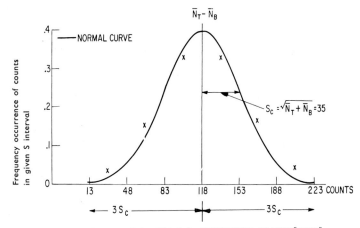

VALUES OF $N_T - N_B$ FROM INDIVIDUAL EXPERIMENTS ON ZINC "SPOT"

Fig. 5. Distribution of 91 values of $N_T - N_B$ from a zinc "spot". Note that the experimental values conform to the predicted unique Gaussian curve.

Risks in trace detection

The detection of E encounters two kinds of risks: that of reporting E absent though present (Producer Risk) and that of reporting E present though absent

References p. 330

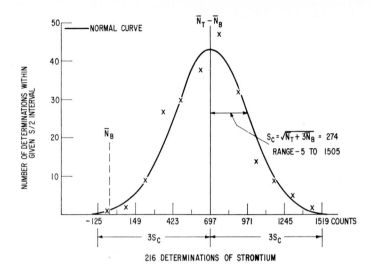

Fig. 6. Distribution of 216 values of $N_T - N_B$ from a strontium "spot". Note that the experimental values conform to the predicted unique Gaussian curve.

(Consumer Risk). As the amount of E approaches zero, the mean $\overline{N}_T$ approaches the mean $\overline{N}_B$, and the two Gaussian distributions on the right of Fig. 4 fuse into a single curve. Fig. 7 shows an evaluation of producer and consumer risks for this case, in which N_T and N_B both lie upon the Gaussian with mean $\overline{N}_B$ and $S_c = \sqrt{N}_B$.

This evaluation is based upon the "operating rule" [6] that one may safely ignore the occurrence of errors greater than three standard errors (here $3S_c$) in "guaranteeing" an analytical result. In a Gaussian distribution, only 0.135 % of

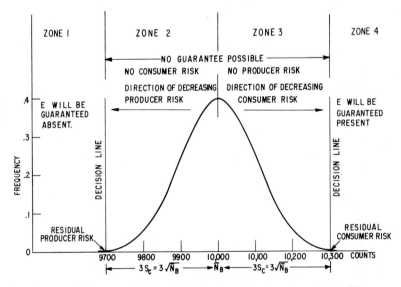

Fig. 7. Producer and consumer risks in the detection of traces so small that $\overline{N}_T$ approaches $\overline{N}_B$.

the values will exceed the mean by more than three standard deviations; and a like proportion will fall below the mean by more than this amount.

Fig. 7 is conveniently divided into four zones as follows:

TABLE II

Zone	Relationship of N_T to $\overline{N}_B$	Characterization of Zone
I	$N_T < \overline{N}_B - 3\sqrt{\overline{N}_B}$	E will be guaranteed absent
2	$\overline{N}_B > N_T > \overline{N}_B - 3\sqrt{\overline{N}_B}$	Consumer risk absent because $\overline{N}_B > N_T$
3	$\overline{N}_B < N_T < \overline{N}_B + 3\sqrt{\overline{N}_B}$	Producer risk absent because $N_T > \overline{N}_B$
4	$N_T > \overline{N}_B + 3\sqrt{\overline{N}_B}$	E will be guaranteed present

The guarantees in Zones I and 4 are in conformity with the operating rule. Because the report "E present" may be ruled out when $N_T < \overline{N}_B$, we may neglect the consumer risk in Zone 2. But the producer risk is so great in this zone as to make no highly reliable guarantee possible. This situation is reversed in Zone 3, in which the great consumer risk vitiates any such guarantee.

The argument illustrated in Fig. 7 therefore leads to the conclusion that a guarantee of "E present" or "E absent" is justified only in 0.27 % of all determinations made when the amount of E present is very close to zero. This is an impractical state of affairs.

To arrive at a more useful criterion for trace detection, let us give up all hope of guaranteeing the absence of E. This amounts to fusing Zones I, 2 and 3 in Fig. 7, and retaining only the decision line between Zones 3 and 4. Two kinds of reports are then possible: "E guaranteed present" when $N_T > \overline{N}_B + 3\sqrt{\overline{N}_B}$, and "Presence of E not proved" (which includes "E absent") for all other values of N_T.

With $\overline{N}_B = 10,000$ and $S_e = 100$ arbitrarily chosen for Fig. 7, it is easy to clarify the arguments of this section with numerical illustrations.

EXPERIMENTAL DETAILS

The argument illustrated in Fig. 7 was tested experimentally by the following technique, which differs only in detail from that used to obtain the experimental results plotted in Figs. I, 5, and 6.

Conditions

General Electric XRD-5 Diffractometer-Spectrograph. Tungsten-target X-ray tube operated at 50 mA and 50 kV to excite the analytical lines. X-ray detector, SPG-7 (krypton-filled) proportional counter. Lithium fluoride analyzing crystal without electronic (pulse-height) discrimination. Soller-slit collimator; 0.25-mm spacing. Helium in X-ray path to enhance N_T and N_B. Counting interval, $\Delta t = 1000$ sec, over which time experience has shown the spectrograph system to be highly stable.

A complete determination, preparation of sample and counting of blank included, required about one hour under favorable conditions.

Background

A value of N_B was established for each sample run.

To minimize the background, which increases with the thickness of the substrate

References p. 330

that carries the sample, Mylar film only 0.0075 mm thick was chosen as substrate. A strip of this film, about 3 mm wide, was placed in the sample holder, and N_B was established by counting this strip for 1000 sec at the goniometer setting for the analytical line (manganese $K\alpha$). Results for 49 determinations of $N_B : \overline{N}_B = 4870$ counts; $S_c = \sqrt{N_B} = 70$ counts; range of N_B, from 4340 to 5500 counts.

Detection of manganese

Manganese was selected as the element on which to test the criteria developed above for the detection of traces. Manganese samples were prepared by evaporating a drop of proper volume upon the Mylar strip after N_B had been established. The drops were delivered from a micrometer syringe containing manganous sulfate solution of such concentration that 0.002 ml of solution contained about 0.001 μg manganese. When the water had been evaporated by use of an infrared lamp, a single value of N_T was obtained by counting for 1000 sec at the setting for manganese $K\alpha$.

The positioning of the sample, done with respect to reference lines on the sample holder, required utmost care. A displacement of the sample center by 2 mm from the optimum position caused the measured intensity of the analytical line to decrease by about 30 %. Overheating the sample during drying had to be avoided. Drafts could blow away the dry residue. In all, 3 samples were lost, 42 manganese samples and 7 additional blanks were successfully run. In no case did the operator know the composition of a sample in the spectrograph.

RESULTS OF DETECTION EXPERIMENTS

The scheme outlined for the detection of traces leads to the following criteria for the experiments with manganese: 1. If $N_T > N_B + 3$ (70), report "Manganese guaranteed present." 2. If $N_T < N_B + 3$ (70), report "Presence of manganese not proved." The results are summarized in Table II according to these criteria. In these criteria, the individual value N_B for each experiment was substituted for $\overline{N}_B$ to compensate for uncontrollable (non-random) variations in the Mylar strips.

TABLE III

RESULTS ON THE DETECTION OF MANGANESE

Mn added (microgram)	Number of runs	Report "Present"	Report "Not proved"
None	7	None	7
0.001	22	9	13
0.002	14	13	1
0.003	6	6	0

Two conclusions that may be drawn from Table III are: 1. The consumer risk has been reduced as Fig. 7 indicates: manganese was never reported present when absent. 2. If one wishes to be sure of finding manganese whenever it is present, the amount present should exceed 0.002 μg.

Minimum amount guaranteed detectable

The second conclusion just stated can be made more precise. To do this, it is necessary to express amounts of manganese in counts, or standard deviations, as well as in micrograms.

References p. 330

If R^{Mn} is the counts/μg manganese/sec, which implies that background has been properly allowed for, then the standard counting error for Table III will be

$$(3) \qquad S_e = \sqrt{2} \ \sqrt{\bar{N}_B}/R^{Mn} \triangle t \ \mu g \ Mn$$

(The $\sqrt{2}$ enters from eqn. (2) with $N_T = N_B$.) To establish R^{Mn}, spots containing "large" amounts of manganese were counted. These experiments gave $R^{Mn} = 170$ counts/sec/μg Mn, in good agreement with 174, the value obtained by averaging the results of the 42 manganese experiments in Table III. Substitution of numerical values in eqn. (3) gives

$$(4) \qquad S_e = \sqrt{2} \ (70)/(170)(1000) = 0.0006 \ \mu g$$

The last column of Table III shows that the risk of failing to report "Present" when manganese is present decreases as the amount of sample increases. For simplicity's sake, we shall call this a modified producer risk. It is worth while defining the "minimum amount guaranteed detectable" (MAGD) as that amount for which

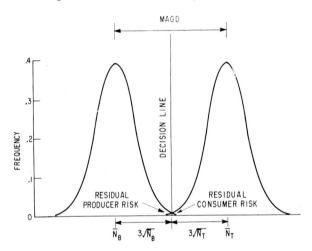

Fig. 8. Graphical definition of the minimum amount guaranteed detectable.

this risk becomes negligible as $\bar{N}_T - \bar{N}_B$ increases. In conformity with previous practice, this amount is defined graphically in Fig. 8. Analytically, it is for the present case,

$$(5) \qquad MAGD = 3 \ \sqrt{\bar{N}_B} + 3 \ \sqrt{\bar{N}_T}$$

whence

$$(6) \qquad MAGD = 430/170,000 \ \mu g, \ or \ 0.003 \ \mu g$$

The indications from Table III are that the rounded value, 0.003 μg, is a reasonable choice for the minimum amount one could safely guarantee to detect by the X-ray method under discussion.

In conclusion, we wish to suggest that the MAGD is a logical position for the boundary between Region III and Region II in Table I and Fig. 1. The sample size at the appearance of a measurable absorption effect fixes the boundary between Regions II and I. We thus arrive at a logical subdivision of the entire region of trace determinations.

References p. 330

REFERENCES

[1] H. A. LIEBHAFSKY and E. H. WINSLOW, *Anal. Chem.*, 30 (1958) 580.
[2] L. v. HÁMOS and A. ENGSTRÖM, *Acta Radiol.*, 25 (1944) 325.
[3] E. VON SCHWEIDLER, *Premier Congr. intern. Radiologie, Liège*, 1905, H. Dunod, Paris, 1906.
[4] H. A. LIEBHAFSKY, H. G. PFEIFFER and P. D. ZEMANY, *Anal. Chem.*, 27 (1955) 1257.
[5] P. D. ZEMANY, H. G. PFEIFFER and H. A. LIEBHAFSKY, *Anal. Chem.*, 31 (1959) 1776.
[6] H. A. LIEBHAFSKY, H. G. PFEIFFER and E. W. BALIS, *Anal. Chem.*, 23 (1951) 1531.

THE INTENSITIES OF CHARACTERISTIC X-RAYS EMITTED FROM TARGETS BOMBARDED BY ELECTRONS

G. D. ARCHARD

Associated Electrical Industries Ltd. Research Laboratory, Aldermaston, Berkshire
(Great Britain)

ABSTRACT

Universalised curves are given for the intensities of characteristic X-rays emitted from targets of various materials bombarded by electrons. Some of the corrections which must be taken into consideration for a proper use of these curves are discussed.

A knowledge of the intensities of characteristic X-rays emitted from targets bombarded by electrons is of particular importance in X-ray micro-analysis.

The calculation would be quite easy [1] if the following two conditions were true:

(A) that every ionization caused by an electron produced one (and only one) quantum of $K\alpha$ radiation

(B) that every electron moved through the target in a straight line until, due to its decreasing velocity, it no longer caused X-radiation.

Neither of these conditions is true, and corrections must be made to allow for the following facts:

(a) some electrons cause Auger rather than X-emission,

(b) not all K radiation is $K\alpha$ radiation,

(c) some electrons are scattered back from the target after penetrating only a short way,

(d) some $K\alpha$ radiation occurs in the form of fluorescence, due to the absorption of continuous radiation excited by the same electron beam,

(e) the electrons do not travel in straight lines in the target; many are scattered to one side and some return through the surface of the target.

WORTHINGTON and TOMLIN [2] made corrections for (a), (b), (c) and (d) by reference to COMPTON and ALLISON [3] and STEPHENSON [4] (for a), WILLIAMS [5] (for b), KIRKPATRICK and BAEZ [6] (for c), and WEBSTER [7] (for d). No account was taken of (e).

The significance of this omission is clear when WORTHINGTON and TOMLIN's results are compared with the experimental work of CASTAING and DESCAMPS [8]. Fig. 1 shows the intensities of X-rays produced at different depths in a copper target. WORTHINGTON and TOMLIN's results are given by curve A, CASTAING and DESCAMPS' by curve B. Both curves give the same total range, but their shapes are quite different.

According to CASTAING and DESCAMPS, the maximum in curve B is caused by the gradual diffusion of electrons. As the beam enters the target, it spreads outwards, and the paths of individual electrons become more oblique. The average distance travelled per unit depth therefore increases, until a state of complete diffusion is reached. After this the intensity falls, because the velocity of the electrons is smaller, and they therefore produce less X-rays.

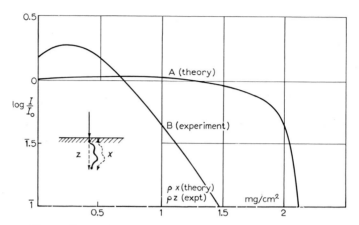

Fig. 1. Theoretical and experimental intensity-depth curves.

Real electron paths contain many random changes of direction; those shown in Fig. 2a are idealized paths — some moving straight into the target, others turning through various angles, and some returning through the surface of the target. WORTHINGTON and TOMLIN considered only the electrons moving straight into the target; hence they overestimated the mean depth at which X-rays are produced and underestimated the total intensity of X-rays leaving the target at a given angle (this is because X-rays produced near the surface lose less by absorption than those produced lower down).

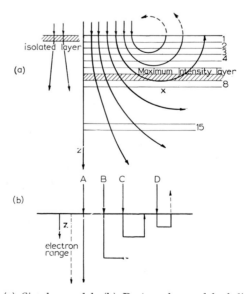

Fig. 2.(a) Circular model, (b) Rectangular model of diffusion.

References p. 336

A good idea of the effect of this may be obtained by selecting a set of electron paths giving a mean intensity-depth distribution similar in form to that of CASTAING and DESCAMPS, and averaging WORTHINGTON and TOMLIN's calculations over the several paths in order to obtain the total intensity. It has been found empirically that a set of only two paths (A and C, Fig. 2b) will give a fair approximation to CASTAING and DESCAMPS' intensity-depth distribution. The corresponding total intensities are compared with WORTHINGTON and TOMLIN's original calculation for titanium in Fig. 3. The effect of considering two paths is plainly to shift the maxima of the curves to the right and to raise the intensity everywhere.

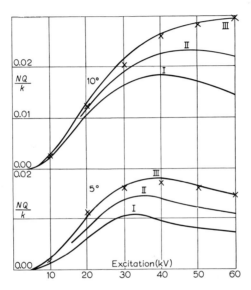

Fig. 3. X-ray intensities for titanium at two different viewing angles. (I) Using path A only (WORTHINGTON and TOMLIN); (II) Using paths A and C; (III) Using paths C only; (XX) Experimental points (arbitrary units).

It would be too much to say that this single comparison justified the universal use of two simple electron paths in intensity calculations. Indeed there is some evidence that still better agreement with experiment can be obtained by using the rectangular path C on its own. The intensity for this path is compared in Fig. 3 with the experimental curve of MULVEY and ALFORD[9], to which it approximates much more closely than either of the earlier curves. This indicates that most of the observed X-rays come from a region not more than one third of the electron's range below the target surface. It should be mentioned that the experimental curves give *relative* intensities; it is the shapes, and in particular the position of the maxima, which are of interest here.

Quite apart from the question of diffusion, it is of importance to extend knowledge of intensities to elements of low atomic number, in particular carbon. In this the determination of correcting factors (a) and (d) (Auger emission and fluorescence, respectively) is fundamental.

With regard to Auger emission, the correcting factor has been accurately determined for elements of intermediate atomic number [3]. The factor becomes small and uncertain for elements below aluminium, and use has to be made of an extrapolation formula provided by COMPTON and ALLISON, or of a slightly different formula given by BLOCHIN[10]. New experimental work by DOLBY [11] suggests that these formulae may be in error at low atomic numbers. Pending confirmation of this, the COMPTON and ALLISON formula has been used in the present work.

With regard to fluorescence, there is a conflict of opinion. Values of the correcting factor obtained by WEBSTER[7] were in the region of 1.5 for silver, and this was supported by later results of STODDARD[12], who found still higher values for heavier elements. This would have serious consequences for X-ray micro-analysis, since X-rays penetrate much further than electrons, so that there would be no way of telling from which part of the target characteristic X-rays came. On the other hand, more recent work of CASTAING[13] indicates that the correcting factor for copper differs from unity by no more than a few percent. This is supported by MULVEY and BERNARD[14] who found that, when a thin sheet of copper (thick enough to stop electrons) is placed over a hole in a copper block and bombarded by electrons, it is impossible to detect the hole by measuring changes in X-ray emission from the thin sheet. If appreciable fluorescence had occurred, the hole would have been seen as a sharp discontinuity in X-ray intensity as the electron beam passed over it. Pending fresh evidence, it is believed that the more recent experiments are to be preferred, and the overall correction factor plotted in Fig. 4 has been obtained on the assumption that the fluorescence factor may be set equal to unity.

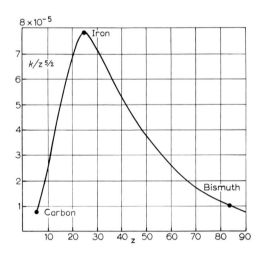

Fig. 4. Values of R-factor.

Fig. 5 shows a generalized set of intensity-excitation curves valid for the range of elements carbon to silver; used in conjunction with Fig. 4 it gives absolute intensities (in deriving these curves the mean intensity calculated for paths A and C in Fig. 2b has been taken). Fig. 6 gives the absolute intensities for electrons of fixed energy $3 V_K$ when the X-rays are observed at an angle of $45°$ to the surface.

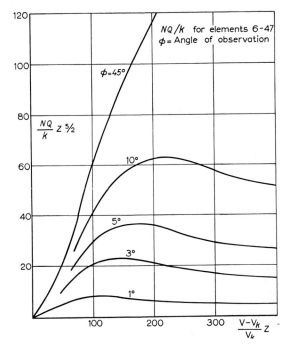

Fig. 5. X-ray intensity factor.

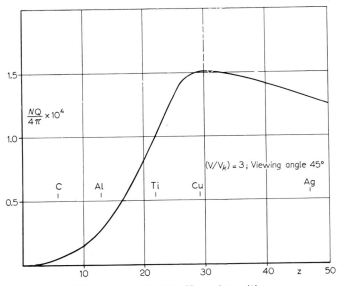

Fig. 6. Characteristic X-ray intensities.

CONCLUSIONS

WORTHINGTON and TOMLIN's theoretical intensity-depth curves differ from CASTAING and DESCAMPS' experiments because only the undeflected electron path was considered. Experiments indicate that far more weight should be given to electrons turned back towards the surface — the mean depth from which X-rays come appears to be approximately 1/6 of the electrons' (linear) range.

Corrections for Auger effect and fluorescence require further study — the former for elements of low atomic number, the latter for elements of intermediate atomic number.

REFERENCES

[1] N. F. MOTT and H. S. W. MASSEY, *Theory of Atomic Collisions*, Clarendon Press, Oxford, 1949.
[2] C. R. WORTHINGTON and S. G. TOMLIN, *Proc. Phys. Soc. (London)*, A 69 (1956) 401.
[3] A. H. COMPTON and S. K. ALLISON, *X-rays in Theory and Experiment*, Van Nostrand, New York, 1935, p. 803.
[4] A. J. STEPHENSON, *Phys. Rev.*, 51 (1937) 637.
[5] J. H. WILLIAMS, *Phys. Rev.*, 44 (1933) 146.
[6] P. KIRKPATRICK and A. V. BAEZ, *Phys. Rev.*, 71 (1947) 521.
[7] D. L. WEBSTER, *Proc. Natl. Acad. Sci. U.S.*, 14 (1928) 337.
[8] R. CASTAING and J. DESCAMPS, *J. phys. radium*, 16 (1955) 304.
[9] T. MULVEY and N. ALFORD, unpublished (1959).
[10] M. A. BLOCHIN, *Physik der Röntgenstrahlen*, VEB Verlag Technik, Berlin, 1957.
[11] R. M. DOLBY, personal communication, 1959.
[12] K. B. STODDARD, *Phys. Rev.*, 48 (1935) 43.
[13] R. CASTAING, *Thesis*, University of Paris, 1951.
[14] T. MULVEY and A. BERNARD, to be published (1959).

PROPOSED SYSTEM FOR MAGNETIC ELECTRON PROBE

G. D. ARCHARD

Associated Electrical Industries Ltd., Research Laboratory, Aldermaston, Berkshire
(Great Britain)

ABSTRACT

Systems originally designed for the correction of spherical aberration can, with little modification, be converted into electron probe systems, suitable for use in X-ray microanalysis. A possible arrangement incorporating magnetic quadrupoles and octupoles is described.

In conventional X-ray micro-analyzers the electron beam is concentrated by means of a magnetic lens into a small spot close to the bore of the lens. The spot is then imaged on the specimen by a second lens designed to have a convenient working distance. As most of the spherical aberration arises from the second lens, it would be very useful if this could be replaced by an aberration-free lens. This would enable a larger current to be obtained for a given spot size, or a smaller spot for a given current. A larger current would be particularly desirable in the soft X-ray region, where the voltage required is low and heat dissipation is not at present a limiting factor.

In this paper a theoretical investigation is made of a possible aberration-free system working at unit magnification.

Quite complicated systems are needed for the correction of spherical aberration[1-3]. These systems deflect an electron beam nearly as much as the lenses which they are designed to correct, and it has from time to time been suggested that the ordinary lenses could be omitted, leaving the correction systems as aberration-free lenses on their own[4,5].

BURFOOT proposed an electrostatic system consisting of four plane electrodes, in each of which appeared an aperture of complicated shape. This system could not be realized, because the apertures would have to be formed with much greater accuracy than is at present possible. In a system intended to avoid this difficulty[6] the four plane electrodes were replaced by electrostatic quadrupoles and octupoles. This system would require fairly high voltages, and the electrodes would be inconveniently close together. These disadvantages are well known in connection with conventional electrostatic lenses, and are largely responsible for the more general use of magnetic lenses. A magnetic quadrupole system will now be considered.

A simple magnetic quadrupole is shown in Fig. 1a. It deflects electrons travelling in plane *ab* (into the plane of the paper) towards the axis, and those travelling in plane *cd* away from the axis. It behaves like an electrostatic quadrupole turned through 45° in its own plane (Fig. 1b). In the same way a magnetic octupole (Fig. 1c) behaves like an electrostatic octupole turned in its own plane through $22\frac{1}{2}°$ (Fig. 1d).

A correction system must be designed in accordance with certain broad principles.

SCHERZER[1] gave expressions for third-order spherical aberration, incorporating electrostatic octupole fields, and these show that the aberration cannot be made zero unless both quadrupole and octupole components of potential are present. The

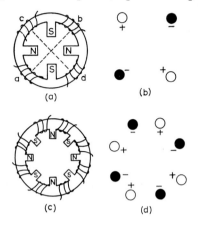

Fig. 1. Magnetic and electrostatic quadrupoles and octupoles.

electron beam must pass through a quadrupole first, because complete correction can only be attained when octupoles are set up in a region in which the beam is astigmatic (that is, in which rays travelling in two planes at right angles are at different distances from the axis), and it is the property of quadrupoles to produce an astigmatic beam.

In order to set up the correction conditions it is necessary to know the relation between the vector potential (used in the ray equations) and the ampere turns on the pole pieces. This can be derived in a convenient form from an expression given by STURROCK[7], in which quadrupole and octupole components appear explicitly.

Before proceeding to correct a system for spherical aberration, it is important to ensure that the conditions for first-order distortion-free imaging be satisfied. The system shown in Fig. 2 satisfies this condition if the outer two quadrupoles have focal lengths $-3/2$ times that of the central quadrupole. This may easily be checked by applying the elementary optical lens formula

$$\frac{1}{v} - \frac{1}{u} = \frac{1}{f}$$

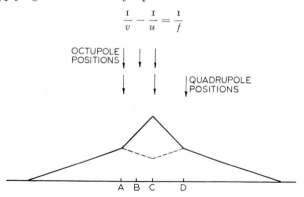

Fig. 2. Possible arrangement of probe system. ——— Paths in xz plane. – – – Paths in yz plane

References p. 343

to the three quadrupoles for rays travelling in both the xz and yz planes; magnification is unity in both cases.

On the assumption that both octupoles and quadrupoles are formed from thin rods separated diametrally by a distance $2a$, the conditions for zero aberration run:

$$5 \sum (NI)_2 \int \frac{z}{(1 + z^2/a^2)^{\frac{7}{2}}} \left(\frac{y'}{y} - \frac{x'}{x} \right) \frac{x^2 y^2}{a^4} \, dz$$

$$+ \, 12 \sum (NI)_4 \int \frac{1}{(1 + z^2/a^2)^{\frac{9}{2}}} \frac{x^2 y^2}{a^4} \, dz$$

$$+ \, \frac{4}{3} (NI)_{2c} \, (f/a)_c \int x'^2 y'^2 \, dz = 0$$

$$5 \sum (NI)_2 \int \frac{1 - 6z^2/a^2}{(1 + z^2/a^2)^{\frac{9}{2}}} \frac{x^4}{a^4} \, dz$$

$$- \, 24 \sum (NI)_4 \int \frac{1}{(1 + z^2/a^2)^{\frac{9}{2}}} \frac{x^4}{a^4} \, dz$$

$$+ \, 8 \, (NI)_{2c} \, (f/a)_c \int x'^4 \, dz = 0$$

$$5 \sum (NI)_2 \int \frac{1 - 6z^2/a^2}{(1 + z^2/a^2)^{\frac{9}{2}}} \frac{y^4}{a^4} \, dz$$

$$+ \, 24 \sum (NI)_4 \int \frac{1}{(1 + z^2/a^2)^{\frac{9}{2}}} \frac{y^4}{a^4} \, dz$$

$$- \, 8 (NI)_{2c} \, (f/a)_c \int y'^4 \, dz = 0$$

the focal length of the central quadrupole being given by

$$(f/a)_c = \sqrt{V_A}/(NI)_{2c}$$

In these expressions $(NI)_2$, $(NI)_4$ represent the number of ampere turns on the respective pole pieces, V_A is the accelerating potential measured in volts, and x, y refer to the co-ordinates of the paths shown in Fig. 2. The summations are taken over the individual octupole and quadrupole elements, the zero of z being taken at the centre in each case.

For the values $(f/a)_c = 2$ and $V_A = 10$ kV, the central quadrupole requires 50 ampere turns and the outer two -33 ampere turns each, while the octupoles at positions A, B, and C (Fig. 2) require respectively 15, -25 and 10 ampere turns. These values have been calculated by the simple theory; preliminary experiments indicate that in practice higher excitations (possibly a factor of 2) are needed.

There is one difficulty in magnetic systems which has not yet been mentioned. This is that the octupole and quadrupole components are separated in azimuth by an angle of $22\frac{1}{2}°$. Thus the form of the deflecting elements at A and C should strictly be as shown in Fig. 3a, incorporating twelve projections. This can be simplified, however, by "spreading" the excitation of the quadrupole projections equally over the neighbouring octupole projections. Thus the system of Fig. 3a should collapse into that of Fig. 3b, incorporating only eight projections.

In conclusion, it should be emphasized that the particular arrangement described is only one of an infinite number of possible arrangements, and was chosen purely

References p. 343

to illustrate the mathematical method of devising such systems. It is not claimed
that this particular arrangement is necessarily a good one for practical use, and
in fact later work has indicated that much better arrangements exist which have a
much smaller spherical aberration before correction is applied.

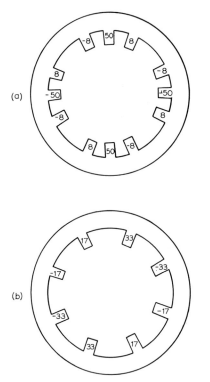

Fig. 3. Superimposed octupole and quadrupole.

APPENDIX

The scalar and vector potentials of a magnetic system may be conveniently interrelated by means of the following expressions:

(1)
$$\phi = \sum_{h \geq l \geq 0}^{\infty} \frac{(-1)^l}{2^{h+l} h! \, l!} \left(\bar{u}^h u^l \Phi_{h-l}^{(2l)} + u^h \bar{u}^l \bar{\Phi}_{h-l}^{(2l)} \right)$$

(2)
$$U = \sum_{h \geq l \geq 0}^{\infty} \frac{i(-1)^l}{2^{h+l} (h+1)! \, l!} \, u^{h+1} \bar{u}^l \bar{\Phi}_{h-l}^{(2l)}$$

(3)
$$A_x + iA_y = -\partial U/\partial z; \quad A_z = \partial U/\partial u + \partial \bar{U}/\partial \bar{u}$$

where $u = x + iy$, bars signify complex conjugates, bracketed superfixes indicate
differentiation with respect to z, ϕ is scalar potential, and A_x, A_y, A_z are the components of vector potential[7]. In this notation Φ_0 corresponds to rotationally symmetric
systems, Φ_2 to quadrupoles, and Φ_4 to octupoles. Φ_0 may be taken as real. The
orientation of quadrupole and octupole components is at present arbitrary. For
later convenience we shall regard Φ_2 as a pure imaginary equal to $i\Phi_2^R$ and Φ_4
as a pure imaginary equal to $i\Phi_4^R$.

References p. 343

Up to the fourth order in u the expression for ϕ runs:

(4)
$$\phi = 2\Phi_0 - \tfrac{1}{2}(x^2 + y^2)\,\Phi_0{}'' + \frac{1}{32}(x^2 + y^2)^2\,\Phi_0{}''''$$
$$+ \frac{xy}{2}\,\Phi_2^R - \frac{xy}{24}(x^2 + y^2)\,\Phi_2^R{}'' + \frac{1}{192}4xy(x^2 - y^2)\,\Phi_4^R$$

primes indicating differentiation with respect to z. If consideration is restricted to systems containing only quadrupoles and octupoles, the terms in Φ_0 may be omitted. The expression for U is then:

(5)
$$iU = (i/24)u^3\,\Phi_2 - (i/384)u^4\,\bar{u}\,\Phi_2{}'' + (i/1920)u^5\,\Phi_4$$

and, to the order required for present purposes, the vector potential components are:

(6)
$$A_x = \frac{1}{24}(3xy^2 - x^3)\,\Phi_2^{R'}$$

(7)
$$A_y = \frac{1}{24}(y^3 - 3x^2y)\,\Phi_2^{R'}$$

(8)
$$A_z = \frac{x^2 - y^2}{4}\,\Phi_2^R - \frac{1}{48}(x^4 - y^4)\,\Phi_2^{R''} + \frac{1}{192}(x^4 - 6x^2y^2 + y^4)\,\Phi_4^R$$

The equations of motion of an electron accelerated by a voltage V_A and subsequently travelling through the magnetic system are:

$$\partial F/\partial x - (\mathrm{d}/\mathrm{d}z)\,\partial F/\partial x' = 0$$
$$\partial F/\partial y - (\mathrm{d}/\mathrm{d}z)\,\partial F/\partial y' = 0$$

where

(9)
$$F = \left[V_A(1 + x'^2 + y'^2)\right]^{\frac{1}{2}} - (e/2mc^2)^{\frac{1}{2}}(A_x x' + A_y y' + A_z)$$

These reduce to:

(10)
$$x'' + (e/8mc^2V_A)^{\frac{1}{2}}\Phi_2^R x = \tfrac{1}{2}\left[x'(x'^2 + y'^2)\right]'$$
$$+ (e/8mc^2V_A)^{\frac{1}{2}}\left\{xyy'\,\Phi_2^{R'} + \frac{1}{12}(x^3 + 3xy^2)\,\Phi_2^{R''} - \frac{1}{24}(3xy^2 - x^3)\,\Phi_4^R\right\}$$

and

(11)
$$y'' - (e/8mc^2V_A)^{\frac{1}{2}}\Phi_2^R y = \tfrac{1}{2}\left[y'(x'^2 + y'^2)\right]'$$
$$+ (e/8mc^2V_A)^{\frac{1}{2}}\left\{-yxx'\,\Phi_2^{R'} - \frac{1}{12}(y^3 + 3yx^2)\,\Phi_2^{R''} - \frac{1}{24}(3yx^2 - y^3)\,\Phi_4^R\right\}$$

It will be observed that Φ_2 and Φ_4 are associated with quantities of the same kind in both equations so that elimination of aberrations is possible. This is the reason for the initial selection of Φ_2 and Φ_4 orientation; if Φ_2 and Φ_4 had both been real, the latter would have been associated with quantities of the forms y^3 and x^2y in the x equation, and x^3 and xy^2 in the y equation, precluding the desired compensation.

If now x_α and y_α are solutions of equations (10), (11) with the right hand sides set equal to zero, the initial conditions being $x_\alpha = 0 = y_\alpha$, $x_\alpha' = 1 = y_\alpha'$, then the general ray leaving the axis at angles α, β in the xz, yz planes respectively may be written

(12)
$$x = \alpha x_\alpha,\quad y = \beta y_\alpha$$

According to the perturbation procedure of SCHERZER[1] these quantities are substituted for x, y on the right hand sides of equations (10), (11), and the following deviations from the Gaussian ray in the image plane are deduced:

$$(13) \quad \delta x = \frac{M}{2} \int_a^b x_\alpha \left[\alpha^3 x_\alpha'^3 + \alpha\beta^2 x_\alpha' y_\alpha'^2 \right]' \mathrm{d}z + M(e/8mc^2 \, V_A)^{\frac{1}{2}} \int_a^b \left[\Phi_2^{R'} \alpha\beta^2 x_\alpha^2 y_\alpha y_\alpha' \right. $$
$$+ \frac{1}{12} \Phi_2^{R''} (\alpha^3 x_\alpha^4 + 3\alpha\beta^2 x_\alpha^2 y_\alpha^2) - \frac{1}{24} \Phi_4^R (3\alpha\beta^2 x_\alpha^2 y_\alpha^2 - \alpha^3 x_\alpha^4) \left. \right] \mathrm{d}z$$

$$(14) \quad \delta y = \frac{M}{2} \int_a^b y_\alpha \left[\beta^3 y_\alpha'^3 + \beta\alpha^2 y_\alpha' x_\alpha'^2 \right]' \mathrm{d}z$$
$$+ M(e/8mc^2 \, V_A)^{\frac{1}{2}} \int_a^b \left[- \Phi_2^{R'} \alpha^2 \beta x_\alpha x_\alpha' y_\alpha^2 - \frac{1}{12} \Phi_2^{R''} (\beta^3 y_\alpha^4 \right. $$
$$+ 3\alpha^2 \beta y_\alpha^2 x_\alpha^2) - \frac{1}{24} \Phi_4^R (3\alpha^2 \beta x_\alpha^2 y_\alpha^2 - \beta^3 y_\alpha^4) \left. \right] \mathrm{d}z$$

a and b indicating object and image positions, and M being the magnification. It is not an essential part of the conditions for zero aberration that x'_α, y'_α should have an initial slope unity, and for the purpose of Fig. 2, a much smaller initial slope is chosen.

The condition for third-order aberrations to vanish is that the coefficients of α^3, β^3, $\alpha\beta^2$ and $\alpha^2\beta$ vanish independently. The coefficients of $\alpha\beta^2$ and $\alpha^2\beta$ are equal (a single partial integration step confirms this) so that in fact only three conditions have to be fulfilled, namely:

$$(15) \quad \int \left[4 \Phi_2^{R'} \left(\frac{y_\alpha'}{y_\alpha} - \frac{x_\alpha'}{x_\alpha} \right) - \Phi_4^R \right] x_\alpha^2 y_\alpha^2 \, \mathrm{d}z - 4 \int x_\alpha'^2 y_\alpha'^2 \, \mathrm{d}z/(e/8mc^2 \, V_A)^{\frac{1}{2}} = 0$$

$$(16) \quad \int \left[2 \Phi_2^{R''} + \Phi_4^R \right] x_\alpha^4 \, \mathrm{d}z - 12 \int x_\alpha'^4 \, \mathrm{d}z/(e/8mc^2 \, V_A)^{\frac{1}{2}} = 0$$

$$(17) \quad \int \left[- 2 \Phi_2^{R''} + \Phi_4^R \right] y_\alpha^4 \, \mathrm{d}z - 12 \int y_\alpha'^4 \, \mathrm{d}z/(e/8mc^2 \, V_A)^{\frac{1}{2}} = 0$$

Before these conditions can be applied to a specific system, the system must first be checked for stigmatic first-order focussing. This holds for the system of Fig. 2, as can easily be verified by using the elementary optical lens formula. The focal lengths of the outer quadrupoles are $-3/2$ times that of the central quadrupole. The focal length of the whole system is twice that of the central quadrupole.

The integrals not explicitly involving Φ_2^R and Φ_4^R in equations (15), (16) and (17) can be immediately evaluated on the assumption that the paths shown in Fig. 2 are not very different from the actual electron paths, which are, of course, curved. The integrals involving Φ_4^R can be fairly approximated by taking $x^2 y^2$, x^4, or y^4 outside the integral sign and evaluating $\int \Phi_4^R \, \mathrm{d}z$ analytically. This is because in the envisaged embodiment Φ_4^R falls off very sharply from its peak value, so that one may reasonably insert the value of $x^2 y^2$, etc., corresponding to the peak of each octupole and sum over the octupoles.

The integrals involving $\Phi_2^{R'}$ and $\Phi_2^{R''}$ are not so easily approximated, since these quantities fall off less sharply and x, y cannot be regarded as constant over the range in which they remain appreciable. It is, therefore, necessary to integrate step by step over the whole system, using the values of x, y and x', y' from Fig. 2.

In order to demonstrate this, it is necessary to assume a particular form of quadrupole and octupole. If these are formed from fairly thin rods, they may be

References p. 343

regarded as a group of point poles. A group of four point poles has a potential distribution of the form

(18)
$$\phi = 2xy\, \Phi_{20}/(1 + z^2/a^2)^{5/2}$$

opposite poles being separated by a distance $2a$ and Φ_{20} denoting peak value. Comparison with equation (4) gives

(19)
$$\Phi_2^R = 4\,\Phi_{20}/(1 + z^2/a^2)^{5/2}$$

Similarly a group of eight point poles has a distribution

(20)
$$\phi = 4\,\Phi_{40}\,xy\,(x^2 + y^2)/(1 + z^2/a^2)^{9/2}$$

To compare this with equation (4), the axes of the octupole must be rotated $\pi/8$; the $x^4 - 6x^2y^2 + y^4$ then becomes $4xy(x^2 - y^2)$ and the following results:

(21)
$$\Phi_4^R = 192\,\Phi_{40}/(1 + z^2/a^2)^{9/2}$$

The scalar potential at any pole face being

(22)
$$\phi = 4\pi\,(NI)/10$$

ampere turns are related to potential peaks by

(23)
$$\Phi_{20} = \frac{4\pi}{10}\,(NI)_2\,\frac{1}{a^2}$$

(24)
$$\Phi_{40} = \frac{4\pi}{10}\,(NI)_4\,\frac{1}{a^4}$$

Further, from the paraxial ray equation (left hand side of equation (10) equated to zero) one gets

(25)
$$x' \doteq (e/8mc^2\,V_A)^{\frac{1}{2}}\,x\int \Phi_2^R\,dz$$

so that the focal length of a quadrupole is given by

(26)
$$1/f = x'/x = (e/8mc^2\,V_A)^{\frac{1}{2}}\,(64\pi/30)\,(NI)_2/a$$

When V_A is measured in volts this gives the simple equation

(26a)
$$(NI)_2(f/a) \doteq \sqrt{V_A}$$

This enables one conveniently to eliminate the $(e/8mc^2\,V_A)^{\frac{1}{2}}$ from the aberration condition by reference to the focal length and ampere turns of the central quadrupole (position C, Fig. 2). Hence, the conditions become those given in the text.

ACKNOWLEDGEMENTS

The author wishes to thank Mr. D. P. R. PETRIE and Mr. T. MULVEY for helpful comment, and Dr. T. E. ALLIBONE, F.R.S., Director of the Research Laboratory, Associated Electrical Industries, for permission to publish this note.

REFERENCES

[1] O. SCHERZER, Optik, 2 (1947) 114.
[2] R. SEELIGER, Optik, 5 (1949) 490.
[3] R. SEELIGER, Optik, 8 (1951) 311.
[4] J. C. BURFOOT, Proc. Phys. Soc. London, B 66 (1953) 775.
[5] R. F. WHITMER, J. Appl. Phys., 27 (1956) 808.
[6] G. D. ARCHARD, Proc. Phys. Soc. London, 72 (1958) 135.
[7] P. A. STURROCK, Phil. Trans. Roy. Soc. London, A 243 (1951) 387.

SEVERAL RESULTS OF THE APPLICATION OF X-RAY SPECTRAL ANALYSES TO THE INVESTIGATION OF MICRO-VOLUMES OF METALLIC SYSTEMS

I. B. BOROVSKY

Baikov Institute of Metallurgy, Academy of Sciences, Moscow (U.S.S.R.)

ABSTRACT

The development of studies of physics of the solid state during the past ten years required the wide application of special methods which permit the study of various changes in structure and composition in very small regions (submicroscopic zones in processes of aging and deformation, substructures in the growth of single crystals, and so forth).

Contemporary technology makes use of alloys of complex composition (heat-resisting, super-hard, special-constructional), sometimes containing as many as twenty elements.

In the processes of heat treatment, elastic and plastic deformation, interaction with active media and so forth, diffusional motion of the elements of alloys occurs within the grains and along grain boundaries. As a result, certain distributions of atoms are produced whose stability against external influences determines the suitability of the alloy and the length of its useful life. Complex alloys as a rule are heterogeneous: various grains have different chemical composition and crystal structure. The linear dimensions of the heterophase regions that determine many properties of alloys lie in the range from 10^{-6} to 10^{-2} cm.

To obtain the complete characteristics of chemical composition and structure of such regions, special methods of investigation are required. Previously existing methods of analyses for small volumes were poorly suited to many-component complex alloys and compounds, since these methods did not permit exact specification of the region being analyzed nor analysis of regions less than 10 to 50 μ in size. The range of their application was limited, and procedures were worked out separately for each element.

In 1951 in France, and independently in the Soviet Union, a method was proposed for X-ray spectral analysis of composition in microvolumes of a substance. The new method is characterized by the following features: with its aid it is possible to study and to determine quantitative chemical composition on specimens of alloys, minerals, slags, organic and inorganic compounds for elements from lithium to uranium in a locality of 0.1 to 2 μ, and to investigate the distribution of any of the elements observed "at a point" in any previously chosen direction on the specimen. By "locality" in the present instance is meant that in an area 0.1 to 2 μ in diameter, affecting 10^{-13} to 10^{-14} g of material, it is possible to determine with an accuracy of 2 to 10 % the quantity of any of the elements listed above, and to follow their possible quantitative variations in each successive 0.1 to 2 μ.

In the apparatus RSASh-2, designed at the Baikov Institute of Metallurgy of the U.S.S.R. Academy of Sciences, for the first time the reverse transmission method (the so-called method of Du Mond) was used for the purpose of X-ray spectral studies. Thanks to the high intensity of the apparatus at the working current of 10^{-6} to 10^{-8} A, in a focus 1 to 3 μ in diameter the number of counts in the recording of the most intense line for a pure element amounts to 10^3 to 10^5 counts/sec. These parameters of the apparatus permit automatic recording of concentration curves at a concentration of the element from 0.2 to 0.5 %. The sensitivity of determination of the elements is 0.05 to 0.5 %. Owing to various rates of motion of the table and specimen (10 to 100 μ/min) and of the take of the self-recording potentiometer, it is possible to obtain concentration curves with various effective concentrations (up to 16,000).

The high local sensitivity of the new method, the possibility of choosing and locating the micro-volume to be analyzed, and also the automatic recording of concentration curves, permit the solution of an exceptionally wide range of problems in the most varied regions of science and technology.

Exact quantitative analysis is done by the method of comparison of the intensity of lines of elements "at a point" with lines from a standard specimen containing the specified elements in known amounts.

The new method has been widely applied for determining diffusion constants, for studying the effect of ordering processes on the magnitude of mutual diffusion, for studying peculiarities in diffusion processes during the formation of structure in single crystals, for studying transfer processes between solid and liquid media, and a series of analogous questions.

THE EFFICIENCY OF CHARACTERISTIC X-RAY PRODUCTION IN CARBON AND COPPER

V. E. COSSLETT

Cavendish Laboratory, University of Cambridge (Great Britain)

ABSTRACT

When X-ray intensities are recorded with a counter it is the quantum efficiency of production and not the usually quoted energy efficiency which is in question. The quantum efficiency, both for the continuous spectrum as a whole and for the characteristic radiation, rises steeply with applied voltage and the ratio of K-quanta to total output does not show the flat maximum of the energy ratio curve. Values have been calculated for copper and for carbon, for high angles of collection of the beam; at low angles, correction for absorption in the target becomes important. At given ratio of applied voltage to that needed to excite the K line, the output from carbon is estimated to be about 5 % that from copper. The accuracy with which carbon content can be determined with the X-ray emission microanalyser will therefore be better than previously anticipated.

INTRODUCTION

The efficiency of X-ray production usually quoted is the energy efficiency (η_E), that is to say, the ratio of the energy in the emitted X-rays to that in the electron beam incident on the target. When the means of detection is a counter, instead of a photographic plate or ionisation chamber, the quantity of interest is the quantum efficiency (η_Q) defined as the ratio of the number of X-ray quanta emitted to the number of electrons incident, per unit time. In quantum terms, the variation of output with voltage is different and in particular no optimum operating voltage exists for a characteristic spectral line as it does for energy efficiency. Further, the theoretical treatment of X-ray production is conducted in terms of quantum processes, so that direct comparison of observed absolute efficiencies with prediction must be made on this basis. The variation with atomic number Z is of particular interest in emission microanalysis, but the state of the subject is such that only an order of magnitude calculation appears justified at present.

QUANTUM EFFICIENCY OF THE CONTINUOUS AND CHARACTERISTIC X-RAY SPECTRA

(a) The energy efficiency for production of *the continuous spectrum* is well-known to be given by the expression:

$$(1) \qquad \eta_{CE} = kZV_0$$

where V_0 is the voltage of the electron beam striking the target and k is a numerical constant given as 1.1×10^{-9} by COMPTON and ALLISON[1] and as 1.3×10^{-9} by KIRKPATRICK and WIEDMANN[2] and by DYSON[3,4]. Calculation of the quantum efficiency runs into the difficulty that the number of quanta per unit frequency (or energy) interval tends to infinity at low energies (Fig. 1). By analogy with K-quanta production, however, a lower limit of voltage can be assumed (V_e) below which no

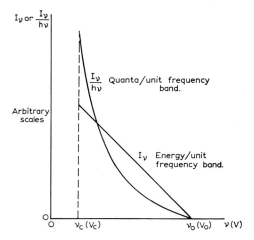

Fig. 1. Variation with frequency ν (or voltage V) of the energy and the number of quanta, per unit frequency (or voltage) band, in the continuous X-ray spectrum above the practical cut-off value ν_c.

quanta are in practice emitted because they are too soft to escape from the target. The quantum efficiency for the continuous spectrum, η_{CQ}, then has the form[5]:

$$(2) \qquad \eta_{CQ} = k_1 Z (V_0 - V_c)^{1.65}/V_c^{0.65}$$

Eqn. (2) was found by DUNCUMB to agree with experiment to within 5 % over a range of 2 to 8 in the ratio V_0/V_c, and for copper the constant k_1 was 1.05×10^{-9} if $V_c = 2$kV. The rapid rise in the number of quanta produced (curve 2) as voltage is increased is compared in Fig. 2 with the steady rise in X-ray beam energy (curve 1). These curves assume negligible absorption in the target, which is true so long as the emergent X-rays make an angle greater than about 30° with the surface. For low take-off angles, as in most X-ray tubes for diffraction, the absorption is appreciable and curve 1 soon reaches a maximum, the position of which will depend on the relative values of the electron range and the X-ray absorption coefficient in the target metal.

  (b) From experimental observations it has long been known that the energy emitted in *the K-line of an element* is proportional to $(V_0 - V_k)^{1.65}$, if V_k is the minimum voltage needed to excite that line. It follows that the energy efficiency for K-line production is given by:

$$(3) \qquad \eta_{KE} = k_2 \cdot V_k (U - 1)^{1.65}/U$$

where $U = V_0/V_k$ and k_2 is a factor which is probably constant for a given element as voltage is varied (neglecting absorption effects), but which will vary with atomic number. The value of η_{KE} rises slowly with voltage (curve 3, Fig. 2) and has no maximum. The existence of a maximum in the corresponding ratio of energy in the K-line to the energy in the continuous spectrum (E_k/E_c) has been noted[6]. As E_k/E_c is proportional to $(U - 1)^{1.65}/U^2$, the maximum occurs at about $U = 6$. The experimental values of this ratio for copper found in the literature vary over more than an order of magnitude, from 0.35 (PARRISH and KOHLER[7]) through 2.2 (BENDIT[8]) up to 5.4 (ARNDT and RILEY[9]), all at $V_0 = 30$ kV. The value of 0.40 obtained by

DYSON[3] appeared to him to agree well with the known data for copper, on which a value for the factor k_2 could be based.

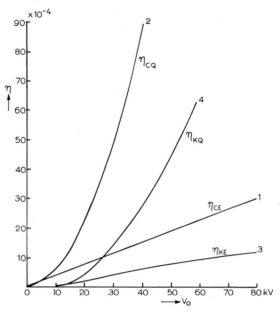

Fig. 2. Variation with excitation voltage V_0 of the efficiency of X-ray production; η_{CE} and η_{CQ} are the energy and quantum efficiencies for the continuous spectrum, η_{KE} and η_{KQ} are the energy and quantum efficiencies for the K-radiation, in ergs per erg and in number of quanta per electron, respectively.

The quantum efficiency for K-line production is given by:

$$(4) \qquad \eta_{KQ} = k_2 \cdot V_k (U - 1)^{1.65}$$

As shown in curve 4 of Fig. 2, it rises almost as rapidly as the quantum efficiency for the continuous spectrum. So long as absorption in the target (or windows) is negligible, no maximum occurs and therefore it is advantageous to use as high an over-voltage ratio U as other experimental factors may allow. By combining eqn. (4) with eqn. (2), we have the ratio of the number of K-quanta to the total quanta in the continuous spectrum as a whole:

$$(5) \qquad N_k/N_c = \eta_{KQ}/\eta_{CQ} = (k_2/k_1 Z) \cdot \left\{ \frac{V_0 - V_k}{V_0 - V_c} \right\}^{1.65} \left\{ \frac{V_c}{V_k} \right\}^{0.65}$$

On the basis of DYSON's measurements, with $V_c = 2$ kV, this ratio has a value of 0.25 for copper at 25 kV and 0.40 at 45 kV. It has no maximum with voltage, but tends to a constant value of 0.50 at very high voltage. The agreement with the value for the ratio E_k/E_c is incidental to the value chosen for V_c, and has no significance.

For assessing the limits of sensitivity in emission microanalysis, it is more important to consider the ratio of the number of K-quanta proper to the number emitted in the continuous spectrum in a voltage channel of width ΔV centred on the emission voltage V_k. This ratio is given by:

$$(6) \qquad N_k/N_{ck} = E_k/E_{ck} \cdot \Delta V = (k_2/kZ) \cdot V_k (U - 1)^{0.65}/\Delta V$$

For copper the ratio of the constants k_2/kZ is almost exactly unity. The signal to background ratio is seen to increase only slowly with overvoltage, but again has no maximum.

VARIATION WITH ATOMIC NUMBER

For emission microanalysis it is desirable to know how the quantum efficiency of K-line production (eqn. 4) varies with atomic number Z. For elements other than copper there is hardly any experimental data available for the value of the constant k_2, so that an appeal must be made to theory.

Calculation of the yield of characteristic X-rays from a target of a given element will involve the number (n) of K-shell ionisations per incident electron, and the probability (w) that ionisation will be followed by emission of a K-quantum rather than by ejection of an electron (and subsequent emission of softer X-quanta). Absorption in the target can be neglected, unless the take-off angle is small, so long as U is not too large. In copper, the electron half-range does not exceed the half-value layer for absorption of the K-line until $U = 7$, and in carbon not until $U = 22$.

The number of K-quanta per electron, at given value of U, can thus be taken as proportional to the product (nw). An expression for n has been derived by WORTHINGTON and TOMLIN[10] on the basis of quantum theory, giving the dependence on atomic number as:

(7) $$n \propto (1/V_k) \cdot \log (23Z/4V_k)$$

for values of U up to 4. By Moseley's law for the frequencies of the K-lines of the elements, $V_k \propto (Z-1)^2$, and, within the present approximation, we can neglect the logarithmic term, so that:

(8) $$n \doteqdot 1/(Z-1)^2$$

The relation for w given by COMPTON and ALLISON[1] is of the form:

(9) $$w = (Z-1)^4/\{K + (Z-1)^4\}$$

the constant K having a value of order 10^6. Combining eqn. (8) and eqn. (9), we see that the quantum output of characteristic radiation depends on Z in the following manner, so long as Z is less than about 30:

(10) $$N_k = nw \doteqdot Z^2$$

Hence the ratio of output in the K-line from carbon and from copper would be about 1 : 25. Taking into account the appreciably greater absorption in copper than in carbon, even at moderate values of U, the ratio might in practice be nearer to 1 : 15.

The deduction that the K-radiation from carbon would only be an order of magnitude less than that from copper, at given overvoltage ratio U, seemed to be at variance with statements in the literature on characteristic X-ray emission. We have therefore made some preliminary measurements of the absolute efficiency of K-emission from carbon and aluminium[11]. As shown in Fig. 3 the output, in terms of quanta per electron per unit solid angle ($N_k/4\pi$), is appreciable. After correcting for absorption in the counter window and for surface roughness of the target, which is important in the soft X-ray region, the same quantum output is obtained from carbon at 2.3 kV ($U = 8$) as for aluminium at 5.7 kV ($U = 4$) and for copper at 20 kV ($U = 2.2$). Or, in terms of the above treatment, the ratio N_C/N_{Cu} is found to be about 1 : 20 at a given value of U, in reasonable agreement with the order of magnitude calculation above. More detailed calculations of the absolute efficiency and its variation with Z have been made by WORTHINGTON and TOMLIN[10] and

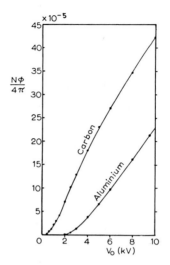

Fig. 3. Variation with excitation voltage V_0 of the quantum efficiency for K-radiation from carbon and aluminium, in quanta per electron per unit solid angle. (DOLBY[11]).

recently by ARCHARD[12]. For aluminium the K-output at 5 kV is found by DOLBY to be about twice that predicted by ARCHARD and one-quarter that by WORTHINGTON and TOMLIN. The agreement with theory may thus be regarded as satisfactory, in view of the uncertainty in some of the fundamental data. More importantly, the outlook for the microanalysis of light elements such as carbon, nitrogen and oxygen, by emission spectrometry, is now much more promising than was previously supposed.

REFERENCES

[1] A. H. COMPTON and S. K. ALLISON, *X-rays in Theory and Experiment*, Van Nostrand, New York, 1935.
[2] P. KIRKPATRICK and L. WIEDMANN, *Phys. Rev.*, 67 (1945) 321.
[3] N. A. DYSON, *Thesis*, Cambridge, 1956; *Brit. J. Appl. Phys.*, 10 (1959) 505.
[4] N. A. DYSON, *Proc. Phys. Soc., London*, 73 (1959) 924.
[5] P. DUNCUMB, *Thesis*, Cambridge, 1957.
[6] A. GUINIER, *X-ray Crystallographic Technology*, Hilger and Watts, London, 1952, p. 6.
[7] W. PARRISH and T. R. KOHLER, *J. Appl. Phys.*, 27 (1956) 1215.
[8] E. G. BENDIT, *Brit. J. Appl. Phys.*, 9 (1958) 312.
[9] U. W. ARNDT and D. P. RILEY, *Proc. Phys. Soc., London, A* 65 (1952) 74.
[10] C. R. WORTHINGTON and S. G. TOMLIN, *Proc. Phys. Soc., London, A* 69 (1956) 401.
[11] R. DOLBY, *Brit. J. Appl. Phys.*, 11 (1960) 64.
[12] G. D. ARCHARD, this volume, p. 337.

A SPECTROMETER SYSTEM FOR LONG WAVELENGTH X-RAY EMISSION MICROANALYSIS

R. M. DOLBY and V. E. COSSLETT

Cavendish Laboratory, University of Cambridge (Great Britain)

ABSTRACT

Spectrometry has not been a serious problem with the $K\alpha$ characteristic lines down to $Z \sim 15$, and counting rates using crystal spectrometers and proportional counters have been high enough to give usable X-ray scanning pictures. But at the long wavelengths (e.g. 44 Å for carbon) low X-ray generation efficiency, absorption effects, and low spectrometer efficiency combine to make counting rates sufficient for high resolution scanning images quite impossible to obtain. Because of this, a direct attempt has been made towards obtaining an X-ray collection and sorting system with a much higher photon utilization efficiency. A small wide-angle proportional counter is used in conjunction with a pulse analysis technique which permits determination of the $K\alpha$ intensities even of adjacent elements in the periodic table. Resolution of three adjacent elements, magnesium, aluminium, and silicon, is demonstrated in some preliminary scanning picture results.

It has been standard practice in X-ray microanalysis to use crystal spectrometers for selecting a desired characteristic wavelength from the several which emerge from the specimen. Unfortunately, however, there are no crystals available for the very long wavelengths, notably in the oxygen, nitrogen, and carbon region. None of the other classical spectrometer methods are satisfactory for solving this problem, particularly from a quantum collection point of view. High efficiency is necessary to keep the beam voltage and current as low as possible, both from specimen heating and spatial resolution considerations. The quantum efficiency problem is particularly acute when scanning images are desired.

The best available energy-discriminating detector having high collection efficiency is the proportional counter[1]. However, proportional counters do not have sufficient energy resolution for separating the K X-ray lines of elements closer than about three in atomic number. But the collection efficiency consideration overrides this disadvantage, and the present long wavelength microanalysis effort has been centered around the direct use of a proportional counter, followed by a special pulse analysis method which overcomes many of the problems associated with low energy resolution.

PROPORTIONAL COUNTER PERFORMANCE

Preliminary experiments on soft X-ray proportional counter behaviour have first been made using the carbon K (44 Å) and aluminium K (8.34 Å) radiations[2]. For this investigation a small argon-flow proportional counter about 2″ long and 0.5″ diameter was constructed. The counter was situated inside the specimen chamber, with a 3/8″ diameter 6 μ Melinex window being the only obstruction between the specimen and the counting volume itself.

References p. 357

Fig. 1 shows pulse-height distributions obtained at an accelerating voltage of 3 kV using thick carbon and aluminium specimens. This proportional counter exhibited a standard deviation/mean pulse height ratio of about 17 % for aluminium

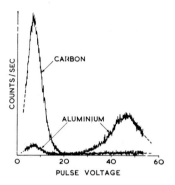

Fig. 1. Carbon and aluminium K pulse-height distributions. Accelerating voltage: 3 kV. (DOLBY[2])

and about 45 % for carbon. These resolution figures indicate that it is not overly difficult to obtain light-element proportional counter performance which is almost as good as that which is usual with heavier elements, considering energy resolution in relation to the K wavelength separations.

ADJACENT ATOMIC NUMBERS

With this encouraging proportional counter performance, the chief remaining problem is that of analysing the output pulses, so that the adjacent K lines of oxygen, nitrogen, and carbon could effectively be resolved. While present counter windows are not suitable for transmitting the oxygen and nitrogen wavelengths, the nature of the pulse analysis problem can be illustrated by experiments using magnesium, aluminium

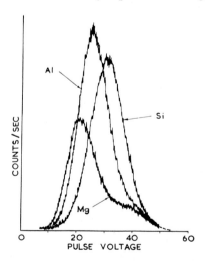

Fig. 2. Magnesium, aluminium, and silicon K pulse-height distributions. Accelerating voltage: 3 kV.

and silicon, which are also adjacent elements in the periodic table. The performance of an argon-flow counter in response to X-rays from these three elements is shown in Fig. 2. Since the same voltage (3 kV) and incident current were used for each specimen, the three pulse-height distributions can be compared directly. The reduction in magnesium response is due mainly to absorption by Melinex windows of 7.4 μ total thickness.

For a specimen containing all three elements, it is evident that there would be considerable difficulty in distinguishing between them with a single-channel pulse-height analyser. The best that could be done to minimize interference would be to position the analyser channel on the outside skirts of the magnesium or silicon curves for detecting these elements; to select aluminium there would be serious interference wherever the analyser channel is placed.

MATRIX METHOD THEORY

A method of pulse analysis which cancels out the interference due to adjacent pulse-height distributions has been discussed by DOLBY[3]. The scheme, which will be referred to as the matrix method, is explained with reference to Fig. 3. For convenience, the three component pulse-height distributions are represented by Gaussian functions whose means are separated by a distance equal to the standard deviation σ, which

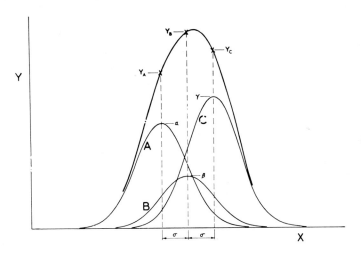

Fig. 3. A composite curve and its constituents, curves A, B, and C.

is the same for all three curves. The composite curve shape is known, but the constituent amplitudes, α, β, and γ, are unknown. They can be found, however, by expressing three ordinate measurements, Y_A, Y_B, and Y_C, of the composite curve in terms of the component amplitudes and solving the resulting three equations simultaneously for α, β, and γ. The resulting answer coefficients depend on the exact shape of the constituent curves, but for the illustration shown the following measurement equations would apply:

$$Y_A = \alpha + .607\beta + .135\gamma$$
$$Y_B = .607\alpha + \beta + .607\gamma$$
$$Y_C = .135\alpha + .607\beta + \gamma$$

The answer equations would then be:

$$\alpha = 1.83Y_A - 1.52Y_B + .68Y_C$$
$$\beta = -1.52Y_A + 2.85Y_B - 1.52Y_C$$
$$\gamma = .68Y_A - 1.52Y_B + 1.83Y_C$$

The coefficients in the answer equations are functions only of the constants in the measurement equations, provided that the constituent curves have been added linearly.

Ordinate measurements have been used by way of illustration, but area measurements (vertical strips), analogous to the pulse height analyser situation, are also applicable.

EQUIPMENT

A practical method for making the measurements and solving the equations automatically on a continuous basis has been developed for use in scanning microanalysis, a block diagram of the equipment being shown in Fig. 4. The basic scanning microanalyser is the system developed by DUNCUMB and COSSLETT[4]. In addition to the usual apparatus, three identical pulse-analysis channels are provided, with

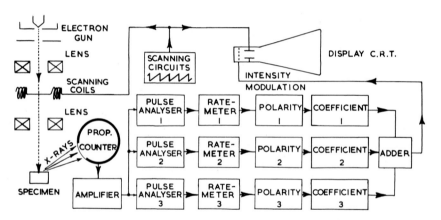

Fig. 4. Scanning X-ray microanalyser incorporating the matrix method of pulse analysis.

the ratemeter time constants being shortened to 1 msec to give sufficient information bandwidth for usable scanning pictures. The ratemeter outputs are fed to the matrixing unit, the elements of which are shown in the figure. After the signal polarities and coefficients (potentiometers) have been set according to the appropriate answer equation, the three signals are combined in the adder. These matrixing operations yield an answer in the form of a voltage proportional to the X-ray concentration of the particular element in question. The answer may then be scanned out on the display tube in the usual manner.

RESULTS

Tests of the system have included magnesium, aluminium, and silicon, the three pulse-height distributions shown in Fig. 2 applying directly. In the calibration

References p. 357

procedure for the figures which will follow, the scanning circuits were stopped and the beam was positioned consecutively on the three pure elements, so that each pulse analyser could be adjusted. The magnesium and silicon analysers were positioned on the advantageous sides of their pulse height distributions, with the aluminium channel being centered on the aluminium peak.

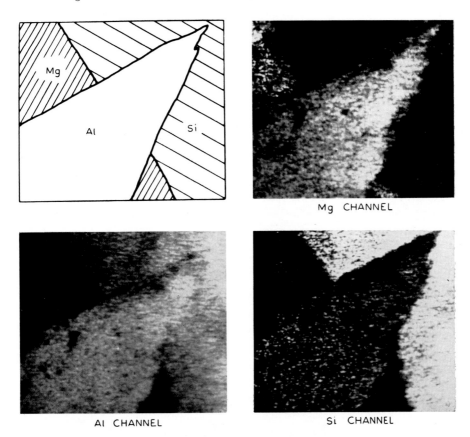

Fig. 5. X-ray scanning pictures from the three pulse-analyser channels, each used alone in the normal way.

Fig. 5 shows test-specimen pictures obtained from each of the pulse-analyser channels and may be taken as being representative of the best that can be done using a proportional counter and the usual method of pulse analysis. The selected element shows up as a bright region, but the undesired elements also appear in varying degrees of brightness, indicating interference from adjacent pulse height distributions.

These pictures, showing an area about 0.5 mm × 0.5 mm in extent, were made using a line rate of about 10/sec and a frame period of 30 sec. Each exposure included 4 full frames, a total of 2 min. The beam current, about 10^{-8} A, was adjusted to give a total count rate of 10,000 pulses/sec on aluminium, using a 3 kV accelerating voltage.

References p. 357

In contrast to Fig. 5, Fig. 6 was made with the matrix pulse-analysis method. There is little interference between the three elements, usable contrast is improved, and misleading changes in brightness have largely been eliminated. A residual background noise remains, an effect which is similar to (but larger than) that with a crystal spectrometer and the continuous radiation of rejected elements.

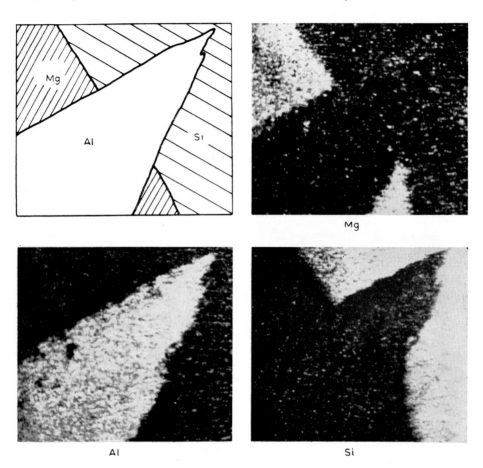

Fig. 6. X-ray scanning pictures obtained by the matrix method.

The last figure, number 7, shows more comparisons between the performance of each pulse-height analyser and the matrix method. The coefficient adjustment procedure for producing such results is very simple, requiring only a few seconds.

CONCLUSION

Even given a suitable counter window, the use of this pulse-analysis system in the carbon, nitrogen, and oxygen region may well disclose unforeseen difficulties, such as interference troubles from the L lines of heavier elements, for example. Nevertheless, these preliminary matrix method results, together with the carbon K proportional counter experiments, are encouraging because they seem to hold out a real hope for an efficient and practical system of soft X-ray spectrometry for micro-analysis purposes.

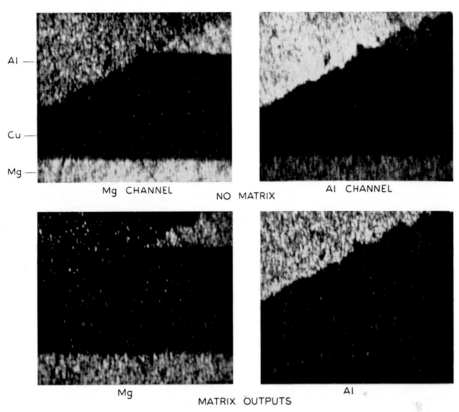

Fig. 7. X-ray scanning pictures showing discrimination between two light elements when present with a heavier element.

ACKNOWLEDGEMENT

One of the authors (R.M.D.) gratefully acknowledges the financial support of a scholarship given by the Marshall Aid Commemoration Commission.

Note added in proof

The attention of the authors has been called to a paper on X-ray counters in which the applicability of the simultaneous equations principle to the overlapping pulse-height distribution problem is pointed out (W. PARRISH and T. R. KOHLER, *Rev. Sci. Inst.*, 27 (1956) 805). It is likely that others, as well, have also appreciated the theoretical possibility of this approach. But it would appear that the incorporation of the principle into a system of microanalysis has not been seriously considered until the present time, now that the growing importance of light element analysis makes the investigation and development of such new methods essential.

REFERENCES

[1] T. MULVEY and A. J. CAMPBELL, *Brit. J. Appl. Phys.*, 9 (1958) 406.
[2] R. M. DOLBY, *Brit. J. Appl. Phys.*, 11 (1960) 64.
[3] R. M. DOLBY, *Proc. Phys. Soc. (London)*, 73 (1959) 81.
[4] P. DUNCUMB and V. E. COSSLETT, *X-ray Microscopy and Microradiography*, Academic Press, Inc., New York, 1957, 374.

DESIGN CONSIDERATIONS OF AN X-RAY SCANNING MICRO-ANALYSER USED MAINLY FOR METALLURGICAL APPLICATIONS

P. DUNCUMB

Cavendish Laboratory, University of Cambridge

and

D. A. MELFORD

Tube Investments Research Laboratories, Hinxton Hall, Cambridge
(Great Britain)

ABSTRACT

The ability of the X-ray scanning microanalyser to display the surface distribution of a given element makes it an important tool for the metallurgist; simultaneous display of both X-ray and scattered electron images facilitates the correlation of element distribution with surface topography and hence optical appearance. To make full use of the rapid analysis possible by the scanning method, an instrument has been built with several new features in the objective lens, specimen chamber and X-ray spectrometer. Specimens up to ¼″ diameter can be accommodated with provision for interchange and manipulation under the electron beam or optical microscope; larger specimens can be examined with some sacrifice in these facilities. A vacuum spectrometer of compact design contains several crystals, which permit analysis over a wide range of wavelengths.

The use of a scanning technique[1-3] in combination with the X-ray emission method of microanalysis initiated by CASTAING[4] allows the rapid study of the surface distribution of different elements. Segregation effects, often not visible optically, can be rapidly detected and the method has proved valuable in metallurgical[5], mineralogical[6] and other problems. The electron probe is scanned over the specimen surface in synchronism with the spot on a cathode ray tube (Fig. 1), which is brightness-modulated by the signal from a spectrometer detecting characteristic emission of the selected element. In this way, an image of the specimen surface showing the distribution of the element is obtained, and, after stopping the scan, the electron probe can be accurately positioned from the image afterglow for quantitative analysis. The method has been mainly used for elements down to atomic number 12 with a resolution of 1 μ, though other papers in this volume[7,8] discuss the extension of these limits.

It is also advantageous to obtain an image in terms of the variation of electron back-scattering over the surface[9]; a scintillation counter is used to collect scattered electrons in the present case (Fig. 1). This shows the surface topography with contrast similar to the optical image obtained in oblique illumination, and gives qualitative information about the variation of atomic number, — a useful feature, for example, in the study of impurities in beryllium.

With the two methods of image formation, it is thus unnecessary to rely on an accurately aligned optical microscope for focusing and probe positioning; improvement of the resolution from 1 μ to 0.1 μ[8] would in any case make the optical method inadequate. In addition, errors due to distortion of the lens field in the neighbourhood of a ferromagnetic specimen are cancelled out.

References p. 364

After the capabilities of the method had been demonstrated on one instrument[3], the need was felt for a second similar to the original but with greater emphasis on ease of operation, particularly in regard to specimen interchange and manipulation. This requirement, combined with the desirability of being able to handle large specimens, made it necessary to develop an objective lens to focus the probe clear of the lens casing. Specimen and standards can then be mounted beneath the lens on a horizontal table, as shown in Fig. 1, so that specimen interchange, movement and rotation can be controlled from outside the vacuum. This also has the advantage that the specimen can be moved under an optical microscope for location of the area to be scanned, no great mechanical accuracy being required since the maximum area of scan is about $\frac{1}{2}$ mm². Finally, to cover elements down to atomic number 12, a vacuum spectrometer is required; in other respects the instrument is similar to the original.

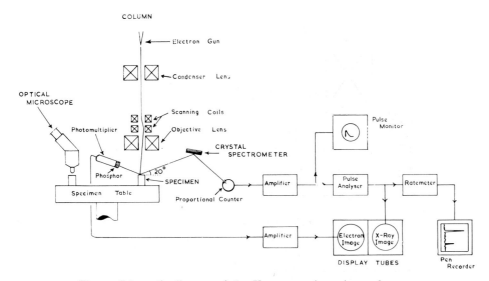

Fig. 1. Schematic diagram of the X-ray scanning microanalyser.

The design of the lens is intimately connected with that of the spectrometer by the requirement that the angle between the analysed X-ray beam and the specimen surface should be as large as possible. This is to reduce absorption within the specimen and variation in the absorption due to surface roughness. In addition, the surface of the specimen should be normal to the electron-optic axis to avoid defocussing of the probe at the edge of the scan. These requirements are not easily met in a lens of low spherical aberration and short working distance, but the arrangement shown in Fig. 2 forms an acceptable compromise. The electron probe is focussed at a point 0.6 mm below the bottom surface of the lens, by a polepiece of the pinhole type[10], giving a focal length of 1.2 cm. X-rays emerge at an angle of 20° through a re-entrant port in the lens casing to the spectrometer. There are six such ports in all, spaced symmetrically about the lens axis. One carries the phosphor and light guide to the photomultiplier for electron collection, and one a copper rod cooled outside the vacuum to prevent carbon contamination; three are at present spare and could be used for additional spectrometers. The upper bore of the lens accommodates the scanning coils, which give the beam a double deflection (see Fig. 1) so that it always passes through the lens aperture in the polepiece gap.

A disadvantage of this form of lens is that the spectrometer becomes unduly bulky if it is to be of the Rowland circle type in a vacuum; the closest the crystal can be moved to the specimen is about 15 cm, necessitating a Rowland circle radius of 45 cm for a minimum Bragg angle of 10°. For most metallurgical work, however, the high resolution given by a quartz spectrometer of this type is not required and cannot in any case be obtained if the electron probe is deflected away from the spectrometer focus. Considerations of compactness and simplicity therefore come foremost, and a curved crystal spectrometer of the semi-focussing type is adequate.

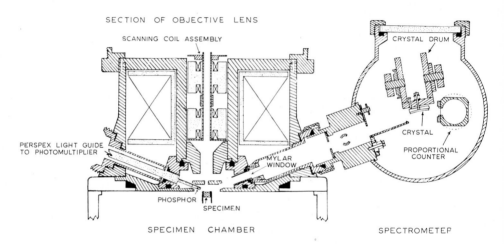

Fig. 2. The objective lens and X-ray spectrometer.

The spectrometer embodies three lithium fluoride crystals curved to different radii and mounted on a drum so as to be interchangeable under vacuum; the axis of drum rotation is in the plane of Fig. 2. A fourth position is available for a different crystal, such as mica or gypsum. Although the focussing conditions of any one crystal are strictly obeyed at only one Bragg angle, the peak width with LiF is at best about 15′, so that some relaxation of the conditions is permitted. The curvatures can thus be chosen so that together the crystals cover a range from 10°—60° without detriment to the resolution. Reflected X-rays are detected by a proportional counter mounted on an arm concentric with the axis of crystal rotation (normal to the plane of Fig. 2), and driven at twice the speed of the crystal. The counter is filled with xenon to give 20 % efficiency for U $L\alpha$ radiation at 0.91 Å, and has a thin beryllium window transmitting 10 % of Mg $K\alpha$ at 9.9 Å; between these extremes the efficiency is much higher. The count rate obtained for the $K\alpha$ emission from pure iron is about 10^4/sec, with a probe current of 10^{-7} A and accelerating voltage of 25 kV. A fifth position on the crystal drum, which is left blank, permits the counter to be rotated into the direct beam for the preliminary exploration of an unknown surface; strong characteristic radiation is immediately detected on the pulse monitoring oscilloscope.

The specimen table is shown in Fig. 3. There are at present eight positions for

References p. 364

specimen and standards although this is soon to be increased to 14. One of these positions holds the specimen itself and is equipped with two orthogonal traversing movements and a rotation about a fixed axis arranged to coincide with the optical and electron-optical axes. Another position is occupied by a Faraday cage and the remaining positions by the standards required for quantitative work. Rotation of the whole table through 180° brings the specimen from optical microscope to electron probe.

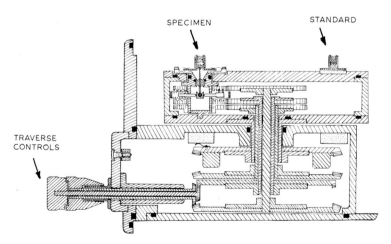

Fig. 3. The specimen table.

The ability to rotate the specimen about the centre of the field was originally specified because it was felt that there would be an advantage in being able to set a linear feature such as a grain boundary into any convenient azimuth so that it might be scanned orthogonally. In practice, it has also proved most helpful in the examination of rough specimens such as fracture surfaces. The restrictions on the accessibility of a field in such a specimen imposed by the emergent angles of 20° for both electron and X-ray images can be largely offset by suitable adjustment of the orientation.

The specimen table is housed in a chamber on the top plate of which are laid out four access positions, namely the optical and electron-optical axes, an airlock

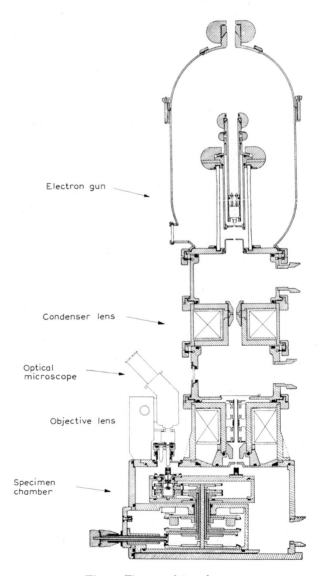

Electron gun

Condenser lens

Optical microscope

Objective lens

Specimen chamber

Fig. 4. The complete column.

References p. 364

and an observation port. The seating for the probe-forming column is at the rear of this plate while in front of the column is mounted a conventional metallurgical microscope. The specimen may be centered at the observation port for withdrawal through the airlock, which works on the caisson tube principle and is large enough for specimens up to $\frac{1}{4}''$ diameter. Larger specimens may be accommodated by removing the specimen table.

The complete column is shown in Fig. 4. The electron gun, which can be operated up to 50 kV, has the filament assembly centrable with respect to the grid during operation; in this way the effect of filament drift on the stability of probe current can be overcome. The condenser lens has a detachable polepiece, and is followed by an intermediate section (containing a fluorescent screen for alignment), objective lens and specimen chamber.

The electronics is shown in block form in Fig. 1. A common scanning generator is used to drive the display tubes and the column, and the normal rate of scan is one picture of 300 lines in 2 sec. The display tubes are identical and have a persistence of about 20 sec; this is long enough to position the probe after the scan is stopped but not so long as to obscure movement of the specimen. One tube displays the electron image and the other has four separate functions: it can display (1) the electron image, (2) the waveform of the signal forming the electron image for rapid focussing of the objective lens, (3) the X-ray image, or (4) the intensity of X-ray emission as a Y deflection proportional to the ratemeter reading. This last facility is used in conjunction with a slow linear scan of 1 line in 15 sec and results in a semi-quantitative

Fig. 5. The complete X-ray scanning microanalyser.

distance/concentration plot being displayed for the path scanned. This is of particular use in demonstrating slight depletions or enrichments which, for statistical reasons, may not be visible in the X-ray image. It also has considerable advantages in the rapid assessment of diffusion gradients. An alternative way of detecting small variations in concentration in the X-ray image would be by the use of a storage tube to increase the persistence time. Although this is essentially no different to recording the image for the same period photographically, the immediate presentation of the image would be a considerable advantage in practice.

The complete instrument, with the exception of the power supplies to the column, is shown in Fig. 5. The desk carrying the column is on the left, the scanning generators and display tubes in the centre, and the electronics for pulse analysis and spectrum plotting on the right. The equipment is being manufactured commercially by the Cambridge Instrument Company.

REFERENCES

[1] V. E. COSSLETT and P. DUNCUMB, *Nature*, 177 (1956) 1172.
[2] P. DUNCUMB and V. E. COSSLETT, *X-ray Microscopy and Microradiography*, Academic Press, Inc., New York, 1957, pp. 374, 617.
[3] P. DUNCUMB, *Brit. J. Appl. Phys.*, 10 (1959) 420.
[4] R. CASTAING, *Thesis*, Paris University, O.N.E.R.A., Publ. No. 55, 1951.
[5] D. A. MELFORD and P. DUNCUMB, *Metallurgia*, 57 (1958) 159.
[6] S. O. AGRELL and J. V. P. LONG, this volume, p. 391.
[7] R. M. DOLBY and V. E. COSSLETT, this volume, p. 351.
[8] P. DUNCUMB, this volume, p. 365.
[9] K. C. A. SMITH and C. W. OATLEY, *Brit. J. Appl. Phys.*, 6 (1955) 391.
[10] G. LIEBMANN, *Proc. Phys. Soc. (London)*, B 68 (1955) 682.

IMPROVED RESOLUTION WITH THE X-RAY SCANNING MICRO-ANALYSER

P. DUNCUMB

Cavendish Laboratory, University of Cambridge (Great Britain)

ABSTRACT

The resolution of an X-ray microanalyser is limited mainly by the penetration of electrons into the specimen, being about $1\ \mu$ at 20 kV in copper. Improvement may be effected either by the use of a specimen thinner than the depth of penetration, or by reduction of the accelerating voltage. The former case has been illustrated previously; the practical limitations of the latter, with particular reference to the scanning microanalyser, are now discussed and examples given.

The principle of the X-ray scanning microanalyser is described elsewhere in the symposium[1]. It is of interest for many applications both metallurgical and biological, to improve the resolving power of the instrument beyond that obtained hitherto. This has been in the region of $1\ \mu$, and, as with the X-ray projection microscope[2], is limited by three main factors: (1) the maximum current which can be delivered by the electron gun into a probe of given Gaussian-optical diameter, (2) the spherical aberration of the objective lens, and (3) the penetration and lateral diffusion of the incident electrons into the specimen. In principle, each of these can be reduced to any desired level by increasing the electron-optical demagnification, reducing the lens aperture or reducing the accelerating voltage respectively, but only at the expense of the available X-ray intensity. It is therefore necessary to fix the minimum X-ray intensity required and to combine these three factors in such a way as to give the minimum overall diameter of the X-ray source. WITTRY[3] has considered this problem, and a simple treatment more easily applied to the scanning microanalyser has been given by the author elsewhere[4]. This is briefly summarised in the following paragraphs, applied to the present conditions and approximately verified by experiment.

The minimum Gaussian-optical probe diameter d_0 for a given probe current i may be derived from LANGMUIR's[5] formula for a thermionic gun of 100 % efficiency:

$$d_o{}^2 = 2.0\ \frac{V_e}{j_c\ V_k}\ \frac{i}{U\ \alpha^2}$$

where V_e, j_c are the thermal energy and current density of electrons leaving the cathode, UV_k is the accelerating voltage and α is the semi-angular aperture of the probe. HAINE, EINSTEIN and BORCHERDS[6] have shown that it is possible to obtain nearly 100 % efficiency from normal tungsten filament guns over a wide range of voltage, though gun design appears to be more critical below 10 kV.

The count rate n from characteristic X-ray emission recorded by a spectrometer of efficiency f is given by:

$$n = f\ A\ i\ (U - 1)^{1.7}$$

neglecting absorption in the specimen, where A is dependent on the target material.

The 1.7 power law has been well verified for elements in the region of copper; few measurements have been made on the value of A for different elements but information is available for copper, aluminium and carbon[7,8].

For a lens of spherical aberration constant C_s the diameter of the disc of least confusion d_s is given by:

$$d_s = \tfrac{1}{2} C_s \alpha^3$$

Finally, the electron penetration gives rise to a disc of confusion d_p, which can be estimated for K_α X-ray emission from the Thomson-Whiddington law, assuming that the lateral spread d_p is equal to the depth of penetration at which the electron energy falls below V_k:

$$d_p = \frac{K V_k^2 (U^2 - 1)}{\rho}$$

The constant K is obtained from measurements by TERRILL[9] as $2.5 \cdot 10^{-12}$ with d_p in cm and V_k in volts, and, except possibly for elements of high atomic number, is sufficiently accurate for energies of 3–30 keV.

Recent measurements by HOLLIDAY and STERNGLASS[10] give good agreement at 10 kV, but below this indicate a variation with voltage to the power of 1.4 rather than 2. Inserting this in the following calculation does not, however, alter the values derived for resolution and accelerating voltage by more than 10 %.

Although the spherical aberration and electron penetration cannot be regarded as imposing a Gaussian spread on each point in the electron probe, it is a better approximation to assume this rather than a linear spread. The diameter d of the X-ray source is thus given by:

$$d^2 = d_o^2 + d_s^2 + d_p^2$$

Inserting the expressions for d_o, d_s and d_p above, and differentiating with respect to α and U, d is found to be minimum for a given count rate n when

$$d = 1.5 d_0 = 2.5 d_s = 1.6 d_p$$

n is then given in terms of d as:

$$n = 1.4 \cdot 10^{18} \cdot \frac{j_c}{V_e C_s^{2/3}} \frac{A \rho^{1.7}}{V_k^{2.4}} f d^{4.4}$$

Thus, under optimum conditions, the count rate varies somewhat more rapidly than the fourth power of the X-ray source diameter, and the coefficient may be split into three parts which depend on the electron-optical system, the nature of the specimen and the spectrometer. It is now possible to evaluate the attainable resolution, taken as equal to d, for certain sets of conditions.

From experiments at different count rates[4], a figure for n of 10^4/sec is taken as being sufficient to produce an X-ray image of useful quality in reasonable exposure time, though this estimate may vary widely depending on the number of lines scanned and the contrast discrimination required. With the present limitation of electron gun and lens, it is unlikely that j_c can be increased much beyond 2 A/cm² nor C_s reduced much below 0.4 cm. With $V_e = 0.25$ V, the factor $j_c/V_e C_s^{2/3}$ for the electron optics thus equals 14.7. The specimen factor $A\rho^{1.7}/V_k^{2.4}$ for Cu K, Al K and C K radiation falls in the region of $1-5 \times 10^7$ (see Table I), though preliminary rough measurements on the efficiency of Cu L production indicate a value an order of magnitude higher than for Cu K; the low value of A for L radiation is more than offset by the lower excitation voltage. Values for the spectrometer factor f vary

TABLE I

Electron optics	Specimen	$\dfrac{A\rho^{1.7}}{V_k^{2.4}}$	Spectrometer	
$j\ = 2$ A/cm^2	Cu K	$2.8 \cdot 10^7$	Li F crystal	$5.5 \cdot 10^{-6}$
$V_e = 0.25$ eV	Al K	$1.1 \cdot 10^7$	Proportional $\left\{ \begin{array}{l} A\ 2.1 \cdot 10^{-3} \\ B\ 10^{-1} \end{array} \right.$	
$C_s = 4$ mm	C $\ K$	$5.0 \cdot 10^7$	counter	

widely, depending on whether a crystal spectrometer or proportional counter is used; j may be increased by over 10^4 using a proportional counter (B in Table I) in place of a typical curved crystal spectrometer, though with the disadvantage of much poorer wavelength resolution. Proportional counter A falls between the extremes and corresponds to the present experimental arrangement.

With these values, the attainable resolution for three different combinations is given in Table II, and varies between $1\ \mu$ for the conventional microanalyser to

TABLE II

Count rate	Specimen	Spectrometer		d	V	i
10^4/sec $\Big\{$	Cu K	Li F crystal		$1\ \mu$	17.4 kV	$1.1\ \mu$A
	Al K	Prop. counter $\left\{ \begin{array}{l} A \\ B \end{array} \right.$	$\begin{array}{l} A \\ B \end{array}$	$\begin{array}{l} 0.31\ \mu \\ 0.12\ \mu \end{array}$	$\begin{array}{l} 4.8 \text{ kV} \\ 3.3 \text{ kV} \end{array}$	$\begin{array}{l} 1.2 \cdot 10^{-2}\ \mu\text{A} \\ 6.9 \cdot 10^{-4}\ \mu\text{A} \end{array}$

$0.1\ \mu$ using a proportional counter. The accelerating voltage required in the latter case is seen to be in the region of $3-5$ kV so that K radiation may be used only for light elements if the excitation ratio U is to be kept sufficiently high; medium and heavy elements must be detected through their L or M emission. The proportional counter window must thus be as thin as possible; "Melinex" foil $6\ \mu$ thick has a $10\ \%$ transmission for wavelengths shorter than 14 Å and for C $K\alpha$ at 44 Å. An argon flow counter using a needle anode with spherical tip was found to be most convenient in the present lens design. This is shown in Fig. 1a and was inserted inside the lens casing just outside the polepiece gap. Pulse-height distributions obtained with this counter for aluminium, copper and carbon at 3 kV are shown in Fig. 1b, the peaks occurring at 8.3 Å, 13 Å and 44 Å respectively. The energy resolution is slightly worse for Al K radiation than the normal counter with cylindrical symmetry, since some 8.3 Å quanta penetrate beyond the tip, but is approximately the same for Cu L and C K. These radiations can thus be at least partially separated with discrimination, but this would not be the case if they lay closer together.

With proportional counter A we should thus expect to obtain a resolution in the region of $0.3\ \mu$ in aluminium (Table II), by using an accelerating voltage in the region of 5 kV and a probe current of about 10^{-8} A. It may be noted at this point that, in the case of a specimen thinner than the electron penetration, such as an extraction replica, a resolution no worse than the specimen thickness can be obtained. Previous results on such a specimen[4] with a voltage of 25 kV, at which the electron penetration is about $2\ \mu$, demonstrated a resolution of $0.3\ \mu$.

References p. 371

The more important practical considerations are listed as follows. The stabilities required of lens current and accelerating voltage are of the order of 0.01 %: care in machining the polepiece removes the need for a stigmator, but this may be

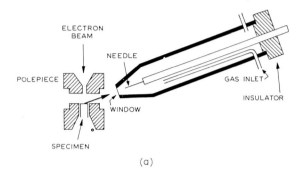

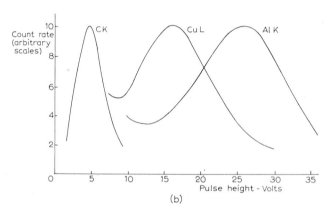

Fig. 1. (a) Proportional counter with needle anode and thin window for detecting soft X-rays. (b) Pulse-height distributions from Al K, Cu L and C K radiations at 8.3, 13 and 44 Å.

necessary if a resolution of 0.1 μ or below is to be achieved[2]: the column should be well shielded against stray magnetic field from the mains, and it may be necessary to lock the frequency of line scan to the mains to reduce the effect on the image: it is convenient to provide a means of collecting back-scattered electrons[11,4] to form a scanning image of topographical detail in the specimen with a resolution much less dependent on electron penetration. In this way the diameter of the electron probe can be estimated, and focussing is greatly facilitated; a similar result is obtained by amplifying the current flowing between the specimen and earth, which was the method used in the present circumstances.

To establish the magnification, a silver grid of 1500 mesh/inch was examined as a test specimen, with the accelerating voltage at 6 kV. Images of the grid, formed from the total X-ray emission, are shown in Fig. 2 (a), (b) and (c), at magnifications of 75, 700 and 3500. (c) may be compared with an electron image at the same magnification (d) which shows the relief of the bars (flat side uppermost). Although this is a poor specimen for estimating X-ray resolution, the electron image shows that the probe diameter is about 0.2 μ.

A better test of X-ray resolution is given by a specimen in which inclusions of one element are present in a matrix of another, the two having low mutual solubility.

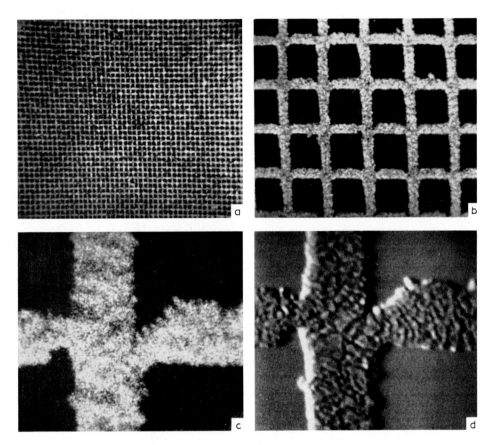

Fig. 2. (a) X-ray scanning image of 1500 mesh/inch silver grid at magnification of 75. (b) Magnification 700. (c) Magnification 3500. (d) Electron scanning image at magnification of 3500.

Such a specimen is provided by the aluminium–tin system, which has been studied by contact microradiography by WILLIAMS[12], and by projection microradiography by NIXON[13]. A polished section of this alloy is shown in Fig. 3. In (a), (b) and (c), which are the electron, Al K and Sn L images respectively at low magnification, the form of the aluminium grain boundaries is clearly revealed by the segregation of the tin. The tip of one such segregation in the middle of the field is shown at high magnification in (d), (e) and (f) which were obtained in a similar way. The shadowing effect in the electron image is not due to relief in the surface but to poor low frequency response in the amplifier. Detail at the tip of the tin segregation shows that the electron probe is about 0.2 μ in diameter, and a resolution of 0.2–0.3 μ is demonstrated in the X-ray images, though somewhat obscured by the effect of quantum noise.

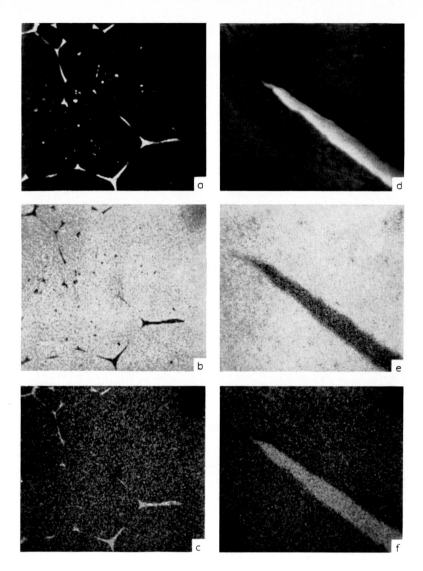

Fig. 3. (a) Electron scanning image of aluminium-tin alloy showing tin segregation at grain boundaries. Magnification 65. (b) X-ray scanning image selecting Al K radiation at same magnification. (c) X-ray scanning image selecting Sn L radiation at same magnification. (d) (e) (f) Tip of segregation in centre of (a), (b) and (c) magnified 3000 times.

It is thus possible to obtain in practice a resolution in the neighbourhood of 0.3 μ using proportional counter discrimination, as indicated by theory. However, the method cannot be universally applied at present owing to insufficient energy resolution of the counter and to absorption in the counter window. Such conditions thus lay even greater stress on the need for improving the proportional counter, as discussed by MULVEY and CAMPBELL[14], or for a system such as that described by DOLBY[15,16], by which the effective resolution may be improved electronically. For

References p. 371

the analysis of single particles with a stationary electron probe, the count rate could be reduced to about 10^2/sec, and an accurate pulse-height distribution obtained in reasonable time with a multi-channel pulse-height analyser to record and sort every pulse. Even if the theory described becomes inaccurate at very low voltages, this would improve the resolving power to better than 0.1 μ, which, in comparison with the normal resolution of 1 μ corresponds to a reduction in the volume analysed of over 1000. The technique of X-ray emission microanalysis may thus be extended to take in a number of metallurgical and biological problems at present inaccessible.

REFERENCES

1 P. DUNCUMB and D. A. MELFORD, this volume, p. 358.
2 W. C. NIXON, *Proc. Roy. Soc. (London)*, A 232 (1955) 475
3 D. B. WITTRY, *J. Appl. Phys.*, 29 (1958) 1543.
4 P. DUNCUMB, *Brit. J. Appl. Phys.*, 10 (1959) 420.
5 D. B. LANGMUIR, *Proc. Inst. Radio Engrs. and Waves and Electrons*, 25 (1937) 977.
6 M. E. HAINE, P. A. EINSTEIN and P. H. BORCHERDS, *Brit. J. Appl. Phys.*, 9 (1958) 482.
7 V. E. COSSLETT, this volume, p. 346.
8 R. M. DOLBY, *Brit. J. Appl. Phys.*, 11 (1960) 64.
9 H. M. TERRILL, *Phys. Rev.*, 22 (1923) 101.
10 J. E. HOLLIDAY and E. J. STERNGLASS, *J. Appl. Phys.*, 30 (1959) 1428.
11 K. C. A. SMITH and C. W. OATLEY, *Brit. J. Appl. Phys.*, 6 (1955) 391.
12 W. M. WILLIAMS and C. S. SMITH, *J. Metals*, 4 (1952) 755.
13 W. C. NIXON, *Proc. Conference on Electron Microscopy, London*, 1954, p. 307.
14 T. MULVEY and A. J. CAMPBELL, *Brit. J. Appl. Phys.*, 9 (1958) 406.
15 R. M. DOLBY, *Proc. Phys. Soc. (London)*, 78 (1959) 81.
16 R. M. DOLBY and V. E. COSSLETT, this volume, p. 351.

A NEW X-RAY MICROANALYZER

T. MULVEY

Research Laboratory, Associated Electrical Industries Limited, Aldermaston, Berkshire
(Great Britain)

ABSTRACT

As a result of experience at the A.E.I. Research Laboratory with an earlier experimental instrument, an X-ray microanalyzer has been designed and constructed to enable the technique to be used in current research problems.

INTRODUCTION

The design of an experimental X-ray microanalyzer at the A.E.I. Research Laboratory has been reported previously[1,2]. Although this instrument was used partly for spectrochemical analysis, its main purpose was the study of instrumental problems and the extension of the CASTAING-GUINIER[3] technique to lighter elements.

The X-ray microanalyzer to be described is similar in general design to the earlier instrument but has been built as an analytical tool for research into problems of surface physics and of metallurgy. Several modifications have been made to the original design either to simplify operation or to extend the usefulness of the method.

In addition, the specimen chamber and spectrometer have been constructed in such a way that the instrument may be readily set up as an X-ray projection microscope for special purposes, *e.g.* the study of impurities in beryllium films.

GENERAL CONSTRUCTION

Fig. 1 is a section drawing showing the probe forming system, the optical microscope, and part of the vacuum spectrometer. An electron gun and two magnetic lenses produce a finely focussed spot on the specimen; the ray paths of the electrons are shown schematically in Fig. 1. The first lens is of the conventional type used in electron microscopy; the second is a long working distance objective[1]. Inside the wide lower bore (6 cm diameter) of this lens are mounted the electrostatic deflector plates which allow small movements of the electron probe to be made accurately and conveniently and which are also used for the electronic scanning of the specimen[4].

Fig. 2 shows these in more detail. They are mounted above the objective aperture which can be changed through the upper bore of the lens. Below the deflectors is an eight-pole electrostatic lens of the BERTEIN type[5] for correcting astigmatism; this arises mainly from charging-up effects in layers of contamination accumulated on the walls of the instrument.

The specimen stage

The specimens are mounted rigidly on a drum which is keyed to the end of a shaft mounted in hardened and ground V blocks. Two micrometers and a lever

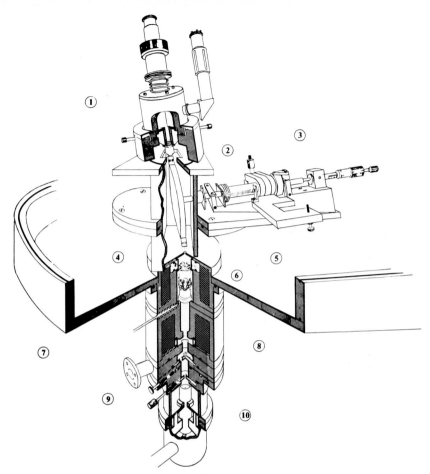

Fig. 1. General arrangement of the X-ray microanalyzer. (1) Optical microscope, (2) Specimen drum, (3) Specimen manipulator, (4) Specimen, (5) X-ray beam, (6) Deflector plates, (7) Vacuum spectrometer, (8) Lens system, (9) Pumping tube, (10) Electron gun.

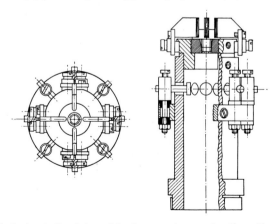

Fig. 2. Assembly of electrostatic plates, objective aperture and astigmatism corrector.

References p. 377

system move the specimen in two directions at right angles as shown in Fig. 1. On rotating the lever system through 180° between fixed stops the micro-area that was under the probe appears under the cross-wires of the optical microscope. The latter is a standard metallurgical microscope with interchangeable objective lenses. Its axis is correctly aligned by making a fine contamination mark on a polished copper specimen, rotating the levers and then placing the cross-wires over the contamination spot by means of four adjusting screws. This alignment is then correct for any setting of the micrometers.

The vacuum spectrometer
Fig. 3 shows a photograph of the equipment. The electron lenses and specimen stage are bolted to the vacuum spectrometer. This is of the JOHANSSON focussing type[6] with a Rowland circle of 25 cm radius which permits the use of a wide range of bent crystals including quartz; the latter is necessary when high spectral resolution is required. The JOHANSSON spectrometer is bulky but combines high resolution with

Fig. 3. Photograph of the X-ray microanalyzer and vacuum spectrometer with counting equipment and electron-scanning display tube.

high intensity and its geometry is particularly suited to the small X-ray source provided by the electron probe. If the resolution of the spectrometer is made too great, however, the intensity of the spectral line falls off rapidly as the probe is moved away from the correct position on the Rowland circle, when using the electrical shift controls or when scanning. With a good quartz crystal the permissible shift might be as small as ± 10 μ. Experience indicates that for many purposes a lithium fluoride crystal gives adequate resolution and permits an area of 100 μ × 100 μ to be scanned without serious loss of intensity at the edges of the field. Crystals can be changed through a porthole in the lid of the spectrometer.

Electronic equipment
The rack behind the spectrometer (Fig. 3) contains the counting equipment, the electronic scanning display tube and various stabilized supplies. The H.T. supply which produces a stabilized output voltage over the range 5—50 kV is not shown.

OPERATION
Specimens for analysis are loaded onto the drum through a port in the specimen chamber (Fig. 3). The drum accommodates six specimens and is insulated thermally, so that it can be heated if required, and electrically, to enable the current arriving at the specimen to be measured. Some applications of the instrument are described elsewhere in these Proceedings[4], but there are several points of operating technique to which attention may be drawn.

Control of contamination
Specimen contamination arising from the breakdown of hydrocarbon vapour[7] under the electron beam furnishes a useful record of the micro-area analyzed, but it is clearly desirable to control the amount that is deposited, and to suppress it during the analysis of very light elements. HEIDE[8] has shown that the contamination rate in demountable vacuum systems depends chiefly on the balance between the oxygen and hydrocarbon vapour pressure. Generally the hydrocarbon vapour predominates leading to the formation of a carbon layer under the action of the electron bombardment. By increasing the oxygen pressure locally in the region of the specimen, HEIDE was able to reduce the contamination rate in an electron microscope and even to remove existing layers.

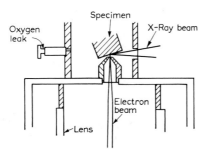

Fig. 4. Control of contamination by local increase of oxygen pressure at the specimen (HEIDE's method).

References p. 377

Fig. 4 shows an arrangement based on this principle which is in use in the present instrument. A conical baffle placed in the bore of the final lens restricts the pumping speed in the specimen chamber and allows a wide range of oxygen pressures to be used without appreciably affecting the mean free path of the electrons since the high pressure region is only 0.5 mm in extent. The pressure in the specimen chamber is adjusted by a needle valve until the desired contamination rate is obtained. Specimens may also be *de-contaminated*; *e.g.*, grease films can be removed in this way.

Backscattering measurements

The current in the specimen will be less than that incident upon it since some electrons are backscattered[9]. The fraction that is backscattered decreases with decreasing atomic number. By measuring the specimen current for different elements a calibration curve can be drawn and subsequently used to determine the average atomic number of a chosen area, for example, an unidentified inclusion. Frequently this gives a clue to the chemical composition and eliminates an extensive search of the spectrum.

Analysis of light elements

Experiments with diffraction gratings[2] and with pulse-height analysis using proportional counters [10] suggest that both methods will be valuable in the soft X-ray region. The poorer resolution of proportional counters compared with that of a grating spectrometer is largely offset by the greatly increased sensitivity. Since neighbouring elements can now be analysed with a proportional counter by the measuring techniques recently devised by DOLBY[11], attention has been concentrated on the design of a suitable proportional counter. Fig. 5 shows the construction of

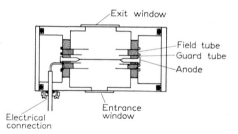

Fig. 5. Vacuum-tight proportional counter for analysis in the soft X-ray region.

this gas-flow counter, 5 cm in diameter, employing an argon–CO_2 mixture. Gas enters the main body, passes into the outer compartments which contain the electrical leads and out into a metering device. The counter is made vacuum-tight by 'O' ring seals giving complete control over gas flow and avoiding a gas-air pocket forming near the insulators. Guard tubes at anode potential prevent leakage currents from reaching the anode which is a Nichrome wire 50 or 100 μ in diameter. Field tubes maintain a purely radial field over the active volume, enabling the physical length of the counter to be reduced to 10 cm, a convenient size for most vacuum spectrometers. "Mylar" entrance and exit windows 6 μ thick are provided.

Quantitative analysis in the soft X-ray region is limited in accuracy at present by uncertainties in the correction factors that must be applied for absorption and fluorescence[12] unless close comparison specimens are available. In order to minimize such corrections the take-off angle of the X-rays is to be increased in the near future from its present value of 10° to 45°, a value which appears to be desirable for the eventual quantitative analysis of elements such as carbon and oxygen.

ACKNOWLEDGEMENTS

The author wishes to thank Mr. R. SMITH and Mr. E. PESTERFIELD for their assistance in the mechanical design, Mr. D. ALLENDEN and R. WINKWORTH for many improvements in the design and construction of the electronic equipment, and Mr. R. ATTWOOD and his staff for carrying out the main construction. He also wishes to thank many colleagues for their advice and help, and Dr. T. E. ALLIBONE, F.R.S., Director of the Research Laboratory, Associated Electrical Industries, for permission to publish this paper.

REFERENCES

[1] T. MULVEY, *Proc. Conf. on Electron Microscopy, Berlin*, 1958, pp. 68, 263.
[2] T. MULVEY, Development of the Castaing-Guinier method of X-ray micro-analysis, *Mém. sci. Rev. mét.*, 56, No. 2, (1959) 163.
[3] R. CASTAING and A. GUINIER, *Proc. Conf. on Electron Microscopy, Delft*, 1949 p. 60.
[4] A. BERNARD, D. BRYSON-HAYNES and T. MULVEY, this volume, p. 379.
[5] F. BERTEIN, *Ann. Radioélectricité*, 3 (1948) 379.
[6] T. JOHANSSON, *Z. Phys.*, 82 (1933) 507.
[7] A. E. ENNOS, *Brit. J. Appl. Phys.*, 4 (1953) 101.
[8] H. G. HEIDE, *Proc. Conf. Electron Microscopy, Berlin*, 1958, p. 88.
[9] J. E. HOLLIDAY and E. J. STERNGLASS, *J. Appl. Phys.*, 28 (1957) 1189.
[10] T. MULVEY and A. J. CAMPBELL, *Brit. J. Appl. Phys.*, 9 (1958) 406.
[11] R. M. DOLBY, *Proc. Phys. Soc. (London)*, 78 (1959) 81.
[12] R. CASTAING and J. DESCAMPS, *Recherche aéronaut.*, No. 63, March—April (1958).

DISCUSSION

JAMES E. MANSON: Microanalysis by X-ray Fluorescence has been used for analysis of stratospheric particulates collected by our group at the Geophysics Research Directorate of the U.S. Air Force. The form of the sample as collected is a line 50 μ wide and 14 mm long, deposited on a plastic film about 0.5 μ thick. This sample is ideally suited to analysis by a focussing spectrometer, since it will be a line source of fluorescent X-rays if irradiated properly, and the background scattering will be a minimum because of the low mass substrate. The work published by BARSTAD and REFSDAL in the May, 1958 issue of the *Review of Scientific Instruments* outlined many of these advantages.

Professor OGILVIE of the Massachusetts Institute of Technology and the Advanced Metals Research Corporation undertook the design and construction of apparatus to accomplish the analysis of our samples. The design involved a rather small and neat attachment for the standard North American Philips Spectrometer. A limiting slit was used to restrict the primary Tungsten exciting radiation to an area 1 mm by 14 mm on the sample. All Soller slits were of course removed from the spectrometer. The attachment provided a cam, cam follower and a three-point bending device to cause a thin LiF crystal to assume the proper curvature at each wavelength setting, thus allowing recording of the response. To allow bending of the thin LiF crystal, it was cemented to a steel frame so machined that it assumed a uniform curvature under the three-point load. The entire attachment was mounted compactly on the spectrometer axis, so that no extra drives were required.

The results obtained with standard samples in the microgram range are shown normalized to 1 μg in Tables I and II. Fig. 6 was obtained with a preliminary design fixed bent crystal but is typical of the results with the elastically bent LiF attachment.

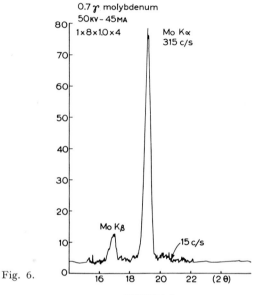

Fig. 6.

TABLE I

(50 kV — 45 mA excitation normalized for a 1 μg sample)

Element	Z	Net I (S)* Counts/sec	Net I (G)** Counts/sec	P/B (S)	P/B (G)
Cr	24	105	49	8	20
Mn	25	250	450	14	70
Fe	26	200	174	41	128
Co	27	700	560	71	223
Ni	28	1220	924	73	368
Cu	29	1160	397	130	308
Zn	30	1340	437	90	175
Sr	38	158	103	25	42
Mo	42	270	51	6	22

*(S) Scintillation counter   **(G)   Geiger counter

TABLE II

Element	Z	Limit (S) g	Limit (G) g
Cr	24	$6.5 \cdot 10^{-9}$	$2.7 \cdot 10^{-9}$
Mn	25	$3.5 \cdot 10^{-9}$	$7.2 \cdot 10^{-10}$
Fe	26	$1.2 \cdot 10^{-9}$	$4.1 \cdot 10^{-10}$
Co	27	$7.2 \cdot 10^{-10}$	$2.3 \cdot 10^{-10}$
Ni	28	$4.5 \cdot 10^{-10}$	$1.4 \cdot 10^{-10}$
Cu	29	$3.8 \cdot 10^{-10}$	$1.7 \cdot 10^{-10}$
Zn	30	$3.7 \cdot 10^{-10}$	$3.0 \cdot 10^{-10}$
Sr	38	$2.2 \cdot 10^{-9}$	$1.3 \cdot 10^{-9}$
Mo	42	$7.0 \cdot 10^{-9}$	$2.6 \cdot 10^{-9}$

AN ELECTROSTATIC SCANNING SYSTEM FOR THE X-RAY MICROANALYZER

A. BERNARD, D. BRYSON-HAYNES and T. MULVEY

Research Laboratory, Associated Electrical Industries Ltd., Aldermaston, Berkshire
(Great Britain)

ABSTRACT

A simple electron scanning system is described which is intended to supplement the information about the specimen obtained with the optical microscope. The system differs from that first described by COSSLETT and DUNCUMB in that electrostatic deflection is used, enabling certain simplifications to be made in the electronic circuitry.

INTRODUCTION

Electron scanning methods of microscopy were first devised by VON ARDENNE[1] and further developed by MCMULLAN[2]. Later DUNCUMB and COSSLETT[3] applied this method to X-ray microanalysis and succeeded in displaying on a cathode ray tube the distribution of a chosen element in the specimen.

A possible deterrent to the construction of electron scanning systems is the complexity of the beam deflector system and the associated electric equipment. The design to be described is simpler than previous ones and is especially suitable for microanalyzers designed primarily for point by point analysis in conjunction with the optical microscope. Means are provided for correlating the electron scanning image with the optical image.

The scanning system

Fig. 1 shows the general arrangement of the scanning system. The electron probe of the X-ray microanalyzer is deflected in synchronism with the spot of a cathode ray tube. For simplicity of mechanical design and electronic circuitry electrostatic deflection was used throughout.

As the electron probe traverses different parts of the specimen the pulse rate of the counter in the spectrometer will vary according to the local composition.

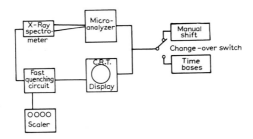

Fig. 1. Schematic arrangement of the scanning system.

References p. 384

These pulses modulate the beam of the cathode ray tube; each pulse results in a flash of light on the screen. By using a long-persistence screen ($\simeq$ 30 sec), an image is obtained showing the distribution of a given element in the area being scanned.

The deflectors
Fig. 3 shows a photograph of the deflector plates which are mounted inside the bore of the final de-magnifying lens of the microanalyzer[4]. They are mounted above the lens aperture which is contained in a conical seating and can be removed through the top bore of the lens for cleaning. The gap between the plates is 5.0 mm

Fig. 2. The electrostatic deflector plates mounted above the removable aperture of the final lens.

to enable this to be done. The plates were dimensioned to give a deflection sensitivity of 1 μ/V at 30 kV. Since deflection takes place after the aperture, the necessity for a double-deflector stage is avoided. The electron probe may be positioned for point analysis by means of suitable d.c. deflecting voltages or scanned in a raster. The two time bases for this are conventional in design and provide a balanced output with respect to earth; this is necessary to avoid astigmatism in the electron probe.

Modulation
In the present instrument a Geiger counter is used for elements heavier than sulphur. A maximum counting rate of 10,000/sec is obtained by using the fast quenching circuit of McKEOWN and UBBELOHDE[5]. This circuit provides large positive pulses that can be fed directly onto the modulator of the cathode ray tube obviating the need for a special amplifier. Other detectors such as proportional or scintillation counters can also be used, of course.

RESULTS

Analysis of spark-hardened layers
Fig. 3(a) shows an optical micrograph of a section of a steel cylinder whose surface had been hardened by the electrospark method[6] using a tungsten carbide

References p. 384

electrode. The specimen was submitted by Dr. N. C. WELSH of this Laboratory. The hardened layer is revealed by a light diagonal band some 30 μ wide. To the left of this layer is the unhardened steel surface. The scanned area is recognisable

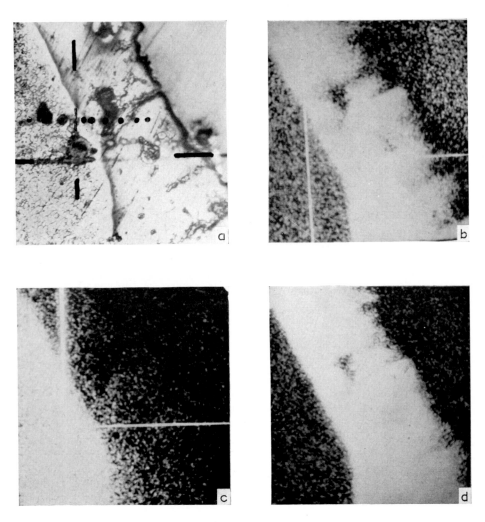

Fig. 3. (a) Optical micro-section of electrospark hardened layer on steel cylinder ($\times$ 385). Co-ordinate axes indicated by contamination marks. Scanned area 130 $\times$ 130 μ. (b) Distribution of cobalt (Co $K\alpha$). Co-ordinate axes superposed on scanning picture. (c) Distribution of iron (Fe $K\alpha$). Co-ordinate axes superposed on scanning picture. (d) Distribution of tungsten (W $L\alpha$).

by a faint rectangle of contamination some 130 μ $\times$ 130 μ. Fig. 3(b) shows the distribution of cobalt in the layer; cobalt is present in the sparking electrode as a bonding agent. The distribution of iron is shown in Fig. 3(c) and that of tungsten in Fig. 3(d). These distributions were obtained by setting the spectrometer to the appropriate spectral line.

In order to correlate the optical and scanning pictures two co-ordinate axes were drawn on the specimen by switching on a line scan and building up a contamination mark. The ends of these lines have been inked in to facilitate identification. By photographing the cathode ray tube, at the same time the corresponding axes are registered on the scanning pictures as shown in Figs. 3(b) and (c). The position of point analyses can be correlated in a similar way.

Metastable Cu–Bi compound

Fig. 4(a) shows an optical micrograph of some needle-like crystals believed to be a metastable compound of copper and bismuth[7]. One specimen was prepared by Dr. COVINGTON and Dr. HOWLETT of this Laboratory in connection with research

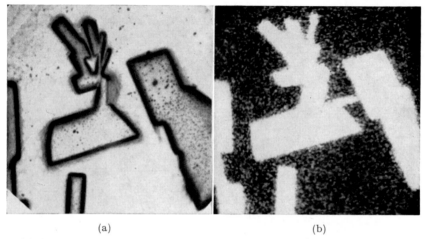

(a)	(b)

Fig. 4. (a) Optical micrograph of metastable Cu-Bi compound. (b) Electron scanning picture (Cu $K\alpha$). Light areas correspond to approximately 44 % Cu.

into mass transfer of metals. The crystals were too small for analysis by chemical means. Fig. 4(b) shows the electron scanning picture (Cu $K\alpha$). The crystals are sharply delineated against the low continuous background from the bismuth and contain approximately 44 % of copper. The resolution is about a micron; slight differences of shape in Fig. 4(a) and (b) were caused by a light polish given to the specimens after analysis to remove dust particles from the vacuum system that had become embedded in the specimen.

Examination of thick oxide layers

During the process of mechanical wear, thick oxide films are sometimes formed on the rubbing surfaces. Their analysis often presents difficulties for electron diffraction and other commonly applied techniques. Electron probe microanalysis can often be useful here since the electron penetration may be reduced below a micron by suitably reducing the accelerating voltage. Fig. 5 shows a scanning picture taken with the Fe $K\alpha$ line and 20 kV accelerating voltage of an oxide film that formed on a brass pin which had been worn against a steel disc. The specimen was submitted by Dr. J. K. LANCASTER of this Laboratory. The thickness of the layers varied between 500 and 5000 A.U. and was not continuous. A quantitative analysis in the thicker parts of the layer showed an iron content of approximately 50 %; copper and zinc were also present in the layer. This analysis, together with the results of electron diffraction enabled the composition and structure of the layer to be determined.

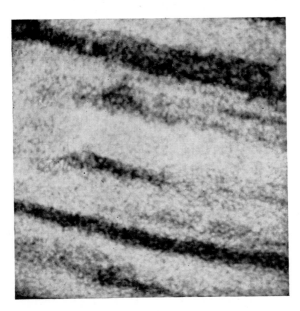

Fig. 5. Electron scanning picture (Fe $K\alpha$) of the distribution of iron in rough oxide layer formed on brass pin worn against steel disc. Accelerating voltage 20 kV.

Statistical considerations

The X-ray quanta arrive at random at the detector and cause a random modulation of the cathode ray tube, obscuring changes of contrast due to real changes in specimen composition. If N random pulses are associated with each picture element then variations of contrast will occur whose root mean square P is equal to $N^{-\frac{1}{2}}$. Sufficient pulses must be accumulated to reduce these variations to a tolerable level. The time required to reduce these variations below an amount P is given by

$$t = \frac{n^2}{P^2 R C}$$

(1)

where n^2 is the number of picture elements
       R is the counting rate from the pure element
       C is the fractional concentration of the element in the specimen.

ROSE[8,9] has investigated this problem experimentally using a specially constructed test chart and he concluded that the value of P should be $\frac{1}{5}$. Fig. 6 shows a series of electron scanning photographs taken with the Cr $K\alpha$ line. They show the distribution of chromium in a grey cast iron containing 2.5 % Cr photographed for 60, 120, 240 and 480 sec respectively; bright areas correspond to $C = 4.7$ % Cr, $R = 6,000$ and $n^2 = 10^4$. From eqn. (1) $t \simeq 890$ sec. This is in qualitative agreement with the images of Fig. 6 in which graininess obscures the fine details even at 240 sec, Fig. 6(c), and is still noticeable at 480 sec, Fig. 6(d). In practice a compromise is usually necessary between exposure time and resolution. The visual image on the tube would normally correspond to Fig. 6(a) (60 sec integration time) and allowance must be made for statistical effects.

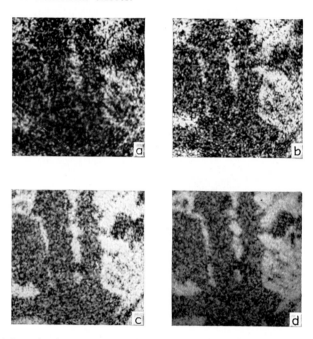

Fig. 6. Graininess in electron scanning pictures caused by random arrival of quanta. (a) $t = 60$ sec, (b) $t = 120$ sec, (c) $t = 240$ sec, (d) $t = 480$ sec. Specimen is cast iron containing 2.5 % of chromium.

CONCLUSION

A simple electronic system has been described which enables the distribution of a chosen element in a specimen to be displayed on a cathode ray tube. Several applications of the instrument are described and attention is directed to certain statistical aspects of the displayed image.

ACKNOWLEDGEMENTS

The authors wish to thank Mr. E. PESTERFIELD for the mechanical design and construction of the deflector system and Dr. J. S. HALLIDAY and Mr. D. P. R. PETRIE for helpful discussion. They also wish to thank Dr. T. E. ALLIBONE, F.R.S., Director of the Research Laboratory, Associated Electrical Industries, for permission to publish this paper.

REFERENCES

[1] M. VON ARDENNE, Z. Physik, 109 (1938) 553.
[2] D. McMULLAN, J. Inst. Elec. Engrs. London, 100, Pt. 1 (1953) 245.
[3] P. DUNCUMB and V. E. COSSLETT, X-ray Microscopy and Microradiography, Academic Press, Inc., New York, 1957, p. 374.
[4] T. MULVEY, this volume, p. 372
[5] P. J. A. McKEOWN and A. R. UBBELOHDE, J. Sci. Instr., 31 (1954) 321.
[6] N. C. WELSH, Nature, 181 (1958) 1005.
[7] A. K. COVINGTON and B. HOWLETT, to be published.
[8] A. ROSE, Advances in Electronics, 1 (1948) 131.
[9] A. ROSE, Optica Acta (Paris), 5, Special Number, Jan. 1958 (Int. Coll. Phys. Probl. in Colour T. V.).

THE METROPOLITAN-VICKERS X-RAY MICROANALYSER

R. S. PAGE and I. K. OPENSHAW

*Scientific Apparatus Department, Metropolitan-Vickers Electrical Company Limited,
Urmston, Manchester (Great Britain)*

ABSTRACT

The Metropolitan-Vickers X-ray microanalyser is a commercial version
of the experimental prototype, built and developed in the A.E.I. Research
Laboratory, Aldermaston.

The electron probe is produced by two reducing magnetic lenses and is
formed about 1 cm from the top surface of the second lens. The minimum
diameter of the electron probe is less than 0.5 μ giving a resolution of 1 μ.

The surface of the specimen is inclined at 30° to the horizontal to permit
a greater take-off angle for the generated X-rays.

The spectrometer uses a bent and ground lithium fluoride crystal and
a Geiger-Müller counter. The range of the present instrument is from
uranium (92) to titanium (22). Provision is made for the evacuation of the
spectrometer to facilitate the future extension of the range to elements of
lower atomic number.

The design of the X-ray microanalyser forms the basis of other electron
probe instruments such as the electron scanning microscope.

INTRODUCTION

The Metropolitan-Vickers X-ray Microanalyser is a commercial version of the
experimental prototype, developed and built at the A.E.I. Research Laboratory,
Aldermaston.

The basic features, *i.e.* method of production of electron probe, specimen
mounting arrangements, spectrometer and operation in general, are similar to the
A.E.I. instrument and have been described in the previous papers[1,2].

The instrument can perform quantitative chemical analyses on volumes as
small as $1\mu^3$ in the range of elements: titanium to uranium. It is possible to
perform an analysis to an accuracy of 1 % after applying corrections for fluorescence
and absorption[3]. A recording time of about 1 to 2 minutes is usually adequate for
the analysis of mass concentrations of about 1 % of the total. Concentrations of about
0.1 % of the total can be detected but it is difficult to get an accurate analysis
because of the long period necessary to collect enough counts to overcome the
statistical error in the counting system. The present range will be extended to
magnesium by the addition of a proportional counter, a pulse-height analyser and
suitable amplifiers.

The distribution of any particular element can be displayed on a cathode ray
tube by scanning the electron probe over a selected area of about 100 μ square[2].
This facility will be shortly available.

References p. 390

GENERAL ARRANGEMENT

Fig. 1 shows the whole instrument which comprises three main items:

The desk

The stabilised electronic supply cubicle

The scaler

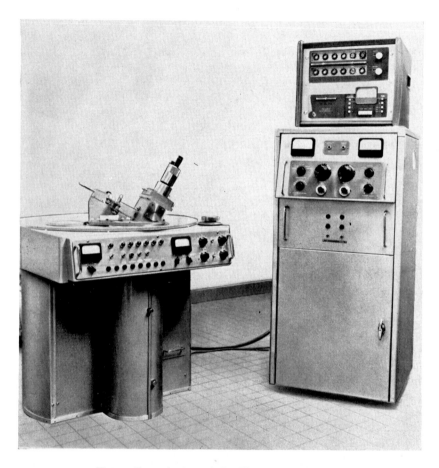

Fig. 1. General view of the X-ray microanalyser.

The desk houses most of the vacuum equipment and protection circuitry, the electron probe-forming stack and the spectrometer tank. In addition to these items, there is a rotary pump and a constant voltage transformer from which the electronic cubicle is supplied.

The electron gun is capable of withstanding 60 kV and the H.V. cable is sealed into the body of the gun using silicone oil as a filling medium. Filaments can be pre-centered into a spare upper half of the cathode assembly and then quickly plugged into the lower half of the cathode by means of a bayonet fastening. A centerable anode plate together with a shift movement provides means of aligning the gun with the remainder of the stack.

The condenser lens is a conventional magnetic lens working at a focal length of about 1 cm. If this lens was used as a microscopic objective lens it would be capable of resolving better than 10 Å U. This lens and the objective lens provide a reduction of the source to less than 0.5 μ diameter. The objective lens is of the asymmetrical type as described by LIEBMANN[4]. This lens works at a focal length of 2.8 cm with a spherical aberration constant (C_s) of about 3 cm and delivers 1 μA into an 0.6 μ diameter spot. Both electron lenses are water-cooled.

The final aperture is mounted behind a system of deflector plates in the wide bore of the objective lens. The whole assembly is mounted on a rotatable turret using the wide bore of the lens as a bearing. The deflector plates can carry astigmatism-correcting potentials or scanning time-base potentials.

A small vacuum valve is placed between the lenses and the electron gun to enable either the gun or the upper section of the stack to be isolated whilst changing filaments or specimens. In the same section of the stack a current-measuring probe is provided for determining the current in the electron beam near the gun.

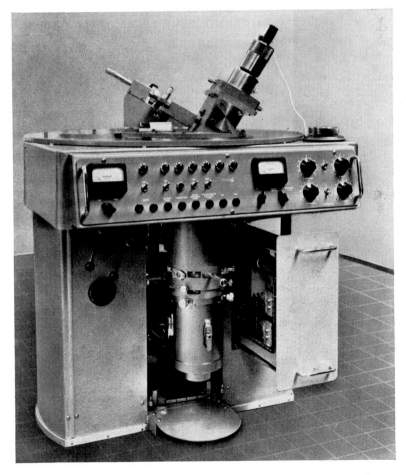

Fig. 2. Front view of desk, showing electron optical stack and controls.

The specimens are mounted on an insulated drum, the plane of which is inclined at 30° to the vertical to facilitate the analysis of elements of low atomic number, otherwise the specimen chamber and optical microscope are similar to the A.E.I. Research Laboratory instrument. Specimen movement is obtained by means of the micrometers shown in Figs. 2 and 3. Specimens can be changed through the small hatch on the side of the specimen chamber.

The X-ray window is made from Melinex (or Mylar) (6 μ thick) which also serves as a vacuum seal when the spectrometer is used in air.

Provision is made for the measurement of specimen current which is amplified and monitored on a meter on the front panel. This facility can be used for aligning the instrument and as an aid for determining the 'backscatter' of electrons from the specimen.

Fig. 2 shows the front of the desk with the vacuum control chassis partly withdrawn and the covers removed from around the electron optical stack. The controls shown on the right of the control panel are used for correcting the astigmatism of the electron probe.

A beam-splitting unit can be mounted onto the eyepiece of the microscope which enables either a 35 mm film camera or $3\frac{1}{2}'' \times 2\frac{1}{2}''$ plate camera to be used. The specimen can be observed through a right-angled eyepiece or on a shielded diffusing screen.

Spectrometer

Fig. 3 shows the spectrometer which is of the JOHANSSON[5] type using a Geiger counter and a curved and ground lithium fluoride crystal; a spring-loaded lead shield is provided, operated by a cam to prevent X-rays entering the Geiger counter directly at low Bragg angles. A quench circuit[6] is used to reduce the dead time of the Geiger counter to about 30 μsec, this is mounted directly underneath the spectrometer. Provision is made for the evacuation of the spectrometer for use with the lighter elements. The correct relative position of the Geiger counter and crystal is controlled by linkages and multiplier arms which are positioned underneath the spectrometer tank. The spectrometer arms are chain-driven from a calibrated knob.

Vacuum system

The rotary pump used is a Metrovac DR210 which consists of two single-stage pumps, each displacing 1 l/sec, in one housing. One half of this pump is continuously used to back the two 3″ diffusion pumps, the other half is used for roughing down either the spectrometer or the electron optical stack.

Magnetic valves and interlocking systems are used to ensure that the vacuum system fails to safety, the supplies for these safety circuits are mounted on the withdrawable chassis (Fig. 2) which is easily accessible for servicing.

Power supplies

The lens and high voltage supplies are housed in the electronics cubicle. These are of conventional design, the latter being generated by means of a Cockcroft-Walton multiplier with metal rectifiers and can supply 5 to 50 kV. The short term stability of the electrical supplies is more than adequate for the X-ray microanalysis, being better than 1 part in 10,000, the long term stability has been achieved by immersing the reference in oil. All amplifying circuits are mounted on plug-in printed circuitry boards. Sufficient room is available for two additional lens stabilisers so that the cubicle could be used for other electron optical devices.

Fig. 3. Top view of desk, showing specimen movement controls and spectrometer tank.

The Isotope Development Scaler 1700 is used, which incorporates a triple range ratemeter with long and short time constants. Other features of the Scaler include a simple pulse-height analyser and an H.T. supply which is sufficiently stable to be used for a proportional counter.

OTHER ELECTRON PROBE INSTRUMENTS

The design of the X-ray microanalyser forms the basis of other electron probe instruments. By using stronger lenses and increasing their separation, an electron probe with a diameter of about 200 Å U. can be obtained. Such a system has been designed for use as an electron scanning microscope.

It is hoped shortly to provide an alternative specimen chamber which would enable the X-ray microanalyser to be used as an X-ray projection microscope.

References p. 390

SPECIFICATION

Electron probe diameter	— less than $\frac{1}{2}$ μ
Optical microscope magnification	— up to 600 $\times$
*Scanning image magnification	— 600 $\times$
Present range of elements	— Titanium (22) to Uranium (92)
*Extended range of elements	— Magnesium (12) to Uranium (92)
Principal crystal	— Lithium fluoride
*Area displayed on C.R.T.	— 100 μ^2
Accelerating voltage	— 5 to 50 kV

* Facilities which will shortly be available.

REFERENCES

[1] T. MULVEY, this volume, p. 372.
[2] A. BERNARD, D. BRYSON-HAYNE and T. MULVEY, this volume, p. 379.
[3] R. CASTAING and J. DESCAMPS, *J. phys. radium*, 16 (1955) 304.
[4] G. LIEBMANN, *Proc. Phys. Soc. (London)*, 68 (1955) 682.
[5] T. JOHANSSON, *Z. Phys.*, 82 (1933) 507.
[6] P. J. A. McKEOWN and A. R. UBBELOHDE, *J. Sci. Instr.*, 31 (1954) 321.

C. APPLICATIONS

THE APPLICATION OF THE SCANNING X-RAY MICROANALYSER TO MINERALOGY

S. O. AGRELL

Department of Mineralogy and Petrology

and

J. V. P. LONG

The Cavendish Laboratory, University of Cambridge, Cambridge (Great Britain)

ABSTRACT

A scanning X-ray microanalyser has been used for determining the composition of fine exsolution intergrowths in natural minerals. Factors affecting the use of the technique for the examination of minerals and rocks are briefly considered, and results obtained from its application in specific cases are presented and discussed.

INTRODUCTION

The present approach to obtaining analytical data on coexisting minerals often involves difficult and tedious separation techniques prior to chemical analysis. The methods of X-ray emission microanalysis allow chemical data to be obtained from extremely small and precisely defined volumes on a polished thin section or mount of a rock or mineral.

Existing microanalysers[1-3] have been designed principally for use with metallic and opaque specimens. The present paper describes briefly an instrument used primarily for non-metallic and transparent materials, but which can also be used for opaque specimens.

The most important factors which influence design of an instrument using this technique in the study of rocks and minerals are:

(1) The difficulty of obtaining a high surface polish on the majority of rock and mineral specimens. This entails the necessity for a high take-off angle for the X-rays, to avoid anomalous absorption effects.

(2) The low electrical and thermal conductivity of most minerals and rocks. This entails the evaporation of a conducting layer (*e.g.* aluminium) on the surface of the specimen and the use of beam currents of the order of 1/100th of the maximum permissible with metals.

(3) The desirability of using petrological thin sections. These, if mounted with Lakeside cement and finished in the normal way but to a thickness of $\sim 45\ \mu$, can be polished adequately for examination.

APPARATUS AND TECHNIQUE

Fig. 1 shows the general arrangement of the apparatus in which an electron beam is focussed by a system of magnetic lenses into a spot about $1\ \mu$ in diameter on the surface of the rock slice. The rock slice is mounted on a mechanical stage and is viewed in transmitted polarised light by means of an optical microscope, and the point of impact of the electron beam may be seen by the visible fluorescence produced in most transparent minerals.

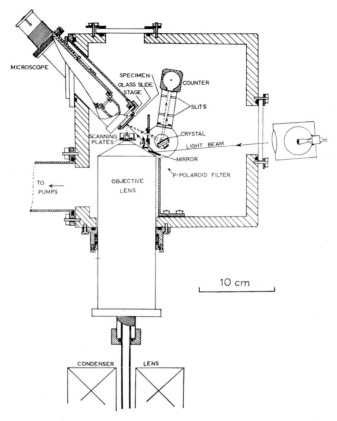

Fig. 1. Cross-section of microanalyser showing part of electron-optical system, light-optical arrangement and X-ray spectrometer.

The spectrometer and the proportional counter which record the intensity of the characteristic X-rays excited by the electron beam are mounted in the same vacuum chamber as the specimen. The X-rays are collected at an angle of 75° to the surface of the specimen. In addition, a scanning device similar to that devised by COSSLETT and DUNCUMB[2], but using electrostatic deflection plates, has been incorporated. This allows an enlarged image showing the distribution of a selected element in the surface of both transparent and opaque materials to be displayed on a cathode ray tube (Figs. 2 and 4). It also allows a trace of the variations in concentration of the element along a traverse of the specimen to be superimposed on the scanning image (Fig. 2).

For quantitative measurements a standard of known composition must be mounted with the thin section to be examined. It is preferable that it should approximate to the composition of the mineral being studied and a most important part of any programme directed towards the study of minerals must be the ac-

References p. 400

cumulation of a wide range of homogeneous standards both of natural and synthetic materials.

QUANTITATIVE MEASUREMENTS ON STANDARD MINERALS

As a preliminary to the analysis of unknown minerals, measurements were made on homogeneous minerals of known composition in order to establish that reliable quantitative data could be obtained from electrically non-conducting specimens. It was in particular desirable to confirm that modification of the backscattering conditions would not occur in these specimens under the conditions of high current density which exist in the electron probe. The results obtained, two of which are given below, are in agreement with the findings of HOLLIDAY and STERNGLASS[4], who demonstrated that the backscattering ratio, η, for secondary electrons of energy 50 eV is a function of atomic number and independent of the conduction properties and crystal structure of the solid. They showed that the backscattering properties of metals and insulators could be expressed on the same curve of η against effective atomic number, at least for the current densities employed by them.

The first measurement was of the iron contents of a magnetite and haematite. The results obtained with pure iron as reference and with a constant *incident* beam current are given in Table I.

TABLE I

Mineral	True % Fe	Measured % Fe
Haematite (Fe_2O_3)	69.9	70.5 ± 0.6
Magnetite (1) (Fe_3O_4)	72.3	71.9 ± 0.6
Magnetite (2)	72.3	72.6 ± 0.6

These are in accordance with the assumption that the effective backscattering is a function only of atomic number.

In the second case, the calcium content of fluorite (CaF_2, cubic) was estimated at three different kilovoltages, calcite ($CaCO_3$, rhombohedral) being used as the standard. The results are given in Table II.

TABLE II

Accelerating voltage (kV)	Measured Ca in fluorite (%)	Mean (%)	Calculated Ca in fluorite (%)
21	50.2 ± 0.3		
25	50.9 ± 0.3	50.6 ± 0.3	51.3
31	50.6 ± 0.3		

In this experiment the result is significantly below the theoretical value but without a chemical analysis to exclude the possibility of substitution, the deviation cannot be ascribed to any physical effect. At worst the error does not appear to be greater than 1.5 %. The variation with accelerating voltage is not significantly greater than the experimental error.

References p. 400

APPLICATIONS

The following preliminary investigations are examples of the application of the technique.

(I) *An inverted pigeonite from the hypersthene gabbro of Bon Accord Quarry, near Pretoria, Transvaal*

A common difficulty in mineralogical studies is the determination of the composition of phases in exsolution intergrowths. This is possible with the apparatus employed down to a size of $\sim 1 - 2\mu$. In Fig. 2, a photomicrograph of the inverted pigeonite is shown and the area studied is outlined. The scanning pictures with a superimposed trace of concentration illustrate visually the distribution of calcium and iron in the hypersthene host and augite lamellae.

With the electron probe stationary and with reference to analysed internal standards cemented into the slice, the following values were obtained: hypersthene — Ca 0.6 %, Fe 18.8 %; augite — Ca 11.4 %, Fe 8.7 %. The measurements on which

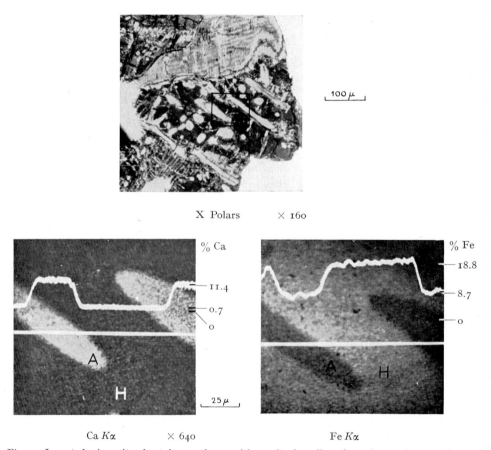

Fig. 2. Inverted pigeonite, host hypersthene with augite lamellae, from hypersthene-gabbro, Bon Accord Quarry, North of Pretoria, Transvaal. Scanning pictures and oscillograph traces show distribution of calcium and iron within area outlined. (A = augite, H = hypersthene).

References p. 400

these values are based were reproducible to within 1 % of the determined value, but owing to uncertainty in one of the internal standards may contain a significant systematic error.

An estimate of the magnesium content can be made on the basis of the inter-section of the calcium and iron values in a ternary plot with $CaSiO_3$ — $MgSiO_3$ — $FeSiO_3$ as co-ordinates and hence the composition can be compared with other pyroxenes falling within this system. The hypersthene gives $Ca_2 Mg_{60} Fe_{38}$ and the augite $Ca_{32} Mg_{51} Fe_{17}$. The calcium content of the augite is low compared with the Skaergaard trend[5] and the significance of our figures has to be checked by further work.

(2) *Preliminary observations on spinels from a metasomatised lithomarge at Tieve-bulliagh, Co. Antrim, N. Ireland*

Thermal metamorphism of a basaltic lithomarge by a dolerite plug gave rise to a mullite-cristobalite-magnesiohercynite-ilmenite hornfels[6]. This assemblage has

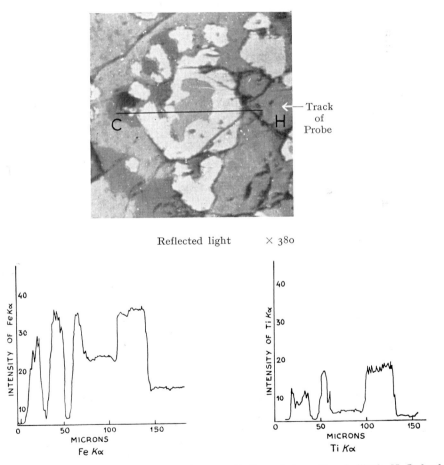

Reflected light   × 380

Fig. 3. Zoned spinel in plagioclase-hypersthene-cordierite rock from Tievebulliagh, N. Ireland. Pen recorder traces showing variation of Fe $K\alpha$ and Ti $K\alpha$ intensity along line marked in photo-micrograph. (C = cordierite, H = hypersthene).

suffered metasomatism at the immediate igneous contact, bytownite and subsequently cordierite and hypersthene developing at the expense of mullite and part of the spinel. Where the hercynite is associated with cordierite it is always mantled by a spinel of higher reflectivity which shows a crenulate outer margin. Fig. 3 shows a photo-micrograph of one such spinel and scanning traces for iron and titanium along the indicated line. In this method the traces are obtained by slowly traversing the specimen relative to the electron probe and plotting the variation in intensity of the characteristic radiation on a pen recorder.

Measurement of the recorded intensities with reference to the core spinel, which was separated from the rock and analysed chemically, gave the following approximate values for iron and titanium expressed as weight percentages, but uncorrected for absorption and fluorescence.

	Titanium	Iron	Magnesium
Core spinel	1	30	5.6
Marginal spinel	5	50	
Hypersthene	0.5	16	15 (inferred)
Cordierite	tr	3	7 (inferred)

The edge of the core spinel shows a significant drop in iron and titanium. Further measurements are required to decide whether this is original composition zoning or a diffusion effect consequent on the development of the marginal iron-rich spinel. The enrichment of titanium relative to iron in the marginal spinel is probably due to the very low titanium to iron ratio of the cordierite. The latter makes up about 50 % of the rock and derives its magnesium in part from what was core spinel. This interpretation is supported by the virtual absence of marginal iron-rich spinel in assemblages free from cordierite. In cordierite and hypersthene, substituting divalent cations other than iron and magnesium are very subordinate. Therefore, assuming all the iron is in the ferrous state, one may determine the magnesium content of these two minerals by graphical methods.

One other rock from Tievebulliagh was examined, namely a bytownite-mullite-spinel-ferropseudobrookite-ilmenite rock. Scanning pictures in calcium, iron, titanium and chromium radiation are shown in Fig. 4 and serve to show in a visual manner the distribution of the elements in these minerals.

(3) The nickel content of kamacite and taenite in the Cañon Diablo and Charcas meteorites

In the study of meteorites there is need for more data on the composition of co-existing phases and by virtue of its non-destructive character quantitative X-ray emission microanalysis is a most valuable technique. As part of a general programme on taenite–kamacite relations in iron meteorites, the nickel content of these phases has been determined in specimens from the Cañon Diablo and Charcas meteorites.

The nickel contents obtained from the pen-recorder traces illustrated in Fig. 5 are given below. They have an accuracy of ± 2 % of the determined value and we are grateful to Henry Wiggin and Co., Ltd., for providing alloys for use as standards.

References p. 400

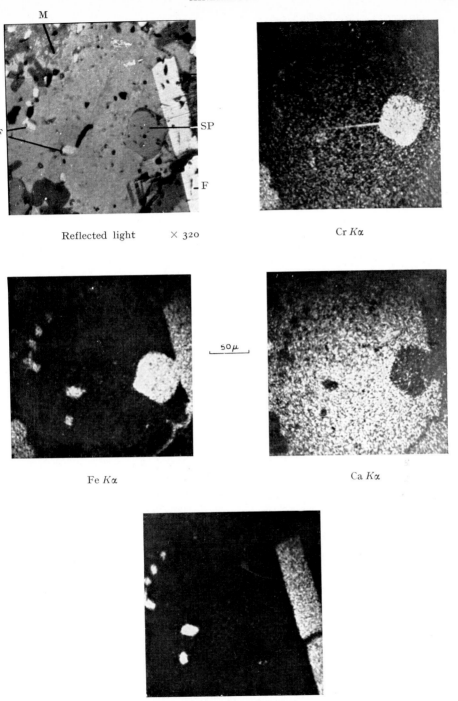

Reflected light $\times$ 320   Cr $K\alpha$

Fe $K\alpha$ Ca $K\alpha$

Ti $K\alpha$

Fig. 4. Metasomatised lithomarge from Tievebulliagh, N. Ireland, showing ferropseudobrookite (F), spinel (SP), mullite (M) set in plagioclase. Scanning pictures in Fe, Ti, Cr, and Ca radiation.

References p. 400

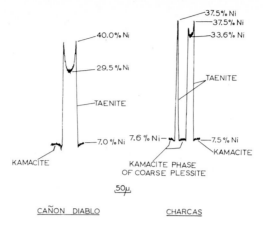

Fig. 5. Pen recorder traces showing distribution of nickel in taenite and kamacite bands of Cañon Diablo and Charcas meteorites. Approximate proportional error $= \pm 2 \%$.

Cañon Diablo meteorite

Kamacite	7.0 %
Taenite at kamacite interface	40.0 %
Taenite at centre of band	29.5 %

Charcas meteorite

Kamacite host			7.6 %
Coarse plessite {	kamacite		7.5 %
	taenite {	margin	37.5 %
		centre	33.6 %

Nickel–iron zoning in taenite has been described by PERRY[7], UHLIG[8] and NICHIPORUK[9] and recently measured in a quantitative manner by YAVNEL et al.[10] in the Chebankol meteorite.

From Fig. 5 it will be seen that the nickel content is at a minimum in the centre of the taenite lamellae and rises to a maximum at the interface with kamacite; also it may be noted that the narrower taenite lamellae of the Charcas meteorite have a higher minimum concentration of nickel. In the Cañon Diablo meteorite, nickel values for the taenite maximum and the kamacite show an 80°C discrepancy on the nickel–iron phase diagram determined by OWEN and LIU[11]. The discrepancy is even greater for the Charcas meteorite, and may be due in part to extrapolation of data from a complex into a binary system. The small drop in nickel content recorded in kamacite at the immediate contact with taenite was consistently reproducible. It may represent a short term reheating effect, or the effect of diffusion in kamacite in the region below 200° C where it may become less rich in nickel with falling temperature[16]. But before this can be elucidated or the effect of pressure discussed, further measurements on these and other meteorites must be made with improved resolution, in order to define accurately the maximum nickel content of the taenite and the corresponding minimum nickel content of the kamacite.

References p. 400

A single scanning trace was made across a rhabdite needle set in kamacite from the Cañon Diablo meteorite giving a nickel content of 50 % ± 5 %, a value higher than any recorded from this or other meteorites.

The preliminary results presented here indicate the wide application of this method of analysis in mineralogy and petrology. Although the measurements described have been confined to elements of atomic number greater than 20 (Ca) improvements in technique such as those described by DOLBY[12] and PHILIBERT[13] will allow an extension to the important light elements Al, Si, Mg and Na. In rock-forming minerals two or more of these neighbouring elements can occur together, often in the presence of heavier elements such as iron. The absorption coefficients for the characteristic X-rays may therefore be high (e.g. μ/ϱ for Si $K\alpha$ in Al $\sim$ 3000) and for this reason the use of a low excitation voltage and a high angle of take-off are desirable in order to minimise the necessary correction.

The scanning technique is useful for the examination of zoned minerals, for the rapid identification of small inclusions and for accurate location of the electron probe. In cases where the minerals present in a rock are sufficiently different in composition to give detectable contrast in the scanning image, the latter could be used to carry out modal analysis, possibly with automatic recording.

The present resolution of the method, which can be less than 1 μ[14], in conjunction with the use of polished thin sections or mounts in which natural mineral associations are preserved, allows application to a range of problems which have so far been difficult or intractable of study. The following are examples of the types of specimens and problems to which the method is particularly suited.

(1) Fine grained materials, either aggregates or intergrowths, including natural rocks, man-made products such as ceramics or cements, or the synthetic products of laboratory studies.

(2) Glasses, metamict, amorphous and crystalline minerals, particularly those in which the chemical composition is not directly determinable from the optical or other properties.

(3) The examination of phases containing elements which are difficult to determine by other methods of analysis, e.g. the rare earths.

(4) Minerals showing composition zoning.

(5) Opaque minerals where the techniques of optical identification are less refined than those applied to transparent minerals.

(6) Scarce minerals of which only small quantities may be available.

(7) The problem of the complete determination of the distribution of elements among the phases of rocks, ores and man-made products.

Qualitative results are readily obtained, particularly by the use of a scanning technique. To obtain an accuracy of the order ± 1 % in quantitative determinations, the use of internal standards or the application of corrections for fluorescence and absorption is necessary. These corrections may be applied directly when the approximate composition of the specimen can be estimated, but for unknown materials

References p. 400

a preliminary semi-quantitative analysis is required. In some cases corrections may be determined without a knowledge of composition[15] by making two or more determinations under different conditions of measurement (*e.g.* with different accelerating voltages).

REFERENCES

[1] R. Castaing, *Thesis*, University of Paris, O.N.E.R.A. publication No. 55, 1951.
[2] V. E. Cosslett and P. Duncumb, *Nature*, 177 (1956) 1172.
[3] P. Duncumb and D. A. Melford, this volume, p. 358.
[4] J. E. Holliday and E. J. Sternglass, *J. Appl. Phys.*, 28 (1957) 1189.
[5] G. M. Brown, *Miner. Mag.*, 31 (1957) 511.
[6] S. O. Agrell and J. M. Langley, *Proc. Roy. Irish Acad.*, B 59 (1958) 93.
[7] S. H. Perry, *Bull. U.S. Natl. Museum*, (1944) 184.
[8] H. H. Uhlig, *Geochim. et Cosmochim. Acta*, 6 (1954) 282.
[9] W. Nichiporuk, *Geochim. et Cosmochim. Acta*, 13 (1958) 233.
[10] A. A. Yavnel, I. B. Borovsky, N. P. Din and I. D. Marchukova, *Doklady Acad. Nauk S.S.S.R.*, 123 (2) (1958) 256.
[11] E. A. Owen and Y. H. Liu, *J. Iron Steel Inst. (London)*, 163 (1949) 132.
[12] R. M. Dolby and V. E. Cosslett, this volume, p. 351.
[13] J. Philibert and H. Bizouard, this volume, p. 416.
[14] P. Duncumb, this volume, p. 365.
[15] J. V. P. Long, *Thesis*, Cambridge University, 1958.
[16] L. Kaufman and M. Cohen *J. Metals*, 8 (1956) 1393.

APPLICATION OF ELECTRON-PROBE MICROANALYSIS TO INTERFACE SEGREGATION

A. E. AUSTIN, N. A. RICHARD and C. M. SCHWARTZ

Batelle Memorial Institute, Columbus, Ohio (U.S.A.)

ABSTRACT

Segregation in alloys may occur during casting, fabrication, and heat treatment. If non-equilibrium conditions exist, further heating will result in diffusion through any concentration gradient. The concentration of constituent elements over distances of the order of microns is determined by X-ray spectral analysis of the region irradiated by the focused electron beam of the electron-probe microanalyzer. However, determination of concentrations at phase and grain boundaries requires geometrical correction for the finite size of the irradiation region. At an abrupt phase boundary, the maximum gradient is limited by the finite diameter of the electron probe. This concentration gradient has been calculated, assuming a uniform circular probe, and compared with that measured for an undiffused interface. This limiting case is used to correct measured concentrations at actual phase boundaries. Applications to problems of segregation in meteorites and other alloys, and to concentration gradients across diffusion interfaces are described.

The work of CASTAING[1] in the development of the first electron-probe microanalyzer demonstrated the means of making quantitative elemental analysis at small localized regions in materials. This indicated the great possibilities for studying interface reactions, segregation, and diffusion. Further development was undertaken at Battelle in 1954.

The present equipment was put in operation in 1957. The electron optical system consists of a self-biased electron gun with double condenser and single objective electromagnet lenses. The system with a nominal reduction of 50 times gives a focused electron beam of 1 μ diameter. The light optics uses conventional lenses with an aluminized tantalum mirror and provides viewing the specimen at 130 $\times$. The X-ray spectrometer consists of a ground and bent crystal and a detector mounted on arms moving together by a pantograph on the Rowland circle. The crystal is quartz and can be replaced by other crystals without changing alignment. The entire spectrometer is mounted within the vacuum system. Fig. 1 shows the completed instrument.

Knowledge of the concentration gradient resulting from diffusion across phase interfaces, and the composition at grain boundaries and in segregation regions in alloys is of particular interest in metallurgical studies. The finite size of the electron probe plus the extent of penetration and scattering in thick specimens produces X-ray sources of about 5 μ diameter. The size of this excited region can be minimized by decreasing the electron accelerating voltage[2] but with attendent decrease in intensity of the characteristic X-rays relative to background. In general, one compromises by using an accelerating voltage about three times the excitation voltage. Thus, the size of the X-ray source is still large compared to grain boundaries and phase interfaces and the measured concentrations are averages over the sample region. Therefore, one must consider the possible correction of the measured X-ray intensities to determine actual concentrations at interfaces.

Fig. 1. Electron-probe microanalyzer.

The X-ray source excited by the electron beam can be approximated as a circular area of uniform intensity. Then the concentration gradient obtained by a traverse of the probe across an abrupt interface between two elements can be calculated as the ratio of the excited area of each element to that for the pure element alone. This ratio is

$$R^2\left(\alpha - \frac{\sin 2\alpha}{2}\right)\bigg/ \pi R^2.$$

where

R is radius of the excited region,

α is $\cos^{-1} X/R$,

X is distance of the probe center from interface.

For an abrupt interface, this gives an apparent gradient which is essentially linear over a distance 0.8 R. Measurements of Cu–Ni and Fe–Ni interfaces made by sectioning electroplated metal verified this range of linearity; however, they show a small tail-off of intensity over a distance greater than calculated by this approximation, indicating that the excited region is not quite uniform. This is shown in Fig. 2 of the Cu–Ni interface.

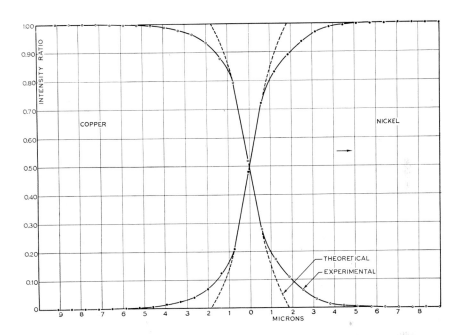

Fig. 2. Electron-probe traverse of a plated copper-nickel interface.

In many cases there may be a concentration gradient up to the interface. Then the measured concentration is an average as follows:

$$1/\pi (C_R + R \tan \phi) \left(\alpha - \frac{\sin 2\alpha}{2} \right) - 2R \tan \phi \frac{\sin^3 \alpha}{3},$$

where ϕ is slope of the concentration gradient and C_R is concentration at distance R from measuring point.

Metallic meteorites are an interesting case of segregation by the formation of two metal phases and growth by diffusion. The study of segregation in metallic meteorites[3] required determination of actual interface compositions. Fig. 3 shows general Widmanstatten structure of iron meteorites. There are three phases; the larger matrix grains of α-iron are called kamacite, the light γ-iron bands are called taenite, and the dark needle-like structure, a mixture of α- and γ-iron, is called plessite. These phases were composed essentially of iron and nickel with trace amounts of vanadium, chromium, manganese, and cobalt. It is believed that the meteorites are fragments of a former large body which cooled slowly under pressure and the phase compositions were at equilibrium when the meteorite was formed[4].

References p. 406

Fig. 3. Widmanstatten structure of metallic meteorite.

Fig. 4. Trace of electron-probe traverse across Widmanstatten band of metallic meteorite.

Fig. 4 shows the course of a traverse across a Widmanstatten band. Fig. 5 is a plot of concentration of nickel and iron for the traverse of Fig. 4. The concentrations of iron and nickel were measured at increments varying from 0.65 to 5, and have been corrected for absorption and fluorescence according to CASTAING's equations[1]. Alloys of 10, 20, 50, and 80 % nickel were used as standards. There is a decrease of nickel and increase of iron in the kamacite within 5 μ of the kamacite–taenite interface. This narrow zone is more apparent by comparison of the measured concentrations with the dashed line showing the concentration to be expected for an abrupt interface and constant concentration in the kamacite. The interface compositions in the taenite shown by the broken line were calculated from the observed data using the equation for a concentration gradient. The maximum nickel concentration was 36 weight per cent. Within the taenite band, the plessite region started at about 18 weight per cent nickel.

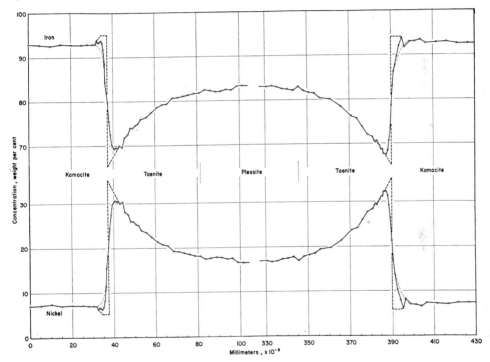

Fig. 5. Concentration gradients across Widmanstatten band of metallic meteorite; the broken line shows the calculated interface concentrations corrected for probe size.

In Fig. 5 the observed nickel concentration for the interface to the left was lower than for the other interface. This effect was due to the direction of emergence of the characteristic X-rays during the traverse relative to the specimen orientation. In this case the X-rays emerged to the left and thus at the left hand interface there was preferential absorption by the iron-rich kamacite. However, there was no appreciable preferential absorption at the right hand interface in going from the taenite into the kamacite.

The analysis of the β-phase region in a copper–zinc diffusion couple shown in

References p. 406

Fig. 6 was done using knowledge of concentration slope at an interface. The center of the linear slopes was taken as the phase interfaces giving a breadth of 7 μ. The limiting concentrations were estimated from the concentration gradient in the β field assuming the concentration at the interface is an average of both β and γ or β and α compositions. This gave β phase boundaries as 51 and 56 weight per cent copper with limiting composition of γ and α field as 43 and 61 weight per cent copper. This couple had been annealed 17 hours at 400° C.

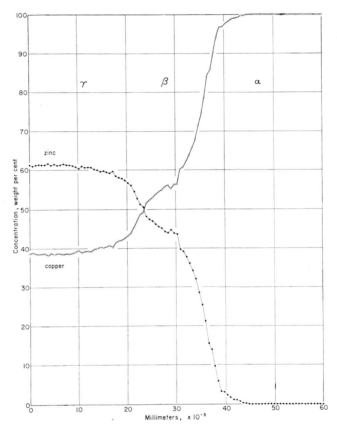

Fig. 6. Concentration gradients across β-phase in copper-zinc diffusion couple.

ACKNOWLEDGEMENT

The authors thank R. E. MARINGER for making available the meteorite study supported by the USAF under Contract No. AF 33 (616)—5080. The copper–zinc diffusion couple study was part of the program of the ASTM Subcommittee XI of Committee E-4.

REFERENCES

[1] R. CASTAING, *Ph. D. Thesis*, University of Paris, O.N.E.R.A., No. 55, 1951.
[2] D. B. WITTRY, *J. Appl. Phys.*, 29 (1958) 1543.
[3] R. E. MARINGER, N. A. RICHARD and A. E. AUSTIN, *Trans. AIME*, 215 (1959) 56.
[4] H. H. UHLIG, *Geochim. et Cosmochim. Acta*, 6 (1954) 282.

THE APPLICATION OF AN IMPROVED X-RAY SCANNING MICRO-ANALYSER TO PROBLEMS IN FERROUS METALLURGY

D. A. MELFORD

Tube Investments Research Laboratories, Hinxton Hall, Saffron Walden, Essex
(Great Britain)

ABSTRACT

Microsegregation of copper and tin at the surface of mild steel can lead to cracking during hot working. The application of an X-ray scanning microanalyser to this problem will be described and results presented to show the type of approach now possible.

EQUIPMENT

The instrument with which these experiments were carried out is described elsewhere in this symposium[1]. For the present purpose, however, one or two aspects of the equipment should be briefly re-stated.

The specimen is prepared as for normal optical metallography and mounted in the microanalyser on a horizontal rotary table. By means of this table it can be transferred *in vacuo* from under an optical microscope, which is used for locating the field of interest, to a position under the electron probe. The reflection electron image is then examined to ensure that the field has been accurately re-located. This image is of great assistance to the metallurgist, being closely similar to an optical image viewed in oblique illumination, and it is displayed on a second long-persistence screen side by side with that displaying the X-ray images. This considerably facilitates correlation of the microstructure as revealed by the surface topography with the compositional information provided by the X-ray images. The results can thus be presented as a set of images of the same field at the same magnification: the optical image, the reflection electron image and the X-ray images taken with appropriate radiations selected.

INTRODUCTION TO THE PROBLEM

The main investigation being carried out at Hinxton Hall with the aid of the scanning microanalyser is concerned with the problem of surface hot shortness in mild steel. It has long been realised that the presence of copper and tin in mild steel could result in the material becoming prone to pronounced surface cracking during hot working. This has been attributed to the formation of a layer at the surface enriched in these elements when the steel is heated in an oxidizing atmosphere. This layer, it has been suggested, can reach a composition which is molten at the temperature of working and show a tendency to penetrate down grain boundaries running inwards from the surface. This can lead to hot tearing if the working process is such as to produce tensile stresses in the surface layers. Hot bending for example is a sensitive index of the susceptibility of a material to this effect. For steels which contain copper alone the situation can be remedied by the addition of nickel. This segregates in the same way as copper and is thought to raise the melting point of the most heavily enriched regions. No such improvement can be obtained if tin is present.

The theory for the mechanism of formation of this enriched layer was first put forward by PFEIL[2]. Nickel, copper and tin being relatively noble metals are less readily oxidized than iron. The first layer of scale formed on a piece of steel heated above 800° C in oxidizing atmosphere will therefore consist mainly of FeO. For oxidation to continue metal ions must diffuse through this first layer to the surface. Iron can diffuse readily through the FeO lattice whereas nickel, copper and tin cannot. Consequently no further oxidation of these latter elements occurs and they collect in a layer at the base of the scale in ever-increasing concentration as the scale/metal interface moves inwards. When the iron concentration in the scale exceeds 22 % in the neighbourhood of, say, such NiO as has initially been formed, this is reduced to nickel and henceforward any nickel occurring at the base of the scale is present as the metal.

Quantitative information on the degree of enrichment which can occur in this subscale is scarce. A micro-sampling technique followed by chemical microanalysis of the swarf is reported by CHILTON and EVANS[3] who were concerned with a similar problem with regard to a wrought-iron containing 0.27 % Ni and 0.20 % Cu. They observed enrichment of nickel up to 2.32 % and copper up to 0.75 %. More recently MOREAU and CAGNET[4] at I.R.S.I.D. have reported very similar results (3 % Ni, 0.75 % Cu) for the metal in the mosaic zone of the scale on steel billet containing 0.2 % Ni and 0.146 % Cu. Reference to copper-rich and copper-coloured phases which would appear to refer to much greater enrichments are quite common in the literature.

EXPERIMENTAL RESULTS

With the aid of the scanning microanalyser it is possible to demonstrate the existence and approximate composition of the sub-scale *in situ* and to study the distribution of the elements within it in relation to the microstructure.

The first set of photographs (Fig. 1) represent a cross section of part of the surface of a steel billet which exhibited surface cracking after the piercing operation prior to tube making.

The composition of this material was:

C	Si	Mn	S	P	Ni	Cu	Sn
0.10	0.07	0.51	0.049	0.018	0.14	0.20	0.059

Before piercing, the billets are heated in a gas-fired furnace at 1,250° C for approximately 3 hours. The field shown in the optical image is compared with a reflection electron image and X-ray images obtained with $FeK\alpha$, $NiK\alpha$, $CuK\alpha$ and $SnL\alpha$ radiations selected. A comparatively uniform enrichment of nickel in a layer $10-15\mu$ thick can be clearly seen. Copper is also present in this layer apparently in comparable or even greater concentrations but is rather more localised. Tin appears equally localised but is not so much in evidence. This is in part due to the fact that all four X-ray images were obtained with a two minute exposure. This discriminates slightly against tin as its L radiation is more easily absorbed than the K radiations of iron,

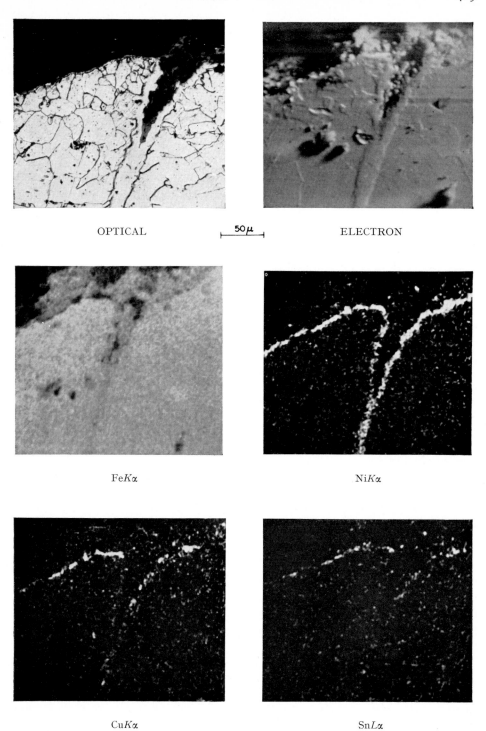

OPTICAL 50μ ELECTRON

FeKα NiKα

CuKα SnLα

Fig. 1. Cross-section of part of the surface of a steel billet.

nickel and copper and the count rate for an equivalent concentration is therefore lower. A fairer visual comparison could probably have been made if the exposure time for the tin image had been approximately doubled.

Rough quantitative analysis carried out at a point in one of the brightest regions in nickel, copper and tin images indicated concentrations of nickel and copper of 30 % and 25 % respectively, very similar in fact to those observed elsewhere in this specimen by DUNCUMB and the author[5] with the aid of the instrument at the Cavendish Laboratory. The concentration of tin at this point appeared to be about 15 %.

Attempts have now been made to reproduce these segregation effects in the laboratory under rather more carefully controlled conditions. The second set of photographs (Fig. 2) show a specimen prepared by heating a typical mild steel in air for 2 hours at 1,100° C.

The composition of the specimen was:

C	Si	S	P	Mn	Ni	Cu	Sn
0.13	0.036	0.032	0.020	0.64	0.20	0.22	0.042

and this section has been prepared by polishing down through the oxide scale to give what is effectively a plan view of the subscale. In the centre of the field is a small region of what may be termed 'continuous' subscale and grain boundaries emanating from this area appear to stand proud of the surface. This geometry is confirmed by the shadowing effects visible in the electron image and is probably due as much to relief polishing as to the effect of the etchant. These are prior austenite grain boundaries and can be seen to be dissociated from the present ferrite network which has been revealed by the light etch. Nickel enrichment at these boundaries is clearly shown by the nickel X-ray image and in particular those in the top left-hand corner of the field exhibit a marked nickel concentration gradient along their length in the X-ray image whereas in the optical image they appear to exhibit a uniform geometry. The level of nickel enrichment required to produce appreciable solution hardening is thus apparently less than that visible on an X-ray image at two minutes exposure. This amount is of the order of 2—3 % nickel under the experimental conditions and the surface relief is thus in this particular instance a more sensitive indication of the presence of enrichment than the X-ray image but gives little or no information as to its extent.

Comparison of the nickel and copper X-ray images reveals once again the more localised nature of the copper enrichment and indicates high levels of copper concentration at these points. This difference in the distribution of nickel and copper is very probably connected with the fact that nickel and iron form a complete range of solid solutions at these temperatures, whereas when the amount of copper in solid solution in iron exceeds about 8 % a molten copper-rich phase is formed.

It is unsafe to apply these observations based on binary equilibrium diagrams to a complex quatenary system except as a qualitative guide to trends in behaviour. In this instance it is of interest that a comparison of the optical and copper images reveals that the areas showing the greatest enrichment in copper correspond to the junction of three austenite grain boundaries, a location where the appearance of a molten phase is most likely. A marked depletion in iron is also apparent at these points.

This example is a good illustration of the advantage of the scanning method to

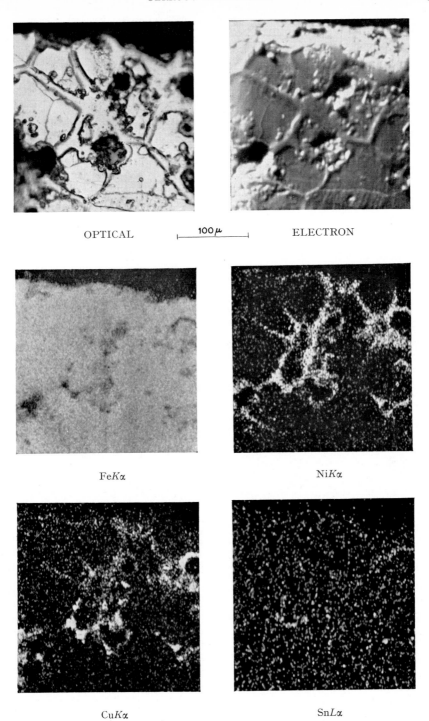

Fig. 2. Section of a specimen of mild steel polished down to give a plan view of the subscale segregation.

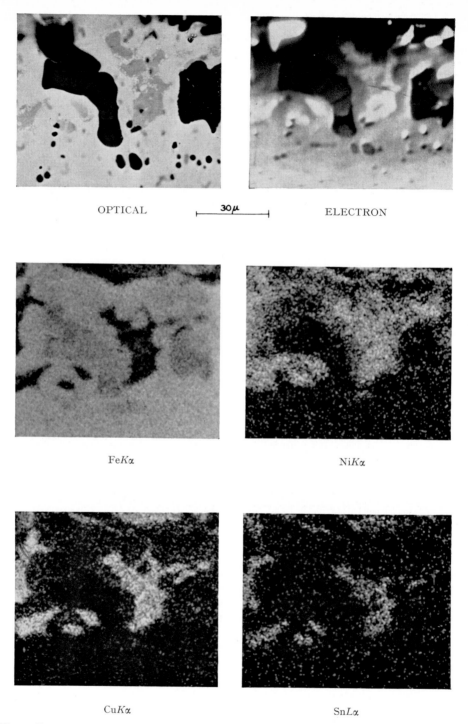

OPTICAL   ⊢——— 30μ ———⊣   ELECTRON

FeKα   NiKα

CuKα   SnLα

Fig. 3. Cross-section of the surface of a specimen of mild steel in the region of the mosaic zone of the scale.

the metallurgist. Much of the information gained has been due to the fact that it has been possible to display the distribution of the constituents over an area which is significant with respect to the scale of the microstructure.

The last specimen of this type was prepared by heating for two hours in air at 1,250° C a mild steel of composition:

C	Si	S	P	Mn	Ni	Cu	Sn
0.19	0.024	0.045	0.033	0.70	0.20	0.31	0.071

The sample was chilled rapidly from the soaking temperature in an attempt to preserve the composition of the enriched regions unchanged. Very heavy oxidation resulted from this heat treatment and this must be regarded as a somewhat extreme case of surface segregation.

The photographs in Fig. 3 are of a cross section of the surface in the region of the mosaic zone of the scale. A striking feature of the iron image is the marked depletion revealed in the regions enriched in nickel, copper and tin. Quantitative analysis revealed an iron content as low as 4.5 % in one of these positions so that here indeed are "copper-rich" regions. As before, the nickel, copper and tin images reveal, in that order, increasing localisation of enrichment.

A portion of this field examined at high magnification (2000 ×) (Fig. 4) reveals still more information. In the optical image some small amount of precipitation does appear to have taken place in spite of the chilling. A priori, these precipitate particles might be expected to be iron-rich since this is the highest melting constituent. Although they appear to be individually beyond the resolution of the instrument, the iron X-ray image does indeed appear to confirm this expectation. Quantitative analysis of the brightest region of the copper image revealed numerically the highest enrichment so far encountered: 69.5 % copper. Of greater significance perhaps is a typical analysis from the tin-rich region:

Cu	Ni	Fe	Sn
42 %	22 %	5 %	28 %

When compared with the bulk analysis for tin of 0.071 % this represents approximately 400 × enrichment indicating that tin can segregate under these circumstances to a greater extent even than copper. An alloy was made up to correspond in composition to this region and a cooling curve plotted for its solidification. Analysis of the results indicated that a molten phase was present at temperatures greater than 900° C. It can thus be asserted with a certain amount of confidence that molten phases do form at the surface of mild steels of this type during oxidation at temperatures of the order of 1,250°C.

One further point is worthy of mention. A close correlation can be seen between the outline of the area showing a light contrast in the electron image and the tin-rich region revealed in the tin X-ray image. This is probably due to the increased back scattering of electrons by the tin atoms ($Z = 50$) compared with that produced by the copper, nickel or iron ($Z = 29, 28, 26$). A certain amount of compositional information is thus being supplied by the electron image. This effect has been found most useful in another context for revealing impurities in beryllium.

CONCLUSIONS

The instrument at Hinxton Hall has been in operation for only five months and experience in its use is as yet extremely limited. The examples quoted represent

References p. 415

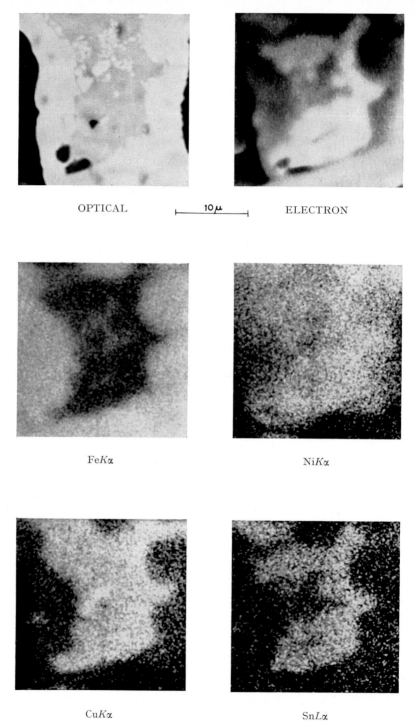

Fig. 4. A portion of the field in Fig. 3 at high magnification.

preliminary investigations into the mechanism behind the micro-scale compositional changes that bring about surface hot-shortness. The main purpose so far has been to explore the possibilities of the technique rather than to make definitive experiments and little accurate quantitative work has yet been attempted. Enough has been done, however, to indicate how fruitful this approach can be.

The technique of X-ray scanning microanalysis is of great value to the metallurgist interested in problems involving micro-segregation effects. A new and direct type of approach has been made possible in these investigation and there is now a most urgent need for user experience in the field. In this way the most effective means of applying this new tool may emerge as soon as possible. Until this experience is built up, there must necessarily be a certain amount of caution in the interpretation of results, particularly where difficult surface geometries are involved.

In view of the fact that the micro-constituents with which the ferrous metallurgist is chiefly concerned are carbides, nitrides and oxides, it is particularly frustrating that the characteristic X-ray emission, from carbon, nitrogen and oxygen are not at present detectable with this equipment. When this difficulty is overcome and a slight increase in resolution achieved, a wider field of application will be opened up in inclusion analysis and the examination of particles on extraction replicas. This is therefore the direction in which the metallurgist would most like to see further development of the technique.

ACKNOWLEDGEMENTS

The author's thanks are due to the Chairman of Tube Investments Ltd. for permission to publish this paper. The assistance of Mr. R. BOULTON with some of the photography is also acknowledged.

REFERENCES

1 P. DUNCUMB and D. A. MELFORD, this volume, p. 358.
2 L. B. PFEIL, J. Iron Steel Inst. (London), 119 (1929) 501.
3 J. P. CHILTON and U. R. EVANS, J. Iron Steel Inst. (London), 181 (1955) 113.
4 J. MOREAU and M. CAGNET, Metal Treatment and Drop Forging, 24 (1957) 362.
5 D. A. MELFORD and P. DUNCUMB, Metallurgia, 57 (1958) 159.

L'ANALYSE DES ÉLÉMENTS LÉGERS AVEC LA „MICROSONDE DE CASTAING"
SES APPLICATIONS MÉTALLURGIQUES ET MINÉRALOGIQUES

J. PHILIBERT et Mme H. BIZOUARD

Institut de Recherches de la Sidérurgie, Saint-Germain-en-Laye (France)

ABSTRACT

THE ANALYSIS OF LIGHT ELEMENTS USING CASTAING'S ELECTRON-PROBE
MICROANALYSER; ITS APPLICATION IN METALLURGY AND MINERALOGY

The field of application of Castaing's electron-probe microanalyser has been considerably extended since the improvement of the second spectrograph. This spectrograph, which is placed in high vacuum and is equipped with a curved mica crystal and a proportional counter, covers the wavelength range from $4-12$ Å, and is thus suited for the analysis of light elements (atomic numbers $11-17$).

The results of some investigations regarding light elements (*e.g.* segregation of P and Si in iron alloys, non-metallic inclusions in steel, mineralogical samples) carried out at IRSID with Castaing's apparatus, are reported. The sensitivity of the method and the importance of the physical corrections to be applied to the intensity measurements in the various cases studied, are briefly discussed.

INTRODUCTION

Le microanalyseur à sonde électronique de CASTAING était équipé à l'origine d'un seul spectromètre (à cristal de quartz courbé et compteur Geiger) qui couvrait le domaine de longueurs d'onde 0,6—4,5 Å. Ce spectromètre permettait l'analyse de tous les éléments de numéro atomique supérieur à 17, soit par leurs raies K (de Cl à Mo), soit par leurs raies L (éléments plus lourds que Mo).

L'analyse a été étendue aux éléments plus légers grâce à un second spectromètre qui couvre le domaine de longueurs d'onde $4 - 12$Å (CASTAING ET DESCAMPS [1]) et permet en particulier l'analyse de Na, Mg, Al, Si et P par leurs raies K. Il comprend un cristal de mica courbé (R = 50 cm) et un compteur proportionnel spécialement étudié; ce compteur est fermé par une fenêtre de mylar de 6 μ, le mélange gazeux (argon + méthane) circule en permanence à une pression légèrement supérieure à 1 atm. L'ensemble est placé sous vide poussé (env. 10^{-5} mm Hg), y compris le pré-amplificateur disposé au voisinage immédiat du compteur. On évite ainsi toute absorption du rayonnement entre l'échantillon et le cristal.

Le préamplificateur a été limité à un seul étage à charge cathodique ("cathode follower"). En effet, les impulsions délivrées par le compteur, alimenté sous 1.500 V, ont une hauteur de 9 mV pour le rayonnement $K\alpha$ de l'aluminium ($\lambda = 8,32$ Å).

Avec un cristal de mica muscovite, on a obtenu des raies dont la largeur à mi-hauteur ne dépasse pas 6'. Notons encore que le cristal de mica donne des réflexions d'ordres multiples particulièrement intenses; c'est ainsi que nous avons pu enregistrer les raies $K\alpha$ du fer du 2ème au 6ème ordre et les raies $K\beta$ du 2ème au 5ème ordre. (*cf.* Fig. 1).

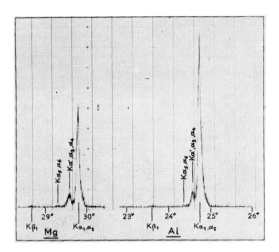

Fig. 1. Spectres K de l'aluminium et du magnésium analysés à l'aide d'un cristal de mica muscovite; dans la partie correspondant au fond continu, les impulsions sont visibles sous forme de ,,tops'' isolés.

Un discriminateur électronique permet d'éviter, lors de l'analyse d'un élément léger, la superposition de la raie étudiée avec des réflexions d'ordre élevé dues soit à des raies, soit au spectre continu émis par des éléments plus lourds.

INTERPRÉTATION DES RÉSULTATS

Soit k_A le rapport des intensités $I(A)$ et I_A d'une raie donnée émise respectivement par l'échantillon et par le témoin A. Ce rapport doit être corrigé des effets d'absorption du rayonnement ou d'émission secondaire (fluorescence) à l'intérieur de l'échantillon, en utilisant les fonctions $f(\chi)$ et les formules de CASTAING [2, 3]. La valeur k'_A ainsi obtenue est reliée à la concentration c_A par la relation:

$$(1) \qquad c_A = k'_A \left[S(A) / S_A \right],$$

obtenue en considérant l'absorption et la diffusion des électrons au cours de leur pénétration. Quand les numéros atomiques Z des éléments constitutifs de l'échantillon sont voisins $S(A)/S(A) \neq 1$ et le calcul des concentrations s'effectue simplement:

$$(1\,bis) \qquad c_A = k'_A$$

Il n'en est pas de même dans le cas de numéros atomiques fort différents et il n'existe pas de relation linéaire entre c_A et k'_A. Il faut de plus tenir compte de la différence des proportions r d'électrons retrodiffusés par l'échantillon et le témoin (r est une fonction croissante de Z [4] (*). Dans ce cas il est préférable d'effectuer un étalonnage expérimental et de calculer des coefficients α empiriques en utilisant des relations du type:

$$(2) \qquad \alpha_i\, c_i - k'_i\, \Sigma_j\, \alpha_j\, c_j = 0$$

---

* Il n'est pas possible de calculer cette correction, car on ne connaît pas la fraction d'électrons retrodiffusés d'énergie *supérieure à l'énergie d'ionisation*.

1. Cas des alliages métalliques

Dans le cas des éléments légers, les corrections peuvent être très importantes. Citons par exemple les résultats de CASTAING ET DESCAMPS [1], qui ont analysé de gros cristaux polygonaux de Mg_2Si présents dans un alliage Al Mg Si brut de coulée. La correction d'absorption pour la raie Si $K\alpha$ — sous une excitation de 9,7 kV — atteint 55% en valeur relative; mais les résultats expérimentaux après correction sont en excellent accord avec les valeurs stoechiométriques.

Cependant, dès que les numéros atomiques des éléments de l'alliage sont assez différents:

— la correction de rétrodiffusion ne doit pas être négligée; pour un alliage Fe-Al, p. ex., on a: $(1-r_{Al})/(1-r_{Fe}) = 1,18$.

— la correction α' d'absorption devient considérable; dans le cas des alliages Fe–P, Fe–Si ou Fe–Al, elle peut dépasser 200%.

— l'écart entre les valeurs de la concentration données par les équations (1bis) et (2) peut être supérieur à k'_A.

Étant donné que les divers termes correctifs sont tous fonction des concentrations, on effectue, dans la pratique, le calcul de la façon suivante. Partant des concentrations réelles c_i — connues par analyse chimique ou théoriquement quand il s'agit de composés définis — on calcule par la relation (2) les valeurs k' au moyen d'un jeu de coefficients α. On applique alors à ces k' les corrections d'absorption ou de fluorescence. Les valeurs k ainsi obtenues sont comparées aux résultats expérimentaux $I(A)/I_A$ et on peut ajuster les coefficients correctifs α.

Partant d'alliages binaires, puis ternaires... soigneusement homogénéisés et bien dosés, on peut alors calculer les coefficients α, ou même tracer des courbes d'étalonnage reliant directement C_A et $I(A)/I_A$.

2. Cas des échantillons non-conducteurs

Il s'agit de composés chimiques renfermant souvent des éléments de numéro atomique inférieur à 11; il n'est plus possible alors de vérifier la condition $\sum k'_A = 1$.

Cependant, dans certains cas, l'examen micrographique et la détermination de la nature des éléments chimiques présents, permettent de connaître le type de composé étudié; ce sera par exemple un alumino-silicate. On calculera alors, à partir des concentrations mesurées, puis corrigées des divers termes analysés plus haut, les concentrations en oxydes respectifs: Al_2O_3, SiO_2, FeO, MnO, TiO_2, CaO... et l'on vérifiera que leur somme est bien égale à 100 %.

Il est donc nécessaire d'effectuer des étalonnages sur des composés chimiques choisis pour leur intérêt et leur bonne pureté, ce qui doit permettre de calculer des coefficients de correction α. On a tout d'abord analysé un échantillon de fer pur recouvert d'une succession nette des trois oxydes FeO, Fe_3O_4 et Fe_2O_3 et l'on a obtenu les résultats suivants:

Composé	FeO	Fe_3O_4	Fe_2O_3
$I(Fe)/I_{Fe}$ = Fe % mesuré	69,5—72,5	66—69	61—64
Fe % theorique	77,8	72,3	70

On observe une certaine dispersion des résultats, qui est d'ailleurs assez fréquente lors de l'analyse d'échantillons non-métalliques. On ne peut probablement pas l'attribuer à des écarts à la stoechiométrie, mais plutôt à des défauts de la surface après polissage, défauts dont de petits pores, des microfissures, etc. peuvent être responsables.

Des mesures analogues ont été faites sur de l'oxyde Fe_2O_3, H_2O, de l'oxyde de manganèse, du carbonate des manganèse et divers sulfures de fer et de manganèse. La relation (2) permet d'écrire:

$$(3) \qquad C_A = \frac{k_A}{(1 - \alpha)k_A + \alpha}$$

et de déterminer un coefficient α pour Fe ou Mn. On peut n'effectuer aucun autre calcul de correction et déterminer simplement par la relation (3) un coefficient empirique que l'on désignera par α'. Le tableau suivant donne les valeurs de α' obtenues avec une tension d'accélération des électrons de 29,5 kV.

$$\alpha' \simeq \quad 0,92 \quad \text{dans le sulfure}$$
$$0,80—0,82 \quad \text{dans les oxydes}$$
$$0,71 \quad \text{dans les carbonates}$$

Cependant, dès que des éléments légers sont dosés, l'absorption de leur rayonnement par l'oxygène par exemple n'est pas négligeable. Aussi est-il préférable de calculer rigoureusement les coefficients α, au moyen de la relation (2), qui relie les concentrations réelles aux valeurs mesurées corrigées de l'absorption. Il faut également prendre garde à la nature de la couche de métallisation déposée à la surface.

Nous avons donc analysé le *silicate de fer* de formule $SiFe_2O_4$ (fayalite) en mesurant les intensités des raies $K\alpha$ Si et $K\alpha$ Fe sous diverses excitations, —l'échantillon étant recouvert d'une couche de carbone ou de cuivre par vaporisation.

On a choisi dans le tableau ci-dessous les résultats des mesures effectuées sous 25,8 kV après métallisation au cuivre:

Élément	Fe	Si
$I(A)/I_A$ (%)	49,5	3,8
conc. théorique	54,8	13,8

On notera l'importance de la correction à appliquer aux intensités mesurées du silicium. Après calcul des corrections d'absorption, on a déterminé les valeurs du coefficient α, pour une tension de 25,8 kV:

$$\alpha_{Si} = 0,59$$
$$\alpha_{Fe} = 0,77$$

Remarque sur le calcul de la correction d'absorption. On ne trouve pas dans les tables toutes les valeurs des coefficients d'absorption dont on a besoin pour les calculs de correction. Pour les grandes longueurs d'ondes en particulier, il n'est plus permis d'effectuer les interpolations suivant une loi en $Z^3\lambda^3$. Aussi avons-nous établi une table de ces coefficients en utilisant les valeurs données par ALLEN[5] et par HENKE et al.[6], et en les complétant par le calcul au moyen soit des fonctions de HENKE, soit de la courbe universelle de JÖNSSON, soit encore par interpolation graphique[7].

Utilisation de témoins autres que des éléments purs. Il n'est pas toujours possible de choisir comme témoin l'élément pur, par exemple dans le cas des métalloïdes ou de métaux très oxydables. Soient I_A et $I(A)$ les intensités que donneraient un témoin formé de l'élément pur, et un échantillon de concentration c_A. Et soit (*cf.* schéma, Fig. 2)

$$(4) \qquad\qquad c_A = \varphi\,[I(A)/I_A]$$

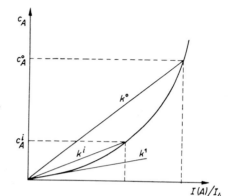

Fig. 2. Courbe d'étalonnage.

la courbe d'étalonnage. Si le témoin choisi a une concentration c_A°, on peut écrire d'après (4), pour l'émission $I^\circ(A)$ de ce témoin:

$$c_A^\circ = k^\circ I^\circ(A)/I_A$$

et pour un échantillon de concentration c_A^i

$$(5) \qquad\qquad c_A^i/c_A^\circ = (k^i/k^\circ)\cdot I^i(A)/I^\circ(A)$$

On mesure donc le rapport $I^i(A)/I^\circ(A)$, et c_A°/k° étant donné par la courbe d'étalonnage théorique, on calcule par cette relation c_A^i/k^i, d'où c_A^i de nouveau d'après la courbe d'étalonnage. Pour les faibles concentrations de l'alliage analysé celle-ci peut être assimilée à une droite de pente constante k^1 d'où

$$(6) \qquad\qquad c_A^i = kI^i(A)/I^\circ(A)$$

avec

$$k = c_A{}^\circ\,k^1/k^\circ$$

On a appliqué cette méthode à l'analyse du phosphore dans le fer. Après l'examen de divers alliages purs Fe–P, on a choisi pour témoin les gros globules de phase Fe_2P contenus dans un alliage à 19 % P. On a alors calculé théoriquement la courbe d'étalonnage en tenant compte de la correction d'absorption. On a ensuite vérifié sa validité en analysant les phases suivantes: Fe_3P, eutectique α/Fe_3P, et la solution α saturée. Les résultats sont en bon accord avec les diagrammes publiés.

EXEMPLES D'APPLICATIONS

1. *Ségrégation dendritique dans les alliages de fer*

A la suite d'une étude de la ségrégation dendritique dans des alliages purs du type Fe–X ou Fe–C–X (X = Mo, Cr, Mn, Ni, As)[8], nous avons analysé des alliages similaires, l'élément X étant P ou Si. Ces alliages ont été préparés sous forme de petits lingotins de 1 kg et refroidis à une vitesse d'environ 2°/min.

Dans l'alliage Fe–C–Si (C = 0,51 %, Si = 0,49 %) où le faciès dendritique n'a pas pu être mis en évidence par attaque micrographique, on a effectué des analyses le long de directions traversant les grains, en partant d'un maximum de concentration de Si systématiquement recherché. Un exemple de courbe concentration-distance est donné dans la Fig. 3. Le taux de ségrégation, déterminé comme le rapport de la concentration maximum dans l'espace interdendritique à son minimum dans l'axe de la dendrite, est égal, dans le cas de Si, à environ 2,5.

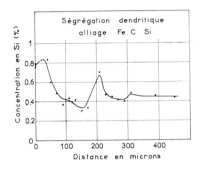

Fig. 3. Courbe de ségrégation du Si à travers les dendrites d'un alliage Fe–C–Si solidifié lentement (refroidissement 4° / min).

Une attaque micrographique (réactif de Comstock) met bien en évidence le faciès dendritique dans les alliages de phosphore, et rend plus aisé l'établissement des courbes de ségrégation. Dans un alliage Fe–C–P (C = 0,45 %, P = 0,032 %) nous n'avons pu déterminer la teneur en P des axes dendritiques; la courbe de ségrégation n'a été établie qu'au cœur des espaces interdendritiques, où l'on a trouvé un maximum égal à 0,36 % P. On peut penser que le taux de ségrégation est supérieur à 12.

Ces résultats complètent ceux qui avaient été obtenus précédemment avec d'autres éléments d'alliage. Finalement, dans des alliages du type Fe–C–X (C ≃ 0,4 ou 0,5 %) les éléments d'alliage X peuvent être classés dans l'ordre suivant, le taux de ségrégation décroissant de gauche à droite:

As, P, Mo, Cr, Si, Mn, Ni.

Dans une autre série d'alliages Fe–P ou Fe–C–P, on a pu mettre en évidence d'une part l'influence considérable du carbone, confirmant ainsi nos résultats relatifs aux alliages Fe–C–As et Fe–As et d'autre part celle de la vitesse de refroidissement durant la solidification *. Mais ces alliages étant assez chargés en P et C, il se forme de l'eutectique phosphoreux dans les espaces interdendritiques (Fig. 4); aussi en évaluant un taux de ségrégation apparent par le rapport de la concentration de l'eutectique à celle de l'axe dendritique, on obtient une valeur par défaut, qui ne tient pas compte de la proportion relative d'eutectique formé. Les comparaisons entre les divers alliages sont donc qualitatives; le rôle de la vitesse de refroidissement est mis en évidence dans le tableau suivant:

C %	P %	Refroidissement	Taux de ségrégation apparent
0,88	1,37	lent	20
		trempé	40

* Les alliages sont soit refroidis lentement dans le creuset à 2°/ min, soit trempés par aspiration du liquide dans un petit tube en réfractaire.

Bibliographie p. 426

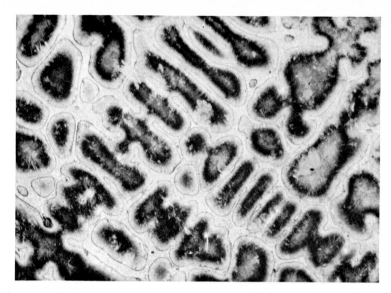

Fig. 4. Attaque nital + Dickensson. × 35. Micrographie d'un alliage Fe–C–P (C=0,88%; P=1,37%) solidifié avec une vitesse de refroidissement de 2°/min.

Le carbone accentue considérablement la ségrégation du phosphore et l'eutectique n'apparaît en quantité appréciable que dans les alliages Fe–C–P. Dans un alliage à 0,75 % de P, le taux de ségrégation passe de 5 à 40 quand la teneur en carbone passe de 0 à 1 %. Enfin dans un alliage Fe–P à 1,1 % P et trempé, on a obtenu des courbes de ségrégation en „accolade", qui présentent un „minimum minimorum" dont la valeur correspond assez bien à la concentration du solidus d'un alliage à 1,1 % P (Fig. 5).

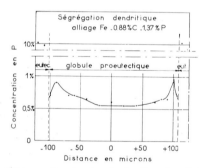

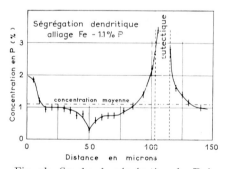

Fig. 5a. Courbe de ségrégation du P à travers une dendrite de l'alliage de la Fig. 4.

Fig. 5b. Courbe de ségrégation du P à travers deux branches de dendrite d'un alliage Fe–P refroidi très rapidement.

2. Examen d'échantillons prélevés au cours de la conversion Thomas

A la suite d'une étude de l'évolution de la composition et de la température du bain au cours de la conversion Thomas, GALEY et al.[9] ont examiné micrographiquement des échantillons prélevés en cours d'opération et trempés à l'eau. Les examens micrographiques ont utilisé deux modes d'attaque: le réactif de Comstock, qui provoque un dépôt de cuivre sur les zones pauvres en phosphore, et le bisulfite, qui met en évidence les hétérogénéités de la solution solide. En particulier, les échantillons prélevés à la rentrée de la flamme, c'est-à-dire au début du palier de température mis en évidence au moyen de l'appareil Galey ($T = 1490°$ C), renferment des *„noyaux" probablement solides au moment du prélèvement* (micrographie, Fig. 6).

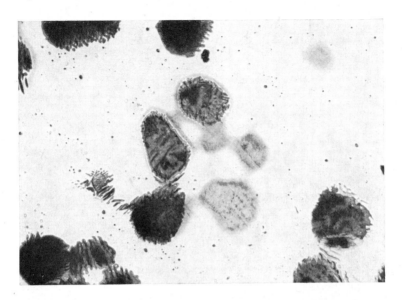

Fig. 6. Attaque Comstock. × 200. Échantillon trempé après prélèvement au cours de l'opération Thomas.

Cette hypothèse a été pleinement confirmée par les analyses que nous avons effectuées sur les mêmes échantillons au moyen de la microsonde. Voici l'essentiel de nos résultats:

— la matrice titre en moyenne 1,35 ± 0,2 % de phosphore.

— les noyaux à contours nets, qui ont subi des transformations $\delta \to \gamma$ et $\gamma \to \alpha$ sont très pauvres: 0,15 à 0,20 % de P; il n'existe pas de gradient de concentrations ni dans le noyau, ni dans la matrice environnante.

— les noyaux „flous" n'ont pas subi la transformation $\delta \to \gamma$ par suite de la diffusion du phosphore: leur concentration, égale à 0,1—0,2 % au centre, s'élève graduellement à 0,5 % sur les bords, cependant que la matrice environnante est appauvrie (Fig. 7).

— la couche de métal, présumée solide au moment du prélèvement, et qui entoure les inclusions de laitier (Fig. 8) est pauvre en phosphore: la concentration en cet élément varie graduellement de 0,1 à 0,5 % quand on traverse cette couche en allant du laitier vers le métal. Elle renferme de plus des filets d'un constituant non métallique; nos analyses ont permis de l'identifier: il s'agit de phosphate de chaux pur. De plus ces filets semblent en continuité avec le laitier, qui a été lui aussi analysé: c'est un silico-phosphate de chaux présentant un gradient de silicium (appauvrissement en Si au voisinage de la couche métallique). Notons en passant

Bibliographie p. 426

que les auteurs du mémoire cité[9] ont montré que cette couche solide était responsable du blocage de la déphosphoration constaté à ce stade de la conversion.

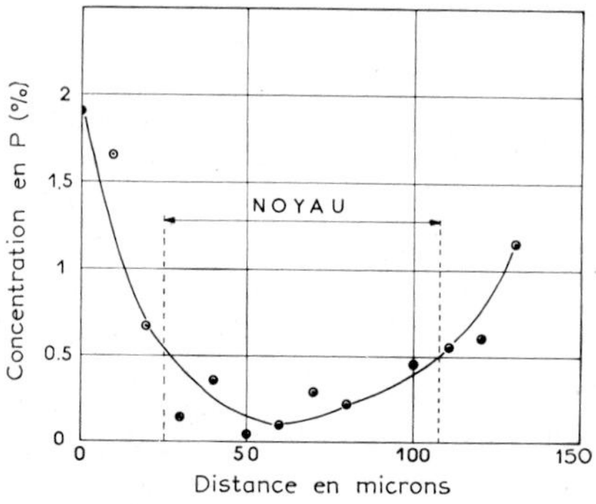

Fig. 7. Courbe de répartition du Phosphore.

Fig. 8. Attaque bisulfite. × 200. Pellicule solide entourant une inclusion de laitier.

3. *Analyse d'échantillons non-métalliques*

Nous nous limiterons ici à l'analyse des inclusions non-métalliques dans les aciers. En fait, ce cas est tout-à-fait analogue à celui de l'analyse des minerais. Il s'agit en effet d'agrégats polyphasés, constitués de sulfures, oxydes, silicates, etc. On donnera ici les résultats relatifs aux deux derniers types de constituants nommés, l'analyse de la phase sulfure ne présentant pas de difficultés particulières.

La Fig. 9 montre une inclusion tétraphasée dans un échantillon d'acier mi-dur calmé au titane (acier à rail, analyse A dans le Tableau I donné en annexe). Une matrice alumino-silicatée contient des cristaux de sulfures et de deux autres phases I et II (oxydes mixtes) dont l'analyse est donnée dans le Tableau II.

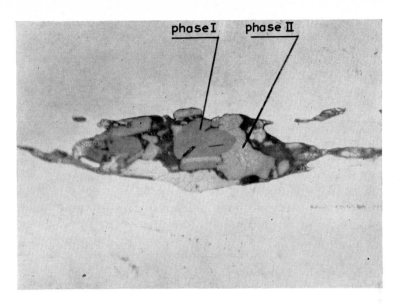

Fig. 9. Polissage mécanique. × 1.000. Inclusion tétraphasée dans un acier mi-dur.

TABLEAU II

	Concentration en %			
	Al	Ti	Mn	Fe
Phase I	3	54	6,5	0,7
Phase II	0,8	39	25	0,8

L'analyse de la matrice alumino-silicatée de ces mêmes inclusions est portée dans la première ligne du Tableau III, où elle est comparée aux analyses d'inclusions analogues rencontrées dans trois autres aciers (deux aciers à rail B et C, un acier doux calmé à l'aluminium D, dont l'analyse chimique est donnée dans le Tableau I en annexe). On remarquera que tous ces alumino-silicates sont très riches en manganèse et très pauvres en fer, et que, dans le cas de l'acier calmé au titane, la forte teneur en titane est compensée par une réduction de moitié de la teneur en silicium.

TABLEAU III

Acier	Concentration %					
	Al	Si	Ca	Ti	Mn	Fe
A	7,1	9	—	12,3	27,5	0,7
B	7	20	6	0,3	26	—
C	7,4	15,8	—	1,3	34	1,2
D	10	18,2	—	—	31,6	1,2

Remarque. Dans les Tableaux II et III, les concentrations sont données avec une précision relative de ± 5 % à ± 10 % suivant les cas, tous calculs de corrections effectués. Une part notable de l'incertitude vient d'ailleurs de l'importance de ces corrections. On peut remarquer que des valeurs expérimentales trouvées pour

Bibliographie p. 426

Al et Si doivent subir une forte correction du fait de la faible valeur du coefficient α correspondant ($\simeq$ 0,6), mais que d'autre part, du fait de la forte absorption du rayonnement $K\alpha$ Si par l'aluminium ($\mu/\varrho = 3000$) une faible variation de la teneur en aluminium entraîne des corrections très différentes sur le silicium, ce qui rend d'ailleurs délicat le calcul de ces corrections.

CONCLUSION

Ce bref aperçu de quelques applications de la Microsonde de CASTAING à l'analyse des éléments légers n'avait pas seulement pour but de donner un aperçu des possibilités de cet instrument dans les domaines de recherches métallurgiques ou minéralogiques. On a également insisté sur la plus grande complexité que présentent les calculs de corrections dès que l'on utilise des rayonnements de longueurs d'onde supérieure à 4 Å d'une part, et lorsque, d'autre part, les éléments constitutifs de l'échantillon étudié ont des numéros atomiques assez différents — cas que l'on rencontre très fréquemment aussi bien dans l'étude des alliages que des corps non-métalliques (inclusions, laitiers, minerais, ciments, etc.).

ANNEXE
TABLEAU I
ANALYSE CHIMIQUE DES ACIERS UTILISÉS POUR L'ANALYSE DES INCLUSIONS NON-MÉTALLIQUES

Acier	C	S	P	Mn	Si	Al	O_2
A	0,44	0,037	0,035	0,95	0,090	0,01	0,024
B	0,46	—	0,042	1	0,10	0,009	
C	0,47	0,045	0,040	0,97	0,150	0,014	0,01
D	0,17	0,025	0,025	0,80	0,20	0,03	

RÉSUMÉ

La „Microsonde de Castaing" a vu son champ d'applications considérablement étendu par la mise au point de son second spectrographe[1]. Celui-ci, placé sous vide poussé, équipé d'un cristal de mica courbé et d'un compteur proportionnel couvre le domaine de longueur d'ondes 4—12 Å, ce qui permet l'analyse des éléments légers (numéros atomiques 11 à 17). La présente communication expose les résultats de quelques études effectuées à l'IRSID au moyen de l'appareil de CASTAING dans le domaine des éléments légers (ségrégation de P et Si dans les alliages de fer, inclusions non-métalliques dans les aciers, échantillons minéralogiques . . .). On discute brièvement la sensibilité de la méthode et l'importance des corrections physiques à apporter aux mesures des intensités dans les divers cas étudiés.

BIBLIOGRAPHIE

[1] R. CASTAING et J. DESCAMPS, Recherche aéronaut., 63 (1958) 41.
[2] R. CASTAING, Thèse, Paris, publication O.N.E.R.A. No. 55, 1951.
[3] R. CASTAING et J. DESCAMPS, J. phys. radium, 16 (1955) 304.
[4] P. PALLUEL, Compt. rend., 224 (1947) 1492 et 1551.
[5] S. J. M. ALLEN, Appendix 9, dans A. H. COMPTON et S. K. ALLISON, X-rays in Theory and Experiment, Van Nostrand, Princeton, 1935.
[6] B. HENKE, R. WHITE et B. LUNDBERG, J. Appl. Phys., 28 (1957) 98.
[7] H. BIZOUARD et J. PHILIBERT, résultats non publiés.
[8] J. PHILIBERT et C. DE BEAULIEU, Rev. mét., 56 (1959) 171.
[9] J. GALEY, L. BEAUJARD, P. VALLET, G. URBAIN, J. TORDEUX, J. FOULARD et P. VILLETTE, Rev. mét., 56 (1959) 69.

X-RAY MICRODIFFRACTION

A. INTRODUCTION

ARNE ENGSTRÖM

Department of Medical Physics, Karolinska Institute, Stockholm (Sweden)

X-ray microanalytical methods are now well established and are currently used in a variety of research fields ranging from the study of the physical properties of metals and alloys to the examination of the microstructure of components in living systems.

The previous trend in the development of X-ray microdiffraction studies was mainly in the direction of diminishing the size of existing diffraction cameras. As small apertures have to be used, the specific output of the primary X-ray source must be as high as possible in such microdiffraction experiments. X-ray tubes with rotating anodes were therefore used. Through the work of EHRENBERG and SPEAR[1] it became evident that X-ray tubes with small local spots of the order 10—100 μ in diameter gave a higher specific output than ordinary X-ray tubes. The real gain in high brilliance was however achieved with the introduction of the point projection X-ray microscope (COSSLETT and co-workers)[2]. For the latter type of instrument special types of microcameras have to be constructed.

Not very many applications of the point projection microscope for diffraction studies have been published, though the method has very promising properties. Perhaps one of the most promising fields of application is its use for divergent beam diffraction according to the method of LONSDALE[3]. The principle of the technique is apparent from Fig. 1 which is taken from CARLSTRÖM and LUNDBERG[4]. A divergent beam diffractogram is reproduced in Fig. 2 and the high resolution is clearly shown. Extremely small crystals can be examined and the small dimensions of the camera necessitate the use of extremely fine-grained film emulsions. The diffractograms are

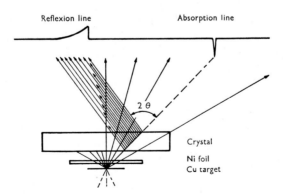

Fig. 1. Formation of absorption and reflection lines when a divergent beam of X-rays from a point source traverses a single crystal[4].

References p. 430

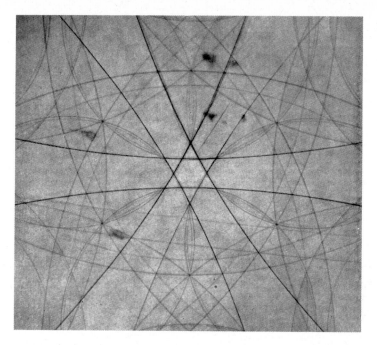

Fig. 2. Negative print of the central part of a divergent-beam diffraction pattern from a spinel twin diamond. Octahedral face parallel to target surface. Thickness of specimen 1.2 mm. Cu target, 21 μ Ni filter, 17 kV and 15 μA. Exposure time 30 min. Black dots are caused by minute inclusions in the specimen. Note the splitting of some lines in the upper part of the picture due to distortions in the crystal[4]. × 10.

magnified by photomicrography and the separation of the α_1—α_2 doublet serves as an internal calibration. By this technique interplanar spacings in tiny crystals can be determined with high accuracy.

The microdiffraction camera designed by CHESLEY[5] is a versatile camera especially in laboratories not equipped with microfocus tubes. The robust construction and the simple alignment of specimen and camera makes it an excellent supplementary tool in ordinary crystallographic laboratories. In fact most of the microdiffraction studies of biological materials have been made with this camera.

Few attempts have been made to increase the resolution of the microdiffraction cameras so as to permit the recording of long interplanar distances. With some modifications of the Chesley camera interplanar spacings in the order 60—100 Å can be recorded. For the study of the long-order range in, for example, biological macromolecules, a better resolution is desired. Perhaps the use of longer wavelengths, for example the Al $K\alpha$ line, will assist in reaching this goal.

As evidenced by the papers in this section, microdiffraction may contribute a unique type of information to a wide range of problems. We may safely predict that X-ray microdiffraction instruments and techniques will come more and more into use in biological and technological research.

REFERENCES

1 W. EHRENBERG and W. E. SPEAR, *Proc. Phys. Soc. (London)*, B 64 (1951) 67.
2 V. E. COSSLETT and co-workers, *Proceedings of the First International Symposium on X-ray Microscopy and Microradiography*, Academic Press, Inc., New York, 1957.
3 K. LONSDALE, *Trans. Roy. Soc. (London)*, A 240 (1947) 219.
4 D. CARLSTRÖM and B. LUNDBERG, *J. Ultrastruct. Research*, 2 (1958) 261.
5 F. G. CHESLEY, *Rev. Sci. Instr.*, 18 (1947) 422.

B. APPARATUS AND TECHNIQUE

X-RAY MICRODIFFRACTION TECHNIQUES

MARGOT E. BERGMANN

*Division of Applied Physics, Polytechnic Institute of Brooklyn,
Brooklyn, N.Y. (U.S.A.)*

ABSTRACT

X-ray microdiffraction is the method of choice in the identification of small samples, and in texture and orientation studies of crystalline materials. In many investigations it is necessary to select the small area to be irradiated by other means (such as optical or microradiographic), or to irradiate the same area repeatedly at several stages of treatment (cold work, annealing, radiation damage, chemical treatment). In all these applications knowledge of the actual size, shape, and intensity distribution of the beam in the specimen plane and of its angular collimation is of the essence. With the help of a specially designed high-precision camera of great flexibility, experiments have been performed that give information on these characteristics for various collimating systems. These experiments have been supplemented by actual diffraction studies, so as to bring out the relative significance of beam characteristics for different applications.

INTRODUCTION

Microdiffraction methods lend themselves to the study of minute crystals either isolated or imbedded in a matrix. In the latter case the X-ray beam itself determines the domain within the sample that gives rise to the diffraction pattern. Various areas of an irradiated sample may show differences in chemical composition, differences in orientation of chemically identical crystallites, and different sizes of particles[1-14].

The relationship of matrix crystals and inclusion crystals may be explored with respect to these same characteristics. Problems of this kind are found, for instance, in the study of bone tissues, or of inclusions of foreign particles in animal or plant tissues. They are also met with in the study of photographic emulsions and in a variety of technically important manufacturing processes. In the study of metals and of fibers, man-made as well as those occurring in nature, the orientation, size, and degree of perfection of crystals and their relation to the mechanical properties of materials are of importance.

In the application of microdiffraction techniques, the collimation of the X-ray beam is frequently one of the decisive camera parameters. For the observation of long spacings a well collimated primary beam is essential, as it is for the observation of continuous low-angle scattering for particle-size determination. In texture studies in particular, knowledge of the collimation of the primary X-ray beam, as well as of its intensity in the specimen plane, is needed in order to evaluate details of the diffraction pattern with regard to number and shapes of the particles. Needless to say, the line width in the wide-angle diagram is also affected by the collimation of the beam.

References p. 439

The actual characteristics of a microbeam in these respects may differ significantly from what one might expect from a purely geometric consideration of the collimating system. By informing oneself of the actual situation in this respect, and by selecting one's collimating system judiciously in accordance with the requirements of a given investigation, one may expect to enhance the efficacy of microdiffraction techniques.

With the help of a microcamera that had been specially designed and built in our laboratory, we have examined the degree of collimation, and the intensity patterns and actual cross sections in the specimen plane of several microbeams; we have also related these beam characteristics to the actual microdiffraction patterns that the various beams produce from typical specimens, and to the information that may be obtained from them.

In this paper we shall first describe our microcamera, and then go over to the experiments performed with this instrument that bear on microbeam characteristics.

THE CAMERA

In order to permit wide latitude in the variation of the angular collimation of the beam, its cross section in the specimen plane, and of the specimen-to-film distance, it was desirable that the internal optical axis of the camera should be so well defined that each individual component of the camera, and in some instances each component of the collimating system, could be centered on the camera axis. Accordingly we have assembled all the components of the microdiffraction camera proper on a carefully machined X-ray track that serves as an optical bench (Figs. 1, 2, and 3). The optical axis of the camera is parallel to that track and passes through one point that is kept fixed. The specimen, likewise, is positioned with reference to that axis.

The X-ray track is supported so that it can be aimed precisely at the source of the X rays; these supports incorporate four degrees of freedom which make it possible not only to train the camera at a specified point of the target within the X-ray tube but to do so with an equally precisely defined orientation in space (Fig. 1: I, II, 1, and 2).

All adjustments once made are maintained. This is so because the internal alignment is accomplished with the help of controls entirely independent of those by which the camera is aimed at the X-ray source. Moreover, the parts of the camera may be lifted off the track individually, and subsequently replaced, without requiring a new alignment.

All components of the diffraction camera above the track are combined into two subassemblies, III and IV. The subassembly III contains both the collimating system and the specimen holder. These two parts were combined in order to minimize the distance between the collimating system and the specimen. The specimen holder is a mechanical microscope stage. For mounting a specimen and for choosing the precise area to be placed into the microbeam, the whole subassembly may be removed from the track and placed e.g. under a petrographic microscope. Both entrance and exit pinholes were drilled into platinum sheets, mounted in inserts so that each pinhole is centered independently of the other, and so that the distance between the two pinholes can be varied. Inserts with glass capillaries may be used also.

The cassette is subassembly IV. A special feature is the slender hollow beam trap, which protrudes slightly, so that it minimizes air scattering just in front of

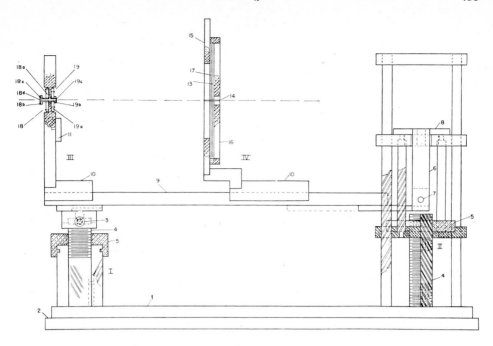

Fig. 1. Line drawing of camera. The numbers in this drawing refer to the list of components.

(I)   Track support, front
(II)   Track support, rear
(III)   Subassembly containing collimating system and specimen holder
(IV)   Cassette holder
(1)   Upper heavy plate
(2)   Lower heavy plate
(3)   Micrometer screw
(4)   Vertical adjustment, rod
(5)   Vertical adjustment, nut
(6)   Parallel bar supporting track
(7)   Connecting joint
(8)   Pivoting circular disk
(9)   Track
(10)   Foot of (III) and (IV)
(11)   Specimen holder (mechanical microscope stage)
(11a, 11b) Specimen mounting frames
(12)   Plate

(13)   Film
(14)   Beam trap
(15)   Front plate of cassette
(15a)   Punch disk
(15b)   Punch guide
(15c, d) Beam trap holders
(15e)   Spacer
(16)   Rear plate of cassette with beam trap guide
(17)   Aluminum foil
(18)   Entrance pinhole assembly
(18a)   Adjustable disk
(18b)   Entrance pinhole insert
(18c)   Entrance platinum sheet with pinhole
(18d)   Entrance leadshield with pinhole
(19)   Exit pinhole assembly
(19a)   Adjustable disk
(19b)   Exit pinhole insert
(19c)   Exit platinum sheet with pinhole

the film and thereby reduces blackening close to the center. The X-ray beam emerging from the exit of the beam trap may be monitored during exposure. The beam trap consists of a piece of stainless steel tubing as used in syringes. Whenever it is to be used, it serves as its own punch. For this purpose the back plate of the cassette is provided with a guide. After the film, covered with a sheet of thin aluminum foil, has been placed in the cassette, a punch guide is also inserted into the opening of the front plate, Fig. 4. The beam trap is then punched through the aluminum foil and film; it forms a light-tight seal with the former. It is held securely by the back plate guide, so that the punch guide in front can be removed before exposure is to begin.

Fig. 2. Camera aligned with the Ehrenberg-Spear microfocus X-ray tube by Hilger.

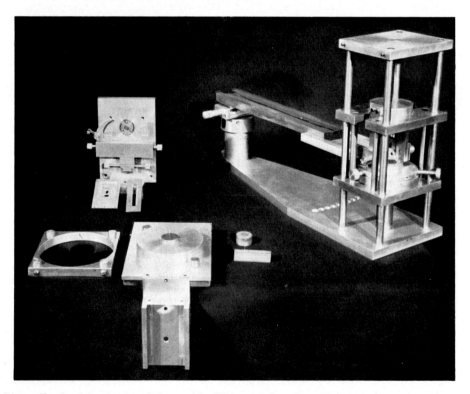

Fig. 3. Track with supports. Subassembly III, containing the collimating system and the mechanical stage, and two different specimen mounts. Cassette holder, with punching mechanism inserted.

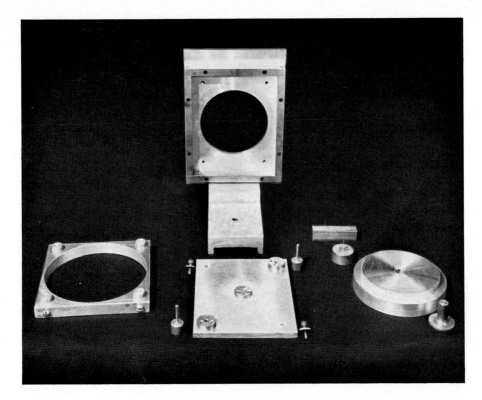

Fig. 4. Cassette and punching mechanism, disassembled.

In the course of working with the camera it was found that its alignment remains stable for months; from that point of view the need for monitoring is greatly reduced.

For aligning the camera internally, the center of the cross section of the beam trap serves as the fixed point that defines the optical axis. In order to align the collimating system, a microscope that is equipped with an appropriately shaped foot is placed temporarily on the X-ray track, and its cross hair is centered on the beam trap. Then the exit and entrance pinholes are centered separately on the cross hair of the microscope. The specimen may be positioned in the same manner, or alternatively, the whole subassembly III may be removed from the track; in that case the specimen is aligned with respect to the exit pinhole while being viewed through any microscope.

BEAM COLLIMATION STUDIES

Before presenting experimental work on beam collimation we shall start out with a theoretical discussion based on purely geometric considerations, which will serve as a frame of reference for the experimental findings. We shall assume a pinhole system, denoting the diameter of the entrance pinhole by S_1, that of the exit pinhole by S_2, and the distance between them by L. The angle of divergence of the emerging beam will be:

$$\psi_c = \frac{1}{L}\Big(S_1 + S_2\Big).$$

(1)

If the specimen plane is a distance r from the exit pinhole, then the diameter of the irradiated area in the specimen will be:

$$(2) \qquad\qquad D_s = S_2 + r\psi_c.$$

In the film plane the diameter of the primary beam will be:

$$(3) \qquad\qquad D_f = S_2 + (R + r)\psi_c,$$

where R is the specimen-to-film distance.

With a fine-focus tube the beam may be defined by the diameter of the focal spot on the tube target, S_t, and the exit pinhole, the entrance pinhole serving more or less as a guard slit. If we denote the distance between the tube target and the entrance pinhole by R', then the angle of divergence of the primary beam will be given by

$$(4) \qquad\qquad \psi_t = \frac{S_t + S_2}{L + R'},$$

rather than by the expression (1). S_t represents the "effective" diameter of the focal spot, that is to say its projection on a plane perpendicular to the camera axis. In eqns. (2) and (3) ψ_c should be replaced by ψ_t, except that eqn. (3) should be retained unchanged for an estimate of the size of the area in which the low-angle pattern will be obscured by the primary beam; there is always some diffuse emission of X-rays outside the focal spot, which cannot be disregarded as contributing to the background.

The adjustments below the track allow an observation of the effects of small displacements of the optical axis with respect to the focal spot of the X-ray tube. Fig. 5 shows enlargements of photographs of the X-ray beams obtained by viewing the microfocal spot of the Ehrenberg-Spear tube built by Hilger through a 60 μ pinhole system at slightly varying positions of the camera axis. Fig. 6 is a view of the line focus of a North American Philips tube through the identical collimator. These photographs of the direct beam demonstrate the importance of the alignment of the camera axis with the focal spot. They also show that the analysis of the

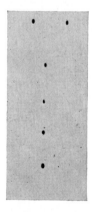

Fig. 5. Enlarged cross sections of X-ray beams obtained by viewing the microfocal spot of the Ehrenberg-Spear tube through a 60 μ pinhole system at slightly varying positions of the camera axis.

References p. 439

geometric relationship given above applies. In addition, they point to the importance of the stability of the focal spot itself with respect to size, shape, and location.

Fig. 6. Cross sections of X-ray beams (natural size) obtained by viewing the line focus of a Norelco tube through the same pinhole system as used for Fig. 5. (a) shows the variation of cross section with collimator-to-film distance. (b) shows a sequence of spots at constant large distance corresponding to increasingly good alignment. The pictures at the larger distance demonstrate that in the horizontal direction the beam is defined by the alignment of the pinhole system with the source, whereas vertically the width of the line focus controls.

Fig. 7 shows a picture of the primary beam collimated by means of a lead glass capillary with a bore of 50 μ. The focal spot viewed was that of the line focus of the North American Philips tube. The film was 10 cm behind the exit of the capillary. Exposure was varied from 1 to 30 minutes. Comparison of these pictures with those of Fig. 8, which was obtained with a pinhole system, shows a marked difference in the intensity distribution within the beam as well as in overall beam cross section, the most striking difference being that of the effect of the time of exposure.

Fig. 7. Variation with exposure time of cross sections of the beam obtained with a lead glass capillary (50 μ bore). To demonstrate the irregular intensity distribution, both first and second films are shown.

Fig. 8. Variation with exposure time of cross sections of the beam obtained with a 60 μ pinhole system. First and second films.

References p. 439

The results of Fig. 7 cannot be explained on the basis of the simple geometric analysis underlying eqns. (1) through (4). These photographs can be understood only on the assumption that a very considerable part of the beam has been totally reflected several times by the walls of the capillary. It can be shown that because of total reflection at glancing angles below the critical value, part of the X-ray beam will be reflected multiply in such a manner that its path through the capillary forms a spiral, and so that upon emerging at the exit this part of the beam has an angle with the optical axis much larger than the critical angle of total reflection. The sequence of Fig. 7 shows evidence that with increasing length of exposure additional arms of such spirals become visible. Though their intensity is low compared to that of the more centrally located part of the primary beam, it is still sufficient to obscure any low-angle diffraction effects. No improvement in collimation can be obtained by lengthening the capillary. Many additional pictures that were taken under the same circumstances as those of Fig. 7 show that minute changes in the alignment of the capillary relative to the X-ray source may give rise to many different and complex intensity patterns in the primary beam.

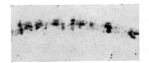

Fig. 9. Effects of collimating system and of texture of sample on the detailed structure of Debye-Scherrer rings. (a) and (b) were obtained from the AgBr grains in an undeveloped X-ray film, (a) with a lead glass capillary, (b) with a pinhole system, (c) represents the transmission pattern of a thin Ni foil, obtained with the pinhole collimating system. All three photographs are enlarged.

The effect of such complex and broad beam patterns on wide-angle diagrams was also investigated. For Figs. 9a, b the specimen used was a piece of undeveloped X-ray film. The enlarged sector of a diffraction ring shown in Fig. 9a was obtained with a 50 μ lead glass capillary, that of Fig. 9b with a 60 μ pinhole system. When the two original films were viewed under the microscope (100 $\times$ to 200 $\times$ magnification), the diffraction spots in Fig. 9a showed curved tails, whereas those of Fig. 9b were round and lacked internal structure. Fig. 9c represents part of a diffraction ring of a transmission pattern obtained from a thin nickel foil; it was included to afford a comparison between samples of different textures exposed to the beam of the same 60 μ pinhole system.

The unevenness of the intensity distribution across the primary beam is also of importance for estimates of the total volume irradiated, as in texture studies.

Finally, the intensity distribution bears on the problem of positioning to best advantage specimens that are significantly smaller than the cross section of the collimator. With a pinhole system one may locate the most intense part of the beam by photographing the X-ray shadow of an absorbent object, which may be the specimen itself or a "stand-in". With a glass capillary the angular collimation is too poor to give enough resolution for a shadow. In this case the best location must be searched for with the help of diffraction diagrams of a suitable standard substance.

References p. 439

ACKNOWLEDGEMENTS

The author wishes to express her appreciation to Professor I. FANKUCHEN, who introduced her to microdiffraction techniques and who made many valuable suggestions, particularly concerning design requirements; to Professors P. P. EWALD and D. HARKER for discussions. Special thanks are due to Mr. K. HALE, of the instrument shop of the Physics Department of Polytechnic Institute of Brooklyn, who built and assembled all the parts of the camera.

REFERENCES

1 M. E. BERGMANN and I. FANKUCHEN, *Rev. Sci. Instr.*, 20 (1949) 696; *Science*, 113 (1951) 415.
2 G. F. CHESLEY, *Rev. Sci. Instr.*, 18 (1947) 422.
3 I. FANKUCHEN and H. MARK, *J. Appl. Phys.*, 15 (1944) 364.
4 P. GAY, P. B. HIRSCH and A. KELLY, *Acta Cryst.*, 7 (1954) 41.
5 P. GAY and R. W. K. HONEYCOMBE, *Proc. Phys. Soc. (London)*, A 64 (1951) 844.
6 P. GAY and A. KELLY, *Acta Cryst.*, 6 (1953) 165, 172; 7 (1954) 333.
7 P. B. HIRSCH, *Acta Cryst.*, 5 (1952) 172.
8 P. B. HIRSCH and J. N. KELLAR, *Acta Cryst.*, 5 (1952) 162.
9 J. N. KELLAR, P. B. HIRSCH and J. S. THORP, *Nature*, 165 (1950) 554.
10 A. KELLY, *Acta Cryst.*, 7 (1954) 554.
11 E. KLEIN, O. R. TRAUTZ, I. FANKUCHEN and H. K. ADDELSTON, *J. Dental Research*, 30 (1951) 439.
12 D. R. KREGER, Ch. IV in J. BOUMAN, *Selected Topics in X-ray Crystallography from the Delft X-ray Institute*, Interscience, New York, 1951.
13 R. D. PRESTON, *Phil. Trans. Roy. Soc. London*, B 224 (1934) 131.
14 J. SINGER, J. A. RICHARDS, and W. C. MOXLEY, *Can. J. Technol.*, 31 (1953) 155.

NEW MICROBEAM CAMERAS AND THEIR USE IN IDENTIFICATION AND TEXTURE PROBLEMS

J. W. JEFFERY and H. E. BULLEN

Birkbeck College Research Laboratory, University of London,
(Great Britain)

ABSTRACT

The cameras described consist of a miniature version of the normal single-crystal rotation camera, and a modified version of the selected area microbeam camera described by LEWIS which allows low-angle as well as back-reflection lines to be registered.

These cameras have been used on the following problems: (1) The identification of very small inclusions by selected area diffraction; (2) The investigation of quartz inclusions in garnet crystallised during rock movement; (3) The identification of very small single crystals; (4) The determination of the effect of heat treatment on the grain structure of special alloy steels; (5) The investigation of fracture bands in aluminium alloy; (6) The investigation of biological fibres.

INTRODUCTION

The cameras to be described are designed to enable the normal techniques for single crystal and poly-crystalline specimens to be employed when the size of the specimen is too small for normal cameras. They are essentially cases of miniaturisation rather than new devices, except for the means of location of the beam relative to the specimen in the second camera which is new. This simple and positive method was developed in these laboratories and has been described[1] for a back-reflection camera. The method has now been extended to allow the whole range of diffraction angles to be recorded up to a spacing of nearly 10 Å for Co K_α radiation. The cameras have been designed for use in conjunction with an Ehrenberg-Spear fine or semi-fine focus tube.

The examples given of the use of the cameras are in the main either parts of larger problems or preliminary investigations made to assess the possibility of obtaining useful information in more specialised problems. Only examples leading to positive conclusions have been cited. All the X-ray work has been carried out in this laboratory.

CAMERAS

The miniature single-crystal oscillation and rotation camera (Camera 1)

Description. Fig. 1 shows the construction of the camera and Fig. 2 is a photograph of the camera in use against a semi-fine focus tube, with the length of the focus horizontal. The camera base is from a modified Unicam single crystal goniometer. The normal plain bearings of the spindle have been replaced by taper roller bearings, but this is probably unnecessary and improved plain bearings might be sufficient. The camera has to be raised clear of the normal size arcs on which the specimen is mounted. The platform on which it is located is made by cutting down a standard cylindrical film holder to about two thirds the normal height and fixing a horizontal platform across the top so that the underside just clears the arcs when they are at the top of the height adjustment. The specimen must then be raised about 3 cm above the top of the arcs, instead of the normal 1—1.5 cm. In the case

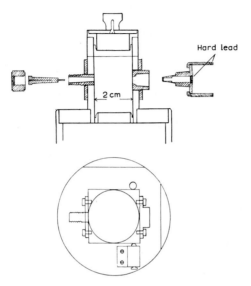

Fig. 1. Drawing of Camera 1 to scale (except base). Camera body of aluminium alloy, with steel side plates for locating pins. Collimator hole diam. 100 μ. Guard slit diam. 450 μ. Beam trap from hypodermic needle tubing, 0.80 mm I.D. and 1.22 mm O.D.

of single crystal specimens this is best done by using a lead wire support of about 1 mm diameter, and attaching the glass fibre carrying the crystal to it. Rough angular adjustments are then made by bending the wire at the top and final adjustments are made on the arcs. The cylindrical base for the camera is cut away at the side and front to allow access to the arcs. This method of adjustment is necessary because angular adjustment of the arcs involves large translations of the specimen, and it would not be possible to bring the specimen back on to the rotation axis without fouling the camera or its supporting base if these adjustments were more than a few degrees.

The raising of the camera involves raising the collimator height. As the collimator is attached to the camera, and the original collimator holder has been removed, this only causes difficulties in the adjustment of the microscope. This must be raised to the same height as the collimator by the insertion of a parallel block. The normal objective of the microscope is too low a power and is replaced by a $\frac{2}{3}''$ ($\times$ 10) objective, except for certain adjustments.

Adjustments. Clearances are arranged to give the possibility of small lateral adjustments to the collimator and backstop housings. The collimator is filled with light from an extended source and the beam defined by the collimating hole and guard slit is observed with the low power microscope focused on a fine glass fibre

References p. 457

Fig. 2. Photograph of Camera I in position against a horizontal semi-fine focus tube, which runs at 2 mA, 50 kV, with a copper target and horizontal line focus of 1.5 × 0.1 mm.

on the rotation axis. The collimator housing is moved until the beam is symmetrical about the fibre. This beam is used to adjust the microscope so that its mechanical traverse is parallel to the beam, and the backstop housing is then adjusted so that the backstop is symmetrical about the beam. The tip of the fibre is next brought to the centre of the beam, the high power substituted for the low power objective and the microscope given final slight lateral adjustments to bring the image of the tip of the fibre on to the crosswires. The instrument is then ready for use and the only running adjustments required are slight movements of the horizontal and vertical slow motion slides at the front of the camera stand. The X-ray beam is observed on a very thin fluorescent screen (powder sprinkled on to cellophane tape) at the rear of the backstop. When the beam is symmetrical about the crosswires the camera is in adjustment. The foreshortened focus of the tube must not be more than 0.1 mm² or the direct beam will hit the guard slit.

Loading. The camera is designed to take normal 35 mm X-ray film (Ilford

Industrial G) and a length of 52 mm just allows the collimator to protrude between the ends of the film. It is just possible for most people to get one finger into the camera, and it can be loaded by hand, but the loading tool shown in Fig. 3a ensures

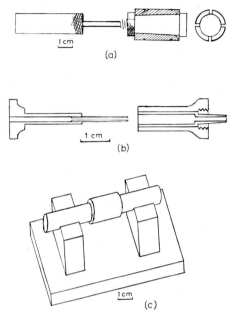

(a)

(b)

(c)

Fig. 3. (a) Loading tool for expanding the film; (b) Film punch; hypodermic needle tubing, 1.28 mm I.D. and 1.80 mm O.D. A clearing rod (not shown) is also provided. (c) Hardwood supporting cylinder and stand.

that the film is pressed out against the camera walls and avoids doubling back the black paper folder where it enters the retaining rings. The film is turned by hand until the collimator can be placed in position and the hole for the backstop is then punched. This is done with a special punch, shown in Fig. 3b, which screws on in place of the backstop cover and cuts against the wood cylinder supported on a stand shown in Fig. 3c. Since this process puts a certain amount of strain on the backstop housing, it is as well to have it pinned in position after the adjustments described above.

The located microbeam camera (Camera 2)

Description. The back reflection camera differs slightly from that described by LEWIS[1]. The wedge is made entirely of brass and is held in position on the tube by four screws passing through oversize holes, thus allowing slight adjustment of the collimator with respect to the X-ray tube focus. The collimator is located in a small hole in the front brass plate (dimensions $1\frac{1}{2} \times 1\frac{1}{16}''$) and is held in position by a 12 BA nut (tapped out to 10 BA) which screws on to the collimator. This small nut and a frame which fits round the edge keep the film flat against the plate. The whole assembly is located on two pins on the wedge and held rigidly against the latter by two spring-loaded clips visible in Fig. 4.

References p. 457

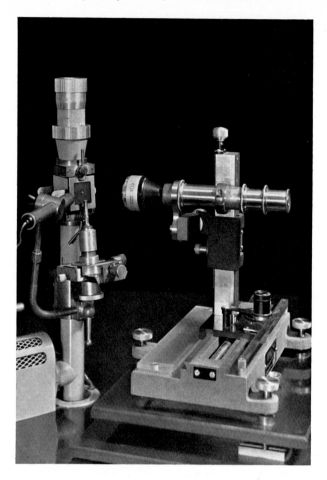

Fig. 4. Photograph of Camera 2 showing general lay-out for taking back-reflection photographs using a vertical semi-fine focus tube which runs at 0.25 mA, 50 kV with a Co target and line focus of 1 × 0.1 mm. A scatter shield (not shown) goes over the film during the preliminary adjustment and carries the mirrors for illuminating and viewing the specimen.

The newly developed 2 cm-diameter semi-cylindrical camera, which can be fitted as an alternative to record the powder diffraction pattern by glancing-angle incidence on the specimen is shown in position on a vertical semi-fine focus tube in Fig. 5. The diffraction pattern is recorded on a strip of film over a width of 1 cm. The semi-cylindrical side of the camera is hinged at one end (shown open in Fig. 5) and after insertion of the film against the frame the side is held closed by means of a spring-loaded plunger. The camera is located on the same pins as the front plate holding the collimator and is held in position by the two spring-loaded clips. Means of accurately setting and oscillating the specimen about a vertical axis are under construction. Collimators of 30, 60, and 90 μ diameter are available.

Adjustments. The procedure for setting up the back-reflection camera for examination of a selected area has been described by LEWIS[1].

In the case of the semi-cylindrical camera it is first necessary to ensure that the

X-ray beam passes through the axis of the cylinder of which the camera forms slightly more than half. This is done using a simple centering jig which consists of a finely-pointed rod of ⅛ inch silver-steel passing through the centre of a brass plug

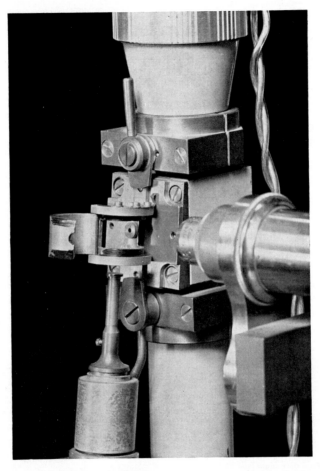

Fig. 5. Close-up of semi-cylindrical film holder for camera 2 in position, but with film-retaining flap swung back.

which would serve as a lid if the whole cylinder were present. After coating the tip of the rod with a little fine fluorescent powder the jig is placed in position so as to form a 'lid' for the camera. The tip is then on the axis of the cylinder; rotation of the jig whilst observing the tip in a microscope through the open-hinged side verifies that this is so. It would improve the present design to increase the height of the film holder so that a high-power objective could be brought up to the pointed rod. At present the working distance required demands a 25 mm objective. The screws clamping the wedge to the X-ray tube are loosened and whilst observing the tip of the rod through a microscope, in a darkened room, the whole assembly is adjusted until the X-ray beam is seen to strike the fluorescent powder. The screws are then tightened and the alignment checked. The cross wires are focussed on the fluorescent point, and the microscope clamped. The jig is then removed and the required area on the illuminated specimen brought on to the cross wires, using the translations on the specimen holder. The camera may be removed for loading before or after this last operation.

Loading. When loading the back-reflection camera it is necessary to take the front brass plate, collimator and nut, and the film retaining frame into the dark room. A piece of film $1^1/_{16}'' \times 1^1/_{16}''$ is cut and a small hole of diameter 0.069'' is punched in it using a specially made film punch. The film, in a black paper envelope, is fitted on to the plate and the assembly transferred to its position on the X-ray tube. Either single or double emulsion film is used. In the latter case the outside of the double emulsion film is stripped off after development.

In the case of the semicylindrical camera, the hinged side is opened, a piece of film (1.3 × 2.7 cm) in a black paper folder inserted against the radius defining flanges and the hinged side closed.

EXAMPLES OF DIFFRACTION MICROANALYSIS
The identification of very small polycrystalline specimens

Selected area diffraction using camera 2. Polished transverse sections of boiler corrosion products frequently show banded structures under the microscope. The bands vary from $1\ \mu$ or less up to 1 mm thick, and glancing-incidence photographs identified the following as the major components of different bands: copper; haematite (α-Fe_2O_3); delafossite ($CuFeO_2$); and magnetite (Fe_3O_4). In the case of one compact black deposit the normal powder pattern from the bulk sample showed only magnetite present. A glancing-angle photograph was taken of the area on one of the bands shown in Fig. 6. This pattern (Fig. 7) shows only magnetite lines. In

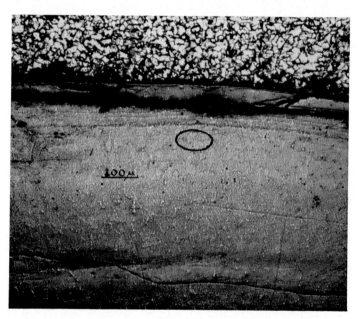

Fig. 6. Section of boiler tube showing banded corrosion product with striations within bands.

this case the layers causing striations were so thin that no pattern could be observed from them. The problem was aggravated by the fact that the layers were softer than the magnetite and polishing etched them below the surface. However, on breaking

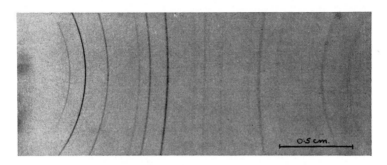

Fig. 7. Glancing-angle photograph with beam located on area outlined in Fig. 6. Camera 2, 60 μ collimator, 1 h.

up the specimen it sometimes parted along layers giving surfaces usually of several mm² covered with a very thin layer of the inclusion. This layer could usually be identified using normal cameras and glancing-angle incidence on the surface, and Na_2SO_4, chalcocite (α-Cu_2S), and digenite ($Cu_{1.8}S$), were identified in this way. In one case, however, only a very small area was available. Camera 2 was used to identify this deposit and Fig. 8 shows the pattern. The smooth lines are magnetite (Fe_3O_4) and the spotty lines bornite (Cu_5FeS_4). The longest spacing line in this photograph is 4.86 Å and shows that spacings up to about 9 Å could be registered with Co K_α

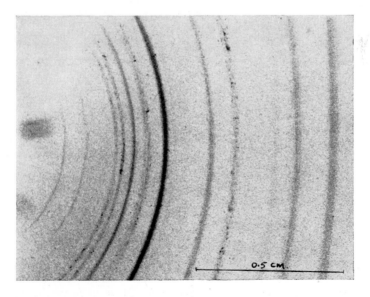

Fig. 8. Glancing angle photograph of parting surface of dense black corrosion product (similar to that of Fig. 6). The smooth lines are from magnetite (Fe_3O_4), the spotty ones from bornite (Cu_5FeS_4). Camera 2, 60 μ collimator, 1 h.

References p. 457

radiation. In none of these cases could sufficient material be obtained for identification by scraping the surface.

In the case of thin surface deposits the microbeam camera can also aid identification of surface layers by high resolution. Fig. 9 shows a portion of the pattern ($\times$ 10) from the surface of scale produced during the heat treatment of a boiler tube. The

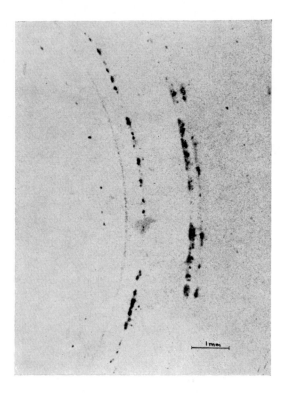

Fig. 9. Low angle (3—2 Å) portion of glancing angle photograph from boiler scale, showing one smooth line from haematite (Fe_2O_3), single spotty lines of magnetite (Fe_3O_4) and a double line from two phases of wustite (FeO). Camera 2, 60 μ collimator, 1 h.

smooth line is from haematite (Fe_2O_3), the single spotty lines from magnetite (Fe_3O_4) and the double spotty line from wustite (FeO). The spacings shown are between 3 and 2 Å. The splitting of the FeO line is due to a near stoichiometric FeO and an iron-rich FeO, both present in the same small area of about 0.03 mm², and with parameters differing by less than 1 %. On a normal powder photograph the iron-rich lines are relatively very much weaker and the splitting difficult to establish, showing that most of this phase is near the surface of the flake.

Identification using camera 1. Patterns can be obtained from very small specimens in a comparatively short time. Fig. 10 shows the pattern obtained from a small white bead (*ca.* 100μ) of a type which was occasionally observed under the microscope in powder from a boiler mud drum. The photograph shows that it is a mixture of aragonite (smooth lines) and calcite (spotty lines).

References p. 457

The identification of very small single crystals using camera I

Identification, and, indeed, complete investigation of small ($< 50\ \mu$) single crystals can be undertaken with this camera. The photographs can be put in an inverted enlarger and the image viewed on a screen with a magnification of $\times 3$. The

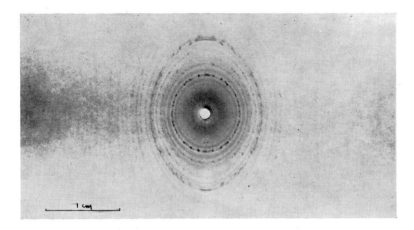

Fig. 10. Photograph of small (*ca.* 100 μ) white bead, showing spotty calcite lines and smooth aragonite lines. Camera I, 2 h.

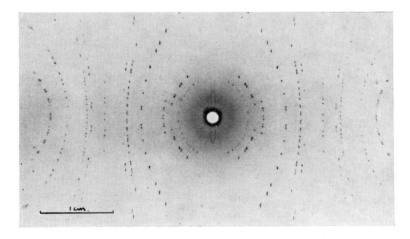

Fig. 11. Multi-rotation photograph of small (*ca.* 50 μ) cuprite (Cu_2O) crystal. Camera I, total 1.5 h.

normal charts can then be used to interpret the photograph and at least rough estimates of intensity made. From the crystal system and cell size, identification can be achieved if the substance is listed in *Crystal Data*[2].

For cubic crystals (and others with small, symmetrical cells) it may be simpler for identification to take a multi-rotation photograph. Fig. 11 shows such a photograph for small (50 μ) red crystals occurring in a de-superheater tube plate corrosion deposit. It immediately identifies the substance as cuprite (Cu_2O).

The investigation of quartz inclusions in garnet single crystals using camera 2

Mineralogical investigation by RAST and STURT[3] suggested that the garnet had crystallised in two stages, the second during movement of the matrix which had rotated and bent the quartz inclusions in the outer zones of the garnet. The specimens for X-ray examination were in the form of thin sections mounted on microscope slides. A strip a few mm wide was cut from the slide containing the garnet. Back-reflection Laue photographs were taken. The beam and the specimen could in this case be located optically by transmission and the use of two pieces of polaroid helped greatly in locating the quartz grains. The inclusions were only about 10 μ across and the beam used was nearly 70 μ on the specimen. However, by taking two photographs, one with the

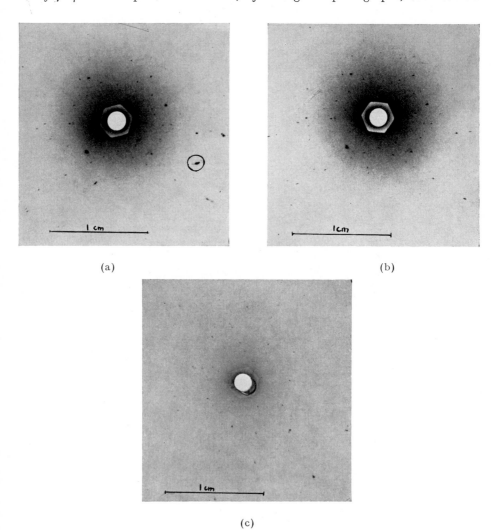

(a)   (b)

(c)

Fig. 12. Back-reflection photographs of (a) area of garnet including small (*ca.* 10 μ) quartz inclusion; one quartz reflection ringed; (b) an adjacent area of garnet without inclusions; (c) an equidimensional quartz grain crystallised under static conditions. Camera 2, 60 μ collimator, (a) 2 h; (b) and (c) 1 h.

References p. 457

inclusion in the beam (Fig. 12a) and one of a closely adjacent area of the garnet (Fig. 12b), it was possible to identify the quartz reflections. These certainly showed signs of bending as can be seen by comparing the reflection ringed in Fig. 12a with the reflections in Fig. 12c which are from a quartz grain which had crystallised under static conditions.

Metallurgical investigations

The effect of warm working on the grain structure of a creep-resistant alloy steel. The grain size of the specimens before treatment was 20—30 μ, and with normal equipment spotty powder rings were obtained. After warm working the photographs showed only smooth, rather broad rings, with no indication of what had happened to individual grains. Pointed specimens were prepared and photographs taken of the tip in camera 1. Fig. 13a shows the centre (low angle) portion of a photograph from the tip of an untreated specimen. The spots are typical Laue reflections from a small number of crystallites. Fig. 13b is the corresponding photograph from the warm worked specimen. Although the specimen was stationary, the photograph is very similar to an oscillation photograph from the untreated specimen, except that the

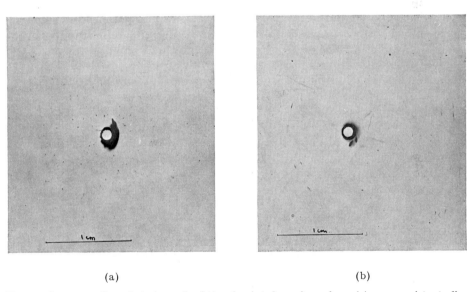

(a)   (b)

Fig. 13. Centre portion of photograph of tip of pointed specimen from (a) creep-resistant alloy before warm working; (b) a similar specimen after warm working. Camera 1, 20 min each; point focus (0.3 mA).

reflections are spread out along constant θ curves. Back reflections also show a certain amount of 'line broadening' so that the α_1, α_2, separation is almost obscured, compared with a sharp separation in the case of the untreated specimen.

Warm working seems, therefore, to have produced plastic distortion of the grains, which have polygonised, either leaving a certain amount of strain present or giving rise to crystallites small enough to produce line broadening.

The investigation of the fracture bands produced by alternating large and small amplitudes of vibration in the fatigue testing of a light alloy aircraft component. Fig. 14a is a diagram of the fractured end of the component showing the pieces cut out for X-ray investigation heavily outlined and the point where the beam impinged on the specimen for photographs Nos. 86 and 35 (Figs. 16b and c). A large piece of the

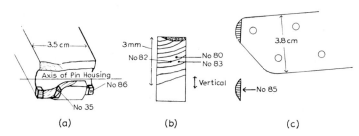

Fig. 14. Diagram showing fractured aircraft part and location of X-ray beam for various (numbered) photographs. (a) Fractured pin housing; (b) enlargement of left-hand cut-away portion; (c) unstressed end of component.

casting had already been cut away before the specimen for No. 86 was taken. Fig. 14b is an enlarged drawing of the front of the left-hand specimen, showing the fracture bands. Each band corresponds to a period of large or small amplitude vibrations and at the boundary of each band the surface changes direction abruptly. The points of impingement of the beam for various photographs are marked. Fig. 14c shows the opposite end of the casting and the specimen cut away from the least stressed part. All cut surfaces from which photographs were taken had been etched to a depth of about 0.2 mm in caustic soda.

All photographs are back-reflection with stationary specimen. All except No. 35 (Fig. 16c) were taken with camera 2. Fig. 16c was taken with a normal, large beam, back-reflection camera. In all cases the X-ray beam was approximately perpendicular to the gross surface. In taking Fig. 16c this meant that the beam was approximately parallel to the pin-housing axis, and in all other cases perpendicular to it. Fig. 15a and c (Nos. 80 and 83) are from adjacent bands, Fig. 15b (No. 82) from the boundary between them.

The specimen was translated without rotation between these last three photographs. All three show considerable preferred orientation and evidence of strain and/or small crystallite size. The orientation on the two bands appears to be the same but definite differences can be seen in Fig. 15b from the boundary. The significance of this difference can only be decided by a series of photographs with the specimen rotated through known angles between each, and the camera is not yet adapted for this operation.

Fig. 16a (No. 85) shows that in an unstressed part of the casting there is preferred orientation but no sign of strain or small crystallite size, but that deep in an unbroken region round the pin housing where the main stress occurs, the signs of stress, Fig. 16b, are as evident as on the surface of the fracture. The macrobeam photograph Fig. 16c seems to show less preferred orientation, but this may be partly due to the size of the beam and partly to its direction. The preferred orientation may tend to be cylindrically symmetrical about the pin axis direction. Again, only further investigation can decide these questions.

References p. 457

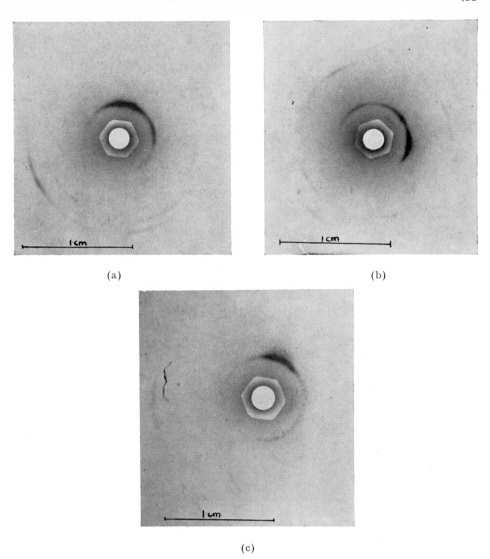

(a)

(b)

(c)

Fig. 15. Back-reflection photographs from areas shown in Fig. 14(b). (a) No. 80 from centre of fracture band; (b) No. 82 from the boundary; (c) No. 83 from the centre of the adjacent band. Camera 2, 90 μ collimator; 1 h each.

The investigation of the sub-grain structure of molybdenum used in neutron bombardment experiments. The effect of neutron bombardment is being investigated by Mr. A. A. JOHNSON at Imperial College, London. It has been shown to vary with grain size and is thought to be dependent on the true grain size, *i.e.* sub-grain boundaries are as important as the main boundaries. It was therefore important to determine the sub-grain structure, and back-reflection photographs of various specimens were taken using camera 2. Fig. 17 is a photograph of a grain (the symmetry is fortuitous) showing no sub-structure over the area of the beam (in this case about 70 μ diam.). Fig. 18 is a photomicrograph of a single reflection from a different specimen.

References p. 457

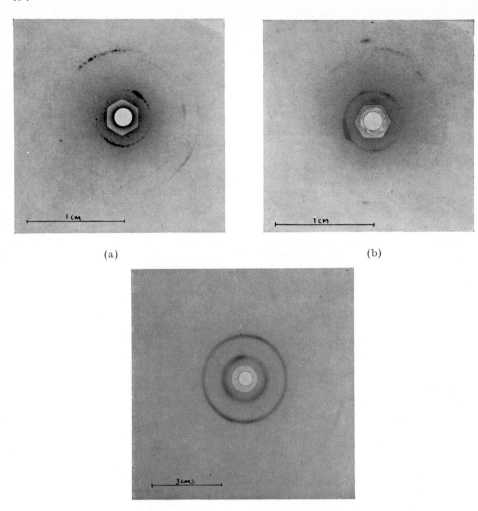

(a) (b)

(c)

Fig. 16. Back-reflection photographs from areas shown in Fig. 14(a) and (c). (a) No. 85 from an un stressed area; (b) No. 86 from a stressed area some distance from the fracture; (c) No. 35 from the area of the final break. (a) and (b) using camera 2, 90 μ collimator, 1 h each. (c) Normal large beam backreflection camera, reproduction reduced to compare better with other photographs, 1.5 h.

Here the splitting of the reflection indicates the presence of sub-grain structure. An attempt is to be made to extend the investigation on a quantitative basis.

Biological investigations of fibres from animal tissue

The general description of these cellulose-like fibres has been given by CRUISE and JEFFERY[4]. Small bundles or single fibres were photographed with camera 1. A variety of specimen holders has been used, but for the later specimens the fibres have been stretched across a 1 mm hole in a strip of copper foil and stuck to the foil at each end. Fig. 19 shows (a), a bundle of cotton fibres, and (b), the X-ray photograph from them. Fig. 20 is (a), a single cotton fibre and (b), its photograph.

References p. 457

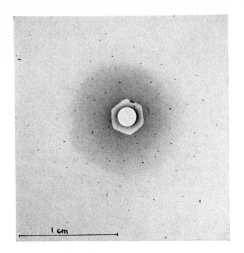

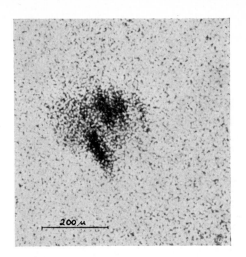

Fig. 17. Back-reflection photograph from a grain in molybdenum sheet. Camera 2, 60 μ collimator, 2 h.

Fig. 18. Photomicrograph of a reflection from a photograph similar to Fig. 17, but from a different specimen. 60 μ collimator, 1 h.

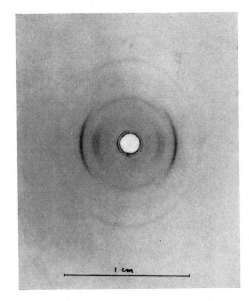

(a)   (b)

Fig. 19. (a) A bundle of cotton fibres; (b) the photograph from them. Camera 1, 12 h, point focus (0.3 mA).

References p. 457

These may be compared with Fig. 21 (a), a tangled bundle of redimiculous fibres from tissue, and (b), its photograph; and Fig. 22(a), a single vitreous fibre, and (b), its photograph. The resemblance is striking and goes a long way towards establishing the existence of cellulose-like fibres in animal tissue.

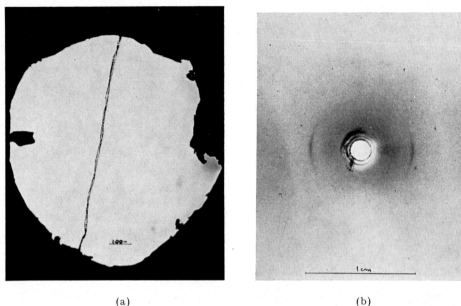

(a)   (b)

Fig. 20. (a) A single cotton fibre; (b) the photograph from it. Camera 1, 16 h.

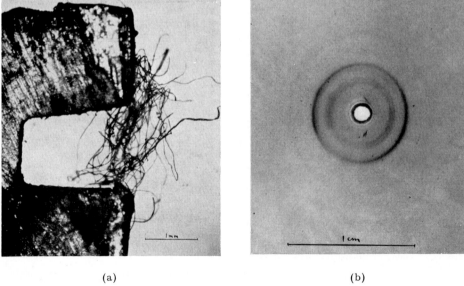

(a)   (b)

Fig. 21. (a) A tangled bundle of redimiculous fibres from animal tissue; (b) the photograph from them. Camera 1, 4 h.

References p. 457

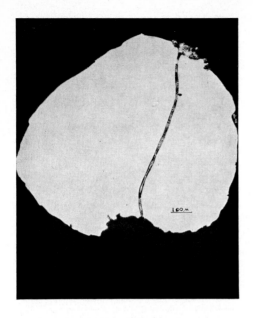
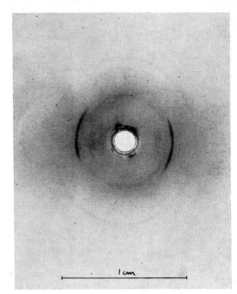

(a)   (b)

Fig. 22. (a) A single vitreous fibre; (b) its photograph. Camera 1, 12 h.

ACKNOWLEDGEMENTS

Camera 2 was developed as part of a programme of research into boiler corrosion sponsored by the Central Electricity Research Council, and the paper includes some of the results of that research. Acknowledgment is made to Mr. K. MELLENFIELD for help in the experimental work, and to Mr. G. ATKINSON for the reproductions. The X-ray tubes and cameras were made in the laboratory workshop under the direction of Mr. L. STEVENS.

REFERENCES

[1] D. LEWIS, *J. Sci. Instr.*, 32 (1955) 467.
[2] J. D. H. DONNAY, *Crystal Data - Determinative Tables*, Memoir 60, The Geological Society of America, 1954.
[3] N. RAST and B. A. STURT, *Nature*, 179 (1957) 215.
[4] A. J. CRUISE and J. W. JEFFERY, *Nature*, 183 (1959) 677.

FACTORS IN THE DETECTION OF LOW CONCENTRATIONS IN X-RAY DIFFRACTOMETRY

WILLIAM PARRISH and JEANNE TAYLOR

Philips Laboratories, Irvington-on-Hudson, N.Y. (U.S.A.)

ABSTRACT

The qualitative and quantitative aspects of measuring a crystalline phase present in small amounts in a relatively large specimen will be described. The sensitivity is dependent upon the peak-to-background ratio (P/B) of the chosen line, and the precision is dependent upon the intensity as well as P/B. Instrument alignment, geometry and counter tube technique have a large effect on these factors and methods of optimizing them will be described. The specimen matrix and the statistical factors involved in specimen preparation and intensity measurements will be discussed. The background always contains a considerable fraction of scattered characteristic radiation that cannot be eliminated with pulse amplitude discrimination or with a monochromator, and this limits the sensitivity of the analysis. The geometry of the focusing diffractometer using a reflection specimen will be compared with that of the transmission specimen followed by a focusing monochromator. The latter has some advantages in P/B, and much smaller volume of specimens can be used. However, in neither case can standard equipment be used effectively with microsamples because the apertures of the system are then limited by the specimen size and cause a large reduction of intensity.

INTRODUCTION

The relative intensities of lines in diffractometer patterns of individual polycrystalline substances may cover a range of two to three orders of magnitude, and in mixtures of substances the concentrations may also vary over wide limits. A question that frequently arises is, "What are the minimum detectable limits?" This question has considerable practical importance because identification of the substance can also be made by its powder diffraction pattern. It is possible by quantitative diffraction analysis to determine the phases present and from these data to calculate the chemical composition. This is an important application because elemental chemical analysis by X-ray fluorescence with presently available equipment is practically impossible for elements up to about atomic number 12 and quite difficult up to about 16.

The various factors that contribute to the precision and limits of the analysis will be outlined and references will be given to key papers in the literature which the reader may consult for further details. Only the modern counter diffractometer which employs a relatively large specimen will be considered[1]. Microsize specimens generally require high brilliance microfocus X-ray tubes and special diffractometer geometries to best utilize the much smaller total intensities.

The peak-to-background ratio of the most intense line of the powder pattern determines the minimum detectable amount of that substance. Obviously, the experimental difficulties increase as the peak-to-background ratio decreases, particularly when it falls below about 1 or 2. The absolute magnitudes of the peak intensity and the background have marked effects on the precision of the measurement and time required for a given precision. It is therefore clear that the maximum peak and minimum background intensities are the conditions that must be reached for the best results. These intensities are strongly affected by the instrument geometry and alignment, the characteristics of the detector system, the specimen properties and preparation, and the statistical factors in the measurements. Many of the factors influence the results in different ways, and since they combine in a complicated interrelated manner it is essential to optimize each.

INSTRUMENTAL FACTORS

In the modern counter tube diffractometer, a divergent primary beam is used with a flat specimen in a "focussing" arrangement[1]. The specimen is automatically rotated at one-half the angular speed of the receiving slit and counter tube in order to obtain the best focussing conditions and hence the sharpest lines at all reflection angles. Parallel or Soller slits are used to limit the axial (or "vertical") divergence of the primary and diffracted beams normal to the focussing plane. They make possible the use of an extended line source to obtain high intensity without causing excessive asymmetric broadening of the line profile.

The focal line of the X-ray tube viewed normal to its short dimension is the geometrical source of the X-ray optical system. In commercial sealed-off diffraction tubes the width varies from about 1.0 to 1.6 mm. When viewed at a small angle ψ the width is foreshortened, the length remaining the same. The effective width may be increased, thereby increasing the intensity and the peak-to-background ratio without decreasing the resolution because the various instrumental aberrations mask the effect of the small increase in source width[2]. The effective width can be doubled by increasing ψ from 3° to 6° and about a 25 % gain of intensity is obtained. If the width is doubled in the manufacture of the tube, the intensity may be increased 100 % for the same specific target loading. Combining the wider focus and the increased ψ results in an even larger increase of intensity with only a small loss of resolution.

The intensity is proportional to the angular aperture α of the primary beam in the focussing plane and the length of specimen illuminated is $l = \alpha R \sin \theta$ where R is the goniometer radius. It is therefore desirable to use the maximum α consistent with the length of specimen illuminated at the smallest diffraction angle. The use of a flat specimen rather than one whose front surface is curved to fit the focussing circle causes an asymmetric broadening of the line profile but has little effect on the peak intensity[3].

The receiving slit width is a major factor in determining the shape of the line profiles from well-crystallized substances. For the case of an unresolved Cu $K\alpha$ doublet, increasing the receiving slit width by a factor of 10 from 0.025° to 0.25° (2θ) increases the peak intensity by a factor of 4 but decreases the peak-to-background ratio and resolution by more than a factor of 2 ([2, 4]). It is therefore necessary to select the receiving slit width according to whether the intensity or peak-to-background ratio is the more important factor for a particular analysis.

To achieve optimum performance it is, of course, necessary to align the goniometer and its slits correctly with the X-ray source and mechanical devices have been developed for this purpose[5]. The goniometer specimen post must be set to the correct θ-angle when the middle of the receiving slit is at 2 θ. If this is not done accurately, the peak intensity and peak-to-background ratio will decrease by an amount dependent upon the missetting and the diffraction angle, and in addition may cause a systematic error when several lines are measured[2].

There is always a certain amount of scattering in the X-ray optical system and it is essential to align the anti-scatter slits properly to achieve a minimum background level. One of the important advantages of the diffractometer over film methods is that by the proper use of anti-scatter slits the counter tube receives radiation only from the irradiated portion of the sample regardless of the diffraction angle. The background at any angle is therefore related to a small angular range rather than to the entire pattern.

Detector system

It is now well accepted that counter tubes are far superior to film for the direct, rapid and accurate measurement of X-ray intensities. Proportional and scintillation counters are better suited to measurements of lines with low peak-to-background ratios than Geiger-Mueller counters because they make it possible to use electronic discrimination methods[6,7]. For a given instrument, the measured intensity is determined by the quantum counting efficiency of the counter tube[8], and the peak-to-background ratio by the spectral response of the counter-discriminator system.

The quantum counting efficiency of the NaI·Tl scintillation counter is nearly 100 % for all the wavelengths normally used in diffractometry. Since the polycrystalline specimen scatters the entire incident X-ray spectrum with varying efficiency, it is essential to use a single channel pulse-height analyzer whose window is set to transmit the characteristic X-ray line pulses and eliminate most of the non-characteristic X-ray pulses reaching the scaling circuit, thereby decreasing the recorded background. The effectiveness of the electronic discrimination method is illustrated in Fig. 1 for a copper target tube operated at 40 kVp with full-wave rectification. The analyzer set to transmit about 90 % of Cu $K\alpha$ removes practically the entire short wavelength continuum, and the nickel filter removes the Cu $K\beta$ line and the continuum just below the Ni K absorption edge. The pulses recorded by the scaler are thus almost entirely due to Cu $K\alpha$ plus a small amount of the long wavelength continuum that is not removed by the analyzer or filter. In the case of the (111) line of a pure silicon polycrystalline specimen, discrimination increased the peak-to-background ratio from 12 to 134 while the peak intensity decreased by only 10 %. The remaining background consisted mainly of scattered Cu $K\alpha$ radiation. Hence further narrowing of the analyzer window caused the peak intensity to decrease at a more rapid rate than the rate of gain in peak-to-background ratio.

The quantum counting efficiency of the xenon proportional counter is about one-half that of the scintillation counter for Cu $K\alpha$ and longer wavelengths (mainly because of window absorption) and falls off to lower values with decreasing wavelength, being about one-seventh that of the scintillation counter at Mo $K\alpha$ (because of low absorption in the gas). Hence, background caused by scattered radiation is much lower than that observed with the scintillation counter with no discrimination. The peak-to-background ratio for the same condition mentioned above was 57 without the analyzer and 146 with it. Although the energy resolution of the proportional counter is about 2.5 times better than that of the scintillation counter, there is little improvement in the recorded peak-to-background ratio using non-fluorescent polycrystalline specimens.

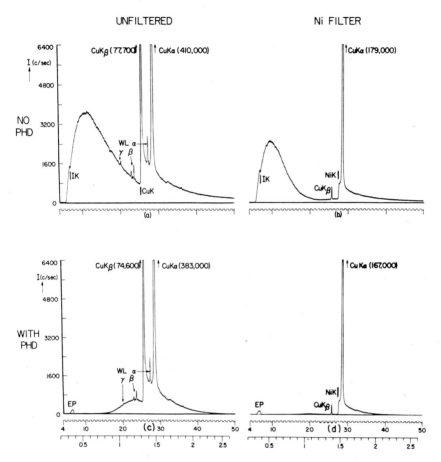

Fig. 1. Effect of setting pulse-height analyzer to detect 90 % of Cu $K\alpha$ and of 0.0007 in. Ni filter on the spectrum of a Cu target X-ray tube. Si (111) analyzer, scintillation counter. The upper scale gives the 2θ-angle and the lower scale the wavelength in Å.

The energy resolution of the proportional and scintillation counters is not very high, and hence the degree of monochromatization achieved by electronic discrimination is not comparable with that of a crystal monochromator. Nevertheless it is of some interest to compare the peak-to-background ratios of the discrimination method with those obtained with a crystal monochromator [9,10]. The monochromator may reflect the subharmonic wavelengths $\lambda/2$ and $\lambda/3$ which could easily be eliminated by the discriminator. The monochromator reduces the intensity and the amount of reduction depends on the particular monochromator geometry used. In the case of reflecting specimen arrangements, the intensities are reduced by factors of 5 to 20 compared to the standard diffractometer. The most efficient arrangement is to use the specimen in transmission because the angular aperture can be increased so that much of the intensity lost in the monochromatization is restored. Using a transmission specimen followed by a monochromator bent in the form of a logarithmic spiral it is possible to obtain intensities up to about one-half of those obtained with a standard diffractometer set up for maximum resolution[11]. (A Johansson-type monochromator may also be used.) Although the continuum is entirely eliminated, there remains the scattered characteristic Cu $K\alpha$ background and the peak-to-background ratios are not much better than those obtained with the discriminator. The monochromator in this arrangement is of course most advantageous in eliminating specimen fluorescence.

The use of such short wavelength radiations as Mo $K\alpha$ increases the scattering cross-section of the specimen. The peak-to-background ratios are always lower than those obtained with Cu $K\alpha$ because the short wavelength Mo $K\alpha$ lines occur near the peak of the continuum and the electronic discrimination is not effective in the immediate vicinity of the spectral lines[12]. Under the same experimental conditions and using the pulse-height analyzer, the peak-to-background ratio is more than 3 times higher for Cu $K\alpha$ than for Mo $K\alpha$.

Although fluorescent sources have no continuum, their brightness is about $1/1000$ of the direct electron-excited X-ray source and hence the intensities are much too low for powder diffractometry[13].

COUNTING STATISTICS

When the intensities and peak-to-background ratios are low, the counting statistics play an important part in determining the precision of the analysis[4]. The relative error of an individual measurement is $\varepsilon = Q/N^{1/2}$ where N is the total number of counts and Q is a constant determined by the confidence level. $Q = 0.67$, 1.64 and 2.58 for the 50 %, 90 % and 99 % confidence levels, respectively. Thus to obtain a result within 1 % of the true value requires the accumulation of 4,500, 27,000 or 67,000 counts depending on the confidence level chosen. However, the background may markedly influence the results, and in practically all analyses two measurements are required — one on the peak plus background, and another on the background. If n_1 is the counting rate of the former, and n_2 of the latter, and ε_1 and ε_2 are the relative errors, the absolute errors are $n_1\varepsilon_1$ and $n_2\varepsilon_2$ and the relative error of the difference is

$$\varepsilon_d = \frac{\left[(n_1\varepsilon_1)^2 + (n_2\varepsilon_2)^2\right]^{1/2}}{n_1 - n_2}.$$

Hence the absolute errors of both the peak and background have about the same influence on ε_d. When a large number of measurements is required and the total time is limited, it is advisable to apportion the time in an optimum manner so as to obtain the maximum precision of $n_1 - n_2$ in the available time[14].

Table I shows the effect of intensity and peak-to-background ratio on the number of counts that must be accumulated and the total time required for 1 % accuracy of $n_1 - n_2$ at the 50 % and 90 % confidence levels. The peak and background counting rates have been chosen to represent typical cases which might be encountered in the determination of small concentrations of a polycrystalline substance. The table shows the number of counts required in measuring the intensities of the peak-plus-background N_1 and the background N_2 for 1 % accuracy in the peak

References p. 466

TABLE I

$P, c/s$ n_1-n_2	$B, c/s$ n_2	P/B $(n_1-n_2)/n_2$	1% accuracy					
			50% confidence level			90% confidence level		
			N_1 (10^3 counts)	N_2 (10^3 counts)	$T(min)$	N_1 (10^3 counts)	N_2 (10^3 counts)	$T(min)$
250	50	5	9	1	0.7	55	4	4.3
250	125	2	16	3	1.2	95	18	6.7
250	250	1	31	11	1.8	184	65	10.4
250	500	0.5	75	41	3.0	441	239	17.8
100	50	2	16	3	2.8	95	18	16.7
100	100	1	31	11	4.4	184	65	26.1
100	500	0.2	313	239	16.7	1850	1409	98.4
10	10	1	31	11	44.2	184	65	261.1
10	50	0.2	313	239	166.7	1850	1409	983.8

intensity. It can be seen from the table that the total time spent for a given accuracy increases rapidly with decreasing peak-to-background ratio.

SPECIMEN CHARACTERISTICS

The specimen preparation is usually the limiting factor in the precision of the data. The specimen must be homogeneous and unstrained, and its surface representative of the bulk of the sample because only a thin surface layer contributes to the diffraction except in the case of very low absorbing samples. In the latter case the sample should be thick enough to absorb the entire beam at all diffraction angles for otherwise corrections must be applied to intensities of lines occurring at different diffraction angles[15] to account for the variation in effective scattering volume. However, thick low absorbing specimens may cause undesirable asymmetric broadening of the line profiles. If this effect is to be avoided, a thin layer of the sample should be mounted on a low reflecting surface, such as a single-crystal quartz plate, Mylar, or properly oriented cellophane. For this case the intensity corrections described above are necessary. The intensity is a function of the effective diffracting volume of the sample and the absorption of the matrix, decreasing with increasing absorption.

The crystallite sizes may have a large effect on the relative and absolute intensities. To reproduce the relative intensities of different specimen preparations to about 1 % the crystallite sizes should be in the range 1 to 5 μ. Larger sizes cause variations in the relative intensities of the lines which may result in a considerable random error[16]. Rapid rotation of the specimen in its own plane averages the intensity fluctuations, and this technique should be used to avoid large specimen statistical errors in the relative intensities. Rotating the specimen has no effect on the absolute intensities which are influenced by the packing density, extinction, etc., and usually increase with decreasing crystallite size.

Preferred orientation of the crystallites has a profound effect on the observed relative intensities of the lines. For an oriented specimen the intensities of the planes parallel to the specimen surface are enhanced and those normal are reduced compared to the random specimen. A comparison of the relative intensities of, say ool and hko, reflections obtained with the *same* specimen, in a standard goniometer and in transmission using the monochromator arrangement referred to above, gives the degree of preferred orientation. Rotating the sample reduces the effects of the preferred orientation only within the plane and is not helpful in the situation just described.

Specimen fluorescence may be a problem in causing high backgrounds, but can often be controlled by the proper choice of X-ray tube target to avoid fluorescence, or placement of the β filter — either on the divergence slit if the β radiation from the target is causing fluorescence, or on the receiving slit if it will screen out undesired wavelengths. Other filters may also be used to selectively absorb the fluorescent and transmit the characteristic radiation. In general, the discrimination method is helpful in reducing the fluorescent background only when the wavelength is relatively far removed from the characteristic wavelength.

EXPERIMENTAL RESULTS

A Norelco diffractometer[1] was used with 1° angular aperture, 0.05° receiving slit and scintillation counter with the pulse-height analyzer window set to transmit about 90 % Ni-filtered Cu $K\alpha$ radiation.

To illustrate the effect of matrix absorption on the minimum detectable limits, mixtures were prepared of various compositions of silicon in tungsten and in lithium fluoride. The materials were weighed on an analytical balance and the mixtures were blended until homogeneous as determined by reproducible X-ray intensities from several specimens prepared from each composition. The compositions represented were nominally 0.1, 1, 5, and 10 % by weight of silicon in tungsten (approximately 1, 8, 29, and 45 % by volume) and 0.01, 0.1, 1, 5, and 10 % by weight of silicon in lithium fluoride (approximately the same composition by volume).

Both peak and integrated intensity measurements were made of the silicon (111), (220) and (400) reflections from rotating specimens. The peak measurements proved to be the more desirable both from the standpoint of convenience in measuring and consideration of counting statistics. Plots of the peak counting rates with background subtracted against percentage composition are given in Fig. 2. Since the background is essentially constant for the low concentrations involved, plots of peak-to-background ratios against composition would be virtually the same as those shown in Fig. 2.

For 0.1 % silicon in tungsten, only the silicon (111) reflection could barely be detected above background, and this composition represents the approximate lower limit of sensitivity for this case. For the lower absorbing lithium fluoride matrix, the sensitivity is greater by almost an order of magnitude, the lowest detectable limit being about 0.01 % silicon. Here, however, the background is considerably higher than for the tungsten matrix and this must be taken into account in apportioning the measuring time as discussed in the section on counting statistics.

It is possible to use a strong line of the matrix as a standard. In this case, the working curves are plots of the ratio of the intensity of the line of the unknown to the matrix line intensity as illustrated in Fig. 3. This procedure eliminates the effects of small day-to-day variations in experimental conditions such as the primary beam intensity. Of course, if the matrix is amorphous, this method cannot be used, and either a standard reference substance must be added in a known amount or the intensity measurements from various samples must be made under the same conditions used for preparation of the working curves.

References p. 466

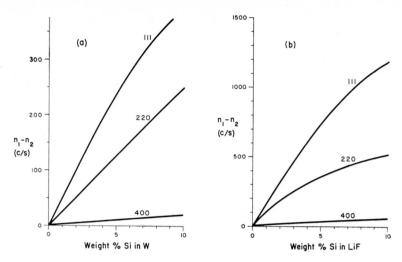

Fig. 2. Peak counting rates $(n_1 - n_2)$ of silicon reflections plotted against percentage composition of silicon in tungsten (a) and in lithium fluoride (b). Ni-filtered Cu K radiation, scintillation counter with pulse-height discrimination.

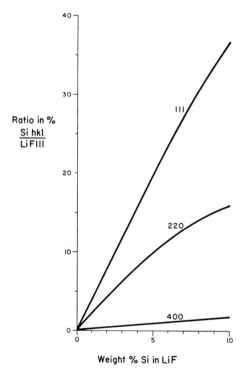

Fig. 3. Ratio of the intensity of various silicon reflections to the intensity of the lithium fluoride (111) reflection plotted against percentage composition. Ni-filtered Cu K radiation, scintillation counter with pulse-height discrimination.

REFERENCES

[1] W. Parrish, E. A. Hamacher and K. Lowitzsch, *Philips Tech. Rev.*, 16 (1954/55) 123.

[2] W. Parrish, Advances in X-ray diffractometry of clay minerals, *Proc. Seventh Natl. Conf. Clays and Clay Minerals, Washington, D.C.*, 1958, Pergamon Press, London (in the press).

[3] A. J. C. Wilson, *J. Sci. Instr.*, 27 (1950) 321.

[4] W. Parrish, *Philips Tech. Rev.*, 17 (1955/56) 206.

[5] W. Parrish and K. Lowitzsch, *Am. Mineralogist*, 44 (1959) 765.

[6] W. Parrish and T. R. Kohler, *Rev. Sci. Instr.*, 27 (1956) 795.

[7] A. Trost, *Z. angew. Phys.*, 10 (1958) 404.

[8] J. Taylor and W. Parrish, *Rev. Sci. Instr.*, 26 (1955) 367; *ibid.*, 27 (1956) 108.

[9] A. R. Lang, *Rev. Sci. Instr.*, 27 (1956) 17.

[10] G. Leineweber and E. Heller, *Z. Krist.*, 109 (1957) 198.

[11] P. M. de Wolff, W. Parrish and K. Lowitzsch, *Diffractometer with transmission specimen and focussing monochromator*, (in preparation).

[12] W. Parrish and T. R. Kohler, *J. Appl. Phys.*, 27 (1956) 1215.

[13] W. Parrish, K. Lowitzsch and N. Spielberg, *Acta Cryst.*, 11 (1958) 400.

[14] M. Mack and N. Spielberg, *Spectrochim. Acta*, 12 (1958) 169.

[15] M. E. Milberg, *J. Appl. Phys.*, 29 (1958) 64.

[16] P. M. de Wolff, J. M. Taylor and W. Parrish, *J. Appl. Phys.*, 30 (1959) 63.

SMALL-ANGLE SCATTERING APPARATUS WITH A POINT-FOCUSING MONOCHROMATOR

K. SIEGBAHN and S. HAGSTRÖM

Institute of Physics, University of Uppsala (Sweden)

ABSTRACT

An instrument for studying small-angle scattering of X-rays with a point-focusing monochromator has been designed and built. A circular lamina (diameter 60 mm, thickness 0.5 mm) cut along the atomic planes 10$\bar{1}$0, is bent between two concentric circular edges which gives a point-to-point focusing system. The X-ray tube has a focal area as seen under an angle of 6° of 0.14 × 0.10 mm². The atomic planes chosen give a Bragg angle of approximately 80° for Al K_α in the first order, Ag L_α in the second and Cr K_β, Mn K_α, in the fourth order. The distance between the X-ray tube and the crystal is 1 m. Samples of powders or solutions are held in a cell with windows of thin mylar films. The distance sample–focus can be varied continuously from about 80 cm. The recording of the scattering curves can be made either photographically or by means of a counting tube. Investigations are made on Dow Polystyrene Latex with particle diameters: 0.340, 0.264, 0.138 μ. To get the first ten rings of the 0.264 μ fraction with a distance sample–focus 850 mm, an exposure time of 3 h was needed. The camera resolved the central first order of the 640 Å period of dry kangeroo-tail-tendon collagen and is capable of resolving consecutive orders of spacings as high as 10,000 Å.

A number of crystal point-focusing monochromators for X-rays have been designed and built. A method is described below of bending a single quartz crystal with a rather simple device for a point-focusing monochromator.

For focusing of X-rays in one dimension the crystal must have a shape according to JOHANSSON (Fig. 1b). A Johann-bent crystal, however, gives nearly perfect focusing for large Bragg angles. In order to obtain a point-focusing crystal the

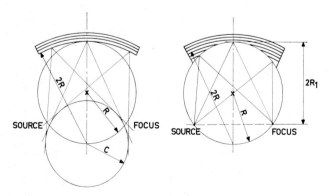

Fig. 1. Bendings of a crystal for focusing of X-rays in one dimension. (a) Johann; (b) Johansson.

atomic planes must have two principal radii of curvature, $2R$ and $2R_1$ in planes perpendicular to each other. These radii are related to the Bragg angle θ by the relation:

$$R_1 = R\sin^2\theta$$

Fig. 2 shows the cross section of the crystal holder. The crystal used is a circular quartz lamina (diameter 60 mm, thickness 0.5 mm) with the atomic planes ($10\bar{1}0$) parallel to the crystal surface. The spacing is 4.24602 kX-unit. The lamina is bent

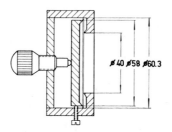

Fig. 2. Cross section of the crystal holder. Dimensions and atomic planes of the quartz crystal used. Diameter of crystal 60 mm. Thickness of crystal: 0.5 mm. Atomic planes: ($10\bar{1}0$). Spacing: 4.24602 kX-units.

between the two concentric circular edges of hardened steel by means of a finely threaded screw. Due to the anisotropically elastic properties of the crystal the central portion of the surface has different radii of curvature for different azimuths. The atomic planes chosen give a Bragg angle of approximately 80° for the following wavelengths and reflection orders:

$$
\begin{aligned}
&\text{Al} \quad K\alpha\,; \quad &\lambda = 8.03 \text{ Å} \quad &\text{(1. order)}\\
&\text{Ag} \quad L\alpha_1; \quad &\lambda = 4.15 \text{ Å} \quad &\text{(2. order)}\\
&\text{Cr} \quad K\beta_1; \quad &\lambda = 2.08 \text{ Å} \quad &\text{(4. order)}\\
&\text{Mn} \quad K\alpha_1; \quad &\lambda = 2.10 \text{ Å} \quad &\text{(4. order)}
\end{aligned}
$$

The curvature was adjusted by means of an optical device so that the distance between the X-ray source and the crystal becomes 1 m for a Bragg angle of about

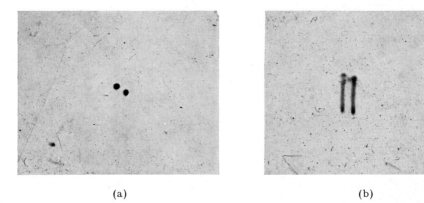

(a)   (b)

Fig. 3. Focusing properties of the crystal: (a) Image with crystal in point-focusing position; (b) image with crystal rotated 90° from position (a).

80°. Fig. 3a illustrates the good focusing properties of the crystal surface, which forms an image of a point light source placed in the position of the X-ray source. The crystal holder has then been rotated 90° around its axis of symmetry and in Fig. 3b the astigmatic error is quite pronounced. The two images come from reflection in the front and back surfaces of the crystal. The point-focusing properties also hold for X-rays.

The monochromator is used in an apparatus for studying small-angle scattering of X-rays. The X-ray source consists of a Hilger micro-focus tube with a focal area of 1.4×0.1 mm^2 which is reduced to 0.14×0.1 mm^2 by the viewing angle. The characteristic radiation $K\alpha_1$ from a manganese anode is used. As there are no commercial manganese anodes available these are prepared by evaporating or electroplating a thin manganese metal layer on a silver base.

The principles of the apparatus are shown in Fig. 4. From the crystal a monochromatic beam of X-rays converges to a point focus. The sample to be investigated

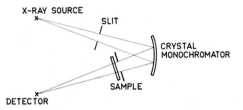

Fig. 4. Principles of the small-angle scattering apparatus.

Fig. 5. Total view of the equipment.

is placed in this beam. The detection of the scattered intensity can be made either photographically or by means of a proportional counter. The latter is a Norelco flow-proportional counter which can be provided with very thin windows. The pulses are selected in a single-channel pulse analyzer. The scattered intensity for different angles is obtained by placing an annular slit in front of the counter window at the focal plane and varying the distance between the sample and the slit. For this reason the sample holder is placed on a long screw which can be operated from the outside of the container. The maximum distance between the sample and the focus is 85 cm.

Fig. 6. Container with cover withdrawn.

In order to avoid air absorption and scattering the container is filled with hydrogen gas at atmospheric pressure. This has also the advantage that liquid samples can be held in very thin-walled cells. The samples are brought into the apparatus *via* a sluice. In order to decrease parasitic scattering from the crystal surface this has been etched with hydrofluoric acid.

Investigations have so far been made mainly on different fractions of Dow Polystyrene Latex, Fig. 7. These consist of very uniform spheres. Three different samples have been used with stated diameters of 0.340 μ, 0.264 μ and 0.138 μ respectively. The scattering function for a uniform sphere shows secondary maxima and these can be seen very well separated on the film. By measuring the diameters of the diffraction rings the size of the scattering particles can be obtained. It should be observed that the ring next to the direct beam is actually the zero order maximum which has "moved out" due to interparticle interference. Some exposures have also been made on dry collagen from kangaroo tail tendon, Fig. 8. The first order of the 637 Å spacing is well resolved from the direct beam. The camera is capable of resolving consecutive orders of spacings as high as 10,000 Å.

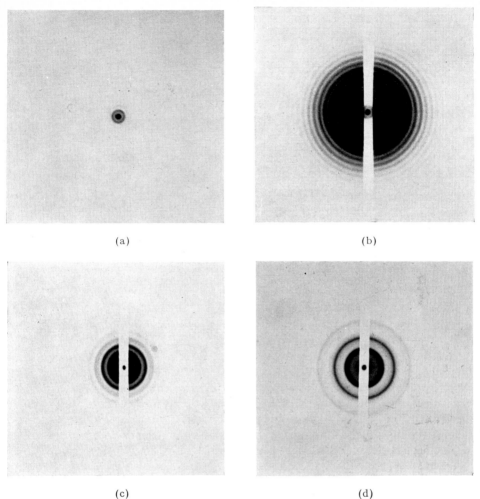

Fig. 7. Exposures on different fractions of Dow Polystyrene Latex with the following diameters and exposure times: a, 0.340 μ, 15 sec; b, 0.340 μ, 19 h; c, 0.264 μ, 15 min; d, 0 138 μ, 15 min.

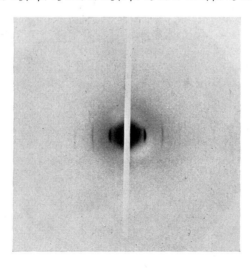

Fig. 8. Exposure on dry kangaroo tail tendon. Exposure time 20 h.

A SENSITIVE X-RAY DIFFRACTOMETER FOR MICRO-DIFFRACTION STUDIES

ALLAN SKERTCHLY

Textile Physics Laboratory, University of Leeds (Great Britain)

ABSTRACT

The mechanical details and electronic circuitry of a versatile diffractometer suitable for micro-diffraction studies are described. Emphasis is placed on the rapidity of securing the diffraction data together with convenient facilities to provide quantitative analysis of permanently stored magnetic tape records of observations. Incorporated is a memory loop which enables successive diffraction records to be stored and integrated until a sufficiently accurate record is obtained.

An analysis of errors and actual performance data is given.

GENERAL DESCRIPTION OF THE INSTRUMENT

Details of a similar but simpler type of apparatus for use with gross specimens possessing a longitudinal uniaxial orientation have recently been described elsewhere[1].

The microdiffractometer as finally evolved consists of two scanning arms attached to which are the radiation-sensitive detectors, usually Geiger-Müller or proportional counters (P.C.). The arms traverse planar paths at equiangular separations from the main beam with a rate of scan that is variable between wide limits, but is usually fixed near $1°$ of Bragg θ per second in order to make the apparatus "direct reading". The photograph, Fig. 1, and Figs. 2 and 3, enable the salient features of the micro-diffractometer scanning assembly to be portrayed. The drive to the scanning arms is taken *via* a series of reduction gears to a pair of bevel gears which are allowed to rotate continuously in opposite directions. Actual engagement of the arms occurs only in the direction of increasing Bragg θ by means of magnetic clutches attached to the underside of each arm. The duration of engagement of the clutches is controlled between $2\theta_S$ and $2\theta_L$ from the Dekatron Master Timer which is described later. In order to retrace their paths back to the starting place near zero angle a spring-loaded restoring force is used at high values of Bragg θ, this being replaced by magnetic attraction when nearing and in the rest position.

The pulses from the radiation detectors are amplified, displayed, recorded and analyzed by means of apparatus shown schematically in Fig. 2. The main facilities available are shown, but a brief additional description here is perhaps not amiss since there are certain novel features. Most important is the direct recording of the entire diffraction data on magnetic tape in order to facilitate permanent storage and subsequent analysis. Since an important objective of apparatus of this type is to enable difficult experiments, involving time-dependent phenomena, to be carried out, the preservation of the entire set of observations with high fidelity is highly regarded. In order to allow of visual comparison with different diffraction patterns, a ratemeter and direct current oscilloscope fitted with an automatic recording camera

References p. 482

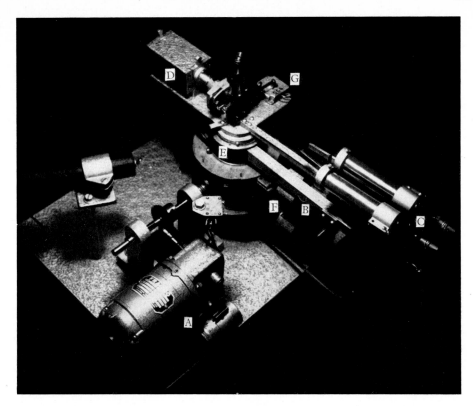

Fig. 1. Photograph of the scanning section of the microdiffractometer. A, Drive motor; B, Scanning arms; C, Geiger-Müller counter; D, Incident X-ray beam collimator; E, Trigger photocell; F, Magnetic clutches; G, Specimen-absorption and angle-calibration device.

are also incorporated. Normally, photographic recordings are only made of particular traces. The quantitative evaluation of the recordings (or of the current scan) is readily carried out using the Intensity Analyzer. With this component the number of pulses (and hence the integrated intensity) occurring between any two particular Bragg θ positions may be measured, and the results printed on paper tape.

A dual magnetic tape-recording channel is used. Channel 1 carries the timing and diffraction information and channel 2 enables a simultaneous description (or associated measurement) of the experiment to be recorded.

Since the normal rate of scanning is high, one scan alone may not yield a sufficiently accurate record. To enable integration of the effects of successive scans to be carried out, a memory-loop integrator has been developed. This enables each new scan to be recorded on top of the previous one until a sufficient number of quanta have been received.

MAIN FEATURES

The main features of the technique may thus be summarized as follows.

(1) Dual fast-scanning X-ray detectors of high quantum efficiency.

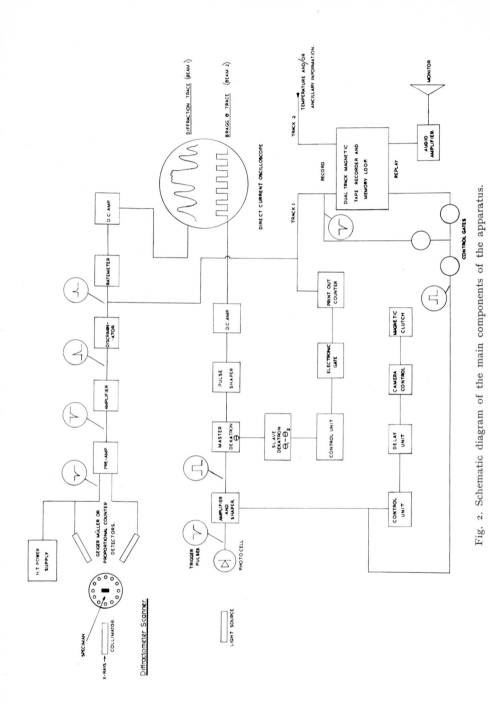

Fig. 2. Schematic diagram of the main components of the apparatus.

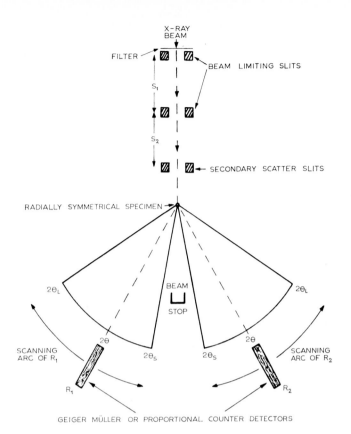

Fig. 3. Plan of the collimating and scanning section. The radiation detectors R_1 and R_2 perform symmetrical scans over the arcs defined by $2\,\theta_S$ to $2\,\theta_L$. $S_1 = 8$ cm $S_2 = 5$ cm. The incident beam collimating slits are adjustable from $0-1$ mm.

(2) Magnetic tape recording of the diffraction data with high fidelity and low operating costs.

(3) A memory loop for the integration of successive traces to ensure the desired accuracy of the diffraction data.

(4) Variable scanning rates.

(5) Oscilloscopic display and photographic recording of the *desired* diffraction patterns.

(6) An intensity analyzer for the rapid evaluation of records.

(7) Printing-out counter to enable the analyzer to perform unattended.

(8) Automatic operation during both the initial scanning and analytical functions.

Specimen absorption, angle calibration and incident beam-intensity monitoring

A suitable system of calibration for the apparatus is provided by means of two silver foils which may be simultaneously placed in position both before and after the specimen. The calibration is not provided continuously but is usually introduced during a portion of the scan that is not otherwise required.

References p. 482

Fig. 4 shows the details schematically together with the relevant parameters for an analysis of the method. The usual specimen shape is cylindrical, but if this is irradiated with a fine beam and we concern ourselves only with diffraction at the lower angles then an analytical approximation is afforded by an infinite block.

In this case it is easily shown that the diffracted intensity from the specimen is given by

$$I_{2\theta} = I_0 f(2\theta) e^{-2\mu R \sec 2\theta} \frac{\left(e^{2\mu R (\sec 2\theta - 1)} - 1\right)}{\mu(\sec 2\theta - 1)}$$

where $f(2\theta)$ is the intensity distribution function and $\mu =$ linear absorption coefficient.

If we assume $2\mu R (\sec 2\theta - 1)$, is small, and we let $R_1 =$ ratio of intensities scattered by the foils with the specimen in position and $R_2 =$ corresponding ratio without the specimen then we find

$$f(2\theta) \propto \frac{I_{2\theta} R_2 \sec 2\theta}{R_1 I_0 \propto \ln\left(\frac{R_2}{R_1}\right)}.$$

This factor embodies corrections for:

(a) long-term drift variations in incident beam intensity,
(b) specimen shape,
(c) specimen size.

The foils may also be used as a convenient source of Bragg θ calibration, but since the foils are not mounted coincident with the specimen, there will be an apparent shift in Bragg angle due to longitudinal displacement along the incident beam axis. The change in one recorded angle is given by

$$\Delta\theta \simeq \pm \frac{90}{\pi} \frac{(l_1 + R) \sin 2\theta}{(L + l)}$$

and similarly for the other. These terms may easily be calculated for a fixed specimen–detector distance.

This displacement is shown in the inset diagram in Fig. 4.

Mechanical details of scanning system

To meet the stringent mechanical requirements great care was needed in machining the components. The main requirements of the scanning system were:

(1) A uniform dual equiangular planar scan over the desired range.
(2) Provision for securing near equal repetitive scans with the same duration to within narrow limits.
(3) Adequate stability and rigidity of the components.
(4) An accurately known and maintained centre of rotation.

Double ball races attached to the main central pillar secure accurate alignment of the gears and scanning arms, and the central assembly is held secure by retaining plates at the top and bottom. The zero angle fiducial point and beam stop are both attached to the top retaining plate, which forms an integral part of the incident beam collimating assembly.

In order to safeguard the apparatus, limit switches are provided to cut off the motor drive at a particular preset overdrive angle.

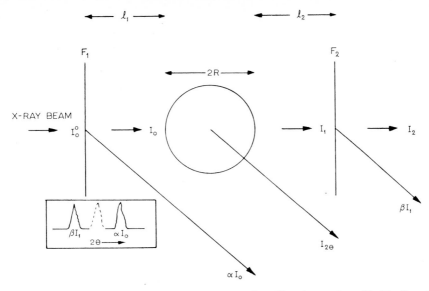

Fig. 4. Geometry of the specimen absorption and angle calibration system. F_1, F_2 silver foils, $I_0^0 \approx I_0$, $I_1 \approx I_2$ X-ray intensities at the indicated positions. l_1, l_2 specimen–foil distances. αI_0, βI_1, $I_{2\theta}$, diffracted beam intensities. The inset diagram shows the displacement of the beam diffracted by the calibrating foils.

X-ray detectors

The choice of X-ray detector is conditioned by the need for a device of high quantum efficiency. Two counters, a Geiger-Müller counter (Type MX 118 by Mullard Ltd.) and a P.C. of special design[2,3] have been used with success. For the high counting rates which are necessary to secure sufficiently accurate data in short times the P.C. has decided advantages, and in particular a low rate of counting loss due to the short resolving time. Further, partial beam monochromatization may be secured with a suitable "kick sorter". This may be useful when using non-filtered X radiation. The P.C. utilizes a diagonal absorption path leading to a high quantum efficiency and a low "wall effect". Other characteristics of the counter make it eminently suitable for the work in hand. However, both these types of detector suffer from the serious drawback of bulk which precludes their use in particular applications. Thus, the use of photoconductors is being investigated, particularly as back-reflection micro-diffraction studies of metal complexes could be investigated with their aid. Low-angle diffraction patterns at short specimen–detector distances must at present be obtained using only one detector in position.

Electronic circuitry

Most of the electrical components used are readily available commercially. A number of minor modifications, such as the alteration of time constants and input and output impedances were necessary in order to secure adequate compatability of the various units.

The Master Timer consists of four Dekatrons driven from a 100 cycles, near constant frequency source. Added to the frequency dividers is an electronic gate, two thyratron control units and a counting register. A Slave set of Dekatrons is used to control the variable-period gate which is used in conjunction with the Intensity Analyzer.

Recording system and memory loop

Suitably attenuated shaped pulses from the ratemeter circuit are used for making a recording of the diffraction patterns. The initial pulses are negative going and this property is retained on the recording input. The trigger pulses, on the other hand, are square and positive going. This difference in polarity facilitates the operation of the various trigger circuits. The frequency response of the recorder is sufficient to enable pulses occurring in times down to 10^{-4} sec to be recorded with fidelity. This is adequate for Geiger-Müller pulses (duration $1—400$ μsec), but is totally inadequate for P.C. work at high intensities. If metallurgic applications of this technique were contemplated, a video-frequency magnetic tape recorder may be required. It might also be mentioned that the resolving time of the Dekatron counting valves in the Intensity Analyzer restricts the use of the apparatus at high counting speeds. For the applications intended these restrictions are not considered to be detrimental. The coefficient of variation of tape velocity should be kept as low as possible. Over a short period this amounts to $\cong 0.1 \%$ and this slightly affects the analytical accuracy.

Fig. 5 shows the high degree of fidelity between the original and recorded intensity distribution. Similar correspondence is obtained up to count rates of 1000/sec. Beyond this rate the system develops non-linearity of response. However, it is possible to do useful work with the P.C.'s up to 10,000 counts/sec if care is taken and suitable corrections are applied.

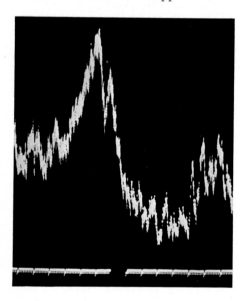 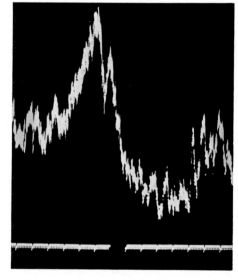

(a)   (b)

Fig. 5. Comparison of a direct (a) and recorded (b) observation. The specimen absorption and angle calibration peaks may be seen on the right hand side of the trace.

References p. 482

In order to overcome the inherent statistical limitations to accuracy at low counting rates, the integrative memory loop may be used. Fig. 6 shows, in outline, the components involved. In this application one track is used for the diffraction

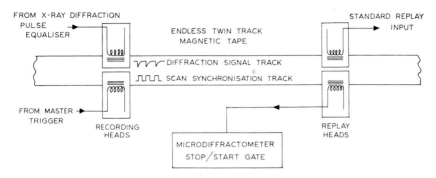

Fig. 6. Memory loop and scan integrator.

data and the second is used to provide accurate scan-synchronisation pulses. At the end of a scan there may be a pause in the drive system which waits to recommence its scan until after the receipt of a trigger pulse from the magnetic tape. In this way accurate integration is obtained without recourse to complex servo mechanisms.

The efficacy of the memory loop is demonstrated in Fig. 7 where successive traces of the same diffraction pattern are recorded.

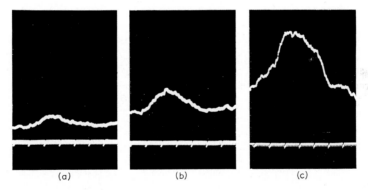

Fig. 7. Integrating effect of the memory loop. Notice the decrease in statistical uncertainty as the number of scans is increased from (a) 1 to (b) 4 to (c) 9. The associated error is reduced in the ratio 3 : 2 : 1. (The reflection is the equatorial 9.8 Å "spot" in wool keratin.)

Intensity Analyzer

The Intensity Analyzer is controlled by the Slave Dekatrons and relay system. It is normally intended as a facility for analysis of the recorded diffraction patterns but may be used directly on the scattered intensity. Since the scanning speed and Master Dekatron oscillator frequency are correlated and the standard scanning speed is $1°$ of Bragg θ/sec, the frequency dividers are also *per se* angle measurers. The Slave Dekatrons are attached to two separate coincidence circuits that actuate

References p. 482

relays at the end of preset intervals. The intervals correspond to values of Bragg θ chosen within the scanning range and may be set to within 0.1° with great accuracy. It has been found that this degree of resolution of the pattern is adequate at present. The counting interval operates a gate on the printing counter and at the end of its analysis a further relay operates the printing sequence to produce a direct count of the number of quanta scattered between the particular chosen limits. The analytical function is automatic and sequential. Analyses of sets of recorded diffraction patterns may be carried out for a duration of up to two hours (the limiting capacity of the magnetic store).

Table I shows the accuracy of the analyzer during successive analyses of a set of diffraction patterns. The Intensity Analyzer provides the more accurate evaluation of the records.

TABLE I

COMPARISON OF ANALYSIS OF AN EQUATORIAL X-RAY INTENSITY DISTRIBUTION

Direct (a)				Recorded (b)				Recorded (c)			
1	0	0	8	1	0	0	0	1	0	0	0
1	0	1	3	1	0	1	3	1	0	0	4
1	5	7	0	1	5	7	3	1	5	6	6
0	9	0	9	0	9	0	7	0	9	0	7
0	5	7	6	0	5	7	2	0	5	7	0
1	3	0	3	1	3	0	0	1	2	9	8

Errors and distortions

A complete analysis of the analytical errors associated with the apparatus has not yet been made. However, it is clearly evident that amidst many minor sources of aberration there are but two dominant factors which must be taken into account.

The subsidiary errors affect the analytical counter much less than the photographic record and include such factors as variation in tape speed, gating errors, lack of linearity in the oscilloscope display, optical errors and aberrations introduced during the photographic process.

However, the sum total of the above errors is small compared with a basic inherent limitation of the method. This is due to the random nature of arrival of quanta leading to a Poisson distribution about a mean rate x, giving the probability of recording n quanta as

$$p(n) = \frac{x^n e^{-x}}{n!}$$

and since the variance is equal to x the coefficient of variation (V) is equal to

$$\frac{100}{\sqrt{xT}}$$

where T is the duration of a scan.

Since accuracy is inversely proportional to $\sqrt{T}$, a tenfold diminution in scanning time only reduces accuracy threefold. Consequently, for a number of applications where highest accuracy is not important, the fast detecting methods may be most useful. When using the ratemeter method of integration, certain other problems present themselves. Consideration of the "flyback" period is governed by the fact that equilibrium of the detector response (to within σ) occurs in time[4]

$$t = \frac{RC}{2} \ln (2NRC) \cdot$$

Thus the "flyback" time for sequential traces can never be less than a value determined by the parameters of the analysis under investigation. For example, with $RC = 1$ and $N = 1000$, $t \simeq 4.0$ sec. Alternatively the maximum value of RC that can be used at this counting rate under the standard conditions is $\simeq 2.3$ sec.

A useful approximation to many scanned diffraction lines is a triangular waveform with a leading edge rising linearly as a function $v = kt$. In this case when $t = T$

$$V = \frac{100}{\sqrt{RCk}} \frac{\sqrt{T/2 + \frac{RC}{4} e^{-2T/RC} - \frac{RC}{4}}}{T + RC\, e^{-T/RC} - RC}$$

and the variation of precision along the diffraction line may be assessed. The importance of high counting rates is evident.

To simplify the comparison of photographic records it is important to appreciate the effect of a finite time constant which causes an apparent shift in lattice spacing.

The true profile $\psi(t)$ is obtained from the observed profile $\theta(t)$ by using the relationship

$$\psi(t) = \dot{\theta}(t) RC + \theta(t).$$

The effect of various time constants on the observed profiles is shown in Fig. 8.

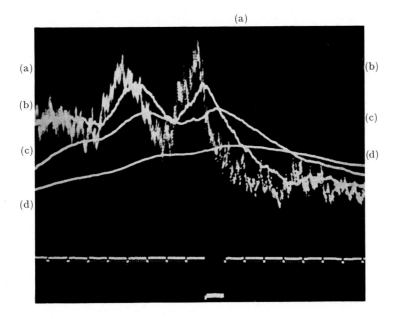

Fig. 8. Distortion of trace due to the finite time constant. (a) $RC = 0.3$ sec. (b) $RC = 1$ sec. (c) $RC = 3$ sec. (d) $RC = 10$ sec. Notice the displacement of apparent Bragg spacing.

ACKNOWLEDGEMENTS

The generous advice and wise counsel of H. J. Woods is appreciatively acknowledged. To Professor J. B. Speakman for his encouragement and continued support, to the Wool Research Council, and to all earlier workers whose ideas have been unconsciously incorporated, I express my deepest thanks.

The mechanical construction of the instrument was carried out under the direction of R. Haynes to whom the author is deeply indebted.

REFERENCES

[1] A. R. B. Skertchly, *Nature*, 180 (1957) 802.
[2] A. R. B. Skertchly, *J. Sci. Instr.*, 33 (1956) 209.
[3] A. R. B. Skertchly, *Rev. Sci. Instr.*, 27 (1956) 324.
[4] L. I. Schiff and R. D. Evans, *Rev. Sci. Instr.*, 7 (1936) 456.

AN X-RAY GENERATOR WITH A WIDE RANGE OF FOCAL AREAS

J. R. STANSFIELD

Hilger & Watts Ltd., London (Great Britain)

ABSTRACT

The target of a fine-focus X-ray tube can be loaded more heavily than the target of a broader focus tube, so that although its total power is smaller, its power per unit area of focus is much greater. The application of this principle is of particular importance in microanalytical techniques since exposure times are often long, and the correct choice of focal area can result in considerable improvements in speed. An X-ray generator will be described which has been developed primarily for diffraction studies, and in which simple interchangeable cathode guns give actual focal areas from a 0.04 mm diameter spot to a line some 5 or 6 mm long by about a tenth of a millimeter broad. Very high specific loadings are possible, depending on the particular focus required, and on the target material.

In X-ray microdiffraction work the intensity of the diffracted beams is usually very low and it is therefore necessary to pay particular attention to the efficient use of a high intensity source. One of the principal factors controlling the energy available for measurement is the power of the X-ray tube within the useful area of the focus. If a collimating system and a specimen define a certain focal area, any X-radiation originating outside that area is wasted, and by limiting the focus to that area unnecessary heating of the target is avoided, and a greater specific loading is possible over that limited area. On other occasions the size of the focus is of importance in itself, as, for example, in the study of individual grains in metals, or in ordinary powder diffractometry where the X-ray tube focal width is one of the factors determining the resolution. For these reasons it is very desirable to be able to select the appropriate focal area for the work in hand.

An X-ray generator which has already proved very useful in diffraction studies is seen in Fig. 1. The tube itself is slim and its focus only 19 mm from the outer wall so that apparatus can be brought very close. It is a demountable tube which allows not only interchangeable cathode guns giving different focal areas, but also target materials can be changed, and if desired a very high target loading may be used which would give an unacceptably short life to a sealed tube. It may be fitted with an EHRENBERG and SPEAR[1] type microfocus gun giving a focal area of 0.04 mm diameter, which with a copper target can be operated at a power of 25 watts or 15 kW per mm², or with a gun giving a larger focal area in the form of a line focus[2] 0.1 × 1.4 mm which operates with a copper target at 150 watts or 1.1 kW per mm². The latter gun is very compact, and it is possible to bring a camera and a diffractometer very close, and to operate the diffractometer up to high angles.

A new cathode gun for this X-ray tube has now been developed giving a larger focus still, approximately 0.1 × 5 mm, and operating at 450 watts or 0.9 kW per mm².

References p. 486

This is still a small area compared with a normal sealed X-ray diffraction tube, but the total power is lower by a factor of only about 2, and the intensity is higher by some 9 times.

Fig. 1. Hilger Microfocus X-ray generator.

Fig. 2 shows a simplified drawing of the new gun. It consists essentially of a curved filament of tungsten wire in a suitably shaped focussing slot which is biassed negatively with respect to the filament. The focussing slot and the tube walls are at earth potential and the anode positive by, say, 50 kV. The negative potential of the tube walls relative to the anode forms an essential part of the electron focussing system of the original versions of the X-ray tube, and may be regarded as producing a highly convergent electrostatic field. Since the new gun was for use in the same X-ray tube, this part of the system had to be retained, but a simple straight filament in a focussing slot was found to produce too short a focal line. By the shaping of the slot and filament an initial divergence in the electron trajectories is introduced, so that the length of the line focus is increased without materially affecting the focussing conditions across the line. The curvature of the filament is also chosen to ensure a

References p. 486

uniform loading along the length of the focus. The results obtained are indicated in
Fig. 3. The tube in this instance was operated at 50 kV. and the automatic biassing
resistance adjusted to give a tube current of 7.5 mA. As the filament current and

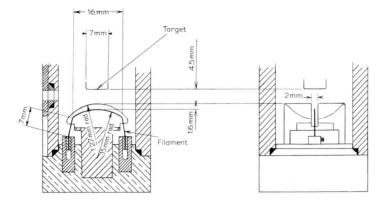

Fig. 2. Cathode assembly (diagrammatic).

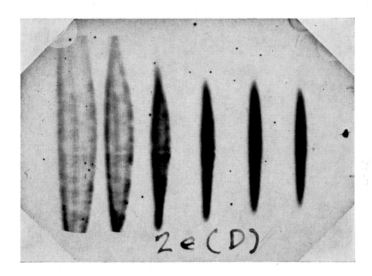

Fig. 3. Effect on focus of increasing bias voltage: Anode voltage 50 kV. Bias voltage increasing,
left to right, from 1020 to 1340 V. Filament current increasing to maintain tube current of 7.5 mA.

emission is increased, the bias may also be increased and the progressive sharpening
of the focus is seen. Further increase of filament current and bias shortens the focus
without materially reducing its width. These photographs were taken using a pinhole
camera technique at a viewing angle to foreshorten the length of the focus. At the
most suitable operating conditions the focal area is about 0.1 × 5 mm.

A set of characteristic curves for the tube is seen in Fig. 4. Tube current is plotted
against filament current for a series of different bias resistances, and the conditions
for optimum focus are indicated by the steeply sloping line. As the filament current

References p. 486

is increased there is a rather gradual approach to a saturation level, and a simple
empirical method has been established to find the correct operating points.

To operate at the high specific loadings possible with this X-ray tube, attention

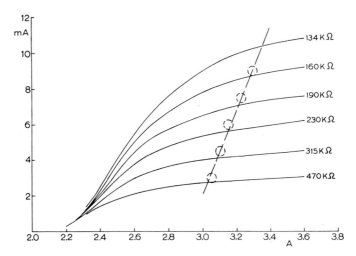

Fig. 4. Typical operating characteristics.

has to be given to the target cooling. In the lower power versions of the tube, interchangeable targets detachable from the main anode rod are used, but for the higher
power an interface between target and anode introduces too great a thermal resistance.
A complete interchangeable oil-cooled anode has, therefore, been developed, and the
mechanical design of the X-ray tube changed somewhat to make its removal and
replacement easier.

The complete instrument now forms a very versatile X-ray generator. The
target material and the focal area can be suited to the problem, the intensity is extremely high and the dimensions allow close approach to the source of radiation. It
is applicable not only in microdiffraction studies, but also over a wide range of more
general X-ray diffraction work.

REFERENCES

[1] W. EHRENBERG and W. E. SPEAR, *Proc. Phys. Soc. (London)*, B 64 (1951) 67.
[2] D. P. RILEY and J. R. STANSFIELD, *Acta Cryst.*, 10 (1957) 737.

C. METALLURGICAL APPLICATIONS

THE OBSERVATION OF DISLOCATIONS AND OTHER SUB-STRUCTURE IN CRYSTALS BY X-RAY DIFFRACTION MICROSCOPY

J. B. NEWKIRK

Research Laboratory, General Electric Co., Schenectady, N.Y. (U.S.A.)

ABSTRACT

An experimental study of silicon and lithium fluoride single crystals, using the BERG-BARRETT X-ray technique[1], has shown that the method is capable of revealing topographically individual undecorated dislocations as well as other subgrain structural details. The increased diffracted intensity at the dislocation sites is due to a local reduction of primary X-ray extinction. Since extinction is a direction-sensitive phenomenon, the direction of the Burgers vector of a dislocation may be found experimentally by comparing the intensity of its image in diffraction micrographs made with different hkl reflections. The best resolution which I have obtained to date, using this method, has been about $2\ \mu$.

Further details of this work have been published elsewhere[2].

REFERENCES

[1] C. S. BARRETT, *Trans. Am. Inst. Mining Met. Petrol. Engrs.*, 161 (1945) 15.
[2] J. B. NEWKIRK, *Am. Inst. Mining Met. Petrol. Engrs.*, 209 (1959).

SUBSTRUCTURE CHARACTERISTICS DISCLOSED BY A COMBINATION OF X-RAY REFLECTION MICROSCOPY AND DIFFRACTION ANALYSIS

S. WEISSMANN

College of Engineering, Rutgers, The State University of New Jersey, New Brunswick, N.J. (U.S.A.)

ABSTRACT

A method is described which combines light microscopy with X-ray reflection microscopy and diffraction analysis. The topographical relationship of the crystallites of a polycrystalline material as well as their fine-structural details are disclosed by a special technique of reflection X-ray microscopy using different portions of the spectrum, including heterogeneous, continuous and crystal-monochromatized radiation. The X-ray observations are correlated to those made by light microscopy and the individual crystallites are subsequently analyzed for their substructure characteristics. This analysis is accomplished by photographic tracing of the X-ray reflection images and by means of a method based on the principle of the X-ray double-crystal diffractometer. For metal specimens quantitative information is obtained concerning the lattice misalignment of the grains, the size of the subgrains, disorientation angle between subgrains, lattice misalignment existing within the subgrains and the structure of low-angle boundaries.

INTRODUCTION

For the solution of various problems in physical metallurgy, it is frequently desirable to investigate a metal or alloy specimen for lattice inhomogeneities and substructure. Various physical methods are used for this purpose, but the most commonly employed are the metallographic and X-ray methods. If these methods are employed it is often important to obtain a correlation of observations with respect to the identical crystallites of the specimen and this is particularly true if structural modifications resulting from physical or chemical processes are studied. Such correlation has been accomplished by a method combining light microscopy with X-ray reflection microscopy and diffraction analysis which will presently be described.

DESCRIPTION OF THE X-RAY METHOD

Referring to Fig. 1, a divergent, unfiltered X-ray beam P emerging from an X-ray tube passes through a collimator C. With the monochromatizing crystal A retracted from the path of the beam, the primary beam P passes unimpeded through a spectroscopic slit system B, which controls the cross-section of the X-ray beam, and impinges at a small grazing angle on the specimen surface of the polycrystalline test specimen S located at the center of a Debye-Scherrer camera E. A fine-grained photographic plate D is placed close to the specimen surface and a reflection X-ray micrograph of the grains on the specimen surface is obtained in the manner described by BERG[1] and BARRETT[2]. This experimental arrangement is depicted in Fig. 2 and schematically indicated by solid lines in Fig. 1. An X-ray micrograph obtained by this

References p. 496

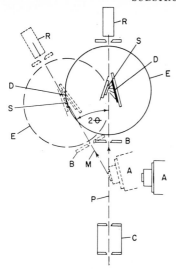

Fig. 1. Experimental arrangement for taking reflection X-ray micrographs. Solid lines with crystal A retracted indicate arrangement for use of heterogeneous and continuous radiation. Dashed lines with crystal A in reflecting position indicate arrangement for use of crystal-monochromatized radiation.

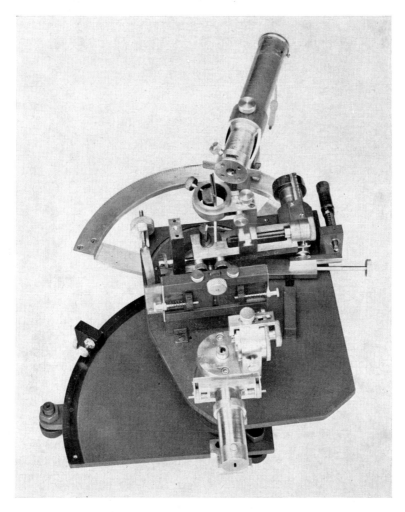

Fig. 2. Photograph of X-ray double-crystal diffractometer with plastic camera removed. Upper movable platform in position for experimental arrangement indicated by solid lines in Fig. 1.

References p. 496

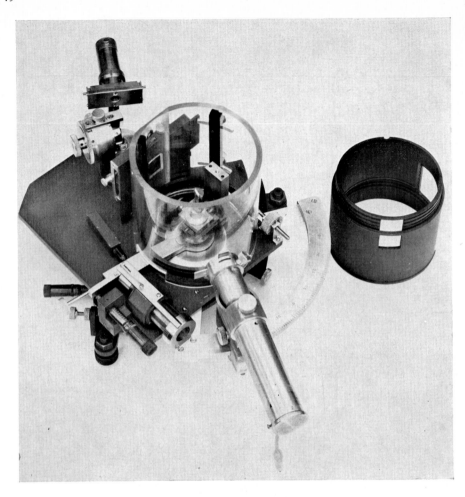

Fig. 3. Photograph of X-ray double-crystal diffractometer. Upper movable platform in position for experimental arrangement indicated by dashed lines in Fig. 1. Plastic camera aids in the location of reflections for the direct recording of intensities by radiation detector.

arrangement is shown in Fig. 4. The specimen which was investigated happened to be a 99.998 % aluminum specimen, cold-worked 81 % and annealed at 400° C for 1 hour. Since a divergent, unfiltered X-ray beam was employed, a great many grains satisfied the Bragg condition of reflection and were, therefore, recorded. The topographical relationship of the grains is clearly outlined on the X-ray micrograph and consequently the images can be directly correlated to those obtained by light microscopy, as shown in Fig. 5.

Although the BERG-BARRETT micrographs of polycrystalline materials supply a great deal of information concerning the surface texture, topography and reflecting power of lattice domains, they have serious limitations. Due to the fact that the incident beam is divergent and unfiltered, fine-structural details of the individual grains cannot be disclosed. Furthermore, from the viewpoint of diffraction analysis

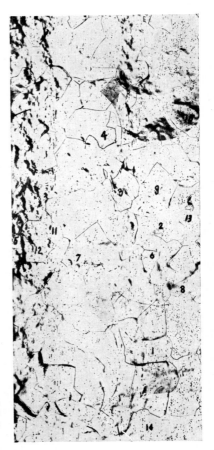

Fig. 4. Reflection X-ray micrograph of 99.998% Al, c. r. 81 %, annealed at 400° C for 1 hour. Unfiltered Cu radiation 35 kV (5 ×).

Fig. 5. Photo micrograph of specimen area shown in Fig 4. (12.5 ×). Numerals indicate outlines of grains corresponding to the respective X-ray reflection images of Figs. 4 and 6.

the X-ray micrographs are quite useless, since the individual reflections cannot be traced to the respective Debye-Scherrer lines without losing their identity and cannot, therefore, be subjected to an analysis based on the powder method. Quite frequently it is impossible to determine whether the images viewed represent a cluster of grains or individual grains containing a cluster of subgrains, a problem that would be solved easily if the reflections could be traced to the respective Debye-Scherrer lines[3]. It is, therefore, evident that the X-ray images registered by the experimental arrangement stated above are not yet amenable to X-ray analysis and further steps presently described have to be taken.

Referring to Fig. 1, a single crystal A is interposed in the path of the primary beam P and adjusted to reflect the incident beam. The reflected, monochromatized beam M will thus subtend an angle of 2θ with the primary beam P, where θ is the Bragg angle of the reflecting (*hkl*) planes of the monochromator. In order to obtain a beam M which is nearly parallel and possesses a high degree of intensity, the (111) reflection of a germanium crystal was used. The total width of its rocking curve measured at half maximum was 20'' of arc. If the entire assembly, consisting of specimen S, photographic plate D, cylindrical camera E, radiation detector R and spectroscopic slit system B, is rotated by the exact angle of 2θ around an axis coincident with the axis of rotation of the monochromatizing crystal, then the identical area of the specimen S is irradiated with crystal-monochromatized radiation M. This new experimental arrangement is depicted in Fig. 3 and schematically represented in Fig. 1 by dashed lines.

Fig. 6 depicts the reflection X-ray micrograph obtained by this experimental arrangement and should be compared with Fig. 4. It will be noted that the X-ray micrograph of Fig. 6 registers fewer grain reflections, due to the stringent reflecting conditions imposed by the parallel, crystal-monochromatized radiation. The resolution of the fine-structural details is now greatly enhanced and because only a few grain reflections are recorded, the outward tracing of the reflected images for the subsequent structural analysis is made possible.

Inspection of Fig. 4 makes it evident that the topographical relationship of

Fig. 6. Reflection X-ray micrograph of specimen area shown in Fig. 4. Crystal-monochromatized Cu K_α radiation 35 kV (5 ×).

References p. 496

the grain reflections has been greatly diminished. It will be shown shortly, however, that by using alternatingly a divergent, unfiltered beam and a crystal-monochromatized beam, knowledge of both the topography and fine-structural details of the grains can be obtained.

In order to establish a correlation between the images recorded by the unfiltered and those by monochromatized radiation the X-ray beam is artificially decomposed in steps. First it is decomposed into a beam consisting of continuous (heterogeneous) radiation only and subsequently into a beam of crystal-monochromatized radiation. To achieve this end, an X-ray micrograph of the specimen surface is taken with the direct beam, using the experimental arrangement depicted in Fig. 1 by solid lines and employing a voltage which is below that of the excitation potential of the characteristic radiation (below 9 kV for CuK_a radiation).

The effect of this decomposition process on the individual reflection images of the X-ray micrograph is best illustrated by Figs. 7a—c. For the sake of illustration the attention is focussed on a single grain reflection which represents a detail of a more complex X-ray reflection micrograph on which actually many grain reflections were recorded. Fig. 7a is an X-ray reflection micrograph obtained by employing continuous radiation only. This micrograph is essentially the same as that obtained with higher voltage except that due to the low operating voltage the contributions of the characteristic radiation and also that of the very short wavelength portion of the spectrum are missing. Actually two X-ray micrographs are taken with this arrangement. One X-ray micrograph is kept for the purpose of reference and comparison, while the second exposed but undeveloped micrograph is rigidly retained in close contact with the specimen surface.

After the interposition of the monochromatizing crystal and subsequent rotation of the camera assembly previously described and depicted in Fig. 1 by dashed lines, the images of the grains, now reflecting the monochromatized radiation at higher voltage (35 kV for CuK_a radiation), are being superimposed on the exposed images obtained with continuous radiation. The exposure time using crystal-monochromatized radiation is purposely prolonged so that the contribution of the monochromatized radiation to the image formation of the X-ray micrograph is clearly tagged. Fig. 7b depicts

X-RAY MICROGRAPH OF GRAIN A

250 μ

(a)   (b)   (c)

Unfiltered Cu radiation, 8.5 kV, exposure time 24 h.

Composite X-ray micrograph. Unfiltered Cu radiation (8.5 kV, exposure time 3 h) and superimposed crystal monochromatized radiation, 35 kV, exposure time 5 h.

Crystal monochromatized Cu radiation, 35 kV, exposure time 5 h.

Fig. 7. Detail of reflection X-ray micrograph disclosing the fine structure of the surface texture of a single grain. 99.998 % Al, c. w. 81 % and annealed at 400° C for 1 hour. × 40.

References p. 496

the detail of the micrograph obtained by this superposition technique. An X-ray micrograph is finally obtained employing only crystal-monochromatized radiation (Fig. 7c) and the topographical relationship of the reflecting crystallites or portion of the crystallites with reference to the adjacent crystallites is established by comparative inspection of the obtained sequence of X-ray micrographs.

After the topographical relationship of the reflecting grains has been established, the few individual images obtained with crystal-monochromatized radiation are traced outward by recording them photographically at increasing distances from the specimen surface. Thus a direct correlation is established between the spot reflections on the Debye-Scherrer lines and the grains on the specimen surface giving rise to these reflections[3]. The series of Figs. 8a—e may serve to illustrate the outward tracing of the reflection images designated with numerals 1 to 7.

A quantitative analysis of the spot reflections is subsequently undertaken. This analysis is based on the principle of the double-crystal diffractometer. According to this principle each reflecting crystallite of the specimen surface may independently be regarded as functioning as the second crystal of a double-crystal diffractometer. By a technique of discrete angular specimen rotation and appropriate film shifts carried out between each discrete specimen rotation, arrays of spots are obtained for each reflecting crystallite[4-6]. These arrays of spots are shown in Fig. 8f, wherein the angular specimen rotation was carried out in discrete intervals of 5′ of arc. From the analysis of the rocking curves one may compute the angular misalignment of the grains and the disorientation angle of the subgrains as well as the angular misalignment within the subgrains[4-6].

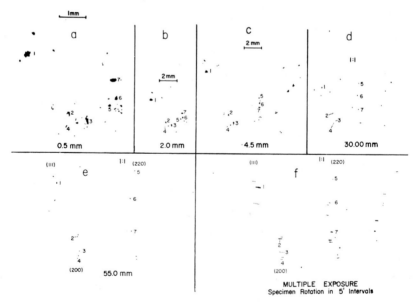

Fig. 8(a)—(e). Photographic tracing of reflection images at increasing distances from specimen surface. (f) Detail of multiple exposure diagram. The arrays of spots are obtained by discrete angular specimen rotation in 5′ intervals and appropriate film shifts between specimen rotations.

The arrays of spots are a visual manifestation of the rocking curves of the grains.

If the grain reflections are not too closely clustered and are intense enough to be picked up by an electronic radiation detector, it is possible to record directly the rocking curves of the individual grains on a chart. In this case the electronic radiation detector is placed in position to register a grain reflection and the specimen is rotated continuously through the reflecting range of the grain. This process is then repeated for other grain reflections. The exact positioning of the radiation detector is greatly facilitated by using an optically transparent Debye-Scherrer camera as depicted in Fig. 3. When the exposed Debye-Scherrer film has been developed and inserted back in the camera the location of the spot reflections is visually aided. After positioning of the radiation detector and removal of camera and film, the intensity values can be directly registered. Should any doubt arise that more than one reflection is simultaneously recorded by the radiation detector for any one angular specimen position, a film strip is placed in a slot behind the receiving slit of the detector and exposed to the radiation entering the receiving slit. Inspection of this film strip after development permits exact adjustment of the receiving slit and the elimination of the recording of simultaneous reflections.

TOPOGRAPHY OF THE SUBSTRUCTURE OF A POLYCRYSTALLINE MATERIAL

Besides correlating the X-ray microscopy phase to the analysis phase of the method, the successive irradiation of the specimen with different portions of the X-ray spectrum is quite useful for mapping out the topography of lattice misorientation within the individual grains. BARRETT[2] has discussed the origin of intensified reflections in terms of strained regions and reflecting power of the crystal. Consider the X-rays of the continuous spectrum striking a concavely misoriented lattice region of a grain. Many of the convergent rays will be reflected because different portions of the misoriented region will satisfy the reflecting condition, owing to the convergence and spread of wavelengths of the continuum. Consequently, the reflection image on the film corresponding to this misoriented region will be intensified. On the other hand, an undistorted lattice region of the grain will select a single ray from the impinging bundle for reflection and since a less efficient use of the incident X-ray energy is made, the corresponding image on the film will be light or even white if the exposure time is short. Fig. 7a is interpreted as an example of such reflecting conditions.

Exactly the opposite case is encountered if crystal-monochromatized radiation is employed. All the lattice domains of the same orientation that satisfy the stringent reflecting condition imposed by the monochromatizing crystal will give rise to dark areas on the film, whereas the misoriented lattice domains will not reflect. The X-ray micrograph of Fig. 7c taken with crystal-monochromatized radiation may serve to illustrate the point. The complementary function of the two types of radiation used is exemplified by the superposition of the radiation shown in Fig. 7b.

The complementary application of continuous and crystal-monochromatized radiation can be fully exploited if an X-ray tube with a tungsten target is used. Tungsten radiation is usually not employed in X-ray diffraction work because of the weak contrast in intensity between the characteristic and continuous spectrum. In the case of X-ray reflection microscopy, however, the use of tungsten radiation with its intense, broad, continuous spectrum is highly advantageous, since a great number of grains of various orientation will be recorded on an X-ray micrograph. Furthermore, because of the presence of very short wavelengths the specimen can be explored in depth. The fine-structural details are again elucidated by the application of crystal-monochromatized radiation. In contrast to copper radiation, however, where only the characteristic K_α line was used for the probing crystal-monochromatized beam, the tungsten radiation offers various characteristic L lines. Thus, referring to Fig. 1, the monochromatizing crystal may be first set to reflect the wavelength of the $L_{\alpha 1}$ line ($\lambda = 1.47635$ Å), and the identity of the grain reflections on the micrograph obtained with this radiation and those obtained by continuous radiation may be again established by the superposition technique outlined above. Subsequently, the monochromatizing crystal may be set to reflect $L_{\beta 1}$ ($\lambda = 1.28176$ Å) and after that to reflect $L_{\beta 2}$ ($\lambda = 1.26285$ Å). In this manner various portions of the X-ray spectrum can be used successively to elucidate the topography of the grains and their fine-structural details.

SUMMARY

A method combining light microscopy with X-ray reflection microscopy and diffraction analysis is described by a sequence of experimental steps.

1. The topographical relationship of the crystallites on the surface of a fine-grained polycrystalline material as well as the fine-structural details of the surface texture of the crystallites are disclosed on reflection X-ray micrographs. This is accomplished by successive irradiation of the specimen with different portions of the X-ray spectrum which include heterogeneous, continuous and crystal-monochromatized radiation. The X-ray reflection images of the crystallites can be directly correlated to the light-micrographic study carried out on the identical crystallites.

2. After the analysis of the topographical relationship and the study of the surface texture of the crystallites have been accomplished, the individual crystallites are quantitatively analyzed for their substructure characteristics. The analysis is based on the principle of the double-crystal diffractometer. Rocking curves of the individual crystallites are obtained by recording either photographically or directly by means of a radiation detector the reflected intensities as a function of specimen rotation.

3. For metal or alloy specimens the analysis of the rocking curves combined with that of the X-ray reflection micrography yields quantitative information concerning the lattice misalignment of the grains, the size of the subgrains, disorientation angle between subgrains, lattice misalignment within the subgrains, and structure of the low-angle boundaries.

ACKNOWLEDGEMENTS

The author is indebted to Dr. T. IMURA for his assistance in this work. The sponsorship of this study by the Office of Naval Research is greatly appreciated.

REFERENCES

[1] W. F. BERG, Naturwiss., 19 (1931) 391.
[2] C. S. BARRETT, Trans. AIME, 161 (1945) 15.
[3] S. WEISSMANN, J. Appl. Phys., 27 (1956) 389.
[4] A. J. REIS, J. J. SLADE JR. and S. WEISSMANN, J. Appl. Phys., 22 (1951) 665.
[5] J. J. SLADE JR. and S. WEISSMANN, J. Appl. Phys., 23 (1952) 323.
[6] S. WEISSMANN and D. L. EVANS, Acta Cryst., 7 (1954) 729.

ON THE MECHANISM OF RECRYSTALLIZATION OF ALUMINUM

S. WEISSMANN

College of Engineering, Rutgers, The State University of New Jersey, New Brunswick, N.J. (U.S.A.)

ABSTRACT

Recrystallization and grain growth of 99.998 % aluminum were studied by methods combining metallographic techniques with X-ray microscopy and diffraction analysis. The recrystallized grains are shown to be the product of preferential subgrain growth whereby subgrains subtending large disorientation angles with respect to their neighbors exhibit the highest velocity of growth. The recrystallized grains emerging from the deformed matrix show at first a high degree of lattice perfection, but incur lattice imperfections during the growth process. At elevated temperatures the sub-boundaries formed are either partially or totally eliminated. Frequently the grains are consumed by grains exhibiting a higher degree of lattice perfection. Values for the local strain-free energy of the deformed matrix surrounding the growing subgrains are obtained from the kinetics of sub-grain growth. This energy is believed to provide the bulk of the driving force for recrystallization.

INTRODUCTION

Considerable evidence has been accumulated in the past years that in various metals subgrains are directly formed during the cold-working process. GAY, HIRSCH and KELLY[1] have investigated the structure of a number of cold-worked metals by means of an X-ray microbeam technique which permitted a resolution of the diffraction spots originating from small subgrains. They interpreted their results in terms of a foam structure in which relatively perfect subgrains are continuously linked with each other by distorted boundary regions. They concluded that the formation of this structure is a direct result of the accumulation of dislocations on slip bands during cold work and is not due to a recovery process subsequent to cold-working. For aluminum cold-worked at room temperature the order of magnitude of the size of subgrains was found to be $1-2 \mu$. The existence and size of these subgrains after cold-working has been convincingly demonstrated by HEIDENREICH[2] and by HIRSCH and his co-workers[3] by means of transmission electron microscope studies of thin metal foils. HEIDENREICH has shown that the subgrains exhibit some strain energy immediately after deformation which, however, on standing at room temperature gradually disappears[2]. This recovery process takes place without advancement of the interfaces.

Primary recrystallization, which may be defined as the disappearance of deformed material and appearance of new grains, has been attributed by various authors to the preferential growth of a few subgrains after an initial period of strain-relief by recovery[4,5]. The mechanism of this preferential growth process, if it exists at all, has, however, not been clarified, and attempts to elucidate the role of subgrains in the mechanism of primary recrystallization utilizing conventional metallographic techniques have not so far been very successful.

References p. 509

The work presented here deals with the experimental investigation of sub-structure and its relation to primary recrystallization, and beyond that it attempts to shed light on the mechanism of grain growth.

Electropolished aluminum specimens of 99.998 % purity, cold-rolled 81.7 %, were used for this investigation. To study the influence of substructure on the mechanism of recrystallization, a high-resolution X-ray method was employed which combines light microscopy with X-ray reflection microscopy and diffraction analysis[6, 7].

Two different kinds of etching solutions were used for the metallographic investigation. One etching solution attacked predominantly the grain boundaries and served to establish the outline of the equivalent grains studied by the X-ray method. The second etching solution was particularly suited to reveal subgrain boundaries and substructural details and represented a modification of Lacombe's solution. When the specimen was etched with the latter solution the substructural details disclosed by X-ray and light microscopy could be compared[7].

In order to observe the growth of subgrains and concomitant modifications of lattice imperfections without changing the specimen area irradiated by the X-ray beam, it was imperative to carry out the annealing of the specimen on the X-ray diffraction unit. A furnace of the electric resistor type was used during the initial stages of the investigation. Subsequently, however, when the series of experiments was repeated on identical samples to verify the obtained results, an elliptical reflector lamp was employed. This reflector lamp was arranged in such a manner that the position of one of the focal points of the ellipse coincided with the filament of the incandescent bulb and that of the other focal point with the specimen surface. A thermocouple in contact with the back of the specimen served to register the exact annealing temperature. This heating arrangement proved to be very convenient and highly efficient.

Preferential subgrain growth at low annealing temperature

The metallographic and X-ray data of the un-annealed specimens were characteristic of the as-cold-worked state. As expected, the X-ray diagrams of the heavily cold-worked samples exhibited smeared-out Debye-Scherrer lines with strong preferred orientation.

When the specimen was annealed at 200° C for one hour, a number of interesting observations could be made, which may best be described with reference to Fig. 1. This figure depicts a detail of a multiple exposure diagram characteristic of this annealing stage. Each individual array of spots represents reflections of a crystallite recorded as a function of specimen rotation. The specimen rotation was carried out in discrete angular intervals and between each angular interval of specimen rotation an appropriate film shift was made to separate the individual intensity contribution. The separation between consecutive spots corresponds to a discrete angular specimen rotation of 10″ of arc. Since these arrays were obtained from crystallites reflecting the incident, crystal-monochromatized radiation, they may be regarded as manifestations of reflection or rocking curves[6, 7].

References p. 509

It will be noted that the annealing treatment gave rise to a fine break-up of the reflections along portions of the Debye-Scherrer lines which happen to be removed from the equator of the diagram. They are hereafter termed azimuthal reflections. Simultaneously, however, the emergence of grain reflections was observed in portions of the Debye-Scherrer lines corresponding to the equatorial region ("equatorial reflection"), where no reflections were observed at all prior to the annealing treatment in the as-cold-worked state. The absence of equatorial reflections for the (111) and (200) lines of this diagram in the case of the cold-rolled specimen was due to the preferred orientation as well as to the severe restrictions which crystal-monochromatized radiation imposes on the number of possible reflections.

When the reflection images on the Debye-Scherrer lines were correlated by means of the photographic tracer technique[6,7] to the corresponding images of the X-ray micrograph of the specimen surface in order to establish a topographical relation between azimuthal and equatorial reflections, it was surprisingly observed that both, the azimuthal as well as the equatorial reflections, emerged from the same region and not from different regions of the specimen surface.

The observations, however, which were most surprising concerned the characteristic differences between the azimuthal and equatorial reflections. These differences refer to (a) the size and (b) the lattice perfection of the crystallites which gave rise to the reflections.

The fine break-up of the azimuthal reflections could be traced to small subgrains on the specimen surface, varying between $1-2\ \mu$. There may very well exist subgrains of smaller size, since the lower limit of the range could not be disclosed with certainty, due to the limit of resolution imposed by the grain size of the available spectroscopic plates. When rocking curves of these subgrains were carried out at the specimen surface by means of X-ray micrographs, the half-width values ranged from $15-25''$ of arc. At the circumference of the Debye-Scherrer camera these rocking curves interweave with those of adjacent subgrains and give rise to wide plateaus of the reflection curve which represent the convolution of rocking curves deriving from a cluster of subgrains.

In contrast to the azimuthal reflections the equatorial reflections emanated from subgrains of larger size, approximately $15-20\ \mu$ in diameter, and exhibited individual well-defined rocking curves, such as array 1 of Fig. 1, with half-width values varying from $40-80''$ of arc. These larger half-width values of the equatorial reflections are indicative of a lattice misalignment of the corresponding subgrains which is larger than that pertaining to the azimuthal reflections. This interpretation is supported by the corresponding images of the X-ray reflection micrographs taken at the specimen surface. It was noted that whereas the subgrain images corresponding to the azimuthal reflections were uniform in intensity, those corresponding to the equatorial reflections exhibited variations in reflecting power. It should be emphasized that none of the inferences with regard to lattice imperfections presented in this paper are obtained from rocking curves alone, but derive from the combined evidence of rocking curve analysis plus corresponding reflection X-ray microscopy.

Isothermal annealing of the specimen at 200° C for 16 hours resulted in a marked degree of break-up of the azimuthal reflections with a concomitant decrease in the diffuse background scattering. The size of the equatorial reflections and corresponding images has sharply increased and so has the angular range of reflection. To display

References p. 509

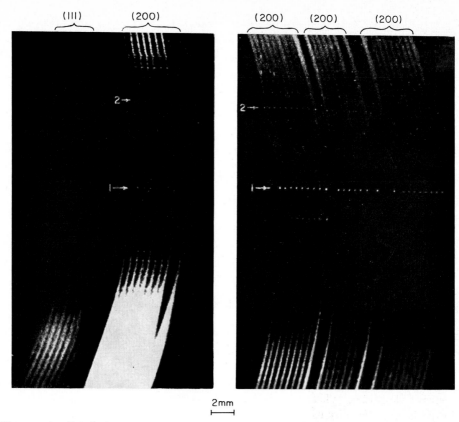

2mm
|——|

Figs. 1 and 2. Detail of a multiple exposure X-ray diagram of 99.998 % Al, c. w. 81 %, exhibiting the dependence of the angular range of grain reflections 1 and 2 on isothermal annealing. Annealing temperature 200° C. Annealing time 1 h (Fig. 1), 16 h (Fig. 2). Rotation of specimen in intervals of 10″ of arc. Crystal-monochromatized Cu radiation.

the extent of the rocking curves of grain reflections 1 and 2 it was necessary to record the angular range of reflections on two subsequent films and to align the corresponding film portions to give the composite, multiple exposure diagram of Fig. 2. The half-width values for these reflections are now, respectively, 4.3 and 2.8′, of arc. That this increase of angular range of reflection was due to an increase of lattice misalignment and not to surface curvature of the growing grain can be seen from Fig. 3. This figure depicts the X-ray micrograph of the grains which gave rise to the reflection curves 1 and 2 of Fig. 2, the correlation being obtained by the previously described tracer technique[6, 7]. It will be noted that the micrographs of these reflections are characterized by a fine maze of subgrain boundaries. Detailed studies of these and other similar grain reflections showed that the greatest concentrations of subboundaries are found in the vicinity of the interface and that these boundaries seem to branch out from nodes at the grain boundary.

Fig. 4 shows the reflection curves of the emerging grains annealed at 200° C for 60 hours. The size, number and extent of the angular range of equatorial reflections have now increased as expected; the specimen rotations have been carried out in discrete intervals of 40 instead of 10″ of arc. The break-up of the azimuthal reflections into

References p. 509

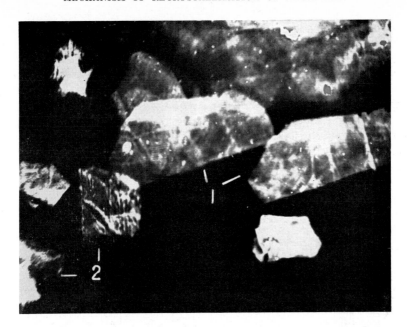

Fig. 3. Reflection X-ray micrograph of grains 1 and 2 (400 ×). Because continuous radiation was employed the same grain reflections are repeated several times, permitting the disclosure of structural details in depth.

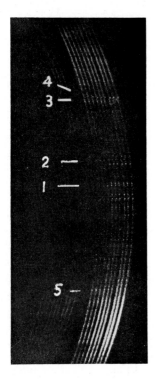

Fig. 4. Detail of multiple exposure X-ray diagram of 99.998 % Al, c. w. 81 %, annealed at 200° C for 60 h. Rotation of specimen in intervals of 40″ of arc. Crystal-monochromatized Cu radiation. Note: For grain reflections at higher azimuths (reflections 3, 4, and 5) there is an apparent increase in the width of the reflection curves due to the vertical divergence of the beam. The true width can, however, be computed from the experimental data.

distinct entities as well as the recession of the diffuse background scattering is now more conspicuous. Simultaneously, individual reflections at higher azimuths (*e.g.*, arrays 3, 4 and 5) emerge, which can also be traced to the identical area of the specimen surface whence the other reflections derived. The orientation difference ψ of the grains 3, 4 and 5 with respect to the mean orientation of the subgrains from which they emerged is about 15, 12 and 8° respectively. Other distinct arrays of spots now become visible, but as the tracer technique disclosed, these derived from different regions of the irradiated specimen area.

For the sake of clarity the X-ray evidence obtained from the isothermal annealing treatment of the specimen is schematically summarized in Fig. 5. In this figure the small blocks represent the subgrains which cluster around a mean orientation

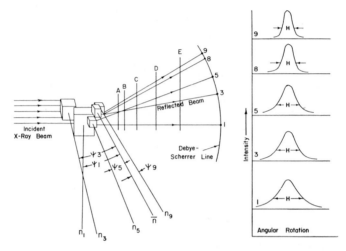

Fig. 5. Schematic drawing summarizing experimental observations of isothermal annealing. Only the topographical relation and reflections of grains 1, 3, 5, 8 and 9 are shown.

expressed by the mean normal *n* of the reflecting (*hkl*) planes. The normals of these small subgrains subtend small disorientation angles ψ with respect to *n*. It will be understood, however, that all the normals subtend an angle $90-\theta$ with respect to the incident monochromatized beam, where θ is the Bragg angle of the reflecting (*hkl*) planes.

As soon as the disorientation angle ψ becomes large, reaching the proportion of large-angle boundaries, shown by ψ_1 and ψ_3, the subgrains grow rapidly in size and this is schematically expressed by the large blocks 1 and 3. The rays reflected from the subgrains give rise to spot reflections on the Debye-Scherrer lines shown by the numbered dots. The vertical lines A, B, C, D and E intersecting the reflecting rays indicate the various locations of the photographic plates used for outward tracing of the reflection images.

The angular misalignment of the subgrains, which by means of the correlated X-ray micrographs has been shown to be intimately linked with the density of sub-boundaries, is schematically expressed in terms of the observed rocking curves. The rocking curves of the subgrains are sketched next to the corresponding dots on

References p. 509

the Debye-Scherrer line and exhibit increasing values of half-width, H, with increasing ψ.

Kinetic study of subgrain growth
In addition to the study of the orientation dependence of subgrain growth a kinetic study was also undertaken. Fig. 6 exhibits the isothermal dependence of the linear growth rate on the time of annealing for grains 1—9. As has been described

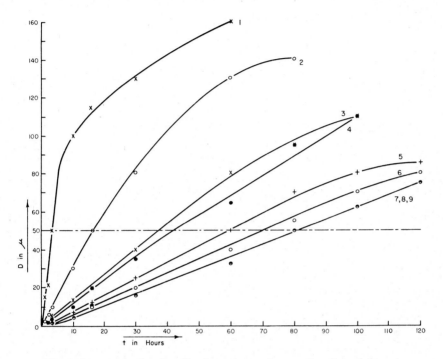

Fig. 6. Increase in the size, D, of growing grains as a function of time, t.

previously, these grains emerged from a cluster of subgrains by the process of subgrain growth and one may note that a linear relationship is satisfactorily maintained approximately up to the average size of 75 μ. Beyond this size limit a general flattening of the curves is observed, presumably due to grain impingement.

For the isothermal kinetic study a convenient grain size of 50 μ was selected. Column 3 of Table I shows the time required for the neighboring subgrains 1—9 to emerge as grains of the selected linear size, and these values were obtained from Fig. 6 as shown by the dashed line.

The orientation dependence of the growth rate is shown in column 2 of Table I and is expressed in terms of the angle ψ, which gives the angle of disorientation of the recrystallized grain relative to the mean orientation of the adjacent subgrains from which it emerges by a preferential growth process. It will be noted that the slowest growth rate is associated with subgrains of small values. Thus grains 7, 8 and 9, having ψ values between 0—1°, emerge as grains of 50 μ after about 80 h, whereas grain 3, with a ψ value of about 30°, reached the same size at about 3 h.

References p. 509

TABLE I

ISOTHERMAL RECRYSTALLIZATION CHARACTERISTICS

99.998 % Al, cold-reduced 81.7 % and annealed at 200° C

	1	2	3	4	5	6	7	8
	Number of grain	ψ in deg.	t observed++ (in h)	t computed (in h)	Z** (erg/cm³)	τ (sec)	σ* (erg/cm²)	H (min)
	1	30	3	—	$5.9 \cdot 10^8$	14.4 (max) 6.5 (min)	500 ($\theta = 30°$) 223 ($\theta = 5°$)	3.1
	2	24	16	—	$1.11 \cdot 10^8$	412 (max) 185 (min)	500 ($\theta = 30°$) 223 ($\theta = 5°$)	2.8
	3	15	38	—	$4.65 \cdot 10^7$	1792 (max) 1050 (min)	381 ($\theta = 15°$) 223 ($\theta = 5°$)	3.4
	4	12	42	—	$4.21 \cdot 10^7$	2018 (max) 1280 (min)	352 ($\theta = 12°$) 223 ($\theta = 5°$)	3.5
	5	8	60	—	$2.95 \cdot 10^7$	3399 (max) 2600 (min)	291 ($\theta = 8°$) 223 ($\theta = 5°$)	3.2
	6	5	70	—	$2.53 \cdot 10^7$	3540	223 ($\theta = 5°$)	2.8
	7							2.3
	8	$0 - 1$	80	82+	$2.16 \cdot 10^{7+}$ $2.21 \cdot 10^7$	1654+ 1578	73.5 ($\theta = 1°$)	2.7
	9							2.5

(Left margin, rotated: *Decreasing disorientation angle θ*)

* σ values were computed from eqn. (5) except for $\theta \geq 24°$, where σ was taken to be 500 erg/cm².

** Except as indicated, Z values were computed from eqn. (3), using the observed t values.

+ Computed from eqn. (5)

++ Observed time refers to $D = 50\ \mu$.

Column 8 of Table I exhibits the total width, H, at half maximum of the rocking curves of the grains and is, therefore, a criterion of their lattice perfection. It will be observed that the H values do not differ appreciably, but it should be remembered that if H values corrresponding to the same time periods of annealing are compared, they differ by orders of magnitude.

Applying the BURKE and TURNBULL treatment[8] of the low energy block hypothesis of nucleation to the kinetic study of subgrain growth, we may express the net driving force of recrystallization ΔF per gram atom as the sum of a free energy term proportional to the surface area of the mass and a free energy term proportional to the volume of the subgrains.

(1) $$\Delta F = -a\sigma D^2/D^3 + ZD^3/D^3 = Z - a\sigma/D$$

where the symbols have the following significance: a is a geometrical factor; Z is the free energy due to the mean strain set up by the dislocation wall making up the sub-boundary of two neighboring subgrains after cold-working; σ is the surface energy of the subgrain, and D is the linear dimension of the sub-boundary. It should be emphasized that in contrast to the treatment of BURKE and TURNBULL, Z does not signify the free energy due to the mean strain of the entire cold-worked specimen, but represents, rather, a local, free energy strain term. The meaning of Z can be better understood from the following consideration, which is based on the concept of the foam structure of cold-worked metals proposed by GAY, HIRSCH and KELLY[1]. The greater the disorientation angle of neighboring subgrains, the more complex is the dislocation wall which separates these subgrains and the greater is the mean, local free energy strain value Z.

For the sake of convenience we may still adhere to the concept of nucleation and growth and correct later by approximation for the initial stage of subgrain growth corresponding to the "apparent" nucleation period, τ.

Consequently we can write for the linear growth rate G

(2) $$G = dD/dt = k(\Delta F).$$

Substituting eqn. (1) into eqn. (2) and performing the integration, we arrive at

(3a) $$D = ktZ + D_0 - (a\sigma/Z) \ln [(D - a\sigma/Z)/(D_0 - a\sigma/Z)].$$

Rearranging,

(3b) $$t = D - D_0/kZ + (a/kZ)^2 \ln (D - a/Z)/(D_0 - a/Z).$$

Since eqn. (3) represents the equation of a straight line with respect to t and since this relationship has been experimentally verified to hold over a considerable range of t values (Fig. 6), eqn. (3) may be utilized for the computation of the Z values associated with the individual growing subgrains. Letting the average size of the subgrains after the deformation, D_0, be equal to $1\ \mu$, Z values were computed for a cluster of grains grown to $50\ \mu$ size which took its origin from adjacent subgrains (column 5 of Table I). These Z values were computed from the corresponding t values which were obtained from the D vs. t curves of Fig. 6 as shown by the dashed line. (See also column 3 of Table I.)

If we consider the grains which exhibited the slowest growth rate, such as grains 7, 8 and 9, which were characterized by low ψ values, that is, small disorientation with respect to one another, we may suppose that Z is contained entirely in the surface energy σ of the sub-boundaries formed in cold-working[9]. For this case

(4) $$Z = K\sigma V/D_0$$

where V is the gram atomic volume of the metal and k varies from 1 to 3. Now, the surface energy, σ, for a small tilt angle θ can be computed from the SHOCKLEY-READ equation[10]:

(5) $$\sigma = \sigma_0 \theta (A - \ln \theta).$$

After deformation the tilt angle of $1°$ was taken to be typical for the average disorientation angle of those subgrains which upon annealing gave rise to recrystallization *in situ*. Since the subgrains 7, 8 and 9 were separated by small-angle boundaries of such an order of magnitude and since they maintained more or less this relationship during the growth process (recrystallization *in situ*), a Z value of $2.16 \cdot 10^7$ erg/cm³ was computed from eqn. (4), using the σ value of 73.5 erg/cm³ which, in turn, was obtained from the SHOCKLEY-READ equation. This Z value is listed in column 5 of Table I. Substituting the computed Z value in eqn. (3), a t value of 82 h was obtained for grains 7, 8 and 9. This computed value was in good agreement with the observed t value of 80 h. This agreement, which was obtained repeatedly, gives one confidence in the idea that subgrains giving rise to recrystallization *in situ* have the strain energy contained entirely in the surface energy of the sub-boundaries.

References p. 509

If we consider τ the apparent nucleation period, we may write

(6) $D - D_0 = G(t - \tau).$

Rearranging eqn. (3) into a convenient form, we obtain

(7) $D - D_0 = kZ \left\{ t - (\sigma a/kZ^2) \ln (D - a\sigma/Z)/D_0 - (a\sigma/Z) \right\}.$

Comparison of eqn. (7) with eqn. (6) identifies τ as the second term on the right-hand side. The τ value may be regarded as the minimum time required before the rate of subgrain growth increases to obey the linear growth relationship.

For grains recrystallized *in situ*, characterized by low Z values, the τ values can be computed with a considerable degree of accuracy. This degree of accuracy, however, cannot be achieved for grains the growth rate of which is strongly orientation-dependent when emerging from a cluster of subgrains and which are associated with large Z values. Since the computation of τ is dependent on the surface energy σ and this in turn is dependent on the disorientation angle θ, the accuracy of the τ values will depend on the accuracy with which the initial disorientation angle can be determined. In most cases it is not possible to determine the initial disorientation angle of the growing subgrains with respect to their neighbors. We observe either the final disorientation angle as in the case of grain 1 or evidence of crystal rotation and increase in the disorientation angle as in grain 2. Nevertheless a maximum and minimum τ value can be estimated by assigning a maximum σ value based on the final observed disorientation angle and a minimum σ value by assuming or estimating some reasonable initial disorientation angle. The τ values for grains 1—9 were either estimated or computed and are listed in column 6 of Table I.

GRAIN GROWTH AT HIGHER ANNEALING TEMPERATURE

If the annealing temperature is raised from 200° C to *e.g.* 350° C the subgrains which, by virtue of their orientation difference with respect to the bulk, have preferentially grown to form individual grains, increase rapidly in size and show at first a marked increase in lattice misalignment and in the density of substructure (Figs. 7 and 8). At prolonged annealing times or at elevated annealing temperatures a reverse trend is observed. Whereas the size of the grain increases, the angular lattice misalignment as well as the density in substructure decreases, indicating that a process of annihilation and rearrangement of dislocations has taken place.

It should be emphasized, however, that at none of the annealing stages at elevated temperatures has it been possible even to approximate that high degree of lattice perfection and low dislocation density which were exhibited when the grains were very small and had just emerged as individual crystallites from the deformed matrix, that is, at low annealing temperature.

It can be shown that at more elevated temperatures of annealing the grains which have first emerged from the deformed matrix and which, due to grain growth and impingement with other grains, are afflicted with lattice imperfection (high dislocation density) are being consumed by grains which emerged at a later annealing stage and which display, therefore, a higher degree of lattice perfection (low dislocation density). Thus the grain whose X-ray micrograph and portion of the reflection curve have been shown in Figs. 7 and 8 respectively for the annealing temperature of 350° C was entirely consumed at 440° C by a grain possessing a higher degree of lattice perfection.

References p. 509

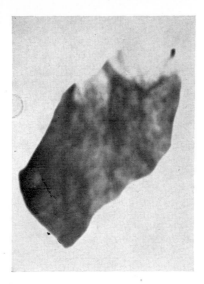

Fig. 7. Reflection X-ray micrograph of aluminum grain annealed at 350° C for 30 min. Continuous X-radiation (250 ×).

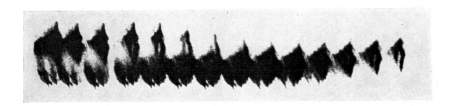

Fig. 8. Detail of angular range of reflection of grain shown in Fig. 7. Specimen rotation 1' of arc. Crystal-monochromatized Cu radiation.

Figs. 9 and 10 show the X-ray micrograph and portion of the corresponding reflection curve of a grain corresponding to an annealing treatment at 440° C for 2 hours. The resulting total angular lattice misalignment may sometimes amount to 0.5—1.5 degree of arc and the microstructure exhibits a corresponding complexity of substructure. The coexistence of various orders of magnitude of substructural entities can be disclosed and at least three orders of magnitude were observed by the X-ray method employed. At more elevated temperature the substructure of the grains was either partially or entirely eliminated. In many instances it was observed that the grains with complex substructure were consumed by more perfect grains which emerged at a more advanced state of annealing.

CONCLUSIONS

(1) Recrystallized grains are the product of preferential subgrain growth.
(2) Subgrains of the deformed matrix subtending small disorientation angles with respect to their neighbors exhibit a low velocity of boundary migration, whereas

Fig. 9. Reflection X-ray micrograph of aluminum grain annealed at 440° C for 2 h. Continuous radiation (250 ×).

Fig. 10. Detail of angular range of reflection of grain shown in Fig. 9. Specimen rotation 1′ of arc. Crystal-monochromatized Cu radiation.

subgrains subtending large disorientation angles exhibit a high velocity and consequently grow very rapidly.

(3) The recrystallized grains emerging from the deformed matrix show at first

a high degree of lattice perfection. As growth proceeds, lattice imperfections are incurred which are manifested by a net of sub-boundaries in the recrystallized grains usually emanating from the advancing interface. These lattice imperfections are associated with the process of grain impingement and adaptation to orientation difference existing between the growing grain and the grain being consumed. At elevated temperatures the sub-boundaries are either partially or totally eliminated. Frequently the grains are consumed by grains exhibiting a higher degree of lattice perfection.

(4) Values for the mean strain-free energy of the deformed matrix surrounding the growing subgrains were obtained from the kinetics of subgrain growth. Subgrains separated by small-angle boundaries and recrystallizing *in situ* have the strain energy contained entirely in the surface energy of the sub-boundaries.

ACKNOWLEDGEMENT

The author is indebted to his colleague, Dr. T. IMURA, for his assistance in this work and to Professor J. J. SLADE, JR., for his valuable critical comments. The sponsorship of this work by the Office of Naval Research is deeply appreciated.

REFERENCES

P. GAY, P. B. HIRSCH and A. KELLY, *Acta Cryst.*, 7 (1954) 41.
[1] R. D. HEIDENREICH, Electron transmission through thin metal sections, *Bell System Tech. J.*,
[2] October, 1951.
[3] P. B. HIRSCH, R. W. HORNE and M. J. WHELAN, *Phil. Mag.*, 1 (1956) 677.
[4] G. BURGERS and P. Z. LOUWERSE, *Z. Physik*, 67 (1931) 605.
[5] R. W. CAHN, *Proc. Phys. Soc. (London)*, *A* 63 (1950) 323.
[6] S. WEISSMANN, *J. Appl. Phys.*, 27 (1956) 389.
[7] S. WEISSMANN, this volume, p. 488.
[8] J. E. BURKE and D. TURNBULL, *Progr. in Metal Phys.*, 3 (1952) 261.
[9] *Ibid.*, p. 245.
[10] W. T. READ and W. SHOCKLEY, in *Imperfections in Nearly Perfect Crystals*, Symposium at Pocono Manor, 1950, John Wiley & Sons, New York, 1952, pp. 365—367.

D. BIOLOGICAL APPLICATIONS

X-RAY MICRORADIOGRAPHY AND DIFFRACTION STUDIES OF IMPREGNATION IN BALSA WOOD

T. S. WYLIE

Department of Natural Philosophy, Royal College of Science and Technology, Glasgow (Great Britain)

ABSTRACT

Preliminary studies of balsa wood impregnated with crystals of the following salts: copper chloride, copper sulphate, nickel sulphate, ferrous sulphate, aluminium sulphate, magnesium sulphate, calcium oxalate, sodium chloride, and aluminium acetate show that preferred orientation is possible in certain cases. The conditions giving rise to such effects are of interest and importance and a detailed study is being made of these.

The definite absence of orientation in other cases should also furnish important information about the responsible factors. Simultaneously, diffraction studies of fibre structure were undertaken and it is hoped to obtain further information on the linkage between fibre and crystal.

INTRODUCTION

The occurrence of crystals in woody tissues has been observed for many years, but few attempts have been made to identify and explore structure as modified by the environment.

In 1955/56 a survey was carried out by CHATTAWAY[1] into the presence of crystals in woody tissue. In the Proceedings of the previous X-ray Microscopy Symposium, JACKSON[2] had a series of microradiographs of wood sections. The sketches and photographs shown in these two papers make it likely that there may be other reasons for the apparent orientation of the crystals in the cells other than that of cell shape and crystal habit. With the object of examining this, the experiments reported below were carried out.

CHOICE OF MATERIALS

The Bombaceae family to which balsa (*Achroma Lagopus*) belongs, according to the survey, does not normally exhibit crystals in any except the upright ray cells. Since it was not the intention in the first instance to grow naturally occurring crystals, this factor was disregarded and the balsa was used because of its lightness and high air content which ensured a faint diffraction pattern.

In the sample obtained for this work masses of crystals were observed in the bark. These are at present being examined.

Copper chloride was chosen as the first salt to be examined using copper K_α radiation. This proved to be rather fortunate. Copper chloride gives marked orientation. Various other salts have been examined. These are listed in Table I.

The gross structure of balsa

Balsa is a hard wood and is composed of cells arranged in (a) a longitudinal system, *i.e.*, parallel to the axis of the tree; the cells of this system are wood fibres and vessels; (b) a radial system of rays. Fig. 1 is a tangential system of balsa showing the non-septate fibres and a section through the heterogeneous rays.

Fig. 1. Tangential section of balsa wood. × 7.2.

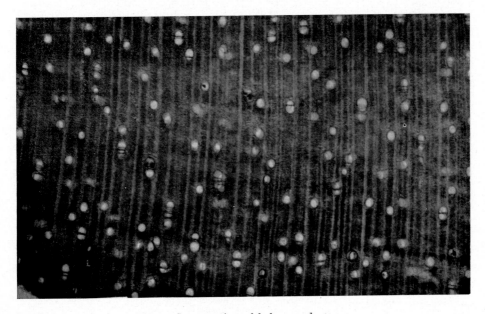

Fig. 2. Cross section of balsa wood. × 7.2.

References p. 517

Fig. 2 is a cross section showing the vessels and parenchyma. Communications between the various fibres, vessels and ray cells takes place through simple pits in the cell walls, through pores in the centre lamella and through the ray cells.

EXPERIMENTAL TECHNIQUES

Four methods were adopted for introducing the concentrates into the balsa.

(1) *Natural method*

A balsa cone was made and inserted into a perspex holder as shown in Fig. 3. The angle θ was made small to obtain a good surface finish ($\theta = 15$ degrees). The

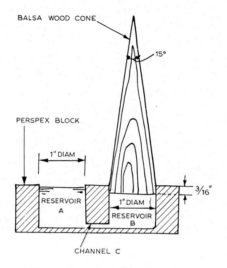

Fig. 3. Perspex holder for cones.

test solution was poured into the reservoir A and it flowed through the channel C to chamber B where it came in contact with the base of the cone and thence by capillary action rose into the cone. After all the liquid in Section A had evaporated, the cone was removed and allowed to dry out. The cone was sectioned radially and a centre section about 1/16″ thick was removed and microradiographs made. This section was then further cut and fibre photographs taken of it in the diffraction camera. Several photographs along the length of the fibre were generally made.

(2) *Boiling*

This method was only used in one instance. A section of balsa about 2″ diameter and $1\frac{1}{2}$″ long was boiled in a concentrated solution of cupric chloride for about ten minutes. Greater penetration was achieved than by simple diffusion.

(3) *Total immersion*

In this series of experiments specimens $1\frac{1}{2}$″ × $\frac{3}{8}$″ sq. cross section were immersed in concentrated solutions of the salts at 70° C and maintained at this temperature for 36 h, after which they were dried and examined.

(4) *Partial immersion*

Balsa specimens 5″ long and 1″ sq. cross section were allowed to float in concentrated solutions of salts maintained at constant temperature in closed tubes for 12 h. The specimens were then removed and dried.

(5) *Vacuum impregnation*

A section was placed in a vacuum chamber attached to a rotary pump and the chamber pumped out until constant vacuum was obtained of order 0.01 mm Hg. Vacuum was maintained for about 15 min after which a concentrated solution at room temperature was introduced; when conditions had settled the specimen was removed and dried.

CAMERA

An important consideration for clear interpretation of the photographs is that a large field be radiographed. A small simple camera designed to do this is shown in Fig. 4. The brass insert "A" seen in the photograph is removed for large

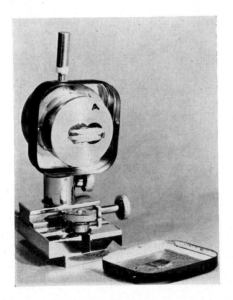

Fig. 4. Microradiographic camera.

radiographs. For small radiographs the off-set hole in the insert is centred on the axis of the camera, *i.e.*, at 90° to the position in the illustration. The illustration shows the camera in position for taking one of a stereo pair. To take the second, the camera is inverted and at the same time the plate holder rotated through 180°. The negative is printed on to a piece of positive film, cut up and mounted in correct orientation.

RESULTS

The results obtained for the different salts are tabulated in the table where details are given under the following heads: (a) Microscopic examination, (b) Crystals, (c) Orientation, (d) Particle size.

References p. 517

In general the results of the various methods of impregnation differed only in degree of penetration. The cone experiments gave the most information. The cones showed a marked difference in their external and internal appearance. In the case of copper chloride a thin surface layer was present with little penetration, Fig. 5a.

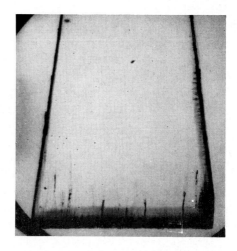

Fig. 5a. Section of copper chloride cone. × 1.7.

Fig. 5b. Fibre photograph, copper chloride cone.

Where penetration was present there was preferred orientation, as shown by the fibre photograph, Fig. 5b. On the other hand, the palladium chloride solution rapidly penetrated. It was found concentrated at the apex and also showed a depth of penetration into the sides, Fig. 5c. Crystals were seen growing at the tip of the cone; all these observations were confirmed by the fibre photograph which resembled

References p. 517

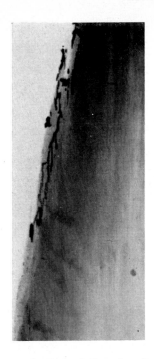

Fig. 5c. Section of tip of palladium chloride cone. × 3.75.

Fig. 5d. Fibre photograph, palladium chloride cone tip.

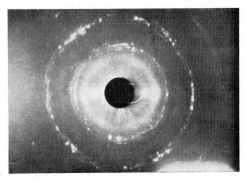

Fig. 5e. Section of potassium chloride cone. × 1.7.

Fig. 5f. Fibre photograph, potassium chloride cone.

References p. 517

TABLE I

Technique	Substance	Ref.	Microscopic examination (a)	Crystals (b)			Ref.	Orientation (c)	Particle size (d)	
				Vessels	Fibres	Rays			small	large
									(i)	(ii)
1	Copper chloride	(08)	Penetration from cone side into fibres (Fig. 5a)	+	+	+	(03)	Present [001]	+	+
1	Potassium chloride	(09)	Crystals throughout specimen (Fig. 5e)	+ 20	+ 12	+ 12	(42)	Present [100]	+	+
1	Palladium chloride	(15)	Single crystals at tip (Fig. 5c)	·	·	·	(52)	Laue photo	−	+
1	Sodium chloride	(60)	Slight penetration into the fibres	−	+ +	−	(02)	Inconclusive	−	+
1	Nickel chloride	(43)	Penetration from base and sides into cone (in magnetic field)	+ 12	+ 2	−	(46)	Absent	+	+
1	Potassium iodide	(22)	Heavy deposit on cone 3 mm thick	−	+	+ 1	(49)	Inconclusive	+	+
2	Copper chloride	(16)	Acicular crystals in vessels	+	+	+	·	·	·	·
3	Copper chloride	(47)	Penetration at base and sides	++	++	+	·	·	·	·
3	Aluminium sulphate	(47)	Fine crystals dispersed throughout specimen	++	++	−	·	·	·	·
3	Copper sulphate	(47)	Medium size (100 μ) crystals throughout specimen	+	+	−		Absent	−	+
3	Magnesium sulphate	(47)	Very fine crystals (below 5 μ) throughout specimen	+ 12	+ 3	+ 3	(58)	Absent	+	+
3	Nickel sulphate	(67)	Very large crystals	+	+	−	(68)	Laue pattern	−	+
5	Copper chloride	(45)	No large crystals in vessels	−	+ 3	+ 2	(26)	Present [001]	+	+
5	Potassium chloride	(40)	Crystals throughout specimen	++	++	++	(54)	Present [100]	++	+
5	Aluminium sulphate	(19)	Very fine crystals throughout	++	++	++	(50)	Present	++	−
5	Nickel chloride	(17)	Large crystals in vessels	++	++	+	(53)	Absent	−	−
1s	Oxalic acid cone immersed in a solution of calcium thiosulphate		Cone coated with layer of calcium oxalate. A few rosettes found in vessels					Inconclusive		
1	Calcium oxalate in 20 % HCl		A few crystals in vessels at the surface of the cone					Inconclusive		

Legend   + Present   − Absent   Figures in column (b) give maximum penetration in mm.
        (i) Rings   (ii) Spots

References p. 517

a Laue photograph, Fig. 5d. The effects using potassium chloride solution as the penetrant were the most impressive. Here the material penetrated the cone readily and whiskers commenced to grow on the outside surface of the cone in great profusion. As time went on the form of the crystalline deposit changed until a solid mass of crystals established themselves, as shown in Fig. 5e. X-ray diffraction photographs of the fibres revealed a certain amount of preferred orientation, Fig. 5f. The tendency for whisker growth was not confined to the outer surface and comparison of the actual deposits corresponding to the last two diagrams showed that whiskers had grown inside as well as out; measurement of the dimensions of the "whiskers" examined and also of the internal deposit did, in fact, agree quite reasonably, being about 10 to 20 μ in diameter. Stereomicroradiographs confirmed this.

CONCLUSIONS

Of the eleven salts examined including the very interesting calcium oxalate, there is predominant evidence of definite and preferred orientation in the cases of copper chloride, potassium chloride and also with aluminium sulphate. This undoubtedly arises from crystal habit in some cases, *e.g.* copper chloride, but it is not clear as to the exact reason in the others. Why no orientation occurs in the majority of cases, including the calcium oxalate remains at the moment obscure. The observations have revealed marked differences in both the rate and character of the diffusion mechanism. In the opinion of the author, polarisation phenomena and differential mobility of the ionic complexes will have to be further studied before a clear interpretation emerges. Some aspects of these topics are being pursued.

REFERENCES

[1] M. MARGARET CHATTAWAY, *Tropical Woods*, 102 (1955); 104 (1956).

[2] C. K. JACKSON, in V. E. COSSLETT, A. ENGSTRÖM and H. H. PATTEE, JR., *X-ray Microscopy and Microradiography*, Academic Press, Inc., New York, 1957, p. 487.

IDENTIFICATION DE MICRO-CRISTAUX DANS DES OBJETS BIOLOGIQUES

FERNAND FOURNIER

Centre National de la Recherche Scientifique, Laboratoire de Verville par Nesles-la-Vallée, Seine et Oise (France)

ABSTRACT

IDENTIFICATION OF MICROCRYSTALS IN BIOLOGICAL MATERIAL

Histological examination of certain intraperitoneal tumours reveals the presence of inclusions of birefringent bodies, the nature of which is not quite clear. After a brief description of the optical findings, the techniques that have been utilized to study these crystals are discussed. These were micro-incineration, contact microradiography and microdiffraction.

The apparatus and techniques used are described, and the results of the examination of several cases are presented.

Nos recherches ont porté sur l'examen de corps biréfringents inclus dans des tumeurs intra-péritonéales. Depuis longtemps il avait été signalé dans ces tumeurs la présence de formations pseudo-cristallines très biréfringentes et dont la nature était très discutée. Ces tumeurs, peu volumineuses, situées en géneral sur l'intestin grêle, dans une région assez bien déterminée, provoquent des désordres qui nécessitent une intervention chirurgicale; il semble que ces lésions apparaissent chez des personnes ayant déjà subi une intervention, souvent bénigne (appendicectomie). Depuis très longtemps on a songé à une réaction de corps étrangers et en particulier à la présence de poudre de talc introduite dans le péritoine au cours d'une première intervention. Les talcomes ont été décrits et constatés par divers auteurs.

Nous nous sommes proposé de rechercher dans les coupes histologiques de tumeurs, la nature des inclusions biréfringentes et de rechercher les cristaux susceptibles d'être identifiés.

Le caractère de biréfringence n'implique pas nécessairement la présence de cristaux mais indique une anisotropie optique dont les origines sont très diverses; en particulier, ces formations peuvent être dûes:

— à de simples souillures: fibres de textile, débris de matériel synthétique de suture.
— à la présence sous des formes très diverses de certains antibiotiques.
— à de minuscules cristaux de paraffine inclus dans les tissus.
— à une biréfringence du Baume du Canada.

On voit de suite la difficulté de distinguer les causes ayant provoqué ces manifestations optiques.

Nous n'avons nullement la compétence nécessaire pour traiter un des cas les plus complexes de la pathogénèse de ces tumeurs, mais nous devons faire remarquer que tous les cristaux introduits dans un organisme vivant subissent, au cours d'un temps plus ou moins long, une altération profonde dans leurs propriétés cristallographiques. Cette action est d'autant plus énergique que les cristaux sont plus petits, une très petite partie du cristal (quartz, talc, etc.) entre en solution dans le sérum physiologique et les produits amorphes portent localement ou à distance des perturbations dans le métabolisme des cellules provoquant des lésions; ceci pour montrer qu'il n'est pas nécessaire de retrouver des cristaux de talc dans une tumeur pour se trouver en présence d'un talcome et que d'autres cristaux que le talc peuvent provoquer des lésions intestinales dont l'évolution est toujours très grave.

Nous avons songé à utiliser le microscope électronique et la diffraction électronique pour examiner nos préparations. Celà est possible dans certains cas mais en général, les formations cristallines ont un volume trop grand pour obtenir des résultats interprétables, aussi avons nous dû employer pour ces examens:

— la micro-radiographie de contact,
— la micro-diffraction par rayons X.

Il ne nous est pas encore possible, pour le moment et avec notre appareillage, d'obtenir des diagrammes de cristal tournant qui permettront de déterminer d'une façon rigoureuse le système cristallin du produit examiné.

Ce travail et l'appareillage convenable sont actuellement en cours d'essais.

TECHNIQUE UTILISÉE

Les tumeurs sont traitées suivant les méthodes habituelles et incluses dans la paraffine. On prépare un ruban de coupe permettant de repérer les éléments dans le ruban, c'est-à-dire que: Un élément B par exemple placé entre deux coupes A et C indique que dans la tumeur les coupes A et C sont immédiatement en avant et en arrière de la coupe B.

Suivant les techniques habituelles, on prépare:

— une lame destinée à la coloration,
— une lame déparaffinée sans coloration,
— deux lames sur verre pour micro-incinération,
— deux lames sur pyrex pour micro-incinération,
— trois lames sur verre et collodion pour micro-radiographie de contact et micro-diffraction,
— une lame sur l'élément No. 10 pour coloration.

De cette façon on peut retrouver en gros, une bonne répartition des corps biréfringents. Un repérage par photographie et un repérage de points remarquables au moyen du micro-viseur de KAZEEF permet de placer le cristal ou la région à étudier devant le faisceau de rayons X du tube à micro-diffraction.

Les micro-radiographies de contact sont effectuées sous deux ou trois tensions différentes pour permettre l'estimation assez grossière des différences d'absorption, par exemple: 1.000 V, 2.000 V, 3.000 V.

La micro-incinération par la méthode classique permet d'éliminer tous les produits se décomposant ou se volatilisant au dessus de 350° C [1].

Les spodogrammes obtenus peuvent être prélevés sur collodion pour examen aux rayons X.

Bibliographie p. 524

APPAREILLAGE UTILISÉ

La micro-radiographie est exécutée au moyen d'un tube radiogène que nous avons fait construire et qui est constitué par un canon à électrons à trois lentilles électrostatiques d'un type utilisé dans les oscillographes cathodiques; le foyer est assez fin (cercle de 0,1 mm environ) et la tension d'alimentation est règlable entre 800 et 3.500 V environ. Les fenêtres de sortie du rayonnement sont constituées par des disques de béryllium de 0,2 mm d'épaisseur, la préparation est placée très près de la fenêtre de sortie pour éviter l'absorption par l'air. L'alimentation est en courant continu et un potentiomètre placé sur la haute tension permet les règlages nécessaires. L'anticathode est, soit en Ag, Pt, W ou Au, selon les besoins.

(a)

(b) (c)

Fig. 1. (a) Tube pour micro-radiographie de contact. (b) Tube pour micro-diffraction. (c) Micro Laue.

Bibliographie p. 524

La distance foyer–film est comprise entre 3 et 6 cm. (Fig. 1, a, b, c).

Le tube utilisé pour la micro-diffraction est aussi avec canon à concentration électrostatique par lentille dissymétrique portée à un potentiel convenable. Il fonctionne correctement avec une tension d'alimentation qui peut varier de 5.000 à 80.000 V, un système potentiométrique règle le potentiel de la lentille et la polarisation du Wehnelt. L'image focale est l'image électronique du filament en vraie grandeur. Il est possible de placer la fenêtre de sortie du rayonnement à 4 mm du foyer. Le collimateur en verre est à l'intérieur du tube. Le diamètre de ces collimateurs varie selon les besoins, entre 10 μ et 100 μ. Comme il est impossible de régler les collimateurs mécaniquement, un système de règlage permet de déplacer le foyer pour le mettre dans l'alignement du collimateur. Un microscope muni d'un illuminateur spécial est monté sur le tube et permet le centrage des préparations, soit par transmission, soit par réflexion.

Deux cas de maladie de Crohn dont les observations ont été recueillies par Tosoni-Pittoni dans le service du Docteur Lambling[2] ont montré des granulomes au

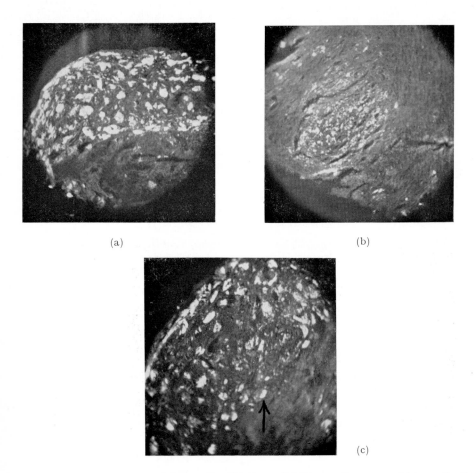

(a) (b)

(c)

Fig. 2. (a) Micro-radio × 300. Cristaux d'antibiotique. (b) Micro-radio × 200. Cristaux d'antibiotique. (c) Micro-radio × 300. Un cristal de talc.

talc associés à une maladie de Crohn. L'identification a été faite par examen des coupes en micro-incinération, repérage des centres biréfringents puis finalement, confirmation de la présence de cristaux minéraux par micro-radiographie. Ces cristaux présentent une biréfringence importante. (Fig. 2).

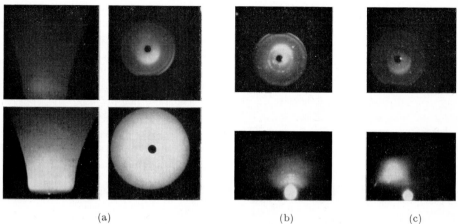

(a) (b) (c)

Fig. 3. (a) Pas de talc. (b) Petits cristaux de talc. (c) Un cristal de talc.

Trois autres cas de granulomes post-opératoires ont été examinés, ces observations nous ont été données par THOMERET; sur ces tumeurs il a été exécuté une micro-radiographie des corps biréfringents, il est constaté une absorption très notable du rayonnement dans un nodule contenant de nombreux cristaloïdes. Il est alors procédé à une micro-diffraction sur ces corps, le diagramme obtenu est celui de corps amorphes. Une vérification sur une préparation de talc dont la répartition des cristaux est identique à ceux de la coupe, montre au contraire un diagramme très net de cristaux de talc (Fig. 3). L'examen aux rayons X montre par réflexion les trois raies les plus intenses du talc; il semble donc vérifié que les coupes des tumeurs ne portent pas de traces appréciables de talc et que les corps biréfringents visibles au microscope sont très vraisemblablement provoqués par des antibiotiques. Les coupes ont été portées à 400° par micro-incinération; sur cinq échantillons examinés on ne retrouve aucun cristal biréfringent après 15 min de chauffage. Sur les corps appartenant au troisième cas, on ne retrouve, après incinération, qu'un seul cristal biréfringent [3,4] (Fig. 4).

CONCLUSIONS

La micro-radiographie et les examens par micro-diffraction des rayons X sur des cristaux inclus dans des objets biologiques permettent de préciser la nature minérale ou organique des formations biréfringentes constatées; elles éliminent les défauts de la méthode optique qui doit cependant être constamment pratiquée. Un appareillage de micro-diffraction a été construit au Laboratoire et permet déjà de nombreux examens. Le diamètre très réduit du faisceau de rayons X et sa grande intensité permettent des temps de pose assez courts entre 1 et 2 heures environ pour des cristaux organiques. La mise en place et le réglage de préparation se font avec une grande facilité grâce au microscope fixé sur le tube radiogène et muni de divers illuminateurs rendant possible la vision et le centrage de très petits cristaux [5].

Bibliographie p. 524

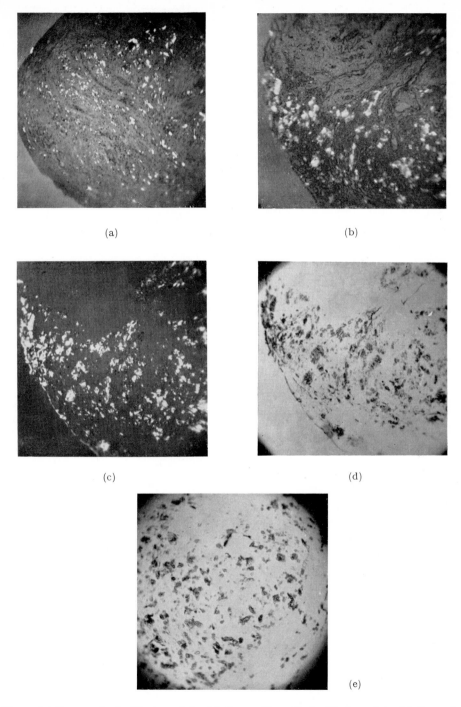

Fig. 4. (a) Coupe colorée, Nicols croisés. (b) Coupe déparaffinée, Nicols croisés. (c) Coupe in-cinérée, Nicols croisés. (d) Même coupe, lumière non polarisée. (e) Cristaux, lumière non polarisée. Grossissement × 200.

RÉSUMÉ

Certaines tumeurs intra-péritonéales présentent à l'examen histologique des inclusions de corps biréfringents dont la nature est assez mal définie. Après un court exposé sur les constatations optiques, il est indiqué les techniques qui ont été utilisées pour examiner ces cristaux. La micro-incinération, la micro-radiographie de contact et la micro-diffraction ont été utilisées pour déterminer la nature de ces formations.

Les appareils et les techniques utilisées sont indiqués et des résultats sont donnés pour plusieurs cas examinés.

BIBLIOGRAPHIE

[1] A. POLICARD, *Actualités sci. et ind.*, 765 (1938).
[2] A. TOSONI-PITTONI, *Thèse de doctorat*, 1958.
[3] CL. OLIVIER, I. BERTRAND et G. CERBONNET, *Mém. acad. chir.*, 22, 23, 24 (1951) 769, 773.
[4] G. THOMERET, M. BAY, J. ORCEL, F. FOURNIER et H. GISSELBRECHT, *Mém. acad. chir.*, 4, 5 (1957) 150.
[5] A. RIMSKY et MIHAILOVIC, *Brevet C.N.R.S.*
[6] CL. OLIVIER et G. CERBONNET, *Mém. acad. chir.*, 4, 5 (1957) 167.

THE USE OF X-RAY DIFFRACTION METHODS IN SOME CLINICAL PROBLEMS

OLGA KENNARD

National Institute for Medical Research, Mill Hill, London (Great Britain)

ABSTRACT

X-ray microanalysis has been of help in a variety of clinical problems either in the identification of substances present in quantities too small to be examined by conventional methods, or in cases where the precise crystal form was of significance. The applications of both powder and single crystal identification using X-ray diffraction will be discussed and illustrated by cases of porphyria, cystinosis, tumour deposits and a number of other clinical conditions.

During the past eight years or so increasing use has been made of X-ray diffraction methods at the National Institute for Medical Research in London, and I thought it would be of interest in this session on the biological applications of microdiffraction analysis if I described some clinical cases where X-ray methods have proved helpful.

Perhaps for the sake of members of the conference who are not crystallographers, I might quickly recapitulate the types of problems one might expect to solve by such methods.

Firstly, X-ray diffraction can be used for the identification of crystalline deposits in cells and tissues, or of substances extracted from the body. For this only sub-microscopic crystals or powders are required. Since the diffraction pattern is dependent both on the kinds of atoms composing the substance and their arrangement, unequivocal identification of the whole chemical entity is possible, provided only that the diffraction pattern can be matched by the pattern of a known substance. Dr. PARRISH has discussed at this symposium the minimum detectable limits, using Geiger-counter techniques, but even with photographic methods one might confidently expect to identify quantities of the order of a few microgrammes. Inorganic deposits can usually be traced by referring to the *X-ray Powder Data File*[1] which lists the three strongest lines in the powder-pattern of several thousand inorganic, and relatively fewer organic, compounds.

A few specialised collections of organic powder patterns, such as that for sterols[2] have recently appeared, but in most actual cases when dealing with organic compounds it is still necessary to take comparison patterns of known substances. Diffraction patterns are also, usually, sensitive to the presence of impurities, either as mechanical mixtures or solid solutions and thus are a useful control for purification procedures.

When single crystals are available the dimensions of the structural unit of the crystal, "the unit cell", can be measured and the substance identified by reference to the determinative tables in *Crystal Data*[3] or if not listed there, by direct comparison with known substances. The single crystal pattern is more detailed than that from a powder and is useful for organic compounds which may exist in polymorphic forms or as solid solutions.

A measurement of unit cell dimensions can also be used in deriving the molecular weight of a crystal, since the only additional constant required is the bulk density of the substance. We can then use the relation $\rho = N \times M/V \times 1.6604$ where ρ is the density, N the number of molecules in the unit cell and V the cell volume. There are evident advantages in being able to determine the molecular weight of a new or unknown substance by such a non-destructive method, especially since the accuracy of the measurement is around 3—4 %. The single crystal pattern will often give additional information about the symmetry and shape of the molecule particularly when used in conjunction with other evidence, such as optics or nuclear magnetic resonance.

A complete interpretation of the diffraction pattern from a single crystal will, of course, describe the stereochemistry of the molecule and I need only mention the work of HODGKIN and her colleagues[4] on *Vitamin B*$_{12}$ as the supreme application of X-ray methods to biochemical problems. However, even a more limited use of these methods will give a wealth of information about both the chemical identity and physical state of solids of biological interest.

To illustrate the scope of these methods I should like to discuss three cases. Each of these represents collaborative work with chemists, biochemists and clinical workers, and X-ray diffraction was used as just one additional tool in the investigation. Indeed I have chosen these cases to emphasise the importance of tackling a biological problem with the widest variety of methods.

The first case concerns cystinosis or the LIGNAC[5-7], FANCONI[8] syndrome. It is a cystine-storage disease, usually found in young children, who rarely survive beyond ten years of age. Clinical symptoms are variable, but rickets, dwarfism, tetanic and uraemic attacks are common. In most patients characteristic crystalline deposits are found in many tissues. The proof that these crystals are indeed cystine was obtained by Dr. SMALL from an X-ray photograph of a biopsy specimen of conjunctiva[9]. I myself, together with Professor CHARLES DENT at University College Hospital Medical School studied liver and lung sections, and Fig. 1 shows some typical crystals as viewed by visual phase-contrast, transmitted and polarised light. The crystals appeared at first sight to be present within the red cells, but a closer study of phase contrast and ultraviolet photomicrographs, Fig. 2, showed that they were lying freely in the plasma. Two types of crystals could be distinguished, hexagonal, highly birefringent plates, with negative uniaxial sign, strongly absorbing at 2750 Å, and columnar, birefringent crystals, only poorly absorbing in the ultraviolet region. Similar, columnar crystals were occasionally observed in liver sections from normal infants and adults. X-ray diffraction patterns of tissue sections were taken, using conventional equipment, and compared with the patterns of normal tissue, and of pure L-cystine. The results are summarised in Table I. The lines at spacings 4.2 Å and 3.7 Å which appear in both normal and pathological tissues may be due to the unidentified columnar crystals.

The last column gives the pattern obtained from a suspected case of cystinosis, which though weak, clearly showed the two strongest lines of cystine, and thus gave confirmation of the diagnosis.

References p. 530

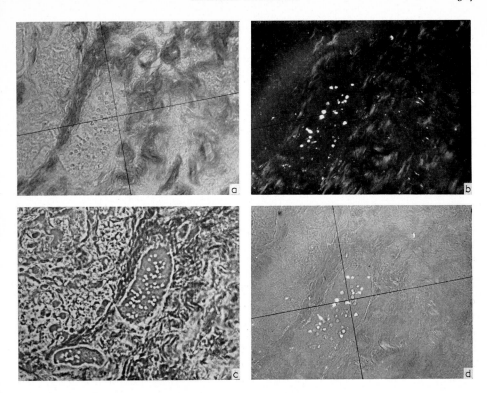

Fig. 1. Photomicrographs of a lung section from a case of cystinosis (Infant G. Day). (a) = Transmitted light; (b) = Polarised light; (c) = Visual phase contrast; (d) = Polarised light, overexposed to show surrounding tissue. Magnification × 250.

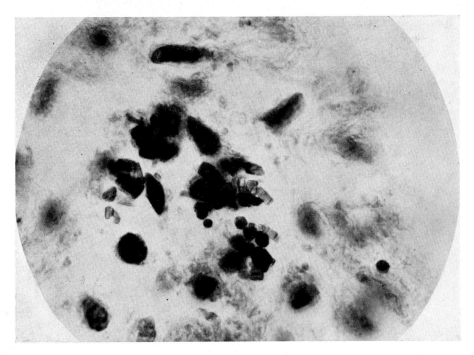

Fig. 2. Photomicrograph of lung section of a case of cystinosis (Infant G. Day). Taken with ultraviolet light $\lambda = 2750$ Å showing heavily absorbing hexagonal crystals of cystine and columnar crystals. Magnification × 2,640.

TABLE I

COMPARISON OF X-RAY DIFFRACTION PATTERNS OF LIVER TISSUES FROM VARIOUS SOURCES WITH
L-CYSTINE
(Interplanar spacings in Ångstrom units)

L-Cystine	Liver tissue "Normal"	Cystinosis U.C.H.	Cystinosis G.O.S.
4.65 s		4.65 m	4.64 m
	4.19 s	4.13 s	4.15 s
4.04 w			
	3.72 m	3.71 m	3.77 w
3.28 w		3.24 m	
3.10 s		3.15 m	3.12 m
2.71 m		2.72 m	
2.57 m		2.59 w	
		2.47 w	
2.32 m		2.30 w	
2.13 m		2.17 w	
2.01 w			

s = strong; w = weak ; m = medium.

Recently a case was reported[10] where similar crystals were observed in the conjunctiva of an otherwise healthy adult, and it was suggested, on basis of chromatographic studies, that this was a case of benign cystinosis. Fig. 3 shows a typical cluster of crystals, in a conjunctiva specimen of this case which Dr. COGAN kindly sent us. We had altogether four sections, about 10 μ thick and 3 mm diameter each. A direct X-ray photograph of one of these sections failed to show the characteristic

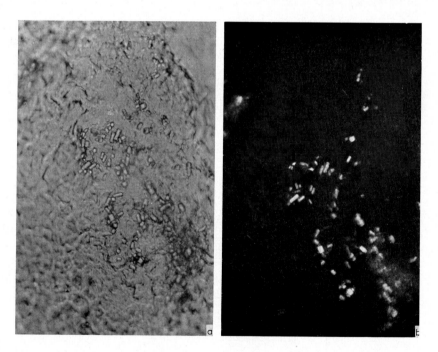

Fig. 3. Photomicrograph of conjunctiva section from an adult. (a) = Transmitted light; (b) = Polarised light. Magnification × 420.

References p. 530

lines of cystine. An attempt was made to concentrate the cystine by extraction but still no cystine lines were observed. We are now working on the hypothesis that these crystals may be a protein. We have evidence suggestive of this, since the crystals lose birefringence on incubating at 60° C and are digested by a proteolytic enzyme. However, we need additional evidence to decide on the nature of the crystals. The existence or not of a benign form of cystinosis would of course be of considerable importance in our understanding of this disease.

The next case I should like to talk about is one of porphyria, on which we have already published some work[11]. I would just like to summarise our findings and quote some more recent work to illustrate the scope of diffraction methods, where applied to closely related isomers.

Porphyria is a comparatively rare disturbance of pigment metabolism, which, however, has been studied extensively, in the hope that it will throw some light on the biosynthesis of haemoglobin and chlorophyll. A variety of porphyrins have been extracted from the urine and faeces of patients, but because of the difficulty of applying the usual biochemical methods to the differentiation of structurally related isomers we decided with Professor C. RIMINGTON of University College Hospital Medical School to try to classify the porphyrins on the basis of powder patterns. We also studied the patterns of known mixtures of isomers and found that these form solid solutions, with abrupt changes of pattern at the eutectic points. By reference to these patterns the purity of various urinary porphyrins could be estimated, and as an example, we could detect 5 % or less of uroporphyrin I tetramethyl ester in a mixture with the III isomer.

Powder patterns have, however, to be used with great caution in such a field as our own experience has shown. In the course of this work we found an unusual urinary porphyrin, the so-called McCawley ester, whose pattern matched that of a synthetic porphyrin, believed to be uroporphyrin II tetramethyl ester prepared by McDONALD[12]. This isomer had never previously been isolated from biological sources and our finding led McDONALD to apply X-ray techniques to his own samples[13], and he then discovered a polymorphic modification of uroporphyrin III tetramethyl ester which also matched the McCawley ester both in infra-red and X-ray spectra, as well as some samples known to have been mixtures. It is evident that real progress can only be made by single crystal studies and we are at present concentrating on the purification and preparation of various porphyrin derivatives.

Finally I would like to say something about some recent work on cortisone acetate, which arose from a suggestion that tablets of this substance prepared by different firms had different efficacy[14-16]. The infra-red spectrum of cortisone acetate from various sources was examined, but no differences could be detected. The X-ray photographs of the whole tablets were also identical, but on extraction with water marked differences in pattern were found. The apparent anomaly was resolved when it was discovered that specimens for infra-red work had been extracted with chloroform and not water.

An examination of single crystals from various non-aqueous solvents showed the existence of three or possibly four distinct crystal forms. On contact with water these changed into a monoclinic form with cell dimensions of a = 15.68 Å, b = 7.52 Å, c = 26.58 Å, β = 83°. This form is not a hydrated one, but is the only structure which is stable in the presence of water. The difference between the tablets

References p. 530

was, as we found, both in the rate of disintegration of the whole tablets and in the rate of transformation to the stable crystal form.

Time does not permit me to quote further examples but I hope these cases have shown that X-ray diffraction methods can with advantage be used to supplement techniques of clinical research, and perhaps even stimulate work in new directions.

REFERENCES

[1] *X-ray Powder Data File*, American Society for Testing Materials, Philadelphia.
[2] J. PARSONS, W. T. BAKER and G. BAKER, *Powder Pattern for Sterols*, Ford Foundation, New York, 1958.
[3] J. D. H. DONNAY and W. NOWACKI, *Crystal Data*, The Geological Society of America, New York, 1954.
[4] D. C. HODGKIN, J. KAMPER, J. LINDSEY, M. MACKAY, J. PICKWORTH, J. H. ROBERTSON, C. B. SHOEMAKER, J. G. WHITE, R. J. PROSEN and K. N. TRUEBLOOD, *Proc. Roy. Soc. (London)*, A 242 (1957) 228.
[5] G. O. E. LIGNAC, *Deut. Arch. klin. Med.*, 145 (1924) 139.
[6] G. O. E. LIGNAC, *Krankheitsforsch.*, 2 (1926a) 43.
[7] G. O. E. LIGNAC, *Verhandl. deut. pathol. Ges.*, 21 (1926b) 303.
[8] G. FANCONI, *Jahrb. Kinderheilk.*, 147 (1936) 299; *Schweiz. med. Wochschr.*, 88 (1950) 757.
[9] H. BICKEL and J. M. SMELLIE, *Lancet*, 262 (1952) 1093.
[10] D. C. COGAN, T. KUWABARA, J. KINOSHITA, L. SHEEHAN and L. MEROLA, *J. Am. Med. Assoc.*, 164 (1957) 397.
[11] C. RIMINGTON and O. KENNARD, *Biochem. J.*, 55 (1953) 105.
[12] S. F. McDONALD, *J. Chem. Soc.*, (1952) 4184.
[13] S. F. McDONALD, personal communication.
[14] M. L. ROSENHEIM and C. F. ROSS, *Lancet*, 274 (1958) 1371.
[15] J. SNOW, J. MOORE, F. RAINE, R. I. S. BAYLISS and C. G. MILLMAN, *Lancet*, 276 (1959) 96.
[16] I. E. BUSH, *Lancet*, 276 (1959) 205.

MICRODIFFRACTION STUDIES OF KERATINIZATION IN THE HAIR FOLLICLE

ALLAN SKERTCHLY

University of Leeds (Great Britain)

ABSTRACT

Following the early qualitative work of Mercer some quantitative diffractometric measurements on the process of keratinization in the hair follicle are presented. The work is mainly carried out using the microdiffractometer described elsewhere and shows the changes in structure as the fibre extrudes from the isotropic bulb region to form anisotropic crystalline material in the fully keratinized fibre.

NATURE OF THE INVESTIGATION

The work reported in this paper consists of a quantitative X-ray diffraction reinvestigation of the process of keratinization in the hair follicle. This system was investigated by MERCER[1] who reported some X-ray microdiffraction results obtained by SIKORSKI using photographic techniques. It was thought to be a useful check on the performance of the microdiffractometer (see page 472), and in particular of its memory loop and intensity analyser, to make some quantitative measurements of the scattered X-ray intensity at various levels in the hair follicle.

Fig. 1 shows a photograph of the system which is the subject of the investigation.

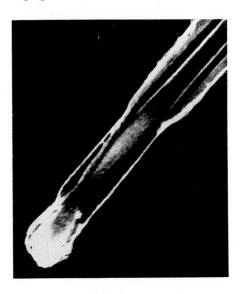

Fig. 1. Photograph of a hair follicle taken using polarized light. Portion of the inner root sheath is also visible. The fibre transforms from the isotropic bulb region of the presumptive cortex to an ordered anisotropic structure in the fully hardened state.

The process of keratinization is characterised by rise in birefringence (with which is associated an increase in order) as the fibre develops. With this development a molecular lattice forms which is sufficiently ordered to give rise to the well known α keratin X-ray diffraction pattern[2] which is now thought to be due to a helical structure[3]. The process is of great intrinsic interest since it represents the synthesis of a fully differentiated protein structure. In view of the extreme complexity of keratin which has been revealed by the technique of electron microscopy[4], any X-ray results obtained from the gross structure will of necessity be the composite additions from the many micro structures present. However, because of the poorly diffracting nature of this low atomic-numbered material it is impracticable at present to investigate less than a single hair and it is with such that we are here concerned.

TECHNIQUE AND MATERIALS

The usual slit system of the microdiffractometer was replaced by pinholes to give a beam of circular cross section approximately 100 μ in diameter. A Raymax rotating anode X-ray generator operating at 60 mA 50 kV was used and a single human hair and follicle was mounted in an adjustable specimen holder. Its position in the X-ray beam was adjusted by eye and the equatorial X-ray diffraction intensity distribution at four levels was obtained using the memory loop and successive integrated scans. In normal use as a diffractometer the air-scattered background radiation is likely to be high, but this can be considerably reduced by means of detector collimators.

Table I shows the backgrounds recorded under various operating conditions. It was important to keep the background as low as possible since non-linearity of the analytical system, due to counting losses, occurs at count rates above about 500/sec. This means that for Geiger-Müller counter operation the maximum per-

TABLE I

Operating conditions	Count rate per scan between 1 and 19° of Bragg θ
Normal diffractometer with no detector collimators	1921
Normal diffractometer with detector collimators	281
Pinhole collimators and detector collimators	58
Non-X-ray back ground	54

missable number of superimposed scans on the memory loop was about 160. With a scan-repeating frequency of 2/min, a single analysis required a little over an hour. This may be compared with 25 h reported for the photographic technique using a stationary anode X-ray generator. In the event, this number of scans is insufficient to provide anything except a marginal improvement in characterisation of the system, and repeated composite scans were necessary to increase accuracy. Fig. 2 shows the results obtained which appear to corroborate those obtained by SIKORSKI.

Since the volume of the specimen which is irradiated by the beam varies from about $9 \cdot 10^{-7}$ cm³ to about $18 \cdot 10^{-7}$ cm³ a correction was necessary to reduce the scattered intensities obtained to equivalent volumes. Ideally equivalent masses would be more

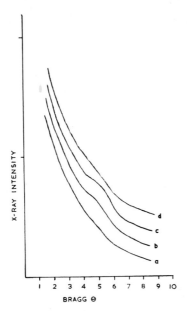

Fig. 2. Equatorial X-ray intensity distribution records obtained using the microdiffractometer (See page 472 of this Symposium). a, 250μ; b, $500\ \mu$; c, $1000\ \mu$; d, $5000\ \mu$. The distances refer to those between the centre of the X-ray spot and the proximal part of the fibre.

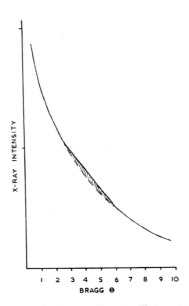

Fig. 3. Diagram showing the method of computing the "integrated" reflection intensity of the *ca.* 9.8 Å equatorial reflection.

References p. 535

suitable, but these are difficult to compute since density variations are unknown. In order to correlate the birefringence with the formation of the lattice which is responsible for the diffraction effects, the reflection on the equator *circa* 9.8 Å was used as a measure of the "X-ray crystalline" material. This may be invalid for two reasons: (a) The lateral order may not be representative of the overall order in the crystal system, although possibly there is a close connection, and (b) the equatorial trace does not give a true integrated reflection intensity since it neglects possible orientation effects. However, with these provisos the results obtained appear to give a reasonable approximation to what would be expected.

The method of separating the "integrated" intensity from the intense general background is shown in Fig. 3.

The background trend is measured on either side of the known limits of the reflection and is estimated between the limits. The difference between the observed and estimated intensity distribution is taken as a measure of the reflection intensity following normal practice. However, such estimates on the steeply sloping background are liable to large errors and the actual results should be taken as indicative only or semi-quantitative in nature.

It is further recognised that this procedure may lead to errors in certain cases. Table II shows the results obtained together with the volume-corrected intensities.

TABLE II

Level	Bragg θ count			Calculated background	Volume $cm^3 \times 10^{-7}$	Corrected intensity	Birefringence
	Observed						
	$3°-4°$	$4°-5°$	$5°-6°$	$4°-5°$			
(a)	36,512	31,467	24,211	31,100	16.1	367	0.0013
(b)	34,286	29,613	22,352	28,900	8.95	1,281	0.0079
(c)	37,429	31,381	25,297	29,700	11.3	2,495	0.0085
(d)	35,821	30,053	24,359	29,100	17.8	1,052	0.0032

Note: the value of the birefringence of the fibre reported for region (d) indicates some disturbance in the normal fibre growth, possibly due to medullation.

The birefringence of the fibre was measured with a Sénarmont compensator mounted on a microscope and the diameters of the various regions with an optical micrometer.

The results of the analysis are plotted in Fig. 4 where it is seen that within the limits of experimental error there is the expected positive correlation.

ACKNOWLEDGEMENT

The generous assistance of the Wool Research Council is appreciatively acknowledged.

References p. 535

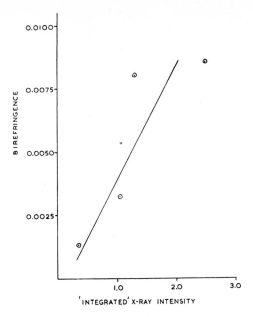

Fig. 4. Graph showing the correlation between birefringence and "integrated" X-ray diffraction intensity of the *ca.* 9.8 Å equatorial reflection. The "integrated" intensity has been corrected to refer to that scattered by constant volume elements.

REFERENCES

[1] E. H. MERCER, *Biochim. Biophys. Acta*, 3 (1949) 161.
[2] W. T. ASTBURY and A. STREET, *Phil. Trans. Roy. Soc. (London), Ser. A*, 230 (1931) 75.
[3] L. PAULING and R. B. COREY, *Nature*, 171 (1953) 59.
[4] J. SIKORSKI and H. J. WOODS, reported by C. E. CHALLICE and T. SIKORSKI, *Brit. J. Appl. Phys.*, 8 (1957) 1, 21.

SUBJECT INDEX

AUTHOR INDEX